6-5-67

70 70 3
1526

THE GEOLOGICAL SOCIETY OF AMERICA, INC.

Memoir 97

Handbook of Physical Constants

Revised Edition

SYDNEY P. CLARK, JR., *Editor*

Yale University, New Haven, Connecticut

PUBLISHED BY THE SOCIETY

1966

PUBLISHED BY

THE GEOLOGICAL SOCIETY OF AMERICA, INC.

231 East 46th Street, New York, New York 10017

Made in the United States of America

The printing of this volume has been made possible by generous contributions to the Memoir Fund of The Geological Society of America by the following industrial concerns:

> *Amerada Petroleum Corporation*
> *The Anaconda Company*
> *The Atlantic Refining Company*
> *Gulf Oil Corporation*
> *Kennecott Copper Corporation*
> *Phelps Dodge Corporation*
> *Standard Oil Company (New Jersey)*
> *Standard Oil Company of California*

and by Fellows and Members of the Society.

FOREWORD

In the "Handbook of Physical Constants," Special Paper Number 36, published by The Geological Society of America in 1942, the editors sought to compile for the first time a wide variety of physical constants needed for geological and geophysical calculations. The choices of data were necessarily arbitrary; the compilations were contributed by the labors of volunteers with little bibliographical assistance. Nevertheless, the usefulness of the Handbook has been demonstrated, both by the exhaustion of several editions and by many citations in subsequent literature.

For at least ten years, the desirability of a revised edition has been recognized: many sections are now badly out of date, and new kinds of measurements have appeared. As the amount of material has increased, however, so has the labor of dealing with it. A preliminary selection of chapters and compilers was drawn up in 1955, and a few manuscripts eventually appeared. It was apparent, however, that a vigorous effort was needed to push the work to completion, and Prof. Sydney P. Clark, Jr., agreed to assume the editorship. The present volume is the result.

A primary consideration has been brevity, on the assumption that a volume of moderate size would be most generally useful. The introductory sections of the chapters have consequently been kept to the minimum length consistent with clarity and usefulness. A critical attitude toward measurements has been encouraged by the inclusion, in many cases, of measurements of ostensibly the same physical property by different observers. Without this confrontation, the real uncertainties of measurements can seldom be judged, although grossly erroneous determinations may sometimes throw suspicion on better ones. The geologist is usually aware of the great possible variations of natural materials lumped in a single descriptive category, such as "shale," or "sandstone"; it is generally impossible to tabulate adequate descriptions of such materials, even when they are available in the original documents, and particular applications may require a return to the source for additional details.

Perhaps one of the most useful functions of such compilations is to draw attention to areas where more adequate data are needed. If a particular measurement cannot be found, it does not necessarily mean that it has never been made —the compiler may have missed a reference—but if a whole category of measurements is conspicuously undernourished, the fact will be evident. A plenitude of data in other categories may serve to discourage unnecessary repetition.

Prof. Clark and I wish to take this opportunity to express our gratitude to those who prepared or contributed to the individual sections. We are especially indebted to the editorial staff of The Geological Society of America for their care in preparing this difficult manuscript for publication, and to the Memoir Fund of The Geological Society of America which helped defray the cost of publication.

FRANCIS BIRCH

October 1965

CONTRIBUTORS

G. E. Andreasen, U. S. Geological Survey.

J. R. Balsley, Wesleyan University.

H. L. Barnes, Pennsylvania State University.

P. M. Bethke, U.S. Geological Survey.

Francis Birch, Harvard University.

J. J. Bradley, Atlantic Refining Company.

A. G. W. Cameron, National Aeronautics and Space Administration.

S. P. Clark, Jr., Yale University.

R. A. Daly (deceased).

J. L. Edwards, U. S. Geological Survey.

A. N. Fort, Jr., Atlantic Refining Company.

H. J. Greenwood, Princeton University.

John Handin, Shell Development Company.

K. S. Heier, Australian National University.

H. C. Helgeson, Northwestern University.

W. T. Holser, Chevron Research Company.

G. V. Keller, Golden, Colorado.

G. C. Kennedy, University of California at Los Angeles.

F. C. Kracek (deceased).

G. Kullerud, Geophysical Laboratory, Washington, D. C.

W. H. K. Lee, University of California at Los Angeles.

D. H. Lindsley, Geophysical Laboratory, Washington, D. C.

G. J. F. MacDonald, University of California at Los Angeles.

G. E. Manger, U.S. Geological Survey.

Z. E. Peterman, U. S. Geological Survey.

Frank Press, Massachusetts Institute of Technology.

R. A. Robie, U. S. Geological Survey.

B. J. Skinner, U. S. Geological Survey.

M. S. Toulmin, U. S. Geological Survey.

G. W. Wetherill, University of California at Los Angeles.

CONTENTS

SECTION 1

COMPOSITION OF ROCKS
by SYDNEY P. CLARK, JR.

CONTENTS

This section deals mainly with petrological terminology and is intended primarily for the nongeologist. It is impossible to cover this subject adequately in a short space, and the reader is referred to standard textbooks on petrography for further details (1, 2, 3, 5). The problem of terminology is complicated by the fact that many samples which have been used for the determination of physical properties of rocks have come from quarries, and terms peculiar to quarrymen have crept into the literature. Since rocks are mixtures of different phases, they can, at least in principle, have a continuous range of composition and of physical properties. Any scheme of classification demands that this potentially continuous series be fitted into more or less distinct and arbitrary compartments.

Three main classes of rocks are recognized: igneous, metamorphic, and sedimentary. Igneous rocks are thought to be in large part the products of crystallization of a silicate melt. Sedimentary rocks result from deposition of material by wind or water at the earth's surface and its later solidification into rock. Metamorphic rocks result from the recrystallization of igneous or sedimentary rocks in the solid state at relatively high temperatures and pressures.

Much of the early effort of petrographers went into the classification of the igneous rocks. The result was a bewildering list of categories, most of which contained rocks of unusual compositions. Only the principal types of rock are mentioned here. The igneous rocks may be divided into plutonic and volcanic types. Plutonic rocks crystallized at depth in the earth and are characterized by relatively coarse grain size, low porosity, and low permeability. Volcanic rocks, which formed at the earth's surface, are commonly poorly aggregated, and some types, known as tuffs, may be very porous and friable. Volcanic rocks may also contain appreciable quantities of glass.

We turn first to the plutonic igneous rocks. *Granite* contains roughly equal amounts of quartz, sodic plagioclase, and potassium feldspar. Dark minerals (amphibole, biotite, or both) rarely exceed 10 per cent. In *diorites*, sodic plagioclase greatly predominates over potassium feldspar. Dark minerals (in most cases amphibole, although biotite is also found) may constitute up to 25 per cent of the rock. Little or no quartz is present. If quartz occurs as a major constituent of such a rock, the term *quartz diorite* or *granodiorite* is used. *Gabbro* consists almost entirely of calcic plagioclase and dark minerals (amphibole, pyroxene, or both). If either quartz or olivine is present in appreciable quantities the term quartz gabbro or olivine gabbro is used.

Diabase is a fine-grained rock consisting almost entirely of calcic plagioclase and pyroxene. Its composition may be similar to some gabbros. This type of rock occurs as dikes or sills, and it is usually relatively fine-grained. Ultramafic rocks have a low content of silica and are characterized by the almost complete absence of feldspar. *Pyroxenite* consists almost entirely of pyroxene. *Peridotites* are mixtures of pyroxene and olivine, and *dunites* are almost entirely olivine. Rocks consisting almost entirely of calcic plagioclase are termed *anorthosites*.

Only four types of volcanic rocks need be considered here. The more siliceous types, the rhyolites and dacites, tend to be largely glassy and commonly very porous. *Rhyolites* contain about 70 per cent silica and are mainly composed of glass with crystals of quartz, alkali feldspar, and in some cases sodic plagioclase. *Dacites* are less siliceous and more sodic than rhyolites, and crystals of pyroxene are commonly found in the glass. Basalts and andesites are considerably less siliceous than dacites and apparently were extruded at considerably higher temperatures. The resulting liquid is much more fluid and crystallizes more readily. *Basalts* invariably contain calcic plagioclase and pyroxene, and commonly also olivine, nepheline, or small amounts of quartz. *Andesites* are more siliceous than basalts and commonly contain amphibole. Glass is usually a relatively minor constituent of basalts and andesites. All volcanic rocks may show considerable porosity, and this as well as the nature of the constituent minerals may influence the physical properties.

Table 1-1 gives average chemical compositions of these and some other types of igneous rocks. Figure 1-1 shows in a generalized way the variation in mineralogical constitution of igneous rocks. It must be realized that any particular rock of a given type may depart markedly from the indicated compositions, although many rocks are well represented in a general way by the diagram.

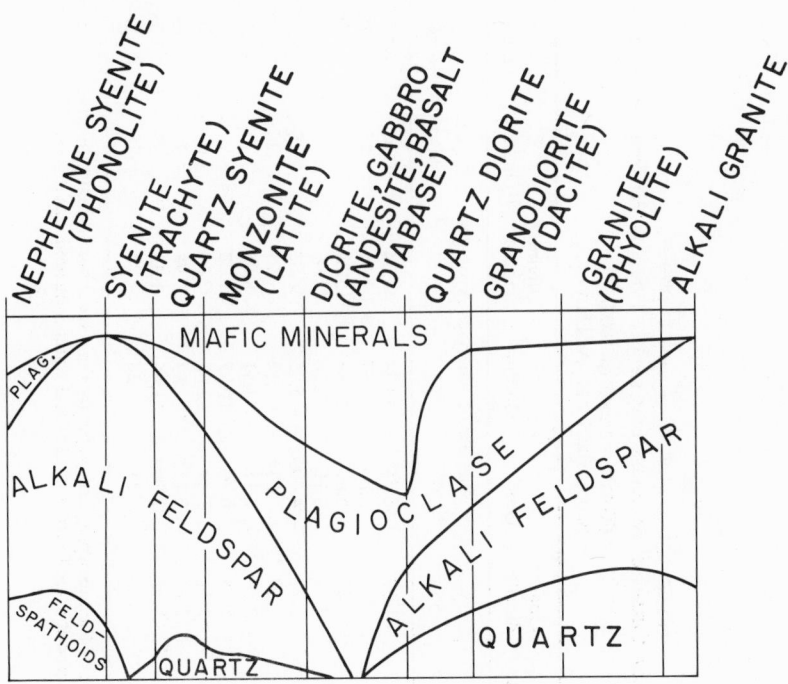

Figure 1-1. Generalized mineralogical constitutions of igneous rocks (after 4)

Sedimentary and metamorphic rocks have not been nearly as extensively studied by petrographers and have not been classified in as much detail as the igneous rocks.

Clastic sediments are commonly classified according to the median diameter of their constituent grains. The mineralogical composition of these materials proves to be fairly closely related to the median diameter. *Sandstones*, which form from coarse clastic sediments, are predominantly composed of quartz and feldspar, whereas *shales*, which form from the finest-grained sediments, contain important quantities of clay minerals as well. The grains comprising these types of rock were shaped by weathering, piled together, and then more or less tightly cemented. The result is that the rocks are relatively porous; this porosity is very important in influencing physical properties. The second important category of sedimentary rocks is that of the so-called chemical sediments. Examples are *limestone* (dominantly $CaCO_3$), *dolomite* (dominantly

TABLE 1-1. AVERAGE CHEMICAL ANALYSES OF CERTAIN TYPES OF PLUTONIC IGNEOUS ROCKS

(Totals reduced to 100.00)

(Compiled by R. A. Daly)

	Granite	Syenite	Granodiorite	Quartz diorite	Diorite	Gabbro	Olivine diabase	Diabase	Dunite	Lherzolite (peridotite)	Plateau basalt
					Number of Analyses Averaged						
	546	50	40	55	70	41	12	90	10	13	43
SiO_2	70.18	60.19	65.01	61.59	56.77	48.24	48.54	50.48	40.49	43.95	48.80
TiO_2	.39	.67	.57	.66	.84	.97	1.31	1.45	.02	.10	2.19
Al_2O_3	14.47	16.28	15.94	16.21	16.67	17.88	15.24	15.34	.86	4.82	13.98
Fe_2O_3	1.57	2.74	1.74	2.54	3.16	3.16	3.06	3.84	2.84	2.20	3.59
FeO	1.78	3.28	2.65	3.77	4.40	5.95	8.88	7.78	5.54	6.34	9.78
MnO	.12	.14	.07	.10	.13	.13	.21	.20	.16	.19	.17
MgO	.88	2.49	1.91	2.80	4.17	7.51	8.08	5.79	46.32	36.81	6.70
CaO	1.99	4.30	4.42	5.38	6.74	10.99	9.38	8.94	.70	3.57	9.38
Na_2O	3.48	3.98	3.70	3.37	3.39	2.55	2.69	3.07	.10	.63	2.59
K_2O	4.11	4.49	2.75	2.10	2.12	.89	.98	.97	.04	.21	.69
H_2O*	.84	1.16	1.04	1.22	1.36	1.45	1.35	1.89	2.88	1.08	1.80
P_2O_5	.19	.28	.20	.26	.25	.28	.28	.25	.05	.10	.33

* Since most of the analysts neglected the effect of the adsorption of water by their specimens when pulverized, the proportion given for this oxide is in general somewhat too high. On the whole, about three fourths of the total water indicated was driven off at temperatures no higher than 105° C.

$CaMg(CO_3)_2$), and *rock salt* (NaCl). These rocks were laid down under water by chemical or biochemical agencies. They tend to be dense and of low porosity, and in this respect resemble the metamorphic and igneous rocks.

Metamorphic rocks result from the recrystallization of pre-existing sedimentary and igneous rocks. They are reconstituted essentially in the solid state, perhaps with the aid of interstitial aqueous fluids. Changes in the bulk composition of the rock may be caused by metamorphism. The most conspicuous is the dehydration of the rock as higher grades of metamorphism are attained. Metamorphic rocks are generally of low porosity and permeability, and hence their physical properties are mainly determined by the properties of the constituent minerals. They are commonly anisotropic owing to a foliation which is caused by parallel arrangement of plates of micas and by planar orientation of rodlike minerals, such as amphiboles. The principal types of metamorphic rocks are *gneisses* and *schists*. They are distinguished by their content of micaceous minerals: gneisses commonly contain less than about 15 per cent, and schists have more than 15 per cent. *Gneisses* may be formed from a variety of rocks, such as granites, rhyolites, and impure sandstones. *Schists* result mainly from the metamorphism of shales. *Slate* is intermediate between shale and schist. The names applied to gneisses and schists may be modified by the names of prominent minerals, as for example hornblende gneiss, or quartz-mica schist.

An *amphibolite* is a metamorphic rock consisting mainly of amphibole with subordinate plagioclase. It is thought to result from the metamorphism of basalt. *Quartzite* results from the metamorphism of sandstone, *marble* from the metamorphism of limestone or dolomite. *Eclogite* is a dense rock consisting mainly of a pink garnet rich in CaO and MgO and a green pyroxene containing Na_2O and Al_2O_3. Most eclogites also contain minor amounts of biotite and amphibole.

REFERENCES FOR SECTION 1

1. Mason, Principles of geochemistry, New York, John Wiley & Sons, 276 p., 1952
2. Pettijohn, Sedimentary rocks, 2d ed., New York, Harper & Bros., 718 p., 1957
3. Turner and Verhoogen, Igneous and metamorphic petrology, 2d ed., New York, McGraw-Hill Book Co., 694 p., 1960
4. Tyrrell, The principles of petrology, 2d ed., New York, Dutton, 349 p., 1929
5. Williams, Turner, and Gilbert, Petrography, San Francisco, W. H. Freeman and Co., 406 p., 1954

SECTION 2

ABUNDANCES OF THE ELEMENTS

by A. G. W. Cameron

Contents

Handbook of Physical Constants—*Revised Edition*
The Geological Society of America Memoir 97, 1966

Table 2-1 contains a compilation of abundances of the elements derived from various sources. The basic purpose behind most of these determinations of abundances has been to attempt to find the over-all composition of the solar system. Some of the volatile elements can be found from the solar spectrum; others must be determined from the spectra of type-B stars, which are believed to be similar in composition to the sun. Some of the nonvolatile elements can also be determined from the solar spectrum, usually with rather low accuracy. Commonly the relative abundances of these elements are better determined from chondritic meteorites, in which not much fractionation of the nonvolatile elements appears to have taken place. Elements in the earth's crust seem to have been fractionated and concentrated to such an extent that it is exceedingly difficult to determine the average abundances and virtually impossible to draw any useful conclusions about the unfractionated abundances, except in a few cases. Meteorites other than chondrites, and certain peculiar classes of stars, may have very different compositions from those listed in Table 2-1.

TABLE 2-1. COMPILATIONS OF ABUNDANCES

Atomic no.	Element	Suess–Urey	Cameron	Clayton–Fowler	Chondrites	Sun	B stars
1	H	4.00×10^{10}	3.2×10^{10}	..	..	3.2×10^{10}	3.6×10^{10}
2	He	3.08×10^{9}	2.6×10^{9}	..	..	..	5.7×10^{9}
3	Li	100	38	..	38	.29	..
4	Be	20	7	..	.64*	7.2	..
5	B	24	6	..	..	..	..
6	C	3.5×10^{6}	1.66×10^{7}	..	..	1.66×10^{7}	7.1×10^{6}
7	N	6.6×10^{6}	3.0×10^{6}	..	..	3.0×10^{6}	5.4×10^{6}
8	O	2.15×10^{7}	2.9×10^{7}	..	..	2.9×10^{7}	2.1×10^{7}
9	F	1600	$\sim 10^{3}$	..	..	..	1.2×10^{5}
10	Ne	8.6×10^{6}	2.9×10^{6}	..	..	..	1.9×10^{7}
11	Na	4.38×10^{4}	4.18×10^{4}	..	..	6.3×10^{4}	..
12	Mg	9.12×10^{5}	1.046×10^{6}	..	..	7.9×10^{5}	3.1×10^{6}
13	Al	9.48×10^{4}	8.93×10^{4}	..	..	5.0×10^{4}	5.8×10^{4}
14	Si	1.00×10^{6}	1.00×10^{6}	..	..	1.00×10^{6}	1.00×10^{6}
15	P	1.00×10^{4}	9320	..	..	6900	1.08×10^{4}
16	S	3.75×10^{5}	6.0×10^{5}	..	..	6.3×10^{5}	1.08×10^{6}
17	Cl	8850	1836	..	..	..	5.8×10^{4}
18	Ar	1.5×10^{5}	2.4×10^{5}	..	..	..	2.9×10^{5}
19	K	3160	2970	..	3290	1580	..
20	Ca	4.90×10^{4}	7.28×10^{4}	..	4.5×10^{4}	4.5×10^{4}	..
21	Sc	28	29	..	32	21	..
22	Ti	2440	3140	..	2090	1510	..
23	V	220	590	..	..	158	..
24	Cr	7800	1.20×10^{4}	..	6400	5000	..
25	Mn	6850	6320	..	7200	2500	..
26	Fe	6.00×10^{5}	8.50×10^{4}	..	..	1.17×10^{5}	..
27	Co	1800	750	..	1190	1380	..
28	Ni	2.74×10^{4}	1.5×10^{4}	..	2.48×10^{4}	2.6×10^{4}	..
29	Cu	212	39	316	186	3500	..
30	Zn	486	202	360	..	800	..
31	Ga	11.4	9.05	32	..	7.2	..
32	Ge	50.5	134	49.1	18.7	62	..
33	As	4.0	4.4	2.18	..	..	..
34	Se	67.6	18.8	30.9	18.8	..	..
35	Br	13.4	3.95	6.9	..	..	..
36	Kr	51.3	20	17.9	..	..	..
37	Rb	6.5	5.0	4.24	4.6–5.8	9.5	..
38	Sr	18.9	21	17.55	..	13.5	..
39	Y	8.9	3.6	11.35	..	5.6	..
40	Zr	54.5	23	39.8	..	54	..
41	Nb	1.00	.81	3.5	..	2.8	..
42	Mo	2.42	2.42	2.77	..	2.5	..

TABLE 2-1.　*Continued*

Atomic no.	Element	Suess–Urey	Cameron	Clayton–Fowler	Chondrites	Sun	B stars
44	Ru	1.49	1.58	.83	1.3†	.93	
45	Rh	.214	.26	.13	.27	.19	
46	Pd	.675	1.00	.601	..	.51	
47	Ag	.26	.26	.166	.131	.044	
48	Cd	.89	.89	.804	..	.91	
49	In	.11	.11	.071	.0013	.46	
50	Sn	1.33	1.33	1.88	..	1.10	
51	Sb	.246	.15	.091	..	2.8	
52	Te	4.67	3.00	1.86	.5–2**	..	
53	I	.80	.46	.21	.02–.3**	..	
54	Xe	4.0	3.15	2.61	..	..	
55	Cs	.456	.25	.13	.10, .14	..	
56	Ba	3.66	4.0	3.68	3.96, 6.44	4.0	
57	La	2.00	.38	.70	.40	..	
58	Ce	2.26	1.08	1.17	.62	..	
59	Pr	.40	.16	.176	.15	..	
60	Nd	1.44	.69	.777	.74	..	
62	Sm	.664	.24	.595	.25	..	
63	Eu	.187	.083	.149	.078, .097	..	
64	Gd	.684	.33	.410	.36	..	
65	Tb	.0956	.054	.083	.056	..	
66	Dy	.556	.33	.449	.39	..	
67	Ho	.118	.076	.084	.078	..	
68	Er	.316	.21	.359	.21	..	
69	Tm	.0318	.032	.060	.039	..	
70	Yb	.220	.18	.387	.19	1.07	
71	Lu	.050	.031	.035	.036	..	
72	Hf	.438	.16	.236	..	..	
73	Ta	.065	.021	.030	.017, .019	..	
74	W	.49	.11	.184	.11	..	
75	Re	.135	.054	.052	..	..	
76	Os	1.00	.73	.511	.73†	..	
77	Ir	.821	.500	.39	.38	..	
78	Pt	1.625	1.157	.80	..	..	
79	Au	.145	.13	.13	.13	..	
80	Hg	.284	.27	.62	.04–8.4	..	
81	Tl	.108	.11	.74	$(3.8–10) \times 10^{-4}$	..	
82	Pb	.47	2.2	6.5	.05–.28	2.5††	
83	Bi	.144	.14	.92	.0016	..	
90	Th	..	.069	..	.026	..	
92	U	..	.042	..	$(7.2–7.9) \times 10^{-3}$	..	

* Sill and Willis, Geochim. Cosmochim. Acta, **26**, 1209, 1962.
† Bate and Huizenga, Geochim. Cosmochim. Acta, **27**, 345, 1963
** Goles and Anders, Jour. Geophys. Res., **66**, 3075, 1961
†† Helliwell, 1961, Astrophys. Jour., **133**, 566, 1961

The first two columns of Table 2-1 contain the atomic number and symbol of the naturally occurring elements. The following paragraphs describe the nature of the abundance information in the remaining columns of the table.

Column three gives the Suess-Urey (1) compilation of abundances. This represents an important pioneering attempt to reconcile astronomical abundance information with abundance analyses of the chondritic meteorites, on the assumption that chondritic meteorites are good samples of solar system nonvolatile material. The results of meteoritic abundance analyses available by 1955 were adjusted by Suess and Urey to give smooth variations in the abundances of the nuclides of odd mass number. The abundance compilation is, therefore, best termed a semiempirical one. This compilation was of very great importance to nuclear physicists when they attempted to deduce the types of nuclear reactions that had been responsible for the synthesis of the elements.

The fourth column of Table 2-1 gives the abundance compilation of Cameron (2). This compilation represents a re-adjustment of that of Suess and Urey, intended to take into account some additional astronomical and meteoritic abundance data and to readjust the abundances of the heavier elements on the basis of specific theories of individual mechanisms of nucleosynthesis.

The fifth column of Table 2-1 lists the abundances of the heavy elements predicted by Clayton and Fowler (3) from an analysis of the formation of heavy elements by the processes of neutron capture on both slow and fast time scales in stellar interiors. These authors emphasize that many of the predicted values are very uncertain.

Column six of Table 2-1 contains new abundance analyses of chondritic meteorites that have been carried out since the compilation of Suess and Urey. Except where noted, these abundances have been taken from the compilation of Ehmann (4). Most of the values usually represent an average of several analyses; in some cases, averages obtained by different analysts are given, separated by a comma; in other cases, where there is a wide variation in the abundances in different chondrites, the range of these values is given. Most of the abundances have been determined by radiochemical analysis and are subject to considerably greater error and intrinsic variation than is indicated by the significant figures that are listed.

The seventh column of Table 2-1 gives a compilation of abundances in the sun, as deduced at the University of Michigan by analysis of the solar spectrum by a method of model atmospheres, and summarized by Aller (5). Some of these abundance values are subject to very great error, owing to some considerable remaining uncertainties in the oscillator strengths of many of the elements. The abundance value given for lead comes from a recent calculation of the oscillator strength of one of the lines in that element by Helliwell (6).

Similar analyses for abundances of the lighter elements in B stars, also summarized by Aller (5), are given in the last column of Table 2-1.

Inspection of Table 2-1 shows that very great uncertainties exist in the relative abundances of many of the elements. It may also be seen that for many elements, such as indium, thallium, lead, and bismuth, the abundance levels in the chondrites are very much lower than would be expected on the basis of nucleosynthesis and on the basis of the solar analyses. The reasons for some of these discrepancies are not at present understood. A great deal of research in many fields remains to be done to improve our knowledge of elemental abundances.

REFERENCES FOR SECTION 2

1. Suess and Urey, Revs. Modern Phys., **28**, 53, 1956
2. Cameron, Astrophys. Jour., **129**, 676, 1959; unpublished notes, 1963
3. Clayton, Fowler, Hull, and Zimmerman, Ann. Phys. (N.Y.), 12, 331, 1961
4. Ehmann, Jour. Chem. Educ., **38**, 53, 1961
5. Aller, The abundance of the elements, Interscience Pub. Inc., 1961
6. Helliwell, Astrophys. Jour., **133**, 566, 1961

SECTION 3

ISOTOPIC ABUNDANCES AND 1961 ATOMIC WEIGHTS
by SYDNEY P. CLARK, JR.

CONTENTS

Handbook of Physical Constants—*Revised Edition*
THE GEOLOGICAL SOCIETY OF AMERICA MEMOIR 97, 1966

Isotopic abundances have been taken from the compilation by Strominger, Hollander, and Seaborg (Revs. Modern Physics, **30,** 585, 1958). Their values have been rounded to the nearest 0.1 per cent, except in cases of very rare isotopes. The natural isotopic variation may exceed this. Atomic weights are on the carbon-12 scale.

TABLE 3-1. ISOTOPIC ABUNDANCES AND ATOMIC WEIGHTS

Atomic no.	Symbol	Mass no.	Abundance (per cent)	1961 Atomic weight
1	H	1	99.99	1.00797
		2	.01	
2	He	3	10^{-4}–10^{-5}	4.0026
		4	100	
3	Li	6	7.4	6.939
		7	92.6	
4	Be	9	100	9.0133
5	B	10	~19	10.811
		11	~81	
6	C	12	98.9	12.01115
		13	1.1	
7	N	14	99.6	14.0067
		15	.4	
8	O	16	99.8	15.9994
		17	.04	
		18	.2	
9	F	19	100	18.9984
10	Ne	20	90.9	20.183
		21	.3	
		22	8.8	
11	Na	23	100	22.9898
12	Mg	24	78.8	24.312
		25	10.2	
		26	11.1	
13	Al	27	100	26.9815
14	Si	28	92.2	28.086
		29	4.7	
		30	3.1	
15	P	31	100	30.9738
16	S	32	95.0	32.064
		33	.8	
		34	4.2	
		36	.02	
17	Cl	35	75.5	35.453
		37	24.5	
18	A	36	.3	39.948
		38	.06	
		40	99.6	
19	K	39	93.1	39.102
		40	.01	
		41	6.9	
20	Ca	40	97.0	40.08
		42	.6	
		43	.1	
		44	2.1	
		46	.003	
		48	.2	

TABLE 3-1.   *Continued*

Atomic no.	Symbol	Mass no.	Abundance (per cent)	1961 Atomic weight
21	Sc	45	100	44.956
22	Ti	46	8.0	47.90
		47	7.7	
		48	73.5	
		49	5.5	
		50	5.3	
23	V	50	.2	50.942
		51	99.8	
24	Cr	50	4.3	51.996
		52	83.8	
		53	9.6	
		54	2.4	
25	Mn	55	100	54.9381
26	Fe	54	5.8	55.847
		56	91.7	
		57	2.2	
		58	.3	
27	Co	59	100	58.9332
28	Ni	58	67.8	58.71
		60	26.2	
		61	1.2	
		62	3.7	
		64	1.2	
29	Cu	63	69.1	63.54
		65	30.9	
30	Zn	64	48.9	65.37
		66	27.8	
		67	4.1	
		68	18.6	
		70	.6	
31	Ga	69	60.5	69.72
		71	39.5	
32	Ge	70	20.6	72.59
		72	27.4	
		73	7.7	
		74	36.7	
		76	7.7	
33	As	75	100	74.9216
34	Se	74	.9	78.96
		76	9.0	
		77	7.6	
		78	23.5	
		80	49.8	
		82	9.2	
35	Br	79	50.6	79.909
		81	49.4	
36	Kr	78	.4	83.80
		80	2.3	
		82	11.6	
		83	11.5	
		84	56.9	
		86	17.4	
37	Rb	85	72.2	85.47
		87	27.8	

TABLE 3-1. *Continued*

Atomic no.	Symbol	Mass no.	Abundance (per cent)	1961 Atomic weight
38	Sr	84	.5	87.62
		86	9.9	
		87	7.0	
		88	82.6	
39	Y	89	100	88.905
40	Zr	90	51.5	91.22
		91	11.2	
		92	17.1	
		94	17.4	
		96	2.8	
41	Nb	93	100	92.906
42	Mo	92	15.9	95.94
		94	9.1	
		95	15.7	
		96	16.5	
		97	9.5	
		98	23.7	
		100	9.6	
44	Ru	96	5.6	101.07
		98	1.9	
		99	12.8	
		100	12.7	
		101	17.0	
		102	31.5	
		104	18.5	
45	Rh	103	100	102.905
46	Pd	102	1.0	106.4
		104	11.0	
		105	22.2	
		106	27.3	
		108	26.7	
		110	11.8	
47	Ag	107	51.4	107.870
		109	48.6	
48	Cd	106	1.2	112.40
		108	.9	
		110	12.4	
		111	12.7	
		112	24.1	
		113	12.3	
		114	28.9	
		116	7.6	
49	In	113	4.3	114.82
		115	95.7	
50	Sn	112	1.0	118.69
		114	.6	
		115	.3	
		116	14.2	
		117	7.6	
		118	24.0	
		119	8.6	
		120	33.0	
		122	4.7	
		124	6.0	

TABLE 3-1. *Continued*

Atomic no.	Symbol	Mass no.	Abundance (per cent)	1961 Atomic weight
51	Sb	121	57.3	121.75
		123	42.7	
52	Te	120	.1	127.60
		122	2.5	
		123	.9	
		124	4.6	
		125	7.0	
		126	18.7	
		128	31.8	
		130	34.5	
53	I	127	100	126.9044
54	Xe	124	.1	131.30
		126	.1	
		128	1.9	
		129	26.4	
		130	4.1	
		131	21.2	
		132	26.9	
		134	10.4	
		136	8.9	
55	Cs	133	100	132.905
56	Ba	130	.1	137.34
		132	.2	
		134	2.6	
		135	6.7	
		136	8.1	
		137	11.9	
		138	70.4	
57	La	138	.1	138.91
		139	99.9	
58	Ce	136	.2	140.12
		138	.2	
		140	88.5	
		142	11.1	
59	Pr	141	100	140.907
60	Nd	142	27.2	144.24
		143	12.2	
		144	23.8	
		145	8.3	
		146	17.2	
		148	5.7	
		150	5.6	
62	Sm	144	3.1	150.35
		147	15.1	
		148	11.3	
		149	13.8	
		150	7.5	
		152	26.6	
		154	22.5	
63	En	151	47.8	151.96
		153	52.2	

Handbook of Physical Constants

TABLE 3-1.   *Continued*

Atomic no.	Symbol	Mass no.	Abundance (per cent)	1961 Atomic weight
64	Gd	152	.2	157.25
		154	2.2	
		155	15.1	
		156	20.6	
		157	15.7	
		158	24.5	
		160	21.6	
65	Tb	159	100	158.924
66	Dy	156	.1	162.50
		158	.1	
		160	2.3	
		161	19.0	
		162	25.5	
		163	24.9	
		164	28.1	
67	Ho	165	100	164.930
68	Er	162	.1	167.26
		164	1.6	
		166	33.4	
		167	22.9	
		168	27.1	
		170	14.9	
69	Tm	169	100	168.934
70	Yb	169	.1	173.04
		170	3.1	
		171	14.4	
		172	21.9	
		173	16.2	
		174	31.6	
		176	12.6	
71	Lu	175	97.4	174.97
		176	2.6	
72	Hf	174	.2	178.49
		176	5.2	
		177	18.5	
		178	27.1	
		179	13.8	
		180	35.2	
73	Ta	180	.01	180.948
		181	100	
74	W	180	.1	183.85
		182	26.4	
		183	14.4	
		184	30.6	
		186	28.4	
75	Re	185	37.1	186.2
		187	62.9	
76	Os	184	.02	190.2
		186	1.6	
		187	1.6	
		188	13.3	
		189	16.1	
		190	26.4	
		192	41.0	

TABLE 3-1.   *Continued*

Atomic no.	Symbol	Mass no.	Abundance (per cent)	1961 Atomic weight
77	Ir	191	38.5	192.2
		193	61.5	
78	Pt	190	.01	195.09
		192	.8	
		194	32.9	
		195	33.8	
		196	25.2	
		198	7.2	
79	Au	197	100	196.967
80	Hg	196	.1	200.59
		198	10.0	
		199	16.8	
		200	23.1	
		201	13.2	
		202	29.8	
		204	6.9	
81	Ti	203	29.5	204.37
		205	70.5	
82	Pb	204	1.4	207.19
		206	25.2	
		207	21.5	
		208	52.0	
83	Bi	209	100	208.980
90	Th	232	100	232.038
92	U	234	∼.006	238.03
		235	.72	
		238	99.28	

SECTION 4

DENSITY OF ROCKS

by R. A. DALY, G. EDWARD MANGER, AND SYDNEY P. CLARK, JR.

CONTENTS

Handbook of Physical Constants—*Revised Edition*
THE GEOLOGICAL SOCIETY OF AMERICA MEMOIR 97, 1966

TABLE 4-1.	AVERAGE DENSITIES OF HOLOCRYSTALLINE IGNEOUS ROCKS
(R. A. Daly)

Rock	Number of samples	Mean density	Range of density
Granite	155	2.667	2.516–2.809
Granodiorite	11	2.716	2.668–2.785
Syenite	24	2.757	2.630–2.899
Quartz diorite	21	2.806	2.680–2.960
Diorite	13	2.839	2.721–2.960
Norite	11	2.984	2.720–3.020
Gabbro, including olivine gabbro	27	2.976	2.850–3.120
Diabase, fresh	40	2.965	2.804–3.110
Peridotite, fresh	3	3.234	3.152–3.276
Dunite*	15	3.277	3.204–3.314
Pyroxenite	8	3.231	3.10 –3.318
Anorthosite	12	2.734	2.640–2.920

* From Birch, Jour. Geophys. Res., **65**, 1083, 1960

TABLE 4-2.	AVERAGE DENSITIES OF NATURAL GLASSES
(R. A. Daly)

Glass	No. of determinations	Range of density	Mean density	Ref.
Rhyolite obsidian	15	2.330–2.413	2.370	2
Trachyte obsidian	3	2.435–2.467	2.450	2
Pitchstone	4	2.321–2.37	2.338	1
Andesite glass	3	2.40 –2.573	2.474	1
Leucite tephrite glass	2	2.52 –2.58	2.55	1
Basalt glass	11	2.704–2.851	2.772	2

REFERENCES FOR TABLE 4-2

1. George, Jour. Geology, **32**, 353, 1924
2. Tilley, Min. Mag., **19**, 275, 1922

Table 4-1 was taken by Daly from a slightly longer compilation in his *Igneous rocks and the depths of the earth* (New York, McGraw-Hill Book Co., 598 p., 1933). It is virtually the same as the list in the first edition of the Handbook of Physical Constants, but with more extensive data for dunites. For further data on the densities of igneous rocks *see* Tables 9-2, 21-2, and 21-4.

Table 4-4 lists a selection of values of porosity and density of sedimentary rocks. The selection illustrates porosity and density variations in relationship to rock type, and to age, locality, and depth of sample.

Porosity is expressed as either total or apparent porosity. Total porosity is a measure of the total void volume and includes those pores which may be sealed off, as well as those which are connected with the surface of the test specimens. It is based on differences in measurement between total or bulk volume (V_B) and grain volume (V_G). The total porosity (P_T) by per cent is

$$P_T = 100\left(1 - \frac{V_G}{V_B}\right) \tag{1}$$

TABLE 4-3.   DENSITY OF CRYSTALLINE ROCK AND CORRESPONDING GLASS
(ARTIFICIALLY PREPARED)
(R. A. Daly)

	Density		Difference per cent of rock density	Ref.
	Rock	Glass		
Granite, Shap Fells	2.656	2.446	7.90	3
Granite, Peterhead	2.630	2.376	9.66	3
Syenite, Plauen'scher Grund	2.724	2.560	6.02	3
Tonalite, New Zealand	2.765	2.575	6.87	3
Diorite, Guernsey	2.833	2.680	5.40	3
Diorite, Markfield	2.880	2.710	5.90	3
Gabbro, Carrock Fell	2.940	2.791	5.07	3
Olivine dolerite, Clee Hills	2.889	2.775	3.95	3
Dolerite, Rowley Rag	2.800	2.640	5.71	3
Dolerite, Whin Sill	2.925	2.800	4.27	3
Diabase, Palisades	2.975	2.761	7.19	1
Diabase, Vinal Haven	2.96	2.76	6.8	2
Eclogite	3.415·	2.746 (?)	19.6	4

REFERENCES FOR TABLE 4-3

1. Day, Sosman, and Hostetter, Am. Jour. Sci., **37**, 1, 1914
2. Dane, E. B., unpublished
3. Douglas, Geol. Soc. London, Quart. Jour., **63**, 145, 1907
4. Joly and Poole, Philos. Mag., **3**, 1242, 1927

Alternatively, and more usually, grain density (D_G) is substituted for grain volume, and bulk density (D_B) for bulk volume. Total porosity by per cent correspondingly is

$$P_T = 100\left(1 - \frac{D_B}{D_G}\right). \tag{2}$$

Apparent porosity, otherwise called effective or net porosity, excludes sealed-off or occluded pores. It is based on a measurement of the pore volume (V_P) which inter-communicates and is connected with the surface of the test specimen. Apparent porosity (P_A) by per cent is

$$P_A = 100\left(\frac{V_P}{V_B}\right).$$

The method of determining porosity may affect porosity values more than true differences between total and apparent porosity. For 10 specimens of fire brick Hart-mann (13) found that the average total porosity, determined by the grain density–bulk density relationship, was 25.5 per cent where bulk volume was obtained by the displacement of water by a previously wetted specimen, but 24.6 per cent where bulk volume was obtained by mercury displacement. Nutting (25) stated that in the determination of grain density by pycnometry the adsorption of water by very finely powdered quartz grains or other material may cause an error of 1 or 2 per cent in the determination of grain density. Apparently, however, such large errors due to the adsorption of water do not commonly occur in practice. Hirschwald (17) showed that an erroneous large deficiency of apparent porosity may result from obtaining pore volume by the imbibition of water under atmospheric pressure. He obtained better results by letting the specimens imbibe water for 3 hours under a partial vacuum equal to the vapor pressure of water at room temperature, but he had to apply a pressure of 50–150 atmospheres to obtain the optimum saturation of the pores.

Among the earlier publications which give extensive data on porosity and bulk density is that of Buckley (5), who determined the porosity of building stones of Wisconsin by slowly immersing the specimens in boiling water and then maintaining a reduced pressure of one twelfth of an atmosphere on the specimens for 36 hours. Gary (9) listed the bulk density of numerous building stones, and the total porosity as determined by the grain density–bulk density relationship. Moore (22) determined the porosity of specimens of sedimentary rocks by saturating them with water under a vacuum of 29 inches of mercury and listed many determinations. Fuller (8) calculated the porosity of some sedimentary and other rocks by using the data of Geikie, Delesse, and Merrill, but the original data were obtained from the imbibition of water under atmospheric pressure. Sorby (33) gave the porosity of sandstone, shale, and slate obtained by imbibition of water for several days under a partial vacuum resulting from the condensation of steam. Hirschwald (17) determined the porosity of many sandstone, limestone, and slate specimens of building stone by saturating the specimens under a partial vacuum and then applying a pressure of 150 atmospheres. Grubenmann, Niggli, and others (11) have presented extensive data on the total porosity and bulk density of the building and roofing stones of Switzerland. Kessler (18) determined the bulk density of commercial marbles of the United States and derived total porosity by the grain density–bulk density relationship.

More recently Melcher (21) gave a critical discussion of previous methods of porosity determination and presented many determinations of bulk density and total porosity of oil sands obtained by the grain density–bulk density relationship. Hedberg (14, 15) and Athy (1) determined the total porosity and bulk density of subsurface samples of shale with particular reference to the relationship of compaction to the thickness of overburden. Stearns (34) determined the bulk density and total porosity of many samples of water-bearing rock. Fancher, Lewis, and Barnes (6) gave extensive references to the various methods of porosity determination, summarized many of the methods and techniques evolved up to the year 1933, and presented many original porosity determinations. A recent extensive list of porosity determinations of oil sands is given by Rall, Hamontre, and Taliaferro (29). In their method pore volume is determined by the pressure and volume relationships of a gas system with and without a rock specimen.

Average values for the porosity of sedimentary rocks have been given by Barrell (2) as: shale, 8.2 per cent; sandstone, 14.8 per cent; limestone, 5.3 per cent; and all sedimentary rocks, 8.5 per cent. Additional data since the publication of Barrell's summary indicate that the average value of 8.2 per cent porosity for shale may be low. Athy's graph (1) for Pennsylvanian and Permian shales from structurally disturbed areas show an average of 8.8 per cent for a depth range from 1000 feet to 5000 feet, but Hedberg's data (15) for undisturbed Tertiary shale show an average porosity of 19.8 per cent for a depth range from 219 feet to 7994 feet.

For further data on the density of sediments and sedimentary rocks, see Tables 21-5 and 21-11.

TABLE 4-4. POROSITY AND BULK DENSITY, DRY AND SATURATED, OF SEDIMENTARY ROCKS*
(G. Edward Manger)

Formation	Age	Locality	Depth of sample, feet	Number of samples	Porosity, per cent Aver.	Min.	Max.	Sat'd. bulk density (average) g per cm⁻³	Ref.	Porosity method: T (Total) A (Apparent)
			SANDSTONE							
"Mount Simon" ss.	Cambrian	W. Va., Wood County	13,005–13,065	9	.7	.2	2.5	2.70	30	A
Southern "Potsdam" ss.	Cambrian	Wis.	quarry	14	11.4	4.8	28.3	2.41	5	A
Northern "Potsdam" ss.	Cambrian	Wis.	quarry	16	19.4	10.4	22.6	2.32	5	A
St. Peter Ss.	Ordovician	Ark., Ozark Plateau	outcrop	12	8.8	3.6	14.1	2.50	4	T
Bradford ss.	Devonian	Pa.	≈600–≈2300	297	15.0	6.0	23.3	2.40 (assumed grain density, 2.65 g cm⁻³)	7	T
Chemung Formation (ss's.)	Devonian	Pa.	≈1700–≈2300	49	9.5	4.5	22.2	2.51	20, 21	T
Berea Ss.	Mississippian	Ohio, W. Va.	0–2160	18	14.1	4.7	19.5	2.39	20, 21 3, 36	T, A
Atoka Formation (and other ss's.)	Pennsylvanian	Ark.: Ozark Plat.	outcrop	17	12.3	4.7	19.8	2.44	4	T
		Ark. Valley	outcrop	35	7.8	0	20.6	2.51	4	T
		Ouachita Mts.	outcrop	25	5.1	0	10.4	2.56	4	T
Bartlesville sand	Pennsylvanian	Okla.	1570–2680	26	18.3	7.6	32.0	2.40	20	T
Bunter Ss.	Triassic	Gt. Britain	outcrop	18	20.4	5.8	30.8	2.29	22	A
Keuper Ss.	Triassic	Gt. Britain	outcrop	16	22.6	16.5	28.6	2.25	22	A
Woodbine sand	Cretaceous	Tex.	2436–3701	10	24.7	19.0	32.0	2.25	28	A
Sandstones and siltstones	Cretaceous	Montana, eastern	outcrop	22	33.7	22.6	38.3	2.17	34	T
Sandstones	Cretaceous	Wyo.	0–3187	38	19.7	8.8	27.0	2.32	20, 21	T
Sandstones	Miocene	Switzerland	quarry	15	18.7 (dips 7° or less)	13.3	22.1	2.37	11	T
			LIMESTONE, DOLOMITE, CHALK, AND MARBLE							
Ellenburger Group (ls. and dol.)	Ordovician	Tex., Llano County	outcrop	57	3.0	.1	12.6	2.75	10	T
Beekmantown Group (dol.)	Ordovician	W. Va., Wood County	10,531–11,945	56	.4	.1	1.1	2.80	30	A
Black River Ls.	Ordovician	Ontario	quarry	11	.46	.07	1.67	2.72	26	A
Niagara Dolomite	Silurian	Wis.	quarry	14	2.9	.5	6.7	2.77	5	A

TABLE 4-4. *Continued*

Formation	Age	Locality	Depth of sample, feet	Number of samples	Porosity, per cent Aver.	Min.	Max.	Sat'd. bulk density (average) g per cm^{-3}	Ref.	Porosity method: T (Total) A (Apparent)
		LIMESTONE, DOLOMITE, CHALK, AND MARBLE *Continued*								
Limestone	Carboniferous	Gt. Britain, Midlands	outcrop	24	5.7	2.2	14.9	2.58	27	T
Marl	Carboniferous	Russia	subsurface	19	8.2	..	..	2.63	24	T
Oolites	Jurassic	Gt. Britain	outcrop	5	14.6	5.5	24.0	2.44	22	A
Limestones	Jurassic	Switzerland	quarry	114	3.6	.4	25.6	2.66	11	T
			(dips 8° or more)							
Glen Rose Ls.	Cretaceous	Tex.	20.5–30.5	10	16.8	16.0	18.8	2.37	28	A
Chalk	Cretaceous	Gt. Britain	outcrop	3	28.8	17.6	42.8	2.23	22	A
Limestone	Cretaceous	Switzerland	quarry	29	4.3	.4	18.3	2.65	11	T
			(dips 10° or more)							
Green River Fm. (marlstone)	Eocene	Colo.	mine	11	2.9	.2	12.0	2.26	36	A
		SHALE, CLAYSTONE, AND SLATE								
Shale	Pennsylvanian	Okla.	1000	..	17	..	..	2.42	1	graph
			3000	..	7	..	..	2.59	1	graph
			5000	..	4	..	..	2.66	1	graph
Shales	Cretaceous	Wyo., Mont.	outcrop	9	29.5	23.8	37.6	2.17	31	T
Shale, nearly horizontal and undisturbed	Oligocene and Miocene	Venezuela	≈600	6	33.5	31.3	35.8	2.06	15	T
			≈2500	9	25.4	22.9	28.9	2.25	15	T
			≈3500	9	21.1	17.8	25.6	2.35	15	T
			≈6100	3	9.6	9.1	10.6	2.52	15	T
			≈7850	2	10.4	10.3	10.4	..	15	T
		SAND, CLAY, GRAVEL, ALLUVIUM, AND SOILS								
Cape May Fm. (sd.)	Pleistocene	N.J.	mostly pits	12	38.9	30.8	45.3	1.93	34	T
Loess soil	Quaternary	Idaho	surface	3	61.2	53.2	69.4	1.61	34	T
Fine sand	Quaternary	Calif.	sea-floor sediments	54	46.2	..	..	1.93	12	†
Very fine sand			0-1 inch below the depositional surface	15	47.7	..	..	1.92	12	†
Sand-silt-clay				3	74.7	..	..	1.44	12	†
Mud	Quaternary	Hudson River	submerged crate	..	88.2	..	..	..	19	†

SAND, CLAY, GRAVEL, ALLUVIUM, AND SOILS *Continued*

Silt	Quaternary	Hudson River	50 ft below river	..	55	..	..	..	..	16	†
Newly deposited material	Quaternary	Mississippi River Delta	..	..	80–90	..	..	..		32	A
Soft mud	Quaternary	Clyde Sea	0–2.5 cm in mud	9	82	80	87	..		23	A
			22.5–25 cm in mud	9	75	72	80	..		23	A
Marble	?	U.S.A., Great Britain	MISCELLANEOUS quarry	112	.7 .4 2.1 (43 + localities)			2.75		18, 22	T, A

* Publication authorized by the Director, U.S. Geological Survey.
† Pore volume by volume of natural-state water.

REFERENCES FOR TABLE 4-4

1. Athy, Am. Assoc. Petroleum Geologists Bull., **14**, 1, 1930
2. Barrell, Jour. Geology, **22**, 214, 1914
3. Bownocker, Ohio Geol. Survey Bull. 18, 1915
4. Branner, Am. Assoc. Petroleum Geologists Bull., **21**, 67, 1937
5. Buckley, Wisconsin Geologists Nat. Hist. Survey Bull. **4**, 401, 1898
6. Fancher, Lewis, and Barnes, Penn. State Coll. Min. Indus. Expt. Sta. Bull. **12**, 65, 1933
7. Fettke, Am. Assoc. Petroleum Geologists Bull., **18**, 191, 1934
8. Fuller, U.S. Geol. Survey Water-Supply Paper **160**, 59, 1906
9. Gary, Mitt. Kgl. tech. Versuchanstalten Berlin, **5**, 243, 1898
10. Goldich and Parmelee, Am. Assoc. Petroleum Geologists Bull., **31**, 1982, 1947
11. Grubenmann et al., Beitr. Geol. Schweiz, Geotech. Ser. 5, 1915
12. Hamilton and Menard, Am. Assoc. Petroleum Geologists Bull., **40**, 755, 1956
13. Hartmann, Fachausschüsse Ver. deutscher Eisenhüttenleute, Ber. 82, 1926
14. Hedberg, Am. Assoc. Petroleum Geologists Bull., **10**, 1035, 1926
15. —— Am. Jour. Sci., [5], **31**, 241, 1936
16. Hewett and Johannesson, Shield and compressed air tunneling, New York, McGraw-Hill Book Co., 291, 1922
17. Hirschwald, Handbuch der bautechnischen Gesteinprüfung, Berlin, Borntraeger, 1912
18. Kessler, U.S. Bur. Stds. Technol. Paper 123, 1919
19. Lewis, Geol. Soc. America Bull., **35**, 557, 1924
20. Melcher, Am. Inst. Min. Metall. Engrs. Trans., **65**, 469, 1921
21. —— Am. Assoc. Petroleum Geologists Bull., **8**, 716, 1924
22. Moore, Geol. Soc. Liverpool Proc., **9**, 129, 1904
23. Moore, Marine Biol. Assoc. (Gt. Brit.) Jour., **17** (new ser.), 325, 1931
24. Nevolin, Galakfionov, and Serova, Priklad. Geofiz., no. 22, 129, 1959
25. Nutting, Am. Assoc. Petroleum Geologists Bull., **14**, 1337, 1930
26. —— quoted in Geol. Soc. Am. Spec. Paper 36, 25, 1942
27. Parks, Report on the building and ornamental stones of Canada, Canada Dept. Mines, 1912
28. Parsons, Geol. Mag. (Gt. Brit.), **59**, 51, 1922
29. Pfeiffer and Dienemann, Preusz. Geol. Landesanstalt Jahrb., **49**, 304, 1928
30. Plummer and Tapp, Am. Assoc. Petroleum Geologists Bull., **27**, 64, 1943
31. Rall, Hamontre, and Taliaferro, U.S. Bur. Mines Rept. Inv. 5025, 1954
32. Robertson, E. C., written communication, 1959
33. Rubey, U.S. Geol. Survey Prof. Paper 165-A, 1930
34. Shaw, *quoted in* Meinzer, U.S. Geol. Survey Water-Supply Paper 489, 8, 1923
35. Sorby, Geol. Soc. London Quart. Jour., **64**, 171, 1908
36. Stearns, U.S. Geol. Survey Water-Supply Paper 596, 1927

There appear to be few systematic studies of the densities of metamorphic rocks; most of the entries in Table 4-5 refer to rocks from New England. Compilation of such a table is complicated by the fact that geologists tend to classify metasedimentary rocks on a stratigraphic basis, rather than on mineralogy. The mineralogy, and hence the density, of a given formation depends in part on the grade of metamorphism, which differs from place to place. The situation may be further complicated by banding and layering, which can cause heterogeneity in the rock on a scale of a few inches to many feet. This makes it difficult to sample adequately and accurately.

For further data on the densities of metamorphic rocks *see* Tables 9-2, 21-2, and 21-4.

TABLE 4-5. AVERAGE DENSITIES OF METAMORPHIC ROCKS
(Sydney P. Clark, Jr.)

Rock	Number of samples	Mean density	Range of density	Ref.
Gneiss, Chester, Vt.	7	2.69	2.66 –2.73	1
Granite gneiss, Hohe Tauern, Austria	19	2.61	2.59 –2.63	3
Gneiss, Grenville, Adirondack Mtns., N.Y.	25	2.84	2.70 –3.06	1
Oligoclase gneiss, Middle Haddam area, Conn.	28	2.67	..	4
Quartz-mica schists, Littleton Fm., N.H. (high-grade metamorphism)	76	2.82	2.70 –2.96	1
Muscovite-biotite schist, Middle Haddam area, Conn.	32	2.76	..	4
Staurolite-garnet and biotite-muscovite schists, Middle Haddam Area, Conn.	22	2.76	..	4
Chlorite-sericite schists, Vt.	50	2.82	2.73 –3.03	1
Slate, Taconic sequence, Vt.	17	2.81	2.72 –2.84	1
Amphibolite, N.H. and Vt.	13	2.99	2.79 –3.14	1
Granulite, Lapland hypersthene-bearing	7	2.93	2.67 –3.10	5
hypersthene-free	5	2.73	2.63 –2.85	5
Eclogite	10	3.392	3.338–3.452	2

REFERENCES FOR TABLE 4-5

1. Bean, Geol. Soc. America Bull., **64,** 509, 1953
2. Birch, Jour. Geophys. Res. **65,** 1083, 1960
3. Clark, Geophys. Jour. **6,** 9, 1961
4. Eaton and Rosenfeld, Rept. XXI Session, Int. Geol. Congr., Pt. II, 168, 1960
5. Eskola, Am. Jour. Sci., Bowen Volume, 133, 1952

SECTION 5

X-RAY CRYSTALLOGRAPHIC DATA, DENSITIES, AND MOLAR VOLUMES OF MINERALS*

by RICHARD A. ROBIE, PHILIP M. BETHKE, MARTHA S. TOULMIN,
AND JERRY L. EDWARDS

CONTENTS

* Publication authorized by the Director, U.S. Geological Survey

Handbook of Physical Constants—*Revised Edition*
THE GEOLOGICAL SOCIETY OF AMERICA MEMOIR 97, 1966

X-ray crystallographic data are of particular importance to the mineralogist. Beyond the considerations of structural chemistry, they provide one of the most accurate methods for phase and/or compositional determination and for obtaining the molar volumes and densities of minerals (Table 5-2).

Selected data for approximately 300 minerals are tabulated in Table 5-1. These are taken from the recent literature or from unpublished sources. With minor exceptions, we have restricted ourselves to data for chemically and physically well-defined phases for which the unit cell parameters are known with an accuracy of the order of .2 per cent or better.

The data are presented by mineral groups following Dana's System. Within a group, however, the order may be alphabetical, structural, or for the sulfides, approximately by increasing sulfur-metal ratio.

Temperatures at which the measurements were made are given in the second column from the right. The letter r indicates the data were obtained at an unspecified room temperature and may be taken as $25° \pm 5° C$. The number of gram formula weights per unit cell is given in the column labeled Z.

Compounds denoted by an asterisk indicate the measurements were made on natural specimens which may have deviated slightly from the listed formula. Substances of rhombohedral symmetry are denoted by the symbol hex-R to distinguish them from materials of true hexagonal symmetry. The space group is given along with its number in the 1952 International Tables for X-ray Crystallography (Henry and Lonsdale, 1952).

All cell dimensions are given in Angstrom units, 10^{-8} cm. Where necessary, older data have been converted from kX units to Angstroms using the conversion factor $1.00204 \pm .000014$ of Cohen, Crowe, and DuMond (1957).

Most natural minerals are intermediate members of multicomponent solid solutions. For this reason data have been included for several phases, not known as minerals but which form the end member of a solid solution. We have also included cell parameters, based on the linear extrapolation of data for incomplete solutions, for several hypothetical compounds.

The uncertainties listed are not necessarily those of the original investigator but represent our attempt to evaluate the true accuracy of the data. In this connection it is worthwhile to restate the results of a recent-co-operative investigation by the International Union of Crystallography (Parrish, 1960), involving more than 20 laboratories, which has shown that although the reproducibility (that is, precision) of an individual may be a few thousandths of a per cent, different investigators working on the same sample showed agreement with one another of only .005 per cent to .015 per cent. Data claiming an accuracy of better than .01 per cent should be considered with these limitations in mind.

For more extensive summaries of X-ray data the reader is referred to the following works:

Berry, L. G., and Thompson, R. M., X-ray powder data for the ore minerals: The Peacock Atlas, Geol. Soc. America Mem. 85, 1962

Donnay, J. D. H., and Nowacki, W., Crystal data, Geol. Soc. America Mem. 60, 1954

International Union of Crystallography, Structure reports (volume 8 through 16 summarize data published from 1940 to 1952)

Pearson, W. B., Handbook of lattice spacing and structure of alloys, New York, Pergamon Press, 1958

REFERENCES

Cohen, E. R., Crowe, K. M., and DuMond, J. W. M., Fundamental constants of physics, New York, Interscience Publisher, 1957

Henry, N. F. M., and Lonsdale, K., Editors, International tables for X-ray crystallography, v. 1, Symmetry groups, Birmingham, England, Kynoch Press, Internat. Union Crystallography, 1952

Parrish, William, Results of the International Union of Crystallography precision lattice parameter project, Acta Cryst., **13**, 833, 1960

The data contained in tables 5-1 and 5-2 was prepared in 1962. This material has since been expanded, a number of corrections made and the formula weights and densities corrected to the unified chemical-physical scale of atomic weights and the 1963 physical constants adopted by NAS-NBS. The revision is available as an open-file U.S. Geological Survey report by R. A. Robie, P. M. Bethke, and K. M. Beardsley.

TABLE 5-1. X-Ray Crystallographic

Formula	Name	Crystal system	Space group	Structure type	Z
Elements					
Ag	silver	cub	Fm3m (225)	f.c.c.[1]	4
Au	gold	cub	Fm3m (225)	f.c.c.	4
C*	diamond	cub	Fd3m (227)	diamond	8
C*	graphite	hex	C6/mmc (194)	graphite	4
Cu	copper	cub	Fm3m (225)	f.c.c.	4
Fe	α-iron	cub	Im3m (229)	b.c.c.[2]	2
Ni	nickel	cub	Fm3m (225)	f.c.c.	4
Pt	platinum	cub	Fm3m (225)	f.c.c.	4
S	α-sulfur	orth	Fddd (70)	S_8 ring molecules	128
S	β-sulfur	mon	$P2_1/c$ (14)	S_8 ring molecules	48
Pb	lead	cub	Fm3m (225)	f.c.c.	4
Sn	β-tin	tet	$I4_1/amd$ (141)	..	4
Sb	antimony	hex-R	R3̄m (166)	arsenic	6
As	Arsenic	hex-R	R3̄m (166)	arsenic	6
Bi	bismuth	hex-R	R3̄m (166)	arsenic	6
Zn	zinc	hex	$P6_3/mmc$ (194)	h.c.p.[3]	2
Se	selenium	hex	$P3_121$ (152) $P3_221$ (154)	chain	3
Te	tellurium	hex	$P3_121$ (152) $P3_221$ (154)	chain	3
Si	silicon	cub	Fd3m (227)	diamond	8
Sulfides, Tellurides, Selenides, and Arsenides					
β-$Ni_3Pb_2S_2$*	shandite	hex-R	R3̄m (166)	..	3
Au_2Bi	maldonite	cub	Fd3m (227)	Cu_2Mg	8
Ag_2S I	hi-argentite	cub	..	..	4
Ag_2S II	argentite	cub	..	..	2
Ag_2S III	acanthite	mon	$P2_1/c$ (14)	..	4
Ag_2Se	hi-naumannite	cub	..	..	..
Ag_2Te I	..	cub	..	..	2

[1] f.c.c., face-centered cubic
[2] b.c.c., body-centered cubic
[3] h.c.p., hexagonal close packed

DATA FOR MINERALS

a_0	b_0	c_0	α_0 or α_r	β_0	γ_0	Temp °C	Ref.
4.0862 ±.0002	..	..	..	..	..	25	146
4.0786 ±.0002	..	..	..	..	..	25	146
3.56703 ±.0001	..	..	..	..	..	25	131, 183
2.4612 ±.0001	..	6.7079 ±.0007	..	..	..	14.6	99
3.6150 ±.0003	..	..	..	..	..	25	146
2.8664 ±.0005	..	..	..	..	..	25	149
3.5238 ±.0005	..	..	..	..	..	25	146
3.9231 ±.0005	..	..	..	..	..	25	146
10.4646 ±.001	12.8660 ±.001	24.4860 ±.002	..	..	..	24.7	178, 21
11.04 ±.03	10.98 ±.03	10.92 ±.03	..	96° 44′ ±30′	..	103	32
4.9505 ±.0005	..	..	..	..	..	25	146
5.83146 ±.0005	..	3.18129 ±.0007	..	..	..	26	69
4.307 ±.001	..	11.273 ±.001	..	..	..	26	148, 126
3.760 ±.002	..	10.548 ±.004	..	..	..	26	148
4.5459 ±.0010	..	11.8622 ±.0030	..	..	..	26	69, 126, 148
2.665 ±.001	..	4.947 ±.0007	..	..	..	25	146
4.3642 ±.0005	..	4.9588 ±.0005	..	..	..	26	143
4.4570 ±.0007	..	5.9290 ±.0010	..	..	..	25	146
5.4305 ±.0003	..	..	..	..	..	25	183
5.576 ±.01	..	13.658 ±.01	..	..	..	r	67, 110
7.958 ±.002	..	..	..	..	..	r	73
6.269 ±.020	..	..	..	..	..	600	30
4.870 ±.008	..	..	..	..	..	189	30
4.228 ±.002	6.928 ±.005	7.862 ±.003	..	99° 35′	..	r	30, 155
4.993 ±.016	..	..	..	..	..	170	116
5.29 ±.01	..	..	..	..	..	825	116

TABLE 5-1. *Continued*

Formula	Name	Crystal system	Space group	Structure type	Z
SULFIDES, TELLURIDES, SELENIDES, AND ARSENIDES. *Continued*					
Ag_2Te II	..	cub	..	..	..
Ag_2Te III*	hessite	mon	$P2_1/c$ (14)	..	4
Cu_2S I*	hi-digenite	cub	..	..	4
Cu_2S II*	hi-chalcocite	hex	..	..	..
Cu_2S III*	chalcocite	orth	Ab2m (39)	..	96
$Cu_{1.79}S$ (Cu rich side)	digenite	pseudo cub	..	deformed CaF_2	4
$Cu_{1.77}S$ (S rich side)	digenite	pseudo cub	..	deformed CaF_2	4
Cu_2Se	..	cub	..	..	4
$Ag_{1.55}Cu_{.45}S$ I	..	cub	..	..	4
$Ag_{1.55}Cu_{.45}S$ II	..	cub	..	..	2
$Ag_{1.55}Cu_{.45}S$ III	jalpaite	tet	..	..	16
$Ag_{.93}Cu_{1.07}S$ I	..	cub	..	..	4
$Ag_{.93}Cu_{1.07}S$ II	..	hex	..	..	2
$Ag_{.93}Cu_{1.07}S$ III	stromeyerite	orth	Cmcn (63)	..	4
AgCuSe	eucairite	orth, pseudo tet	P4/nmm (129)	..	10
Ag_3AuTe_2*	petzite	cub	$I4_132$ (214)	..	8
Cu_3Se_2*	umangite	tet	P4/mmm (123)	..	2
Ni_3S_2	heazlewoodite	hex-R	R32 (155)	Ni_3S_2	3
Cu_5FeS_4*	hi-bornite	cub	..	..	1
Cu_5FeS_4*	metastable bornite	cub	..	..	8
Cu_5FeS_4*	lo-bornite	tet	$P\bar{4}2_1c$ (144)	..	16
$Ni_{11}As_8$	maucherite	tet	$P4_12_12$ (92)	..	4
(Fe, Ni)$_9S_8$ $Fe_{5.25}Ni_{3.75}S_8$	pentlandite	cub	Fm3m (225)	Co_9S_8	4
(Fe, Ni)$_9S_8$ $Fe_{3.75}Ni_{5.25}S_8$	pentlandite	cub	Fm3m (225)	Co_9S_8	4
CaS	oldhamite	cub	Fm3m (225)	NaCl	4
PbS	galena	cub	Fm3m (225)	NaCl	4
PbSe	clausthalite	cub	Fm3m (225)	NaCl	4
PbTe	altaite	cub	Fm3m (225)	NaCl	4

a_0	b_0	c_0	α_0 or α_r	β_0	γ_0	Temp °C	Ref.
6.585 ±.010	..	..	..	..	..	250	116
8.09 ±.02	4.48 ±.01	8.96 ±.02	..	123° 20′	..	r	45
5.725 ±.010	..	..	..	..	..	465	29, 119
3.961 ±.004	..	6.722 ±.007	..	..	..	152	29, 119
11.881 ±.004	27.323 ±.008	13.491 ±.004	..	..	..	r	29, 119
5.5695 ±.001	..	..	..	..	..	25	29, 119
5.5542 ±.001	..	..	..	..	..	25	29, 119
5.85 ±.01	..	..	..	..	..	170	119
6.110 ±.010	..	..	..	..	..	300	30
4.825 ±.005	..	..	..	..	..	116	30
8.673 ±.004	..	11.756 ±.006	..	..	..	r	30
5.961 ±.009	..	..	..	..	..	196	30
4.138 ±.004	..	7.105 ±.007	..	..	..	100	30
4.066 ±.002	6.628 ±.003	7.972 ±.004	..	..	..	r	30
4.105 ±.010	20.35 ±.02	6.31 ±.01	..	..	..	r	43
10.38 ±.02	..	..	..	..	..	r	44
6.402 ±.01	..	4.276 ±.01	..	..	..	r	8, 36
5.746 ±.001	..	7.134 ±.002	..	..	..	r	77, 84
5.50 ±.01	..	..	..	..	..	240	95
10.94 ±.02	..	..	..	..	..	r	95
10.94 ±.02	..	21.88 ±.04	..	..	..	r	95
6.870 ±.001	..	21.81 ±.01	..	..	..	r	176
10.196 ±.010	..	..	..	..	..	r	85
10.095 ± .010	..	..	..	..	..	r	85
5.689 ±.006	..	..	..	..	..	r	152, 62, 115
5.9360 ±.0002	..	..	..	..	..	r	10, 147, 167
6.1255 ±.0005	..	..	..	..	..	r	10
6.4606 ±.0005	..	..	..	..	..	r	9

Table 5-1. *Continued*

Formula	Name	Crystal system	Space group	Structure type	Z
SULFIDES, TELLURIDES, SELENIDES, AND ARSENIDES. *Continued*					
MnS	alabandite	cub	Fm3m (225)	NaCl	4
MnS	sphalerite structure	cub	F$\bar{4}$3m (216)	sphalerite	4
MnS	wurtzite structure	hex	P6$_3$mc (186)	ZnO	2
PtS	cooperite	tet	P4$_2$/mmc (131)	PtS	4
CdS	greenockite	hex	P6$_3$mc (186)	ZnO	2
CdS	hawleyite	cub	F$\bar{4}$3m (216)	sphalerite	4
CdS	(hypothetical)	cub	Fm3m (225)	NaCl	4
ZnS	sphalerite	cub	F$\bar{4}$3m (216)	sphalerite	4
ZnS	wurtzite	hex	P6$_3$mc (186)	ZnO	2
ZnSe	stilleite	cub	F$\bar{4}$3m (216)	sphalerite	4
ZnTe	..	cub	F$\bar{4}$3m(216)	sphalerite	4
HgS	cinnabar	hex	P3$_1$21 (152) P3$_2$21 (154)	cinnabar	3
HgS	metacinnabar	cub	F$\bar{4}$3m (216)	sphalerite	4
HgSe	tiemannite	cub	F$\bar{4}$3m (216)	sphalerite	4
HgTe	coloradoite	cub	F$\bar{4}$3m (216)	sphalerite	4
FeS	(hypothetical)	cub	F$\bar{4}$3m (216)	sphalerite	4
FeS	(hypothetical)	hex	P6$_3$mc (186)	ZnO	2
CoS	(hypothetical)	cub	F$\bar{4}$3m (216)	sphalerite	4
CdSe	cadmoselite	hex	P6$_3$mc (186)	ZnO	2
CdTe	..	cub	F$\bar{4}$3m (216)	sphalerite	4
CuFeS$_2$ CuFeS$_{1.90}$	chalcopyrite	tet	I42d (122)	..	4
CuFeS$_2$S$_3$*	cubanite	orth	Pcmn (62)	cubanite	4
AgFe$_2$S$_3$*	sternbergite	orth	Ccmm (63)	..	8
AgFe$_2$S$_3$*	argentopyrite	orth	Pmmm (47)	..	4
NiAs	niccolite	hex	P6$_3$/mmc (194)	NiAs	2
NiSb	breithauptite	hex	P6$_3$/mmc (194)	NiAs	2
CuS	covellite	hex	P6$_3$/mmc (194)	CuS	6
CuSe	klockmannite	hex	..	deformed CuS	78

a_0	b_0	c_0	α_0 or α_r	β_0	γ_0	Temp °C	Ref.
5.2234 ±.0005	..	..	..	..	..	r	133, 9
5.611 ±.002	..	..	..	..	..	r	132
3.9858 ±.001	..	6.4654 ±.002	..	..	..	r	137
3.4699 ±.0006	..	6.1098 ±.001	..	..	..	r	9, 56
4.1354 ±.0008	..	6.7120 ±.0007	..	..	..	r	137
5.833 ±.002	..	..	..	..	..	r	132, 9, 48 164
5.516 ±.002	..	..	..	..	..	r	10
5.4093 ±.0002	..	..	..	..	..	r	10, 132, 135 136
3.8230 ±.0010	..	6.2565 ±.0010	..	..	..	r	135, 137, 184
5.6685 ±.0004	..	..	..	..	..	r	10, 54
6.1020 ±.0005	..	..	..	..	..	r	9
4.149 ±.001	..	9.495 ±.002	..	..	..	r	9, 149
5.8517 ±.0010	..	..	..	..	..	r	9, 149
6.0853 ±.0005	..	..	..	..	..	r	9, 152
6.4600 ±.0005	..	..	..	..	..	r	9
5.455 ±.001	..	..	..	..	..	r	132, 136
3.872 ±.001	..	6.345 ±.002	..	..	..	r	137
5.339 ±.001	..	..	..	..	..	r	63
4.2977 ±.0004	..	7.0021 ±.0008	..	..	..	r	9
6.4805 ±.0004	..	..	..	..	..	r	9
5.2988 ±.001	..	10.434 ±.005	..	..	..	r	9
6.46 ±.01	11.12 ±.01	6.23 ±.01	..	..	..	r	17
11.60 ±.02	12.675 ±.02	6.63 ±.01	..	..	..	r	109
6.64 ±.01	11.47 ±.02	6.45 ±.02	..	..	..	r	98
3.618 ±.001	..	5.034 ±.001	..	..	..	r	176
3.942 ±.001	..	5.155 ±.001	..	..	..	r	66
3.792 ±.001	..	16.34 ±.01	..	..	..	r	149
$\sqrt{13} \times 3.94$ ±.001	..	17.25 ±.05	..	..	..	r	35, 157

TABLE 5-1. *Continued*

Formula	Name	Crystal system	Space group	Structure type	Z
SULFIDES, TELLURIDES, SELENIDES, AND ARSENIDES. *Continued*					
SnS	herzenbergite	orth	Pbnm (62)	GeS	4
PbSnS$_2$	teallite	orth	Pbnm (62)	GeS	2
AsS*	realgar	mon	P2$_1$/m (11)	..	16
NiS	millerite	hex-R	R3m (160)	millerite	9
Sb$_2$S$_3$	stibnite	orth	Pbnm (62)	Sb$_2$S$_3$	4
Bi$_2$S$_3$	bismuthinite	orth	Pbnm	Sb$_2$S$_3$	4
Bi$_2$Te$_3$	tellurobismuthite	hex-R	R$\overline{3}$m (166)	Bi$_2$Te$_2$S	3
As$_2$S$_3$	orpiment	mon	P2$_1$/n (14)	As$_2$S$_3$	4
Co$_3$S$_4$	linnaeite	cub	Fd3m (227)	spinel	8
Ni$_3$S$_4$	polydymite	cub	Fd3m (227)	spinel	8
FeNi$_2$S$_4$	violarite	cub	Fd3m (227)	spinel	8
FeCr$_2$S$_4$	daubreeite	cub	Fd3m (227)	spinel	8
FeS$_2$	pyrite	cub	Pa3 (205)	pyrite	4
FeS	troilite	hex	P6$_3$/mmc (194)	NiAs	2
Fe$_{.980}$S	pyrrhotite	hex	P6$_3$/mmc (194)	defect NiAs	2
Fe$_{.885}$S	pyrrhotite	hex	P6$_3$/mmc (194)	defect NiAs	2
FeS$_2$*	marcasite	orth	Pnnm (58)	marcasite	2
FeSe$_2$	ferroselite	orth	Pnnm (58)	marcasite	2
FeTe$_2$	frohbergite	orth	Pnnm (58)	marcasite	2
CoS$_2$	cattierite	cub	Pa3 (205)	pyrite	4
CoSe$_2$	trogtalite	cub	Pa3 (205)	pyrite	4
NiS$_2$	vaesite	cub	Pa3 (205)	pyrite	4
NiSe$_2$	..	cub	Pa3 (205)	pyrite	4
NiTe$_2$	melonite	hex	P$\overline{3}$ml (164)	CdI$_2$	1
MnS$_2$	hauerite	cub	Pa3 (205)	pyrite	4
PtAs$_2$*	sperrylite	cub	Pa3 (205)	pyrite	4
RuS$_2$	laurite	cub	Pa3 (205)	pyrite	4
NiAs$_2$	rammelsbergite	ortho	Pnnm (58)	marcasite	2

a_0	b_0	c_0	α_0 or α_r	β_0	γ_0	Temp °C	Ref.
4.328	11.190	3.978	..	..	..	r	96
±.002	±.004	±.001					
4.266	11.419	4.090	..	..	..	r	96
±.003	±.007	±.002					
9.29	13.53	6.57	..	106° 33′	..	r	13, 181
±.05	±.05	±.03		±20′			
9.616	..	3.152	..	..	..	r	9, 156
±.001		±.001					77, 84
11.229	11.310	3.8389	..	..	..	25	150
±.004	±.004	±.0010					
11.150	11.300	3.981	..	..	..	26	149
±.004	±.004	±.001					
4.3835	..	30.487	..	..	..	r	41, 168
±.0005		±.001					
11.49	9.59	4.25	..	90° 27′	..	r	16
±.02	±.02	±.01	,	±20′			
9.401	..	..	..	..	..	r	87
±.005							
9.480	..	..	..	..	..	r	77
±.001							
9.464	..	..	..	..	..	r	86
±.005							
9.966	..	..	..	..	..	r	83
±.005							
5.4175	..	..	..	..	..	r	133, 81, 53
±.0005							
3.446	..	5.877	..	..	..	28 ± 2	186
±.003		±.001					
3.4461	..	5.8479	..	..	..	28 ± 2	186
±.001		±.002					
3.4401	..	5.7090	..	..	..	28 ± 2	186
±.001		±.003					
4.443	5.423	3.3876	..	..	..	25	133, 14
±.002	±.002	±.0015					
4.801	5.778	3.587	..	..	..	r	60, 8
±.005	±.005	±.004					
5.265	6.265	3.869	..	..	..	r	57
±.005	±.005	±.002					
5.535	..	..	..	..	..	r	87
±.005							
5.8588	..	..	..	..	..	r	20
±.001							
5.6873	..	..	..	..	..	r	9, 77, 84
±.0005							
5.9604	..	..	..	..	..	20	58
±.001							
3.869	..	5.308	..	..	..	84	158
±.01		±.01					
6.1014	..	..	..	..	..	28	133
±.0006							
5.968	..	..	..	..	..	r	53, 159
±.005							
5.60	..	..	..	..	..	r	7, 8, 28, 101
±.02							
4.757	5.797	3.542	..	..	..	26	119, 155, 176
±.002	±.004	±.002					

TABLE 5-1. *Continued*

Formula	Name	Crystal system	Space group	Structure type	Z
SULFIDES, TELLURIDES, SELENIDES, AND ARSENIDES. *Continued*					
NiAs$_2$	pararammels- bergite	ortho	Pbca (61)	..	8
FeAs$_2$	loellingite	ortho	Pnnm (58)	marcasite	2
CoAs$_2$	Co-safflorite	mono	..	deformed marcasite	2
(Co, Fe)As$_2$ Co$_{.5}$Fe$_{.5}$As$_2$	safflorite	ortho	Pnnm (58)	marcasite	2
MoS$_2$	molybdenite	hex	P6$_3$/mmc (194)	MoS$_2$	2
WS$_2$	tungstenite	hex	P6$_3$/mmc (194)	MoS$_2$	2
FeAsS*	arsenopyrite	tri	P$\bar{1}$ (2)	..	4
FeSbS*	gudmundite	mono	B2$_1$/d (14)	..	8
(Co, Fe)AsS*	glaucodot	ortho	Cmmm (65)	..	24
CoAsS*	cobaltite	cub	P2$_1$3 (198)	NiSbS	4
NiAsS	gersdorfite	cub	P2$_1$3 (198)	NiAsS	4
FeAs$_{3-x}$ FeAs$_{2.95}$	Fe-skutterudite hypothetical	cub	Im3 (204)	CoAs$_3$	8
CoAs$_{3-x}$ CoAs$_{2.95}$	Co-skutterudite	cub	Im3 (204)	CoAs$_3$	8
NiAs$_{3-x}$ NiAs$_{2.95}$	Ni-skutterudite hypothetical	cub	Im3 (204)	CoAs$_3$	8
Cu$_{12}$As$_4$S$_{13}$	tennantite	cub	I$\bar{4}$3m (217)	..	8
Cu$_{12}$Sb$_4$S$_{13}$	tetrahedrite	cub	I$\bar{4}$3m (217)	..	8
Cu$_3$AsS$_4$	enargite	orth	Pnn2 (34)	..	2
Cu$_3$AsS$_4$	luzonite	tet	I$\bar{4}$2m (121)	..	2
Cu$_3$SbS$_4$	famatinite	tet	I$\bar{4}$2m (121)	..	2
Ag$_3$AsS$_3$	proustite	hex-R	R3c (161)	..	6
Ag$_3$SbS$_3$	pyrargyrite	hex-R	R3c (161)	..	6
OXIDES AND HYDROXIDES					
Al$_2$O$_3$	corundum	hex-R	R$\bar{3}$c (167)	α-Al$_2$O$_3$	6
AlO(OH)	boehmite	orth	Cmcm (63)	γ-FeO(OH)	4
AlO(OH)*	diaspore	orth	Pbnm (62)	..	4
Al(OH)$_3$	gibbsite	mon	P2$_1$/n (14)	..	8
AS$_2$O$_3$	arsenolite	cub	Fd3m (227)	diamond	16
BeO	bromellite	hex	P6$_3$mc (186)	ZnO	2
CaO	lime	cub	Fm3m (225)	NaCl	4
Ca(OH)$_2$	portlandite	hex	P$\bar{3}$ml (164)	CdI$_2$	1

a_0	b_0	c_0	α_0 or α_r	β_0	γ_0	Temp. °C	Ref.
5.75	5.82	11.428	..	..	..	r	107, 76
±.01	±.01	±.02					
5.300	5.981	2.882	..	..	..	26	119, 155
±.002	±.002	±.001					
5.049	5.872	3.127	..	90° 27′	..	26	119, 155
±.002	±.002	±.001		±20′			
5.231	5.953	2.962	..	..	..	26	119, 155
±.002	±.002	±.005					
3.1604	..	12.295	..	..	..	26	150
±.0005		±.002					
3.154	..	12.362	..	..	..	26	153
±.001		±.004					
5.760	5.690	5.785	90°	112° 14′	90°	r	94
±.010	±.005	±.005	±20′	±20′	±20′		
10.00	5.93	6.73	..	~90°	..	r	15
±.05	±.03	±.03					
6.64	28.39	5.64	..	..	..	r	8
±.05	±.10	±.05					
5.60	..	..	..	..	..	r	8
±.05							
5.693	..	..	..	..	..	26	156
±.001							
8.1814	..	..	..	..	..	r	118
±.0009							
8.2060	..	..	..	..	..	r	118
±.0009							
8.3300	..	..	..	..	..	r	118
±.0009							
10.190	..	..	..	..	..	26	133
±.004							
10.327	..	..	..	..	..	26	133
±.004							
6.426	7.422	6.144	..	..	..	26	133
±.006	±.005	±.005					
5.289	..	10.440	..	..	..	26	133, 47
±.005		±.008					
5.384	..	10.770	..	..	..	26	133, 47
±.005		±.008					
10.8160	..	8.6948	..	..	..	26	162
±.0010		±.0013					
11.0520	..	8.7177	..	..	..	26	162
±.0015		±.0016					
4.7591	..	12.9894	..	..	..	25	70, 179
±.0004		±.003					
2.868	12.227	3.700	..	..	..	26	148
±.003	±.003	±.003					
4.401	9.421	2.845	..	..	..	r	19, 148
±.005	±.005	±.002					
9.719	5.0705	8.6412	..	94° 34′	..	r	32
±.002	±.0010	±.0010		±15′			
11.074	..	..	..	..	..	25	146
±.005							
2.698	..	4.380	..	..	..	26	146
±.005		±.005					
4.8108	..	..	..	..	..	26	12, 146
±.0005							
3.5933	..	4.9086	..	..	..	26	12, 146
±.0005		±.002					

TABLE 5-1. *Continued*

Formula	Name	Crystal system	Space group	Structure type	Z
OXIDES AND HYDROXIDES. *Continued*					
CdO	..	cub	Fm3m (225)	NaCl	4
CeO$_2$	cerianite	cub	Fm3m (225)	CaF$_2$	4
CoO	..	cub	Fm3m (225)	NaCl	4
Cr$_2$O$_3$	eskolaite	hex-R	R$\bar{3}$c (167)	α-Al$_2$O$_3$	6
CuO	tenorite	mon	C2/c (15)	..	4
Cu$_2$O	cuprite	cub	Pn3m (224)	Cu$_2$O	2
Fe$_{.953}$O	wustite	cub	Fm3m (225)	NaCl (defect)	4
Fe$_2$O$_3$	hematite	hex-R	R$\bar{3}$c (167)	α-Al$_2$O$_3$	6
Fe$_3$O$_4$	magnetite	cub	Fd3m (227)	spinel	8
α-FeO(OH)*	goethite	orth	Pbnm (62)	..	4
γ-FeO(OH)*	lepidocrocite	orth	Amam (63)	..	4
H$_2$O	ice	hex	P6$_3$/mmc (194)	..	4
HfO$_2$	hafnia	mon	P2$_1$/c (14)	ZrO$_2$	4
HgO	montroydite	orth	Pnma (62)	..	4
MgO	periclase	cub	Fm3m (225)	NaCl	4
Mg(OH)$_2$	brucite	hex	P$\bar{3}$ml (164)	CdI$_2$	1
MnO	manganosite	cub	Fm3m (225)	NaCl	4
MnO$_2$	pyrolusite	tet	P4/mnm (136)	rutile	2
Mn$_2$O$_3$	bixbyite	cub	Ia3 (206)	Tl$_2$O$_3$	16
Mn$_3$O$_4$	hausmanite	tet	I4$_1$/amd (141)	..	8
MoO$_3$	molybdite	orth	Pbnm (62)	..	4
NiO	bunsenite	cub	Fm3m (225)	NaCl	4
PbO	litharge	tet	P4/nmm (129)	..	2
PbO	massicot	orth	Pb2a (32)	..	4
Sb$_2$O$_3$	senarmontite	cub	Fm3m (225)	arsenic trioxide	16
Sb$_2$O$_3$	valentinite	orth	Pccn (56)	antimony trioxide	4
SiO$_2$*	α-quartz	hex	P3$_1$21 (152) P3$_2$21 (154)	..	3

a_0	b_0	c_0	α_0 or α_r	β_0	γ_0	Temp °C	Ref.
4.6953	..	..	..	..	..	27	147
±.001							
5.4110	..	..	..	..	..	26	146
±.002							
4.260	..	..	..	..	..	26	154
±.002							
4.954	..	13.584	..	..	..	26	150
±.002		±.002					
4.684	3.425	5.129	..	99° 28′	..	26	146
±.005	±.005	±.005		±10′			
4.2696	..	..	..	..	..	26	147
±.001							
4.3088	..	..	..	..	..	17	170
±.0003							
5.0329	..	13.749$_2$		..	..	25	59, 169
±.001		±.001					
$a_r = 5.4266$			55° 15.4′				
			±5′				
8.3940	..	..	..	..	..	22	1, 161
±.0005							
4.596	9.957	3.021	..	..	..	r	108
.005	±.010	±.003					
3.868	12.52$_5$	3.066	..	..	..	r	108
±.010	±.010	±.010					
4.5212	..	7.3666	..	..	..	0	79
±.0010		±.0010					
5.1156	5.1722	5.2948	..	99° 11′	..	r	2
±.001	±.001	±.001		±5′			
6.608	5.518	3.519	..	..	..	25	154
±.003	±.003	±.003					
4.2117	..	..	..	..	..	25	131, 146
±.0005							
3.147	..	4.769	..	..	..	26	151
±.004		±.004					
4.4448	..	..	..	..	..	26	150, 49
±.0005							
4.388	..	2.865	..	..	..	r	145, 32
±.003		±.002					
9.411	..	..	..	..	..	25	154
±.005							
8.136	..	9.422	..	..	..	20	165
±.005		±.005					
3.962	13.858	3.697	..	..	..	26	148
±.002	±.005	±.004					
4.177	..	..	..	..	..	26	146
±.002							
3.9759	..	5.023	..	..	..	27	147
±.004		±.004					
5.489	4.755	5.891	..	..	..	27	147
±.003	±.004	±.004					
11.152	..	..	..	..	..	26	148
±.003							
4.914	12.468	5.421	..	..	..	25	155
±.002	±.005	±.004					
4.91355	..	5.40512	..	..	..	25	42, 179
±.0001		±.0001					

TABLE 5-1.   *Continued*

Formula	Name	Crystal system	Space group	Structure type	Z
OXIDES AND HYDROXIDES.	*Continued*				
SiO_2*	β-quartz	hex	$P6_422$ (181) $P6_222$ (180)	..	3
SiO_2	α-cristobalite	tet	$P4_12_12$ (92) $P4_32_12$ (96)	..	4
SiO_2	β-cristobalite	cub	Fd3m (227)	..	8
SiO_2	keatite	tet	$P4_12_12$ (92) $P4_32_12$ (96)	..	12
SiO_2	β-tridymite	hex	$P\bar{6}2c$ (172) $P6_3/mmc$ (194)	..	4
SiO_2*	coesite	mon	B2/b (15)	..	16
SiO_2*	stishovite	tet	P4/mnm (136)	rutile	2
SiO_2*	melanophlogite	cub	$P4_232$ (208)	..	48
SnO_2	cassiterite	tet	P4/mnm (136)	rutile	2
TeO_2*	tellurite	orth	Pbca (61)	tellurite	8
TeO_2	para-tellurite	tet	$P4_12_12$ (92) $P4_32_12$ (96)	..	4
ThO_2	thorianite	cub	Fm3m (225)	CaF_2	4
TiO_2	rutile	tet	P4/mnm (136)	rutile	2
TiO_2	anatase	tet	$I4_1/amd$ (141)	..	4
TiO_2*	brookite	orth	Pcab (61)	..	8
UO_2	uraninite	cub	Fm3m (225)	CaF_2	4
ZnO	zincite	hex	$P6_3mc$ (186)	ZnO	2
ZrO_2	baddeleyite	mon	$P2_1/c$ (14)	ZrO_2	4
SPINELS, ALUMINATES, AND TITINATES					
$BeAl_2O_4$	chrysoberyl	orth	Pnma (62)	olivine	4
$MgAl_2O_4$	spinel	cub	Fd3m (227)	spinel	8
$FeAl_2O_4$	hercynite	cub	Fd3m (227)	spinel	8
$MnAl_2O_4$	galaxite	cub	Fd3m (227)	spinel	8
$ZnAl_2O_4$	gahnite	cub	Fd3m (227)	spinel	8
$FeFe_2O_4$	magnetite	cub	Fd3m (227)	spinel	8
$MnFe_2O_4$	jacobsite	cub	Fd3m (227)	spinel	8
$NiFe_2O_4$	trevorite	cub	Fd3m (227)	spinel	8
$MgCr_2O_4$	picrochromite	cub	Fd3m (227)	spinel	8

a_0	b_0	c_0	α_0 or α_r	β_0	γ_0	Temp °C	Ref.
4.9990 ±.0005	..	5.4592 ±.0005	..	..	..	575	42, 71
4.971 ±.003	.. ..	6.918 ±.003	..	..	..	25	155
7.1382 ±.0010	..	..	..	..	..	405	139
7.456 ±.003	..	8.604 ±.005	..	..	..	r	129, 182
5.0463 ±.0020	..	8.2563 ±.0030	..	..	..	405	139
7.152 ±.001	12.379 ±.002	7.152 ±.001	..	120° 00′ ±10′	..	25	184
4.1790 ±.001	..	2.6649 ±.001	..	..	..	r	23
13.402 ±.004	..	..	..	..	..	r	180
4.738 ±.003	.. ..	3.188 ±.003	..	..	..	26	146
5.607 ±.003	12.034 ±.005	5.463 ±.003	..	..	..	25	154
4.810 ±.002	..	7.613 ±.002	..	..	..	25	155
5.59525 ±.0005	..	..	..	..	..	25	131, 146
4.59374 ±.0005	..	2.9617$_7$ ±.002	..	..	..	25	144, 27, 146
3.785 ±.002	..	9.514 ±.006	..	..	..	r	27, 146
5.447 ±.010	9.185 ±.010	5.145 ±.010	..	..	..	r	32
5.4682 ±.001	..	..	..	..	..	26	147
3.2495 ±.0005	..	5.2069 ±.0005	..	..	..	25	64
5.1454 ±.001	5.2075 ±.001	5.3107 ±.001	..	99° 14′ ±5′	..	r	2
9.4041 ±.003	5.4756 ±.002	4.4267 ±.002	..	..	..	25	154, 185
8.0800 ±.002	..	..	..	..	..	26	147
8.150 ±.004	..	..	..	..	..	25	163
8.258 ±.002	..	..	..	..	..	25	154
8.0848 ±.002	..	..	..	..	..	26	147
8.3940 ±.0005	..	..	..	..	..	22	1, 161
8.499 ±.005	..	..	..	..	..	25	154
8.339 ±.005	..	..	..	..	..	25	155
8.333 ±.005	..	..	..	..	..	26	154

Table 5-1. *Continued*

Formula	Name	Crystal system	Space group	Structure type	Z
Spinels, Aluminates, and Titinates. *Continued*					
CaTiO$_3$	perovskite	orth	Pcmn (62)	perovskite	4
FeTiO$_3$*	ilmenite	hex-R	R$\bar{3}$ (148)	ilmenite	6
MgTiO$_3$	geikielite	hex-R	R$\bar{3}$ (148)	ilmenite	6
Halides					
NaCl	halite	cub	Fm3m (225)	NaCl	4
KCl	sylvite	cub	Fm3m (225)	NaCl	4
NaF	villiaumite	cub	Fm3m (225)	NaCl	4
AgBr	bromyrite	cub	Fm3m (225)	NaCl	4
AgCl	cerargyrite	cub	Fm3m (225)	NaCl	4
AgI	iodyrite	hex	P6$_3$mc (186)	ZnO	2
AgI	miersite	cub	F$\bar{4}$3m (216)	sphalerite	4
CaF$_2$	fluorite	cub	Fm3m (225)	CaF$_2$	4
MgF$_2$	sellaite	tet	P4$_2$/mnm (136)	rutile	2
HgCl	calomel	tet	I4/mm (139)	..	4
Na$_3$AlF$_6$*	cryolite	mon	P2$_1$/n (14)	..	2
NaMgF$_3$	neighborite	orth	Pcmn (62)	perovskite	4
Carbonates and Nitrates					
BaMg(CO$_3$)$_2$*	norsethite	hex-R	R32 (155)	calcite	3
CaCO$_3$	calcite	hex-R	R$\bar{3}$c (167)	calcite	6
CaMg(CO$_3$)$_2$*	dolomite	hex-R	R$\bar{3}$ (148)	calcite	3
CdCO$_3$	otavite	hex-R	R$\bar{3}$c (167)	calcite	6
CoCO$_3$	cobalticalcite	hex-R	R$\bar{3}$c (167)	calcite	6
FeCO$_3$	siderite	hex-R	R$\bar{3}$c (167)	calcite	6
MgCO$_3$	magnesite	hex-R	R$\bar{3}$c (167)	calcite	6

a_0	b_0	c_0	α_0 or α_r	β_0	γ_0	Temp °C	Ref.
5.3670	7.6438	5.4439	..	..	..	r	74
±.0001	±.0001	±.0001					
5.093	..	14.055	..	..	..	r	104
±.005		±.010					
5.054	..	13.898	..	..	..	26	150
±.005		±.005					
5.6402	..	..	..	..	..	26	147
±.0002							
6.2931	..	..	..	..	..	25	146
±.0002							
4.6342	..	..	..	..	..	25	146
±.0005							
5.7745	..	..	..	..	..	26	149
±.0005							
5.5491	..	..	..	..	..	26	149
±.0005							
4.5922	..	7.510	..	..	..	25	153
±.002		±.005					
·6.495	..	..	..	..	..	r	166
±.005							
5.4626	..	..	..	..	..	25	146, 4
±.0003							
4.621	..	3.050	..	..	..	18	34, 149
±.001	..	±.001					
4.478	..	10.91	..	..	..	26	146
±.005	..	±.005					
5.40_0	5.60_1	7.77_6	..	90° 11′	..	r	104
±.01	±.01	±.01		+15′			
5.363	7.676	5.503	..	..	..	18	22
±.001	±.001	±.001					
5.020	..	16.75		..	..	r	97
±.005		±.02	±05′				
$a_r = 6.29$			47° 02′				
4.9899	..	17.064		..	..	26 ± 3	55
±.0002		±.001					
$a_r = 6.3760$			46° 4.3′				
4.8079	..	16.010		..	..	26 ± 3	55
±.0010		±.003					
$a_r = 6.0154$			47° 6.6′				
4.9204	..	16.298		..	..	26 ± 3	55
±.0005		±.003					
$a_r = 6.1306$			47° 19.2′				
4.6581	..	14.958		..	..	26 ± 3	55
±.0005		±.002					
$a_r = 5.6650$			48° 33.1′				
4.6887	..	15.373		..	..	26 ± 3	55
±.0004		±.004					
$a_r = 5.7954$			47° 43.3′				
4.6330	..	15.016		..	..	26 ± 3	55
±.0003		±.002					
$a_r = 5.6752$			48° 10.9′				

TABLE 5.1. *Continued*

Formula	Name	Crystal system	Space group	Structure type	Z
CARBONATES AND NITRATES. *Continued*					
$Mg_3Ca(CO_3)_4$*	huntite	hex-R	R32 (155)	calcite	3
$MnCO_3$	rhodochrosite	hex-R	R$\bar{3}$c (167)	calcite	6
$NiCO_3$	..	hex-R	R$\bar{3}$c (167)	calcite	6
$ZnCO_3$	smithsonite	hex-R	R$\bar{3}$c (167)	calcite	6
$BaCO_3$	witherite	orth	Pmcn (62)	aragonite	4
$CaCO_3$	aragonite	orth	Pmcn (62)	aragonite	4
$PbCO_3$	cerussite	orth	Pmcn (62)	aragonite	4
$SrCO_3$	strontianite	orth	Pmcn (62)	aragonite	4
$Cu_2(OH)_2CO_3$	malachite	mon	P2$_1$/a (14)	complex	4
$Cu_3(OH)_2(CO_3)_2$	azurite	mon	P2$_1$/c (14)	complex	2
$CaCO_3$	vaterite	hex	..	..	6
KNO_3	niter	orth	Pmcn (62)	aragonite	4
$NaNO_3$	soda niter	hex-R	R$\bar{3}$c (167)	calcite	6
$Cu_2(NO_3)(OH)_3$	gerhardite	orth	P2$_1$2$_1$2$_1$ (19)	..	4
SULFATES AND BORATES					
$BaSO_4$	barite	orth	Pnma (62)	$BaSO_4$	4
$CaSO_4$	anhydrite	orth	Ccmm (63) AmmA (63)	$CaSO_4$	4
$PbSO_4$	anglesite	orth	Pnma (62)	$BaSO_4$	4
$SrSO_4$	celestite	orth	Pnma (62)	$BaSO_4$	4
$ZnSO_4$	zinkosite	orth	Pnma (62)	$BaSO_4$	4
K_2SO_4	arcanite	orth	Pnma (62)	K_2SO_4	4
Na_2SO_4	thenardite	orth	Fddd (70)	Na_2SO_4	8
$CaSO_4 \cdot 2H_2O$*	gypsum	mon	C2/c (15)	..	4
$MgSO_4 \cdot 7H_2O$	epsomite	orth	P2$_1$2$_1$2$_1$ (19)	..	4
$Na_2SO_4 \cdot 10H_2O$	mirabilite	mon	P2$_1$/c (14)	..	4

a_0	b_0	c_0	α_0 or α_r	β_0	γ_0	Temp °C	Ref.
9.5062	..	7.8219		..	..	26 ± 3	55
±.003		±.004					
$a_r = 6.0762$			102° 55.9′				
4.7771	..	15.664		..	..	26 ± 3	55
±.0003		±.003					
$a_r = 5.9050$			47° 43.2′				
4.5975	..	14.723		..	..	26 ± 3	55
±.0005		±.002					
$a_r = 5.5795$			48° 39.7′				
4.6528	..	15.025		..	..	26 ± 3	55
±.0003		±.003					
$a_r = 5.6833$			48° 19.6′				
5.314	8.904	6.430	..	..	..	26	147
±.005	±.005	±.005					
4.959	7.968	5.741	..	..	..	26	148
±.005	±.005	±.005					
5.195	8.436	6.152	..	..	..	26	147
±.005	±.005	±.005					
5.107	8.414	6.029	..	..	..	26	148, 184
±.005	±.005	±.005					
9.502	11.974	3.240	..	98° 45′	..	25	155
±.007	±.007	±.003		±15′			
5.008	5.844	10.336	..	92° 27′	..	25	155
±.005	±.005	±.005		±15′			
7.135	..	8.524	..	..	..	r	88
±.005		±.007					
5.414	9.164	6.431	..	..	..	26	148
±.005	±.005	±.005					
5.0696	..	16.829		..	..	25	151
±.0010		±.005					
$a_r = 6.3273$			47° 9.8′				
5.592	6.075	13.812	..	..	..	r	111
±.004	±.004	±.008					
8.878	5.450	7.152	..	..	..	26	148
±.005	±.005	±.003					
6.238	6.991	6.996	..	..	..	26	149
±.005	±.005	±.005					
8.480	5.398	6.958	..	..	..	25	148
±.005	±.005	±.003					
8.359	5.352	6.866	..	..	..	26	147
±.005	±.005	±.005					
8.588	6.740	4.770	..	..	..	25	152
±.008	±.006	±.005					
5.772	10.072	7.483	..	..	..	25	148
±.005	±.005	±.004					
5.863	12.304	9.821	..	..	..	25	147
±.005	±.005	±.005					
5.68	15.18	6.29	..	113° 50′	..	r	104
±.010	±.010	±.010		±15′			
11.964	12.054	6.879	..	..	..	25	104
±.01	±.01	±.01					
11.51	10.38	12.83	..	107° 45′	..	24	121
±.01	±.01	±.01		±10′			

TABLE 5-1. *Continued*

Formula	Name	Crystal system	Space group	Structure type	Z
SULFATES AND BORATES. *Continued*					
$CuSO_4 \cdot 5H_2O$	chalcanthite	tri	P$\bar{1}$ (2)	..	2
$Cu_4SO_4(OH)_6$*	brochantite	mon	P2_1/c (14)	..	4
$K_2Ca(SO_4)_2 \cdot H_2O$	syngenite	mon	P2_1/m (11)	..	2
$CaB_3O_4(OH)_3 \cdot H_2O$*	colemanite	mon	P2_1/a (14)	..	4
$Na_2B_4O_7 \cdot 10H_2O$	borax	mon	C2/c (15)	..	4
$Na_2B_4O_7 \cdot 4H_2O$	kernite	mon	P2_1/c (14)	..	4
$KAl_3(SO_4)_2(OH)_6$	alunite	hex-R	R3m (160)	..	3
$NaAl_3(SO_4)_2(OH)_6$	natroalunite	hex-R	R3m (160)	..	3
PHOSPHATES, MOLYBDATES, AND TUNGSTATES					
$AlPO_4$	berlinite	hex	P$3_1$21 (152) or P$3_2$21 (154)	α-quartz	3
$Ca_5(PO_4)_3OH$	hydroxylapatite	hex	P6_3/m (176)	apatite	2
YPO_4	xenotime	tet	I4_1/amd (141)	zircon	4
$CaMoO_4$	powellite	tet	I4_1/a (100)	calcium tungstate	4
$PbMoO_4$	wulfenite	tet	I4_1/a (100)	calcium tungstate	4
$CaWO_4$	seheelite	tet	I4_1/a (100)	calcium tungstate	4
$PbWO_4$	stolzite	tet	I4_1/a (100)	calcium tungstate	4
$FeWO_4$	ferberite	mon	P2/c (13)	wolframite	2
$MnWO_4$	huebnerite	mon	P2/c (13)	wolframite	2
$Fe_5Mn_5WO_4$	wolframite	mon	P2/c (13)	wolframite	2
$Ca_5(PO_4)_3F$	fluorapatite	hex	P6_3/m (176)	apatite	2
$Ca_5(PO_4)_3Cl$	chlorapatite	hex	P6_3/m (176)	apatite	2
SILICATES					
Al_2SiO_5*	andalusite	orth	Pnnm (58)	..	4
Al_2SiO_5*	kyanite	tri	P$\bar{1}$ (2)	..	4
Al_2SiO_5*	sillimanite	orth	Pbnm (62) Pnma (62)	..	4
$Ca_3Al_2Si_3O_{12}$	grossularite	cub	Ia3d (230)	garnet	8
$Ca_3Cr_2Si_3O_{12}$	uvarovite	cub	Ia3d (230)	garnet	8
$Ca_3Fe_2Si_3O_{12}$	andradite	cub	Ia3d (230)	garnet	8

a_0	b_0	c_0	α_0 or α_r	β_0	γ_0	Temp °C	Ref.
6.104_5	10.72	5.949	97° 34′	107° 17′	77° 26′	r	39
±.005	±.01	±.007	±10′	±10′	±10′		
13.06_6	9.85	6.02_2	..	103° 16′	..	r	32
±.01	±.01	±.01		±15′			
9.775	7.156	6.251	..	104° 00′	..	r	6
±.005	±.005	±.005		±15′			
8.743	11.264	6.102	..	110° 7′	..	r	24
±.004	±.002	±.003		±5′			
11.858	10.674	12.197	..	106° 41′	..	r	92
±.005	±.005	±.005		±2′			
7.022	9.151	15.676	..	108° 50′	..	r	120
±.003	±.004	±.008		±15′			
6.982	..	17.32	..	..	..	r	11, 105
±.005		±.01					
6.974	..	16.69	..	..	..	r	105
±.005		±.01					
4.942	..	10.97	..	..	..	25	155
±.005		±.007					
9.432	..	6.881	..	..	..	r	114
±.005		±.005					
6.885	..	5.982	..	..	..	26	153
±.005		±.005					
5.226	..	11.43	..	..	..	25	151
±.005		±.007					
5.435	..	12.11	..	..	..	25	152
±.007		±.007					
5.242	..	11.372	..	..	..	25	151
±.005		±.005					
5.4616	..	12.046	..	..	..	25	152
±.0020		±.002					
4.732	5.708	4.965	..	90° 00′	..	r	127
±.004	±.003	±.004		±03′			
4.834	5.758	4.999	..	91° 11′	..	r	127
±.004	±.003	±.004		±03′			
4.782	5.731	4.982	..	90° 34′	..	r	127
±.004	±.003	±.004		±03′			
9.369	..	6.884	..	..	..	r	89
±.005		±.003					
9.629	..	6.777	..	..	..	r	89
±.005		±.003					
7.7959	7.8983	5.5583	..	..	..	25	134
±.005	±.002	±.002					
7.123	7.848	5.564	89° 55′	101° 15′	105° 58′	25	134
±.001	±.002	±.008	±09′	±05′	±05′		
7.4843	7.6730	5.7711	..	..	..	25	134
±.003	±.003	±.004					
11.851	..	..	..	..	..	25	130
±.001							
11.999	..	..	..	..	..	26	155
±.002							
12.048	..	..	..	..	..	25	130
±.001							

TABLE 5-1. *Continued*

Formula	Name	Crystal system	Space group	Structure type	Z
SILICATES. *Continued*					
$Fe_3Al_2Si_3O_{12}$	almandite	cub	Ia3d (230)	garnet	8
$Mg_3Al_2Si_3O_{12}$	pyrope	cub	Ia3d (230)	garnet	8
$Mn_3Al_2Si_3O_{12}$	spessartite	cub	Ia3d (230)	garnet	8
γ-Ca_2SiO_4*	lime olivine	orth	Pbnm (62)	olivine	4
Fe_2SiO_4	fayalite	orth	Pbnm (62)	olivine	4
Mg_2SiO_4	forsterite	orth	Pbnm (62)	olivine	4
Mn_2SiO_4*	tephroite	orth	Pbnm (62)	olivine	4
$CaMgSiO_4$*	monticellite	orth	Pbnm (62)	olivine	4
$CaFeSiO_4$	kirschsteinite	orth	Pbnm (62)	olivine	4
β-Ca_2SiO_4*	larnite	mon	$P2_1/n$ (14)	..	4
Be_2SiO_4*	phenacite	hex-R	R$\bar{3}$ (148)	phenacite	18
Zn_2SiO_4	willemite	hex-R	R$\bar{3}$ (148)	phenacite	18
$ThSiO_4$	thorite	tet	I4/amd (141)	zircon	4
$ZrSiO_4$	zircon	tet	I4/amd (141)	zircon	4
$USiO_4$	coffinite	tet	I4/amd (141)	zircon	4
$KAl_2(AlSi_3O_{10})(OH)_2$*	muscovite	mon	C2/c (15)	mica (2M)	4
$KMg_3(AlSi_3O_{10})(OH)_2$*	phlogopite	mon	Cm (8)	mica (1M)	2
$KMg_3(AlSi_3O_{10})F_2$	fluor-phlogopite	mon	Cm (8)	mica (1M)	2
$KFe_3(AlSi_3O_{10})(OH)_2$	annite	mon	Cm (8)	mica (1M)	2
$Al_2Si_4O_{10}(OH)_2$*	pyrophyllite	mon	C2/c (15)	sheet	4
$Mg_3Si_4O_{10}(OH)_2$*	talc	mon	C2/c (15)	sheet	4
$Al_2Si_2O_5(OH)_4$*	kaolinite	tri	..	..	2
$Al_2Si_2O_5(OH)_4$*	dickite	mon	Cc (9)	sheet	4
$Mg_2Al_3(AlSi_5O_{18})$	lo-cordierite	orth	Cccm (66)	..	4
$CaAl_2Si_2O_8$*	anorthite	tri	C$\bar{1}$ (2)	feldspar	4
$NaAlSi_3O_8$*	albite	tri	C$\bar{1}$ (2)	feldspar	4

a_0	b_0	c_0	α_0 or α_r	β_0	γ_0	Temp °C	Ref.
11.526	..	..	..	..	..	25	130
±.001							
11.459	..	..	..	..	..	25	130
±.001							
11.621	..	..	..	..	..	25	130
±.001							
5.07_0	11.30_3	6.79_4	..	..	..	r	102
±.020	±.020	±.020					
4.817	10.477	6.105	..	..	..	r	175
±.005	±.005	±.010					
4.758	10.214	5.984	..	..	..	25	184
±.002	±.003	±.002					
4.871	10.636	6.232	..	..	..	r	68
±.005	±.005	±.005					
4.827	11.084	6.376	..	..	..	r	124
±.005	±.005	±.005					
4.886	11.146	6.434	..	..	..	r	124
±.005	±.005	±.010					
5.48	6.76	9.28	..	94° 33′	..	r	91
±.02	±.02	±.02		±20′			
12.472	..	8.252		..	..	25	153
±.005		±.005					
$a_r = 7.708_2$			108° 0.42′				
13.94	..	9.309		..	..	25	152
±.01		±.003					
$a_r = 8.123$			118° 11′				
7.143	..	6.327	..	..	..	r	46
±.004	..	±.003					
6.604	..	5.979	..	..	..	25	149
±.005		±.005					
6.995	..	6.263	..	..	..	r	46
±.004		±.005					
		7.07					
		±.01					
5.203	8.995	20.030	..	94° 28′	..	r	174, 40
±.005	±.007	±.005		±30′			
5.314	9.204	10.314	..	99° 54′	..	r	173
±.01	±.02	±.005		±10′			
5.299	9.188	10.135	..	99° 55′	..	r	75
±.004	±.002	±.002		±3′			
5.391	9.350	10.313	..	99° 42′	..	r	172
±.01	±.004	±.02		±15′			
5.14	8.90	18.55	..	99° 55′	..	r	61
±.02	±.02	±.03		±5′			
5.28_7	9.15_8	18.95	..	99° 30′	..	r	142
±.007	±.008	±.01					
5.155	8.959	7.407	91° 41′	104° 52′	89° 56′	r	52
±.007	±.010	±.008	±20′	±20′	±20′		
5.150	8.940	14.424	..	96° 44′	..	r	100
±.002	±.003	±.005		±5′			
17.0621	9.7208	9.3389	..	..	..	r	128
±.005	±.003	±.003					
8.1768	12.8768	7.0845	93° 10.0′	115° 50.8′	91° 13.3′	r	25, 51
±.002	±.003	±.002	±2′	±2′	±2′		
8.1353	12.7883	7.1542	94° 13.6′	116° 31.1′	87° 42.5′	r	25, 140, 80
±.002	±.003	±.002	±1′	±1′	±1′		

TABLE 5-1. *Continued*

Formula	Name	Crystal system	Space group	Structure type	Z
SILICATES. *Continued*					
$NaAlSi_3O_8$	hi-albite	tri	..	feldspar	4
$KAlSi_3O_8$*	microcline	tri	C$\bar{1}$ (2)	feldspar	4
$KAlSi_3O_8$	sanidine	mon	C2/m (12)	feldspar	4
$CaTiSiO_5$*	sphene	mon	A2/a (15)	..	4
$Zn_4(OH)_2Si_2O_7 \cdot H_2O$*	hemimorphite	orth	Imm2 (35)	hemimorphite	2
$(AlF)_2SiO_4$*	topaz	orth	Pmnb (62)	..	4
$NaMg_3Al_6B_3Si_6O_{27}(OH)_4$	dravite	hex-R	R3m (160)	tourmaline	3
$CaMg_4Al_5B_3Si_6O_{27}(OH)_4$	uvite	hex-R	R3m (160)	tourmaline	3
$NaAlSi_2O_6 \cdot H_2O$	analcite	cub	Ia3d (230)	zeolite	16
$Na_2Al_2Si_3O_{10} \cdot 2H_2O$	natrolite	orth	Fdd2 (43)	..	8
$CaSiO_3$*	parawollastonite	mon	P2$_1$ (4)	..	12
$CaSiO_3$*	pseudo-wollastonite	tri (mon)	..	..	24
$Ca_2NaHSi_3O_9$*	pectolite	tri	P$\bar{1}$ (2)	wollastonite	2
$CaSiO_3$*	wollastonite	tri	P$\bar{1}$ (2)	wollastonite	6
$MgSiO_3$*	clino-enstatite	mon	P2$_1$/C	diopside	8
$MgSiO_3$*	enstatite	orth	Pcab (61)	..	16
$MnSiO_3$*	rhodonite	tri	P$\bar{1}$ (2)	wollastonite	10
$CaMg(SiO_3)_2$	diopside	mon	C2/c (15)	diopside	4
$CaFe(SiO_3)_2$*	hedenbergite	mon	C2/c (15)	diopside	4
$NaAlSi_2O_6$*	jadeite	mon	C2/c (15)	diopside	4
$Ca_2Mg_5Si_8O_{22}(OH)_2$*	tremolite	mon	C2/m (12)	tremolite	2
$Ca_2Mg_5Si_8O_{22}F_2$	fluor-tremolite	mon	C2/m (12)	tremolite	2
$Na_2Mg_3Fe_2Si_8O_{22}(OH)_2$	Mg-riebecite	mon	I2/m (12)	hornblende	2
$Na_2Mg_3Al_2Si_8O_{22}(OH)_2$	glaucophane	mon	I2/m (12)	hornblende	2
$Be_3Al_2(Si_6O_{18})$*	beryl	hex	P6/mmc (192)	..	2
$Mg_2Al_3(AlSi_5O_{18})$	hi-cordierite	hex	P6/mmc (192)	..	2
$NaAlSiO_4$	lo-nepheline	hex	C6$_3$ (178)	..	8

In the formulas $NaMg_3Al_6B_3Si_6O_{27}(OH)_4$ (dravite) and $CaMg_4Al_5B_3Si_6O_{27}(OH)_4$ (uvite) are grouped as tourmaline.

a_0	b_0	c_0	α_0 or α_r	β_0	γ_0	Temp °C	Ref.
8.151	12.872	7.108	93° 28′	116° 23′	90° 14′	r	140, 80
±.005	±.005	±.005	±10′	±10′	±10′		
8.577	12.967	7.223	90° 39′	115° 56′	87° 42′	r	80
±.01	±.01	±.01	±5′	±5′	±5′		
8.617	13.030	7.176	..	116° 4.6′	..	r	31
±.005	±.005	±.005		±10′			
7.07_4	8.71_8	6.56_3		113° 57′	..	r	32
±.010	±.010	±.010		±15′			
8.370	10.719	5.120	..	..	..	25	147
±.005	±.005	±.005					
8.394	8.792	4.649	..	..	..	25	156
±.005	±.007	±.003					
15.93	..	7.18	..	..	..	r	117
±.01		±.01					
$a_r = 9.50$			113° 53′				
15.86	..	7.19	..	..	..	r	117
±.01		±.01					
$a_r = 9.465$			114° 5′				
13.733	..	..	..	..	..	r	123
±.005							
18.30	18.63	6.60	..	..	..	r	90
±.01	±.01	±.01					
15.417	7.321	7.066	..	95° 24′	..	r	160, 106
±.004	±.002	±.002		±3′			
6.90	11.78	19.65	..	90° 48′	..	r	72
±.02	±.02	±.02		±15′			
7.99	7.04	7.02	90° 03′	95° 17′	102° 28′	r	18
±.01	±.01	±.01	±15′	±15′	±15′		
7.94	7.32	7.07	90° 02′	95° 22′	103° 26′	r	18, 106
±.01	±.01	±.01	±15′	±15′	±15′		
9.618	8.825	5.186	..	108° 21′	..	r	93
±.005	±.005	±.005		±5′			
8.829	18.22	5.192	..	..	..	26	151, 65
±.01	±.01	±.01					
6.68	7.66	12.20	111° 06′	86° 00′	93° 12′	r	82
±.02	±.03	±.04	±20′	±20′	±20′		
9.743	8.923	5.251	..	74° 04′	..	r	125
±.005	±.005	±.005		±15′			
9.854	9.024	5.263	..	75° 46′	..	r	78
±.010	±.010	±.010		±20′			
9.499	8.608	5.241	..	107° 26′	..	r	171
±.020	±.010	±.020		±15′			
9.840	18.052	5.275	..	104° 42′	..	r	177
±.006	±.005	±.005		±15′			
9.781	18.007	5.267	..	104° 30′	..	20	26
±.005	±.004	±.006					
10.04	18.02	5.28	..	72° 00′	..	r	37
±.01	±.01	±.01		±30′			
9.99	17.92	5.27	..	71° 38′	..	r	38
±.01	±.01	±.01		±15′			
9.215	..	9.192	..	..	..	25	154
±.005		±.005					
9.7698	..	9.3517	..	..	..	r	128
±.003		±.003					
9.986	..	8.330	..	..	..	r	33, 141
±.005		±.004					

TABLE 5-1. *Continued*

Formula	Name	Crystal system	Space group	Structure type	Z
SILICATES. *Continued*					
NaAlSiO$_4$	hi-carnegeite	cub	..	..	4
KAlSiO$_4$*	kaliophilite natural	hex	P6$_3$22 (182)	..	54
KAlSiO$_4$	kaliophilite synthetic	hex	P6$_3$ (173) P6$_3$22 (182)	..	2
KAlSiO$_4$	kalsilite	hex	..	..	2
KAlSi$_2$O$_6$*	hi-leucite	cub	..	..	16
LiAlSi$_2$O$_6$	β-spodumene	tet	P4$_3$2$_1$2 (96)	..	..
Ca$_2$MgSi$_2$O$_7$	akermanite	tet	..	..	2
Ca$_2$Al$_2$Si$_2$O$_7$	gehlenite	tet	..	..	2
CaAl$_2$Si$_2$O$_7$(OH)$_2$·H$_2$O	lawsonite	orth	Ccmm (63)	..	4
3Al$_2$O$_3$·2SiO$_2$	3·2 mullite	orth	..	..	3/4
2Al$_2$O$_3$·SiO$_2$	2·1 mullite	orth	Pbam (55)	..	6/5
Ca$_2$Al$_3$(SiO$_4$)$_3$(OH)	zoisite	orth	Pnma (62)	..	4
Ca$_2$Al$_3$(SiO$_4$)$_3$(OH)	clino zoisite	mon	P2$_1$/m (11)	..	2

REFERENCES FOR TABLE 5-1

1. Abrahams and Calhoun, Acta Cryst. 6, 105, 1953
2. Adam and Rodgers, Acta Cryst. 12, 951, 1959
3. Agrell and Smith, Jour. Am. Ceram. Soc. 43, 69, 1960
4. Allen, Am. Min. 37, 910, 1952
5. Andrews, Min. Mag. 28, 374, 1948
6. Aruja, Min. Mag. 31, 943, 1958
7. Bannister, Min. Mag. 23, 195, 1932
8. Berry and Thompson, Mem. 85, Geol. Soc. America, 281 p., 1962
9. Bethke, P. M., unpublished data
10. Bethke and Barton, U.S. Geol. Survey Prof. Paper 424B, 266, 1961
11. Brophy, Scott, and Snellgrove, Am. Min. 47, 112, 1962
12. Brunauer, Kantro, and Weise, Canadian Jour. Chem. 34, 729, 1956
13. Buerger, Am. Min. 20, 36, 1935
14. —— Zeit. Krist. 97, 504, 1937
15. —— Zeit. Krist. 101, 290, 1939
16. —— Am. Min. 27, 301, 1942
17. —— Am. Min. 32, 415, 1945
18. —— Proc. Nat. Acad. Sci. 42, 113, 1956
19. Busing and Levey, Acta Cryst. 11, 798, 1958
20. Bøhm and others, Acta Chem. Scand. 9, 1510, 1955
21. Caron and Donohue, Acta Cryst. 14, 548, 1961
22. Chao, Evans, Skinner, and Milton, Am. Min. 46, 379, 1961
23. Chao, Fahey, Littler, and Milton, Jour. Geophys. Res. 67, 419, 1962
24. Christ, Am. Min. 41, 569, 1956
25. Cole, Sorum, and Taylor, Acta Cryst. 4, 20, 1951
26. Comeforo and Kohn, Am. Min. 39, 537, 1954
27. Cromer and Herrington, Jour. Am. Chem. Soc. 77, 4708, 1955

a_0	b_0	c_0	α_0 or α_r	β_0	γ_0	Temp °C	Ref.
7.325	..	..	..	..	..	750	141
±.007							
26.930	..	8.522	..	..	..	r	141
±.010		±.004					
5.180	..	8.559	..	..	..	r	141
±.002		±.004					
5.159_7	..	8.7032	..	..	..	r	141
±.002		±.002					
13.43	..	..	..	..	..	625	32
±.01							
7.5332	..	9.1540	..	..	..	25	138
±.0008		±.0008					
7.843_5	..	5.010	..	..	..	r	5
±.003		±.003					
7.690	..	5.067_5	..	..	..	r	5
±.003		±.003					
8.787	5.836	13.123	..	..	..	r	112, 103
±.005	±.005	±.008					
7.557	7.687_6	2.884_2	..	..	..	r	3
±.002	±.002	±.001					
7.578_8	7.690_9	2.888_3	..	..	..	r	3, 122
±.001	±.002	±.001					
16.15	5.581	10.06	..	..	..	r	113
±.01	±.005	±.01					
8.887	5.581	10.14	..	115° 56′	..	r	113
±.007	±.005	±.01		±20′			

28. deJong and Hoog, Rec. Trav. Chim. **46**, 173, 1927
29. Djurle, Acta Chem. Scand. **12**, 1415, 1958
30. —— Acta Chem. Scand. **12**, 1427, 1958
31. Donnay and Donnay, Am. Jour. Sci. Bowen volume 115, 1952
32. Donnay and Nowacki, Crystal data, Mem. 60, Geol. Soc. America, 1954
33. Donnay, Schairer, and Donnay, Min. Mag. **32**, 93, 1959
34. Duncanson and Stevenson, Proc. Phys. Soc. **72**, 1001, 1958
35. Earley, Am. Min. **34**, 433, 1949
36. —— Am. Min. **35**, 337, 1950
37. Ernst, Geochim. Cosmochim. Acta. **19**, 10, 1960
38. —— Am. Jour. Sci. **259**, 735, 1961
39. Fisher, Am. Min. **37**, 95, 1952
40. Fournier, R. O., private communication, June 1960
41. Francombe, Brit. Jour. Appl. Phys. **9**, 415, 1958
42. Frondel and Hurlbut, Jour. Chem. Phys. **23**, 1215, 1955
43. Frueh, Geol. Soc. America Bull. **67**, 1697, 1956
44. —— Am. Min. **44**, 693, 1959
45. —— Zeit. Krist. **112**, 44, 1959
46. Fuchs and Gebert, Am. Min. **43**, 243, 1958
47. Gaines, Am. Min. **42**, 766, 1957
48. Goldschmidt, Norsk. Videns, Akad. Oslo I Maf. Nat. Klasse, no. 8, 1927
49. Goldsmith and Graf, Geochim. Cosmochim. Acta **11**, 310, 1957
50. Goldsmith and Laves, Geochim. Cosmochim. Acta **5**, 1, 1954
51. —— Zeit. Krist. **106**, 213, 1955
52. Goodyear and Duffin, Min. Mag. **32**, 902, 1961
53. Gordon, Am. Min. **36**, 918, 1951
54. Goryunova and Fedorova, Sov. Phys. Solid State **1**, 307, 1959
55. Graf, Am. Min. **46**, 1283, 1961
56. Grønvold, Haraldson, and Vinovde, Acta Chem. Scand. **14**, 1879, 1960
57. —— Acta Chem. Scand. **8**, 1927, 1954
58. Grønvold and Jacobsen, Acta Chem. Scand. **10**, 1440, 1956

59. Grønvold and Westrum, Jour. Am. Chem. Soc. **81**, 1780, 1959
60. —— Inorg. Chem. **1**, 36, 1962
61. Gruner, Zeit. Krist. **88**, 412, 1934
62. Güntert and Faessler, Zeit. Krist. **107**, 357, 1956
63. Hall, U.S. Geol. Surv. Prof. Paper 424B, 271, 1961
64. Heller, McGannon, and Weber, Jour. Appl. Phys. **21**, 1283, 1950
65. Hess, Am. Jour. Sci. Bowen volume 173, 1952
66. Hewitt, Econ. Geol. **43**, 408, 1948
67. Hiller, Neues Jahrb. Mineral. Monatsch, 265, 1951
68. Hurlbut, Am. Min. **46**, 549, 1961
69. Ievins, Straumanis, and Karlsons, Zeit. f. Phys. Chem. **40B**, 347, 1938
70. Jan, Steinman, and Dinichert, Jour. Phys. Chem. Solids **12**, 349, 1960
71. Jay, Proc. Roy. Soc. **A142**, 237, 1933
72. Jeffery and Heller, Acta Cryst. **6**, 807, 1953
73. Jurriaanse, Zeit. Krist. **90**, 322, 1953
74. Kay and Bailey, Acta Cryst. **10**, 219,.1957
75. Kohn and Hatch, Am. Min. **40**, 10, 1955
76. Kullerud, unpublished data
77. Kullerud and Yund, Jour. Petrology **3**, 126, 1962
78. Kuno and Hess, Am. Jour. Sci. **251**, 741, 1953
79. LaPlaca and Post, Acta Cryst. **13**, 503, 1960
80. Laves, Jour. Geol. **60**, 549, 1952
81. Lepp, Am. Min. **41**, 347, 1956
82. Liebau, Hilmer, and Lindeman, Acta Cryst. **12**, 182, 1959
83. Lundquist, Ark. Kem. Min. Geol. **17B**, n. 12, 1943
84. —— Ark. Kem. Min. Geol. **24A**, n. 21, 1947
85. —— Ark. Kem. Min. Geol. **24A**, n.22, 1947
86. —— Ark. Kem. Min. Geol. **24A**, n.23, 1947
87. Lundquist and Westgren, Zeit. anorg. Chem. **239**, 85, 1938
88. McConnell, Min. Mag. **32**, 534, 1960
89. —— Science **136**, 241, 1962
90. Meier, Zeit. Krist. **113**, 430, 1960
91. Midgley, Acta Cryst. **5**, 307, 1952
92. Morimoto, Min. Jour. (Japan) **2**, 1, 1956
93. —— Ann. Rept. Dir. Geophys. Lab. **58**, 193, 1959
94. Morimoto and Clark, Am. Min. **46**, 1448, 1961
95. Morimoto and Kullerud, Am. Min. **46**, 1270, 1961
96. Mosberg and others, U.S. Geol. Surv. Prof. Paper 424C, 347, 1961
97. Mrose, Chao, Fahey, and Milton, Am. Min. **46**, 420, 1961
98. Murdoch and Berry, Am. Min. **39**, 475, 1954
99. Nelson and Riley, Proc. Phys. Soc. **57**, 477, 1945
100. Newnham, Min. Mag. **32**, 683, 1961
101. Oftedal, Zeit. Phys. Chem. **135**, 291, 1928
102. O'Daniel and Tscheischwili, Zeit. Krist. **104**, 124, 1942
103. Pabst, Zeits. Krist. **115**, 307, 1961 (Min. Abstracts **15**, 337, 1962)
104. Palache, Berman, and Frondel, Dana's System of Mineralogy, 7th ed., 2 volumes, New York, John Wiley, 1944, 1951
105. Parker, Am. Min. **47**, 127, 1962
106. Peacock, Am. Jour. Sci. **30**, 495, 1935
107. —— Univ. Toronto Stud. Geol. Ser. **42**, 101, 1939
108. —— Trans. Roy. Soc. Canada IV **36**, 107, 1942
109. —— Am. Min. **27**, 229, 1942
110. Peacock and McAndrew, Am. Min. **35**, 425, 1950
111. Oswald, Zeit. Krist. **116**, 210, 1961
112. Pistorius, Am. Min. **46**, 982, 1961
113. —— Jour. Geol. **69**, 604, 1961
114. Posner, Perloff, and Diorio, Acta Cryst. **11**, 308, 1958
115. Primak, Kaufman, and Ward, Jour. Am. Chem. Soc. **70**, 2043, 1948
116. Rahlfs, Zeit. Phys. Chem. **B31**, 157, 1936
117. Robbins, Ann. Rept. Dir. Geophys. Lab. **58**, 137, 1959
118. Roseboom, Am. Min. **47**, 310, 1962
119. —— unpublished data
120. Ross and Edwards, Acta Cryst. **12**, 258, 1959
121. Ruben and Others, Jour. Am. Chem. Soc. **83**, 821, 1961
122. Sadanga, Tokonami, and Takeuchi, Acta Cryst. **15**, 65, 1962
123. Saha, Am. Min. **44**, 300, 1959
124. Sahama and Hytonen, Am. Min. **43**, 862, 1958
125. Sakata, Jap. Jour. Geol. Geog. **28**, 161, 1957

126. Salkovitz, Jour. Metals **8**, 176, 1956
127. Sasaki, Min. Jour. (Japan) **2**, 375, 1959
128. Schreyer and Schairer, Jour. Pet. **2**, 324, 1961
129. Shropshire, Keat, and Vaughan, Zeit. Krist. **112**, 409, 1959
130. Skinner, Am. Min. **41**, 428, 1956
131. —— Am. Min. **42**, 39, 1957
132. —— Am. Min. **46**, 1399, 1961
133. —— unpublished data
134. Skinner, Appelman, and Clark, Am. Jour. Sci. **259**, 651, 1961
135. Skinner and Barton, Am. Min. **45**, 612, 1960
136. Skinner, Barton, and Kullerud, Econ. Geol. **54**, 1040, 1959
137. Skinner and Bethke, Am. Min. **46**, 1382, 1961
138. Skinner and Evans, Am. Jour. Sci. **258A**, 312, 1960
139. Smith, Ann. Rept. Dir. Geophys. Lab. **52**, 61, 1953
140. —— Min. Mag. **31**, 47, 1956
141. Smith and Tuttle, Am. Jour. Sci. **255**, 282, 1957
142. Stemple and Brindley, Jour. Am. Ceram. Soc. **43**, 34, 1960
143. Straumanis, Jour. Appl. Phys. **20**, 726, 1949
144. Straumanis, Ejima, and James, Acta Cryst. **13**, 1022, 1960
145. Structure Reports, 184, 1951
146. Swanson and Tatge, U.S. Nat. Bur. Stds. Circular 539, **1**, Washington, D.C., 1953
147. Swanson and Fuyat, U.S. Nat. Bur. Stds. Circular 539, **2**, Washington, D.C., 1953
148. Swanson, Fuyat, and Ugrinic, U.S. Nat. Bur. Stds. Circular 539, **3**, Washington, D.C., 1954
149. —— U.S. Nat. Bur. Stds. Circular 539, **4**, Washington, D.C., 1955
150. Swanson, Gilfrich, and Ugrinic, U.S. Nat. Bur. Stds. Circular 539, **5**, Washington, D.C., 1955
151. Swanson, Gilfrich, and Cook, U.S. Nat. Bur. Stds. Circular 539, **6**, Washington. D.C., 1956
152. —— U.S. Nat. Bur. Stds. Circular 539, **7**, Washington. D.C., 1957
153. Swanson and others, U.S. Nat. Bur. Stds. Circular 539, **8**, Washington, D.C., 1959
154. —— U.S. Nat. Bur. Stds. Circular 539, **9**, Washington, D.C., 1960
155. —— U.S. Nat. Bur. Stds. Circular 539, **10**, Washington, D.C., 1960
156. —— U.S. Nat. Bur. Stds. Monogr. 25, sec. 1, Washington, D.C., 1962
157. Taylor and Underwood, Acta Cryst. **13**, 361, 1960
158. Tengner, Zeit. anorg. Chem. **239**, 126, 1938
159. Thomassen, Zeit. Phys. Chem. **4**, Abt. B, 277, 1929
160. Tolliday, Nature **182**, 1012, 1958
161. Tombs and Rooksby, Acta Cryst. **4**, 474, 1951
162. Toulmin, Am. Min. **48**, 725, 1963
163. Turnock and Eugster, Jour. Pet., **3**, 533, 1962
164. Ulrich and Zachariasen, Zeit. Krist. **62**, 260, 1925
165. Van Hook and Keith, Am. Min. **43**, 69, 1958
166. Waldbaum, D. R., private communication, August 1961
167. Wasserstein, Am. Min. **36**, 102, 1951
168. Wiese and Muldower, Jour. Phy. and Chem. Solids **15**, 13, 1960
169. Willis and Rooksby, Proc. Phys. Soc. **65B**, 950, 1952
170. —— Acta Cryst. **6**, 827, 1953
171. Wolfe, Am. Min. **40**, 249, 1955
172. Wones, D. R., private communication, February 1961
173. Yoder and Eugster, Geochim. Cosmochim. Acta **6**, 157, 1954
174. —— Geochim. Cosmochim. Acta **8**, 225, 1955
175. Yoder and Sahama, Am. Min. **42**, 475, 1957
176. Yund, Ann. Rept. Dir. Geophys. Lab. Wash. **56**, 148, 1959
177. Zussman, Acta Cryst. **12**, 309, 1959
178. Cooper, Bond and Abrahams, Acta Cryst. **14**, 1008, 1961
179. Cooper, Acta Cryst. **15**, 578, 1962
180. Skinner and Appleman, Am. Min. **48**, 854, 1963
181. Ito, Morimoto and Sadanaga, Acta Cryst. **5**, 775, 1952
182. Frondel, Dana's System of Mineralogy, 7th ed., **III**, Silica minerals, John Wiley, New York, 1962
183. Parrish, Acta Cryst. **13**, 838, 1960
184. Skinner, U.S. Geol. Survey Prof. Paper 450-D, 109, 1962
185. Farrell, Fang, and Newnham, Am. Min. **48**, 804, 1963
186. P. Toulmin, unpublished

Table 5-2 presents critically chosen "best values" for the density and molar volume of selected mineral compounds. No attempt was made to be all-inclusive; rather we have tried to present data for chemically and physically well-defined phases for which the molar volume and/or density was known to the order of 0.2 per cent.

Data are included for several materials not known as minerals but for which the data are necessary for the calculation of partial molar volumes of intermediate members of a solid solution. For similar reasons we have also included a few values of hypothetical phases (e.g. FeS wurtzite and sphalerite structures, and CdS rock-salt structure) based on the extrapolation of measured cell dimensions from incomplete solid solutions. (These theoretical phases are so indicated in Table 5-2.) The majority of the data included are for pure synthetic phases for which unit-cell parameters or densities have been determined with an accuracy of 0.1 per cent or better. In some instances, where the mineral deviates from the stoichiometric composition, either by substitutional or omission solid solution, one or more values are given for materials of known composition as noted in the formula column.

For several substances, measured densities having equal or greater accuracy than the X-ray data are available. For these compounds the molar volume was calculated from (1), and the uncertainty listed with the density.

Molar volumes were calculated from measured densities by the relationship:

$$V = \frac{M}{\rho}, \tag{1}$$

where M is the formula weight in grams and ρ is the density in grams cm^{-3}, or from the unit-cell dimensions,

$$V = \frac{(\text{unit cell volume in } cm^3)(\text{Avogadro's number})}{(\text{number of formulas})/(\text{unit cell})}. \tag{2}$$

Formulas for the volumes of various shaped unit cells are given in Barrett (1952).

Substances of rhombohedral symmetry are denoted by the symbol hex-R to distinguish them from materials of truly hexagonal symmetry. The cell volume and number of formula weights listed for these compounds are, however, given for the larger hexagonal cell.

Substances denoted by an asterisk indicate the data were obtained from natural mineral specimens whose composition may have deviated slightly from the listed composition. Densities given for these minerals were calculated using the formula weight for the stoichiometric phase.

The formula weights are based on the International Atomic Weights for 1957 (Wichers, 1958). Avogadro's number used for these tables is $(6.02322 \pm .00016) \times 10^{23}$ particles $mole^{-1}$ which is the physical value of Cohen, Crowe, and DuMond (1957) converted to the chemical scale, using the conversion factor $1.00027 \pm .000005$ of these authors. Temperatures for which the volumes and density apply are given in the second column from the right. Molar volumes for gases refer to the real gas at 1 atmosphere pressure. The letter r indicates that the measurements were made at an unspecified room temperature. This may be taken as $25 \pm 5°C$. Because of a lack of adequate thermal expansion data, no attempt was made to reduce all the data to the common reference temperature, $25°C$. The uncertainties given for the molar volumes include an estimate of the precision, the reproducibility between different investigators, and in

Work on Table 5-2 was supported in part by the Division of Reactor Development, U.S. Atomic Energy Commission.

some cases slight deviations from stoichiometry. Although the uncertainties are listed only for the molar volumes, it must be understood that an equal percentage uncertainty is associated with the cell volume and the density.

We wish to acknowledge the considerable help rendered in the preparation of Table 5-2 by our colleagues at the U.S. Geological Survey, particularly Mrs. Martha S. Toulmin who aided greatly in compiling and checking the unit-cell parameters of the sulfides and related minerals, and Jerry L. Edwards who checked the majority of the nonsulfide data and prepared the bibliography.

REFERENCES

Barrett, Structure of Metals, McGraw-Hill Book Co., New York, 1952
Wichers, Jour. Am. Chem. Soc. **80**, 4121, 1958
Cohen, Crowe, and DuMond, Fundamental constants of physics, Interscience Pub., New York, 1957

TABLE 5-2. MOLAR VOLUMES AND DENSITIES OF MINERALS
(Richard A. Robie and Philip M. Bethke)

Formula	Name	Formula weight grams	Crystal system	Cell volume 10^{-24} cm³	Z	Molar volume cm³	±	Density grams cm⁻³	Temp °C	Ref.
				ELEMENTS						
Ag	silver	107.880	cub	68.22_7	4	10.274	.005	10.500	25	139
Au	gold	197.0	cub	67.84_7	4	10.216	.005	19.283	25	139
C*	diamond	12.011	cub	45.380	8	3.4167	.0005	3.5154	25	126
C*	graphite	12.011	hex	35.189	4	5.299	.002	2.267	15	98
Cu	copper	63.54	cub	47.24_2	4	7.114	.004	8.932	25	139
Fe	α-iron	55.85	cub	23.55_1	2	7.093	.004	7.874	25	142
Ni	nickel	58.71	cub	43.75_6	4	6.589	.005	8.911	25	139
Pt	platinum	195.09	cub	60.37_9	4	9.092	.005	21.457	25	139
S	α-sulfur	32.066	orth	$3299._4$	128	15.53	.02	2.065	25	147
S	β-sulfur	32.066	mon	$1315._3$	48	16.50	.04	1.943	103	35
Pb	lead	207.2	cub	121.32	4	18.269	.005	11.342	25	139
Sn	β-tin	118.70	tet	108.18	4	16.29	.01	7.286	26	73
Sb	antimony	121.76	hex-R	180.52	6	18.18	.02	6.697	26	141
As	arsenic	74.91	hex-R	129.14	6	12.96	.05	5.778	26	141
Bi	bismuth	209.00	hex-R	212.29	6	21.31	.01	9.807	26	141
Se	selenium	78.96	hex	81.793	3	16.42	.02	4.808	26	137
Te	tellurium	127.61	hex	101.99	3	20.48	.02	6.231	25	139
Zn	zinc	65.38	hex	30.427	2	9.164	.005	7.135	25	139
				SULFIDES, TELLURIDES, SELENIDES, AND ARSENIDES						
β-Ni₃Pb₂S₂*	shandite	654.638	hex-R	367.7_6	3	73.8	.1	8.827	r	71, 108
Au₂Bi	maldonite	603.00	cub	503.9_8	8	37.94	.01	15.892	r	75
Ag₂S I	hi-argentite	247.826	cub	246.3_7	4	37.1	.2	6.680	600	32
Ag₂S II	argentite	247.826	cub	115.50	2	34.8	.1	7.125	189	32
Ag₂S III	acanthite	247.826	orth	227.08	4	34.2	.2	7.254	r	32, 148
Ag₂Se	hi-naumannite	294.72	cub	124.48	2	37.5	.2	7.862	170	113
Ag₂Te I	::	343.37	cub	158.6	2	44.6	.2	7.702	825	113
Ag₂Te II	::	343.37	cub	285.5	4	43.0	.1	7.986	250	113
Ag₂Te III*	hessite	343.37	mon	271.4	4	40.86	.20	8.405	r	49

Formula	Mineral	M	System	V (Å³)	Z	V° (cm³/mol)	±	ρ (g/cm³)	T (°C)	Ref.
Cu_2S I*	hi-digenite	159.146	cub	187.6	4	28.26	.10	5.632	465	31
Cu_2S II*	hi-chalcocite	159.146	hex	91.34	2	27.51	.06	5.786	152	31
Cu_2S III*	chalcocite	159.146	orth	4379.5	96	27.48	.01	5.792	r	31
$Cu_{1.79}S$ (Cu rich side)	digenite	145.803	pseudo-cubic	172.7_6	4	26.01_5	.01	5.605	25	116
$Cu_{1.77}S$ (S rich side)	digenite	144.532	pseudo-cubic	171.34	4	25.80	.01	5.602	25	31, 116
Cu_2Se	berzelianite	206.04	cub	200.2	4	30.15	.15	6.835	170	113
$Ag_{1.55}Cu_{.45}S$ I	jalpaite	227.873	cub	228.1_0	4	34.35	.10	6.634	300	32
$Ag_{1.55}Cu_{.45}S$ II	:	227.873	cub	112.33	2	33.83	.10	6.736	116	32
$Ag_{1.55}Cu_{.45}S$ III	:	227.873	tet	884.30	16	33.29	.03	6.845	r	32
$Ag_{.93}Cu_{1.07}S$ I	:	200.382	cub	211.8	4	31.90	.10	6.282	196	32
$Ag_{.93}Cu_{1.07}S$ II	:	200.382	hex	105.4	2	31.73	.10	6.315	100	32
$Ag_{.93}Cu_{1.07}S$ III	stromeyerite	200.382	orth	214.8	4	32.35	.03	6.194	r	32
$AgCuSe$	eucairite	250.360	orth	527.1	10	31.7	.6	7.887	r	47
Ag_3AuTe_2*	petzite	775.86	cub	1118.4	8	84.2	.2	9.214	r	48
Cu_3Se_2*	umangite	348.54	tet	175.3	2	52.8	.2	6.604	r	9, 38
Ni_3S_2	heazlewoodite	240.262	hex-R	204.0	3	40.95	.02	5.867	r	79, 84
Cu_5FeS_4*	hi-bornite	501.814	cub	166.4	1	100.2	.3	5.008	240	94
Cu_5FeS_4*	metastable bornite	501.814	cub	1309.3	8	98.6	.3	5.090	r	94
Cu_5FeS_4*	lo-bornite	501.814	tet	2618.6	16	98.6	.3	5.090	r	94
$Ni_{11}As_8$	maucherite	1245.09	tet	1029.4	4	155.0	.1	8.033	r	172
$(Fe, Ni)_9S_8$	pentlandite	769.72	cub	1059.96	4	159.6	.3	4.824	:	85
$Fe_{5.25}Ni_{3.75}S_8$	:	774.194	cub	1028.8	4	154.9	.3	4.998	:	85
$Fe_{3.75}Ni_{5.25}S_8$	:								r	
PtS	cooperite	227.156	tet	73.563	2	22.15	.05	10.25_3	r	10, 59
CaS	oldhamite	72.146	cub	184.12	4	27.72	.01	2.602	r	145, 65, 111
PbS	galena	239.276	cub	209.16	4	31.495	.010	7.597	r	11, 140, 160
$PbSe$	clausthalite	286.17	cub	229.84	4	34.609	.010	8.269	r	11
$PbTe$	altaite	334.82	cub	269.66	4	40.606	.020	8.246	r	10
MnS	alabandite	87.006	cub	142.52	4	21.460	.010	4.054	r	129, 10
MnS	sphalerite structure	87.006	cub	176.65	4	26.600	.010	3.271	r	127
MnS	wurtzite structure	87.006	hex	88.952	2	26.79	.01	3.248	r	132
CdS	greenockite	144.476	hex	99.407	2	29.94	.01	4.826	r	132
CdS	hawleyite	144.476	cub	198.46	4	29.88	.01	4.834	r	52, 157, 10

TABLE 5-2. *Continued*

Formula	Name	Formula weight grams	Crystal system	Cell volume 10^{-24} cm³	Z	Molar volume cm³	Density grams cm⁻³	Temp °C	Ref.
				SULFIDES, TELLURIDES, SELENIDES, AND ARSENIDES. *Continued*					
CdS	NaCl structure (hypothetical)	144.476	cub	167.83	4	25.27 ± .01	5.717	r	11
ZnS	sphalerite	97.446	cub	158.279	4	23.834 ± .008	4.088_5	r	11, 127, 130, 131
ZnS	wurtzite	97.446	hex	79.190	2	23.85 ± .01	4.086	r	130, 132
ZnSe	stilleite	144.34	cub	182.14	4	27.427 ± .008	5.263	r	11, 57
ZnTe	··	192.99	cub	227.20	4	34.212 ± .010	5.641	r	10
HgS	cinnabar	232.676	hex	141.55	3	28.419 ± .010	8.187	r	10, 142
HgS	metacinnabar	232.676	cub	200.38	4	30.173 ± .010	7.711	r	10, 142
HgSe	tiemannite	279.57	cub	225.34	4	33.932 ± .015	8.239	r	10, 145
HgTe	coloradoite	328.22	cub	269.59	4	40.594 ± .010	8.085	r	10
FeS	sphalerite structure (hypothetical)	87.916	cub	162.32	4	24.442 ± .010	3.597	r	127, 131
FeS	wurtzite structure (hypothetical)	87.916	hex	82.38	2	24.810 ± .010	3.544	r	132
CoS	sphalerite structure (hypothetical)	91.006	cub	152.18	4	22.916 ± .010	3.971	r	66
CdSe	cadmoselite	191.37	hex	112.00	2	33.731 ± .015	5.673	r	10
CdTe	··	240.020	cub	272.16	4	40.982 ± .020	5.857	r	10
$CuFeS_2$	chalcopyrite	··	··	··	··	··	··	··	··
$CuFeS_{1.90}$	··	180.315	tet	292.96	4	44.11 ± .05	4.088	r	11, 10
$CuFe_2S_3$*	cubanite	271.438	orth	447.5	8	67.39 ± .20	4.028	r	20
$AgFe_2S_3$*	sternbergite	315.756	orth	974.8	8	73.39 ± .20	4.303	r	107
$AgFe_2S_3$*	argentopyrite	315.756	orth	491.2	4	73.97 ± .20	4.269	r	97
NiAs	niccolite	133.62	hex	57.07	2	17.186 ± .020	7.775	r	172
NiSb	breithauptite	180.47	hex	69.37	2	20.893 ± .030	8.639	r	70

Formula	Mineral	Mol wt	System	V	n	Value	±	Density		Refs
CuS	covellite	95.606	hex	203.48	6	20.427	±.020	4.680	r	142
CuSe	klockmannite	142.50	hex	3014.8	78	23.257	±.020	6.128	r	37, 150
SnS	herzenbergite	150.776	orth	192.66	4	29.010	±.020	5.197	r	95
PbSnS$_2$	teallite	390.042	orth	199.24	2	60.002	±.040	6.500	r	95
AsS*	realgar	106.976	mon	791.6	16	29.82	±.10	3.59	r	16
NiS	millerite	90.776	hex-R	252.41	3	16.891	±.008	5.374	r	10, 149, 79, 84
Sb$_2$S$_3$	stibnite	339.718	orth	487.54	4	73.414	±.05	4.696	25	143
Bi$_2$S$_3$	bismuthinite	514.198	orth	501.59	4	75.529	±.07	6.808	26	142
Bi$_2$Te$_3$	tellurobismuthite	800.83	hex-R	507.32	3	101.86	±.10	7.862	r	45, 161
As$_2$S$_3$*	orpiment	246.018	mon	468.3	4	70.52	±.20	3.49	r	19
Co$_3$S$_4$	linnaeite	305.084	cub	830.85	8	62.55	±.05	4.877	r	87
Ni$_3$S$_4$	polydymite	304.394	cub	851.97	8	64.14	±.01	4.746	r	79
FeNi$_2$S$_4$	violarite	301.534	cub	847.66	8	63.82	±.05	4.725	r	86
FeCr$_2$S$_4$	daubreelite	288.134	cub	989.83	8	74.52	±.07	3.866	r	83
FeS$_2$	pyrite	120.082	cub	159.000	4	23.942	±.004	5.016	r	129, 82, 56
FeS	troilite	87.916	hex	60.44	2	18.20	±.01	4.830	r	179
FeS$_2$*	marcasite	120.082	orth	81.622	2	24.58	±.02	4.885	25	128, 17
FeSe$_2$	ferroselite	213.77	orth	99.50	2	29.97	±.05	7.134	r	62, 9
FeTe$_2$	frohbergite	311.07	orth	127.62	2	38.44	±.07	8.092	r	60
CoS$_2$	cattierite	123.072	cub	169.57	4	25.53	±.04	4.820	r	87
CoSe$_2$	trogtalite	216.86	cub	201.106	4	30.28	±.01	7.162	r	23
NiS$_2$	vaesite	122.842	cub	183.96	4	27.700	±.005	4.435	r	10, 79, 84
NiSe$_2$	··	216.63	cub	211.75	4	31.88	±.01	6.795	20	61
NiTe$_2$	melonite	313.93	hex	68.81	1	41.4	±.1	7.58	r	151
MnS$_2$	hauerite	119.072	cub	227.18	4	34.202	±.006	3.481	28	128
PtAs$_2$*	sperrylite	344.91	cub	212.56	4	32.00	±.05	10.778	r	56, 152
RuS$_2$	laurite	165.232	cub	175.6	4	26.4	±.2	6.26	r	8, 9, 30, 101
NiAs$_2$	rammelsbergite	208.53	orth	97.675	2	29.42	±.04	7.088	26	116, 148, 172
NiAs$_2$	pararammelsbergite	208.53	orth	382.4	8	28.8	±.1	7.24	r	78, 105
FeAs$_2$	loellingite	205.67	orth	91.36	2	27.51	±.02	7.476	26	116, 148
CoAs$_2$	Co-safflorite	208.76	mon	92.706	2	27.92	±.02	7.477	26	116, 148
(Co,Fe)As$_2$ Co$_{.5}$Fe$_{.5}$As$_2$	safflorite	207.22	orth	92.23	2	27.78	±.06	7.459	26	116, 148
MoS$_2$	molybdenite	160.082	hex	106.35	2	32.03	±.01	4.998	26	143
WS$_2$	tungstenite	247.992	hex	106.50	2	32.07	±.02	7.733	26	146
FeAsS*	arsenopyrite	162.826	tri	175.49	4	26.42	±.05	6.163	r	93
FeSbS*	gudmundite	209.676	mon	399.1	8	30.05	±.1	6.978	r	18

TABLE 5-2. *Continued*

Formula	Name	Formula weight grams	Crystal system	Cell volume 10^{-24} cm^3	Z	Molar volume cm^3		Density grams cm^{-3}	Temp °C	Ref.
			SULFIDES, TELLURIDES, SELENIDES, AND ARSENIDES. *Continued*							
(Co, Fe)AsS*	glaucodot	164.37	orth	1063.	24	26.7	±.2	6.17	r	9
CoAsS*	cobaltite	165.916	cub	175.6	4	26.4	±.4	6.28	r	9
NiAsS	gersdorffite	165.686	cub	184.51	4	27.78	±.01	5.964	26	149
FeAs$_{3-x}$FeAs$_{2.95}$	Fe-skutterudite (hypothetical)	276.83	cub	547.62	8	41.231	±.010	6.714	r	115
CoAs$_{3-x}$CoAs$_{2.95}$	Co-skutterudite (hypothetical)	279.92	cub	552.57	8	41.604	±.010	6.728	r	115
NiAs$_{3-x}$NiAs$_{2.95}$	Ni-skutterudite (hypothetical)	279.69	cub	578.01	8	43.518	±.010	6.427	r	115
Cu$_{12}$As$_4$S$_{13}$	tennantite	1478.987	cub	1058.1	2	318.7	±.8	4.641	26	129
Cu$_{12}$Sb$_4$S$_{13}$	tetrahedrite	1666.378	cub	1101.3	2	331.7	±.7	5.024	26	129
Cu$_3$AsS$_4$	enargite	393.794	orth	293.0	2	88.2$_5$	±.1	4.46	26	129
Cu$_3$AsS$_4$	luzonite	393.794	tet	292.0	2	87.9$_5$	±.1	4.48	26	129, 51
Cu$_3$SbS$_4$	famatinite	440.644	tet	312.2	2	94.0$_2$	±.1	4.69	26	129, 51
Ag$_3$AsS$_3$	proustite	494.748	hex	880.89	6	88.4	±.1	5.59$_7$	26	155
Ag$_3$SbS$_3$	pyrargyrite	541.598	hex	922.18	6	92.5	±.3	5.85$_5$	26	155
			OXIDES AND HYDROXIDES							
Al$_2$O$_3$	corundum	101.96	hex-R	254.7$_0$	6	25.57	±.01	3.988	26	140
AlO(OH)	boehmite	59.988	orth	129.7$_5$	4	19.54	±.02	3.070	26	141
AlO(OH)	diaspore	59.988	orth	117.9$_6$	4	17.76	±.03	3.377	25	22, 141
Al(OH)$_3$	gibbsite	78.004	mon	424.49	8	31.96	±.06	2.441	r	35
As$_2$O$_3$	arsenolite	197.82	cub	1358.0	16	51.12	±.03	3.869	25	139
BeO	bromellite	25.013	hex	27.61$_2$	2	8.315	±.005	3.008	26	139
CO	..	28.011	..	..	..	22,408.	±15		0	5
CO$_2$	..	44.011	..	..	..	22,263.	±20		0	5
CaO	lime	56.08	cub	111.3$_2$	4	16.76	±.01	3.345	26	139, 15
Ca(OH)$_2$	portlandite	74.096	hex	54.88$_3$	1	33.06	±.04	2.241	26	139, 15
CdO	..	128.41	cub	103.5$_1$	4	15.59	±.01	8.238	27	140
CeO$_2$	cerianite	172.13	cub	158.4$_3$	4	23.86	±.02	7.216	26	139
CoO	..	74.94	cub	77.31	4	11.64	±.01	6.438	26	147

Formula wt.	Formula	Name	System	V (ų)	Z	Molar vol. (cm³)	±	Density (g/cm³)	T (°C)	Ref.
152.02	Cr₂O₃	eskolaite	hex-R	288.7_2	6	28.98	.05	5.245	26	143
79.54	CuO	tenorite	mon	81.16_2	4	12.22	.02	6.508	26	139
143.08	Cu₂O	cuprite	cub	77.83_3	2	23.44	.02	6.104	26	140
69.225	Fe.945O	wüstite	cub	79.99_6	4	12.05	.06	5.745	r	162
159.70	Fe₂O₃	hematite	hex-R	301.6_2	6	30.28	.02	5.274	25	63
231.55	Fe₃O₄	magnetite	cub	591.4_3	8	44.53	.03	5.200	25	1,154
88.858	α-FeO(OH)*	goethite	orth	138.2_7	4	20.82	.03	4.268	r	105
88.858	γ-FeO(OH)*	lepidocrocite	orth	148.5	4	22.37	.08	3.972	r	105
18.016	H₂O	water				18.069	.003	.9971	25	5
18.016	H₂O	ice	hex	130.41	4	19.637	.010	.9174	0	80
210.50	HfO₂	hafnia	mon	138.30	4	20.82	.01	10.108	r	2
216.61	HgO	montroydite	orth	128.3_1	4	19.32	.02	11.211	25	147
40.32	MgO	periclase	cub	74.70_9	4	11.25	.01	3.584	25	126,139
58.336	Mg(OH)₂	brucite	hex	40.90_3	1	24.64	.03	2.368	26	144
70.94	MnO	manganosite	cub	87.81_2	4	13.22	.01	5.365	26	143,53
86.94	MnO₂	pyrolusite	tet	55.16	2	16.61	.06	5.233	r	138
157.88	Mn₂O₃	bixbyite	cub	833.5_0	16	31.38	.03	5.032	25	147
228.82	Mn₃O₄	hausmannite	tet	623.6	8	46.96	.08	4.873	r	158
143.95	MoO₃	molybdite	orth	202.9_8	4	30.56	.02	4.710	26	141
74.71	NiO	bunsenite	cub	72.87_7	4	10.97	.01	6.808	26	139
223.21	PbO	litharge	tet	79.40_2	2	23.91	.02	9.334	27	140
223.21	PbO	massicot	orth	153.7_6	4	23.15	.02	9.641	27	140
64.066	SO₂					21,894.	.15		0	5
291.52	Sb₂O₃	senarmontite	cub	1386.9	16	52.21	.03	5.583	26	141
291.52	Sb₂O₃	valentinite	orth	332.1_3	4	50.01	.06	5.829	25	148
60.09	SiO₂*	α-quartz	hex	113.01_3	3	22.690	.005	2.648	25	46
60.09	SiO₂	α-cristobalite	tet	170.9_5	4	25.74	.02	2.334	25	148
60.09	SiO₂	β-cristobalite	cub	363.7_2	8	27.38	.02	2.194	405	134
60.09	SiO₂	α-tridymite	hex			26.53	.20	2.265	r	43
60.09	SiO₂	β-tridymite	hex	182.0_8	4	27.42	.03	2.192	405	134
60.09	SiO₂*	coesite	mon	548.3_7	16	20.64	.05	2.911	25	128
60.09	SiO₂*	stishovite	tet	46.541	2	14.016	.01	4.287	r	24
60.09	SiO₂	β-quartz	hex	118.15	3	23.72	.01	2.533	575	174
60.09	SiO₂	keatite	tet	478.3	12	24.01	.30	2.503	r	124
60.09	SiO₂	melanophlogite	cub	2407.2	48	30.21	.10	1.989	r	177
150.70	SnO₂	cassiterite	tet	71.56_6	2	21.55	.02	6.992	26	139

TABLE 5-2. *Continued*

Formula	Name	Formula weight grams	Crystal system	Cell volume 10^{-24} cm³	Z	Molar volume cm³	Density grams cm⁻³	Temp °C	Ref.
			OXIDES AND HYDROXIDES. *Continued*						
TeO_2*	tellurite	159.61	orth	368.6₁	8	27.75 ±.02	5.751	25	147
TeO_2	para-tellurite	159.61	tet	176.14	4	26.52 ±.02	6.018	25	148
ThO_2	thorianite	264.05	cub	175.16₉	4	26.38 ±.01	10.011	25	126, 139
TiO_2	rutile	79.90	tet	62.42₈	2	18.80 ±.02	4.250	25	139, 29
TiO_2	anatase	79.90	tet	136.1	4	20.49 ±.03	3.899	26	139, 29
TiO_2*	brookite	79.90	orth	257.4₂	8	19.38 ±.07	4.123	r	35
UO_2	uraninite	270.07	cub	163.5₁	4	24.62 ±.01	10.969	26	140
ZnO	zincite	81.38	hex	47.61₅	2	14.34 ±.01	5.675	25	67
ZrO_2	baddeleyite	123.22	mon	140.4₅	4	21.15 ±.06	5.826	r	2
			SPINELS, ALUMINATES, AND TITANATES						
$BeAl_2O_4$	chrysoberyl	126.973	orth	227.9	4	34.32 ±.06	3.699	25	147
$MgAl_2O_4$	spinel	142.28	cub	527.5	8	39.72 ±.03	3.582	26	140
$FeAl_2O_4$	hercynite	173.81	cub	542.1	8	40.82 ±.06	4.258	25	156
$MnAl_2O_4$	galaxite	172.90	cub	563.2	8	42.40 ±.05	4.078	25	147
$ZnAl_2O_4$	gahnite	183.34	cub	528.5	8	39.79 ±.04	4.608	26	140
$FeFe_2O_4$	magnetite	231.55	cub	590.8	8	44.50 ±.03	5.206	25	1, 154
$MnFe_2O_4$	jacobsite	230.64	cub	613.9	8	46.22 ±.07	4.990	25	147
$NiFe_2O_4$	trevorite	234.41	cub	579.9	8	43.66 ±.08	5.369	25	148
$MgCr_2O_4$	picrochromite	192.34	cub	578.6₁	8	43.57 ±.06	4.415	26	147
$CaTiO_3$	perovskite	135.98	orth	223.33	4	33.63 ±.03	4.043	r	76
$FeTiO_3$*	ilmenite	151.75	hex-R	315.9	6	31.71 ±.05	4.786	r	103, 35
$MgTiO_3$	geikielite	120.22	hex-R	307.4	6	30.86 ±.03	3.895	26	143
			HALIDES						
$NaCl$	halite	58.448	cub	179.42	4	27.018 ±.007	2.163	25	140
KCl	sylvite	74.557	cub	249.23	4	37.528 ±.007	1.987	25	139
NaF	villiaumite	41.991	cub	99.52	4	14.99 ±.01	2.802	25	139
$AgBr$	bromyrite	187.796	cub	192.5₅	4	28.99 ±.01	6.477	26	142
$AgCl$	cerargyrite	143.337	cub	170.8₇	4	25.73 ±.01	5.571	26	142

Mineral	Formula	Formula wt.	System	Cell vol.	Z	Molar vol.	±	Density	T	Ref.
iodyrite	AgI	234.79	hex	137.15	2	41.31	±.02	5.684	25	146
fluorite	CaF$_2$	78.08	cub	163.0$_0$	4	24.54	±.01	3.181	25	139,4
sellaite	MgF$_2$	62.32	tet	65.13	2	19.61	±.02	3.177	27	142,36
calomel	HgCl	236.067	tet	218.8	4	32.94	±.02	7.166	25	139
cryolite	Na$_3$AlF$_6$*	209.953	mon	235.$_3$	2	70.86	±.25	2.963	r	103
HCl	HCl	36.465	..	..	..	22,246.	±.20	...	0	5
neighborite	NaMgF$_3$	104.311	orth	226.5$_4$	4	34.11	±.02	3.058	18	25
miersite	AgI	234.79	cub	273.99	4	41.26	±.08	5.690	r	159
Carbonates and Nitrates										
calcite	CaCO$_3$	100.091	hex-R	367.9$_6$	6	36.94	±.02	2.712	26	58
dolomite	CaMg(CO$_3$)$_2$*	184.422	hex-R	320.5$_1$	3	64.35	±.04	2.866	26±3	58
otavite	CdCO$_3$	172.421	hex-R	341.7$_2$	6	34.30	±.02	5.027	26±3	58
cobalticalcite	CoCO$_3$	118.951	hex-R	281.0$_8$	6	28.22	±.01	4.215	26±3	58
siderite	FeCO$_3$	115.861	hex-R	292.6$_8$	6	29.38	±.02	3.944	26±3	58
magnesite	MgCO$_3$	84.331	hex-R	279.1$_3$	6	28.02	±.01	3.009	26±3	58
huntite	Mg$_3$Ca(CO$_3$)$_4$*	353.084	hex-R	612.1$_5$	3	122.90	±.30	2.873	26±3	58
rhodochrosite	MnCO$_3$	114.951	hex-R	309.5$_5$	6	31.08	±.01	3.698	26±3	58
..	NiCO$_3$	118.721	hex-R	269.5$_1$	6	27.06	±.02	4.387	26±3	58
smithsonite	ZnCO$_3$	125.391	hex-R	281.6$_9$	6	28.28	±.01	4.434	26	58
witherite	BaCO$_3$	197.371	orth	304.2$_4$	4	45.81	±.04	4.308	26	140
aragonite	CaCO$_3$	100.091	orth	226.8$_5$	4	34.16	±.02	2.930	26	141
cerussite	PbCO$_3$	267.221	orth	269.61	4	40.60	±.03	6.581	26	140
strontianite	SrCO$_3$	147.641	orth	259.0$_7$	4	39.01	±.03	3.785	26	141
malachite	Cu$_2$(OH)$_2$CO$_3$	221.107	mon	364.3$_5$	4	54.86	±.05	4.030	25	148
azurite	Cu$_3$(OH)$_2$(CO$_3$)$_2$	344.65	mon	302.2$_3$	2	91.02	±.07	3.787	25	148
niter	KNO$_3$	101.108	orth	319.0$_7$	4	48.04	±.05	2.104	26	141
soda niter	NaNO$_3$	84.999	hex-R	374.5$_7$	6	37.60	±.02	2.260	25	144
norsethite	BaMg(CO$_3$)$_2$*	281.70	hex-R	365.6	3	73.39	±.10	3.838	r	96
vaterite	CaCO$_3$	100.091	hex	375.8$_4$	6	37.73	±.05	2.653	r	88
gerhardite	Cu$_2$(NO$_3$)(OH)$_3$	240.112	orth	469.2	4	70.65	±.10	3.398	r	102
Sulfates and Borates										
barite	BaSO$_4$	233.426	orth	346.0$_5$	4	52.11	±.05	4.480	26	141
anhydrite	CaSO$_4$	136.146	orth	305.0$_9$	4	45.94	±.05	2.963	26	142
anglesite	PbSO$_4$	303.276	orth	318.50	4	47.96	±.05	6.324	25	141
celestite	SrSO$_4$	183.696	orth	307.1$_7$	4	46.25	±.05	3.972	26	140

TABLE 5-2. *Continued*

Formula	Name	Formula weight grams	Crystal system	Cell volume 10^{-24} cm^3	Z	Molar volume cm^3	Density grams cm^{-3}	Temp °C	Ref.
			SULFATES AND BORATES. *Continued*						
ZnSO$_4$	zinkosite	161.446	orth	276.1$_0$	4	41.58 ± .05	3.883	25	145
K$_2$SO$_4$	arcanite	174.266	orth	435.0$_3$	4	65.51 ± .07	2.660	25	141
Na$_2$SO$_4$	thenardite	142.048	orth	708.4$_7$	8	53.34 ± .06	2.663	25	140
CaSO$_4$·2H$_2$O*	gypsum	172.178	mon	(493.5)	4	74.31 ± .16	2.317 ± .005	r	104
MgSO$_4$·7H$_2$O	epsomite	246.498	orth	(975.2)	4	146.85 ± .50	1.677 ± .004	25	104
Na$_2$SO$_4$·10H$_2$O	mirabilite	322.208	mon	1459.$_9$	4	219.83 ± .40	1.466	24	117
CuSO$_4$·5H$_2$O	chalcanthite	249.686	tri	(362.2)	2	109.08 ± .20	2.289 ± .004	r	42,104
Cu$_4$SO$_4$(OH)$_6$*	brochantite	452.274	mon	754.4	4	113.60 ± 1.15	3.981	r	35
Na$_2$B$_4$O$_5$(OH)$_4$·8H$_2$O	borax	381.422	mon	1478.$_8$	4	222.68 ± .40	1.713	r	91
CaB$_3$O$_4$(OH)$_3$·H$_2$O*	colemanite	205.580	mon	564.2$_7$	4	84.97 ± .08	2.419	r	26
K$_2$Ca(SO$_4$)$_2$·H$_2$O	syngenite	328.428	mon	424.2$_7$	2	127.77 ± .15	2.570	r	7
			PHOSPHATES, MOLYBDATES, AND TUNGSTATES						
AlPO$_4$	berlinite	121.955	hex-R	232.0	3	46.59 ± .05	2.618	25	148
Ca$_5$(PO$_4$)$_3$OH	hydroxylapatite	502.333	hex	530.1$_4$	2	159.66 ± .40	3.146	r	110,89
YPO$_4$	xenotime	183.895	tet	283.6	4	42.70 ± .07	4.307	25	146
CaMoO$_4$	powellite	200.03	tet	312.2	4	47.01 ± .08	4.255	25	144
PbMoO$_4$	wulfenite	367.16	tet	357.7	4	53.87 ± .06	6.816	25	145
CaWO$_4$	scheelite	287.94	tet	312.5	4	47.05 ± .04	6.119	25	144
PbWO$_4$	stolzite	455.07	tet	359.3	4	54.11 ± .04	8.411	25	145
FeWO$_4$	ferberite	303.71	mon	134.1$_6$	2	40.40 ± .06	7.517	r	122
MnWO$_4$	huebnerite	302.80	mon	139.0$_6$	2	41.88 ± .06	7.230	r	122
Fe$_{.5}$Mn$_{.5}$WO$_4$	wolframite	303.255	mon	136.6$_8$	2	41.15 ± .06	7.370	r	122
Ca$_5$(PO$_4$)$_3$F	fluorapatite	504.325	hex	523.3	2	157.60 ± .40	3.200	r	89
Ca$_5$(PO$_4$)$_3$Cl	chlorapatite	520.782	hex	544.2	2	163.88 ± .50	3.178	r	89
			SILICATES						
Al$_2$SiO$_5$*	andalusite	162.05	orth	342.2$_6$	4	51.54 ± .01	3.144	25	133
Al$_2$SiO$_5$*	kyanite	162.05	tri	292.9$_0$	4	44.11 ± .02	3.674	25	133
Al$_2$SiO$_5$*	sillimanite	162.05	orth	331.4$_2$	4	49.91 ± .02	3.247	25	133

Formula	Mineral	Mol. wt.	System	Volume	Z	V°	Density	Ref.	T
$Ca_3Al_2Si_3O_{12}$	grossularite	450.47	cub	1664.4_3	8	125.32 ± .04	3.595	125	25
$Ca_3Cr_2Si_3O_{12}$	uvarovite	500.53	cub	1727.5_7	8	129.98 ± .06	3.851	148	26
$Ca_3Fe_2Si_3O_{12}$	andradite	508.21	cub	1748.8_2	8	131.67 ± .04	3.860	125	25
$Fe_3Al_2Si_3O_{12}$	almandite	497.78	cub	1531.2_1	8	115.28 ± .04	4.318	125	25
$Mg_3Al_2Si_3O_{12}$	pyrope	403.19	cub	1504.6_6	8	113.29 ± .04	3.559	125	25
$Mn_3Al_2Si_3O_{12}$	spessartite	495.05	cub	1569.3_9	8	118.16 ± .04	4.190	125	25
$\gamma\text{-}Ca_2SiO_4$*	lime olivine	172.25	orth	389.3_4	4	58.63 ± .35	2.938	100	r
Fe_2SiO_4	fayalite	203.79	orth	308.1_1	4	46.39 ± .08	4.393	170	25
Mg_2SiO_4*	forsterite	140.73	orth	290.8_1	4	43.79 ± .03	3.214	129	25
Mn_2SiO_4*	tephroite	201.97	orth	322.8_7	4	48.62 ± .10	4.154	72	r
$CaMgSiO_4$*	monticellite	156.49	orth	341.1_3	4	51.37 ± .15	3.046	120	r
$CaFeSiO_4$	kirschsteinite	188.02	orth	350.3_9	4	52.76 ± .10	3.564	120	r
$\beta\text{-}Ca_2SiO_4$*	larnite	172.25	mon	342.7	4	51.60 ± .40	3.338	90	r
Be_2SiO_4*	phenacite	110.116	hex-R	1111.6	18	37.20 ± .06	2.960	146	25
Zn_2SiO_4	willemite	222.85	hex-R	1566.6	18	52.42 ± .13	4.251	145	25
$ThSiO_4$*	thorite	324.14	tet	322.7_6	4	48.60 ± .10	6.669	50	r
$ZrSiO_4$*	zircon	183.31	tet	260.7_6	4	39.27 ± .08	4.668	142	25
$USiO_4$	coffinite	330.16	tet	306.4_{45}	4	46.14 ± .10	7.155	50	r
$KAl_2(AlSi_3O_{10})(OH)_2$*	muscovite	398.326	mon (2M)	933.3_9	4	140.55 ± .50	2.834	169,44	27
$KMg_3(AlSi_3O_{10})(OH)_2$*	phlogopite	417.326	mon (1M)	496.9_5	2	149.66 ± 1.0	2.788	168	r
$KMg_3(AlSi_3O_{10})F_2$	fluor-phlogopite	421.31	mon (1M)	486.0_7	2	146.38 ± .50	2.878	77	r
$KFe(AlSi_3O_{10})(OH)_2$	annite	511.916	mon (1M)	512.4_0	2	154.32 ± 1.0	3.317	165	26
$Al_2Si_4O_{10}(OH)_2$*	pyrophyllite	360.336	mon	841.0	4	126.6 ± .50	2.845	64,175	r
$Mg_3Si_4O_{10}(OH)_2$*	talc	379.336	mon	903.7	4	136.7 ± .30	2.788	166,21	r
$CaSiO_3$*	wollastonite	116.17	tri	397.8	6	39.94 ± .08	2.909	153	r
$CaSiO_3$	parawollastonite	116.17	mon	790.3	12	39.67 ± .08	2.928	166,74	r
$CaSiO_3$	pseudowollastonite	116.17	tri (mon)	1597.0_0	24	40.08 ± .08	2.898	92	r
$MgSiO_3$*	clino-enstatite	100.41	mon	417.9_8	8	31.47 ± .07	3.190	69,144	r
$MgSiO_3$	enstatite	100.41	orth	834.0_4	16	31.40 ± .07	3.198 ± .007		26
$MnSiO_3$	rhodonite	131.03	tri	(586.4)	10	35.32 ± .30	3.71 ± .03	..	r
$CaMg(SiO_3)_2$	diopside	216.58	mon	438.9_7	4	66.10 ± .10	3.277	167,121	r
$CaFe(SiO_3)_2$*	hedenbergite	248.11	mon	(438.1)	4	65.97 ± .30	3.55 ± .01	68	r
$NaAlSi_2O_6$*	jadeite	202.151	mon	(405.0)	4	60.98 ± .40	3.315 ± .020	3,164,171	r
$Ca_2Mg_5Si_8O_{22}(OH)_2$*	tremolite	812.496	mon	906.3_4	2	272.95 ± .90	2.976	163,173	r
$Ca_2Mg_5Si_8O_{22}F_2$	fluor-tremolite	816.48	mon	898.0_4	2	270.45 ± .40	3.019	28	20
$Ca_2Fe_5Si_8O_{22}(OH)_2$*	Fe-tremolite	970.146	mon	(947.3)	2	285.3 ± 3.0	3.400 ± .030	163	r

TABLE 5-2. Continued

Formula	Name	Formula weight grams	Crystal system	Cell volume 10^{-24} cm³	Z	Molar volume cm³	Density grams cm⁻³	Temp °C	Ref.
			SILICATES.	Continued					
$Na_2Mg_3Fe_2Si_8O_{22}(OH)_2$	Mg-riebeckite	841.376	mon	908.6	2	$273.6 \pm .8$	3.075	r	39
$Na_2Mg_3Al_2Si_8O_{22}(OH)_2$	glaucophane	783.636	mon	895.4	2	$269.7 \pm .8$	2.906	r	40
$Mg_7Si_8O_{22}(OH)_2$*	anthophyllite	780.976	orth	(1820.0)	4	274.0 ± 3.5	$2.850 \pm .050$	r	112
$Fe_7Si_8O_{22}(OH)_2$*	grunerite	1001.684	mon	(924.7)	2	278.5 ± 1.0	$3.597 \pm .010$	r	13
$Be_3Al_2(Si_6O_{18})$*	beryl	537.539	hex	675.9_8	2	$203.58 \pm .50$	2.640	25	147
$Mg_2Al_3(AlSi_5O_{18})$	hi-cordierite	585.01	hex	773.0_3	2	$232.81 \pm .30$	2.513	r	123
$Mg_2Al_3(AlSi_5O_{18})$	lo-cordierite	585.01	orth	1550.7	4	$233.50 \pm .30$	2.505	r	123
$CaAl_2Si_2O_8$	anorthite	278.22	tri	(668.9_4)	4	$100.73 \pm .15$	$2.762 \pm .004$	r	27, 54, 135
$NaAlSi_3O_8$	albite	262.241	tri	(665.4_9)	4	$100.21 \pm .19$	$2.617 \pm .005$	r	135, 81
$NaAlSi_3O_8$	analbite	262.241	tri	668.2_8	4	$100.63 \pm .15$	$2.606 \pm .004$	r	135, 81
$KAlSi_3O_8$*	microcline	278.35	tri	721.8_3	4	$108.69 \pm .20$	2.561	r	81, 55
$KAlSi_3O_8$	sanidine	278.35	mon	723.7	4	$108.98 \pm .20$	2.554	r	34
$CaTiSiO_5$*	sphene	196.07	mon	369.9	4	$55.70 \pm .30$	3.520	r	35
$Zn_4(OH)_2Si_2O_7 \cdot H_2O$*	hemimorphite	481.732	orth	459.3_6	2	$138.34 \pm .30$	3.482	25	140
$(AlF)_2SiO_4$*	topaz	184.05	orth	343.1	4	$51.66 \pm .10$	3.563	26	149
$NaMg_3Al_6B_3Si_6O_{27}(OH)_4$	dravite	958.863	hex-R	1577.0_9	3	316.80 ± 1.00	3.027	r	114
$CaMg_4Al_5B_3Si_6O_{27}(OH)_4$	uvite	973.292	hex-R	1566.3	3	314.47 ± 1.00	3.095	r	114
$NaAlSi_2O_6 \cdot H_2O$	analcite	220.167	cub	2590.0	16	$97.50 \pm .10$	2.258	r	119
$NaAlSiO_4$	nepheline	142.061	hex	719.5	8	$54.17 \pm .15$	2.623	r	33
$Al_2Si_2O_5(OH)_4$*	dickite	258.172	mon	659.5_1	4	$99.31 \pm .30$	2.600	r	99
$Ca_2MgSi_2O_7$	akermanite	272.68	tet	308.2_2	2	$92.82 \pm .15$	2.938	r	6, 41
$Ca_2Al_2SiO_7$	gehlenite	274.21	tet	299.6_7	2	$90.25 \pm .15$	3.038	r	6, 41
$CaAl_2Si_2O_7(OH)_2 \cdot H_2O$	lawsonite	314.252	orth	672.9_6	4	$101.33 \pm .15$	3.110	r	109
$KAlSiO_4$	kalsilite	158.17	hex	200.66	2	$60.43 \pm .06$	2.617	r	136
$KAlSi_2O_6$*	leucite	218.26	⋯	⋯	⋯	$88.01 \pm .15$	2.480	r	12
$KAlSi_3O_8$*	orthoclase	278.35	mon	(724.6)	4	$109.11 \pm .30$	$2.551 \pm .008$	r	12
$NaAlSiO_4$	lo-carnegieite	142.061	⋯	⋯	⋯	$56.53 \pm .10$	$2.513 \pm .005$	21	14
$3Al_2O_3 \cdot 2SiO_2$	mullite	426.06	orth	167.5_7	3/4	$134.57 \pm .30$	3.166	r	176
$2Al_2O_3 \cdot SiO_2$	mullite	264.01	orth	168.37	6/5	$84.51 \pm .15$	3.124	r	176, 118
$Ca_2Al_3(SiO_4)_3(OH)$	zoisite	454.387	orth	906.7	4	$136.5 \pm .30$	3.328	r	178
$Ca_2Al_3(SiO_4)_3(OH)$	clinozoisite	454.387	mon	452.3	2	$136.2 \pm .30$	3.336	r	178

REFERENCES FOR TABLE 5-2

1. Abrahams and Calhoun, Acta Cryst. **6**, 105, 1953
2. Adam and Rodgers, Acta Cryst. **12**, 951, 1959
3. Adams and Gibson, Proc. Nat. Acd. Sci. **15**, 713, 1929
4. Allen, Am. Min. **37**, 910, 1952
5. American Institute of Physics Handbook, McGraw-Hill Book Co., New York, 1957
6. Andrews, Min. Mag. **28**, 374, 1948
7. Aruja, Min. Mag. **31**, 943, 1958
8. Bannister, Min. Mag. **23**, 195, 1932
9. Berry and Thompson, Mem. 85, Geol. Soc. America, 281 p., 1962
10. Bethke, P. M., unpublished data
11. Bethke and Barton, U.S. Geol. Surv. Prof. Paper 424B, 266, 1961
12. Birch and others, Geol. Soc. America, Special Paper 36, 1942
13. Bowen and Schairer, Am. Min. **543**, 1935
14. Bowen, Am. Jour. Sci. **XLIII**, 115, 1917
15. Brunauer, Kantro, and Weise, Canadian Jour. Chem. **34**, 729, 1956
16. Buerger, Am. Min. **20**, 36, 1935
17. —— Zeit. Krist. **97**, 504, 1937
18. —— Am. Min. **23**, 4, 1939
19. —— Am. Min. **27**, 301, 1942
20. —— Am. Min. **32**, 415, 1947
21. —— Proc. Nat. Acad. Sci. **42**, 113, 1956
22. Busing and Levey, Acta Cryst. **11**, 798, 1958
23. Böhm and others, Acta Chem. Scand. **9**, 1510, 1955
24. Chao, Fahey, Littler, and Milton, Jour. Geophys. Res. **67**, 419, 1962
25. Chao and others, Amer. Min. **46**, 379, 1961
26. Christ, Am. Min. **41**, 569, 1956
27. Cole, Sorum, and Taylor, Acta Cryst. **4**, 20, 1951
28. Comeforo and Kohn, Am. Min. **39**, 537, 1954
29. Cromer and Herrington, Jour. Am. Chem. Soc. **77**, 4708, 1955
30. deJong and Hoog, Rec. Trav. Chim. **46**, 173, 1927
31. Djurle, Acta Chem. Scand. **12**, 1415, 1958
32. —— Acta Chem. Scand. **12**, 1427, 1958
33. Donnay, Ann. Rept. Dir. Geophys. Lab. **56**, 239, 1957
34. Donnay and Donnay, Am. Jour. Sci. Bowen Volume 115, 1952
35. Donnay and Nowacki, Crystal data, Geol. Soc. America Memoir **60**, 1954
36. Duncanson and Stevenson, Proc. Phy. Soc. **72**, 1001, 1958
37. Earley, Am. Min. **34**, 433, 1949
38. —— Am. Min. **35**, 337, 1950
39. Ernst, Geochim. Cosmochim. Acta **19**, 10, 1960
40. —— Am. Jour. Sci. **259**, 735, 1961
41. Ferguson and Buddington, Am. Jour. Sci. **50**, 133, 1920
42. Fisher, Am. Min. **37**, 95, 1952
43. Fleming and Lynton, Phy. Chem. Glasses **1**, 148, 1960
44. Fournier, R. O., private communication, June 1960
45. Francombe, Brit. Jour. Appl. Phys. **9**, 415, 1958
46. Frondel and Hurlbut, Jour. Chem. Phys. **23**, 1215, 1955
47. Frueh, Geol. Soc. America Bull. **67**, 1697, 1956
48. —— Am. Min. **44**, 693, 1959
49. —— Zeit. Krist. **112**, 44, 1959
50. Fuchs and Gebert, Am. Min. **43**, 243, 1958
51. Gaines, Am. Min. **42**, 766, 1957
52. Goldschmidt, Norsk. Videns, Akad. Oslo I Maf. Nat. Klasse, no. 8, 1927
53. Goldsmith and Graf, Geochim. Cosmochim. Acta **11**, 310, 1957

REFERENCES FOR TABLE 5-2. *Continued*

54. Goldsmith and Laves, Zeit. Krist. **106**, 213, 1955
55. —— Geochim. Cosmochim. Acta **5**, 1, 1954
56. Gordon, Am. Min. **36**, 918, 1951
57. Goryunova and Fedorova, Sov. Phys. Solid State, **1**, 307, 1959
58. Graf, Am. Min. **46**, 1283, 1961
59. Grønvold, Haraldsen, and Kjekshus, Acta Chem. Scand. **14**, 1879, 1960
60. Grønvold, Haraldsen, and Vihovde, Acta Chem. Scand. **8**, 1927, 1954
61. Grønvold and Jacobsen, Acta Chem. Scand. **10**, 1440, 1956
62. Grønvold and Westrum, Inorg. Chem. **1**, 36, 1962
63. —— Jour. Am. Chem. Soc. **81**, 1780, 1959
64. Gruner, Zeit. Krist. **88**, 412, 1934
65. Güntert and Faessler, Zeit. Krist. **107**, 357, 1956
66. Hall, U.S. Geol. Surv. Prof. Paper **424B**, 271, 1961
67. Heller, McGannon, and Weber, Jour. Appl. Phys. **21**, 1283, 1950
68. Hess, Am. Min. **34**, 621, 1949
69. —— Am. Jour. Sci. Bowen Volume 173, 1952
70. Hewitt, Econ. Geol. **43**, 408, 1948
71. Hiller, Neues Jahrb. Mineral. Monatsch, 265, 1951
72. Hurlbut, Am. Min. **46**, 549, 1961
73. Ievins, Straumanis, and Karlsons, Zeit. Phys. Chem. **40B**, 347, 1938
74. Jeffery and Heller, Acta Cryst. **6**, 807, 1953
75. Jurriaanse, Zeit. Krist. **90**, 322, 1935
76. Kay and Bailey, Acta Cryst. **10**, 219, 1957
77. Kohn and Hatch, Am. Min. **40**, 10, 1955
78. Kullerud, G., unpublished data
79. Kullerud and Yund, Jour. Petrology **3**, 126, 1962
80. LaPlaca and Post, Acta Cryst. **12**, 951, 1959
81. Laves, Jour. Geol. **60**, 549, 1952
82. Lepp, Am. Min. **41**, 347, 1956
83. Lundquist, Ark. Kem. Min. Geol. **17B**, n. 12, 1943
84. —— Ark. Kem. Min. Geol. **24A**, n. 21, 1947
85. —— Ark. Kem. Min. Geol. **24A**, n. 22, 1947
86. —— Ark. Kem. Min. Geol. **24A**, n. 23, 1947
87. Lundquist and Westgren, Zeit. anorg. Chem. **239**, 85, 1938
88. McConnell, Min. Mag. **32**, 534, 1960
89. —— Science **136**, 241, 1962
90. Midgley, Acta Cryst. **5**, 307, 1952
91. Morimoto, Min. Jour. (Japan) **2**, 1, 1956
92. —— Ann. Rept. Dir. Geophys. Lab. **58**, 193, 1959
93. Morimoto and Clark, Am. Min. **46**, 1448, 1961
94. Morimoto and Kullerud, Am. Min. **46**, 1270, 1961
95. Mosburg and others, U.S. Geol. Surv. Prof. Paper **424C**, 347, 1961
96. Mrose and others, Am. Min. **46**, 420, 1961
97. Murdoch and Berry, Am. Min. **39**, 475, 1954
98. Nelson and Riley, Proc. Phy. Soc. **57**, 477, 1945
99. Newnham, Min. Mag. **32**, 683, 1961
100. O'Daniel and Tscheischwili, Zeit. Krist. **104**, 124, 1942
101. Oftedal, Zeit. Phys. Chem. **135**, 291, 1928
102. Oswald, Zeit. Krist. **116**, 210, 1961
103. Palache, Berman, and Frondel, Dana's System of mineralogy, 7th edition, vol. 1, John Wiley, New York, 1944
104. —— Dana's System of mineralogy, 7th edition, vol. 2, John Wiley, New York, 1951
105. Peacock, Trans. Roy. Soc. Canada (IV) **36**, 107, 1942
106. —— Univ. Toronto Stud. Geol. Ser. **42**, 101, 1939
107. —— Am. Min. **27**, 229, 1942
108. Peacock and McAndrew, Am. Min. **35**, 425, 1950
109. Pistorius, Am. Min. **46**, 982, 1961
110. Posner, Perloff, and Diorio, Acta Cryst. **11**, 308, 1958
111. Primak, Kaufman, and Ward, Jour. Am. Chem. Soc. **70**, 2043, 1948
112. Rabbitt, Am. Min. **33**, 263, 1948
113. Rahlfs, Zeit. Phys. Chem. **B31**, 157, 1936
114. Robbins, Ann. Rept. Dir. Geophys. Lab. **58**, 137, 1959
115. Roseboom, Am. Min. **47**, 310, 1962
116. —— unpublished data
117. Ruben and others, Jour. Am. Chem. Soc. **83**, 821, 1961
118. Sadanga, Tokonami, and Takeuchi, Acta Cryst. **15**, 65, 1962
119. Saha, Am. Min. **44**, 300, 1959
120. Sahama and Hytönen, Am. Min. **43**, 862, 1958
121. Sakata, Japanese Jour. Geol. Geog. **28**, 161, 1957
122. Sasaki, Min. Jour. **2**, 375, 1959
123. Schreyer and Schairer, Jour. Petrology **2**, 324, 1961
124. Shropshire, Keat, and Vaughan, Zeit. Krist. **112**, 409, 1959
125. Skinner, Am. Min. **41**, 428, 1956
126. —— Am. Min. **42**, 39, 1957
127. —— Am. Min. **46**, 1399, 1961
128. —— written communication, June 1962
129. —— unpublished data

130. Skinner and Barton, Am. Min. **45**, 612, 1960
131. Skinner, Barton, and Kullerud, Econ. Geol. **54**, 1040, 1959
132. Skinner and Bethke, Am. Min. **46**, 1382, 1961
133. Skinner, Clark, and Appleman, Am. Jour. Sci. **259**, 651, 1961
134. Smith, Ann. Rept. Dir. Geophys. Lab. **52**, 61, 1953
135. —— Min. Mag. **31**, 47, 1956
136. Smith and Tuttle, Am. Jour. Sci. **255**, 282, 1957
137. Straumanis, Jour. Appl. Phys. **20**, 726, 1949
138. Structure Reports, 184, 1951
139. Swanson and Tatge, U.S. Nat. Bur. Stds. Circular 539, v. 1, Washington, D.C., 1953
140. Swanson and Fuyat, U.S. Nat. Bur. Stds. Circular 539, v. 2, Washington, D.C., 1953
141. Swanson, Fuyat, and Ugrinic, U.S. Nat. Bur. Stds. Circular 539, v. 3, Washington, D.C., 1954
142. —— U.S. Nat. Bur. Stds. Circular 539, v. 4, Washington, D.C., 1955
143. Swanson, Gilfrich, and Ugrinic, U.S. Nat. Bur. Stds. Circular 539, v. 5, Washington, D.C., 1955
144. Swanson, Gilfrich, and Cook, U.S. Nat. Bur. Stds. Circular 539, v. 6, Washington, D.C., 1956
145. —— U.S. Nat. Bur. Stds. Circular 539, v. 7, Washington, D.C., 1957
146. Swanson and others, U.S. Nat. Bur. Stds. Circular 539, v. 8, Washington, D.C., 1959
147. —— U.S. Nat. Bur. Stds. Circular 539, v. 9, Washington, D.C., 1960
148. —— U.S. Nat. Bur. Stds. Circular 539, v. 10, Washington, D.C., 1960
149. —— U.S. Nat. Bur. Stds. Monogr. 25, sec. 1, Washington, D.C., 1962
150. Taylor and Underwood, Acta Cryst. 13, 361, 1960
151. Tengner, Zeit. anorg. Chem. **239**, 126, 1938
152. Thomassen, Zeit. Phys. Chem. **4**, Abt. B, 277, 1929
153. Tolliday, Nature **182**, 1012, 1958
154. Tombs and Rooksby, Acta Cryst. **4**, 474, 1951
155. Toulmin, Am. Min. **48**, 725, 1963
156. Turnock, A., private communication, February 1961
157. Ulrich and Zachariasen, Zeit. Krist. **62**, 260, 1925
158. Van Hook and Keith, Am. Min. **43**, 69, 1958
159. Waldbaum, D. R., private communication, August 1961
160. Wasserstein, Am. Min. **36**, 102, 1951
161. Wiese and Muldawer, Phys. and Chem. Solids **15**, 13, 1960
162. Willis and Rooksby, Acta Cryst. **6**, 827, 1953
163. Winchell, Am. Min. **30**, 33, 1945
164. Wolfe, Am. Min. **40**, 249, 1955
165. Wones, D., private communication, February 1961
166. Wright, Am. Jour. Sci. **189**, 6, 1915
167. Yoder, Jour. Geol. **60**, 364, 1952
168. Yoder and Eugster, Geochim. Cosmochim. Acta **6**, 157, 1954
169. —— Geochim. Cosmochim. Acta **8**, 225, 1955
170. Yoder and Sahama, Am. Min. **42**, 475, 1957
171. Yoder and Weir, Am. Jour. Sci. **249**, 683, 1951
172. Yund, Ann. Rept. Dir. Geophys. Lab. Wash. **58**, 148, 1959
173. Zussman, Acta Cryst. **12**, 309, 1959
174. Calculated from α-quartz cell and thermal expansion of Jay, Proc. Roy. Soc. A**142**, 237, 1933
175. Stemple and Brindley, Jour. Am. Ceram. Soc. **43**, 34, 1960
176. Agrell and Smith, Jour. Am. Ceram. Soc. **43**, 69, 1960
177. Skinner and Appleman, Am. Min. **48**, 854, 1963
178. Pistorius, Jour. Geol. **69**, 604, 1961
179. P. Toulmin, unpublished

SECTION 6

THERMAL EXPANSION

by BRIAN J. SKINNER

CONTENTS

Handbook of Physical Constants—*Revised Edition*
THE GEOLOGICAL SOCIETY OF AMERICA MEMOIR 97, 1966

Thermal expansion is the change in shape and volume of a system due to a temperature change. For liquids, gases, and isotropic solids, thermal expansion is isotropic, involving only a change in volume and requiring, therefore, the measurement of a single parameter to uniquely specify the expansion. Crystalline solids with symmetries other than cubic have anisotropic expansions. In the hexagonal and tetragonal systems, a sphere expands to an ellipsoid of revolution, the unique axis of the ellipsoid coinciding with the unique, or c, crystallographic axis. Two parameters must be measured to uniquely specify the expansion of tetragonal and hexagonal compounds. In the orthorhombic, monoclinic, and triclinic systems a sphere expands to a triaxial ellipsoid. The three principal axes coincide with the three crystallographic axes in the orthorhombic systems, and hence only three parameters are needed to uniquely specify the thermal expansion. In the monoclinic system, the only symmetry requirements are that one axis of the spheroid coincides with the b, or twofold crystallographic axis. Thus, four parameters must be measured to specify the expansion of a monoclinic solid, three giving the axial lengths of the spheroid and one specifying its orientation. In the triclinic system there are no symmetry requirements controlling the orientation of the spheroid of expansion. Consequently, six parameters must be measured to uniquely specify the thermal expansion, three giving the axial lengths of the spheroid, and three specifying their orientations with respect to the crystallographic axes. Complete discussions of the crystallographic relationships of thermal expansions can be found in Voigt's *Lehrbuch der Krystallphysik*, Wooster's *Crystal physics*, or Nye's *Physical properties of crystals*.

Data specifying completely the lengths and orientations of the principal axes of expansion are scarce, particularly for the monoclinic and triclinic systems. The most common procedure has been to measure only the total volume change, without regard to the thermal anisotropy of individual crystals. Fortunately, for most purposes a knowledge of the volume change is adequate.

The thermal expansion coefficient, α, may be defined in several ways. The true, or instantaneous coefficient is $\frac{1}{V}\left(\frac{\partial V}{\partial T}\right)_P$. Measurements are more easily reduced to the form $\frac{1}{V_0}\left(\frac{dV}{dT}\right)$ where V_0 is the volume of the specimen measured at some reference temperature, usually room temperature. The most commonly reported coefficient is the mean coefficient, $\frac{1}{V_0} \cdot \frac{V_T - V_0}{T - T_0}$, where V_0 is the volume at a reference temperature, T_0. The mean coefficient is sometimes given the form $\frac{1}{V_0} \cdot \frac{V_{T_1} - V_{T_2}}{T_1 - T_2}$, and is quoted at a temperature $\frac{T_1 + T_2}{2}$. This form is not frequently used.

Each coefficient has certain advantages, and for this reason the data in Table 6-1 are presented as a percentage change from the volume or length at 20°C to the temperature of reference. The desired coefficient may be calculated from the tables. All cubic compounds, having isotropic expansions, are reported as the volume expansions alone. The linear expansions are, to a very close approximation, one third the volume expansion. The expansions of random aggregates of many noncubic crystals have been measured, and although the measurements give no indication of the anisotropy of expansion of individual crystals, the volume data are useful in themselves. It has been possible to check the figures for volume expansions of random aggregates against the volume expansion of single crystals in several instances, and in each case the answers have been the same within the accuracy of measurements.

Because of the general usefulness of the instantaneous volume coefficient, $\alpha_V = \frac{1}{V}\left(\frac{dV}{dT}\right)$, Table 6-8 presents this coefficient at 20° C, 400° C, and 800° C and atmospheric pressure for a number of interesting silicate minerals. These coefficients were derived by analytically differentiating polynomial functions fitted to the volume-temperature data by the method of least squares. Few silicate compounds are sufficiently well measured for a realistic evaluation of the change in the instantaneous coefficient with temperature to be made. For this reason the instantaneous coefficients are not quoted at intermediate temperatures.

The following tables contain the expansions of a selected list of substances, many artificial and perhaps of more physical or ceramic interest than of geologic interest. However, in view of the relatively limited number of data available above 100° C for inorganic compounds, it is believed that they belong in these tables for the sake of completeness.

In the collection of data for inclusion in the tables some interpretation and selection have been necessary. Where several workers derived essentially the same values for the expansion of a compound, over the same temperature range, preference has been given to the earliest reference. In some instances later work has allowed a reasonable interpretation to be made of apparently confusing data. The measurements reported by Kozu and Saiki (Sci. Rep. Tohoku Univ., Ser. 3, **2**, 203, 1925) for the alkali feldspars show large irreversible effects. These can now be reasonably interpreted as due to the homogenization of alkali ions and indicate that the cooling curves, rather than the heating curves, should be taken as a measure of the thermal expansion.

The data for the expansions of rocks are quoted from the first Handbook of Physical Constants, and the following discussion of rock expansions, by E. B. Dane, Jr., is also quoted from the first Handbook, pages 28–29.

"Thermal expansion data for rocks are given here only to 100° C as tests at high temperature and at one atmosphere pressure on such aggregates of many different anisotropic crystals have little relation to the expansions of rocks buried even to moderate depths. When a rock specimen is measured in the laboratory, it is found that the coefficients of expansion are very different on heating and cooling, with a still different result on each subsequent run. This is due to the unlike expansions of adjacent grains because of differences both of composition and of orientation. As a result, when a rock is heated the grains with the largest thermal dilation tend to determine the apparent change of length of the whole specimen, creating internal fractures and 'pores.' Thus what is actually measured is rather the increase in porosity than the true thermal expansion. In the earth, several factors tend to minimize these effects, The directions of maximum compressibility usually lie close to those of maximum thermal expansion, so that, when temperature and pressure tend to vary in the same direction at the same time, the effects partly cancel each other. Most changes of conditions within the earth proceed slowly so that there is ample time for recrystallization to relieve the points of greatest stress and thus close the pores. However, the fact that all rocks have some porosity, which can be largely eliminated by about 1000 atmospheres of pressure, indicates that such readjustments and compensations are not complete. Considering these facts, it is believed that a better figure for the mean expansion of any rock under the conditions found deep in the earth will be obtained by averaging the weighted volumetric expansions of its constituent minerals. For the mean linear dilatation, this figure must be divided by three."

TABLE 6-1. THERMAL EXPANSIONS OF SELECTED SUBSTANCES
Compositions, where stated, in mole per cent.

The linear expansions of crystals, other than those of the cubic system, depend upon the orientation with respect to the crystallographic axes. The orientations, where known, are given in the second column. For cubic compounds only the volume expansions are quoted. Certain noncubic compounds are also quoted only for their volume expansions, because knowledge of the linear expansions is not available.

	Symmetry and orientation	Expansion from 20°C to indicated temperature, in per cent							Ref.
		100° C	200° C	400° C	600° C	800° C	1000° C	1200° C	
ELEMENTS									
Ag	Cub vol	.463	1.069	2.361	3.779	5.358	...	...	63
Al	Cub vol	.562	1.317	3.049	5.115	...	...	...	70
Au	Cub vol	.343	.784	1.715	2.728	3.842	5.074	...	2
Be	Hex ⊥c	.098	.258	.625	1.032	1.460	1.915	...	19
	‖c	.073	.192	.480	.793	1.147	1.550	...	
	vol	.268	.763	1.740	2.883	4.123	5.476	...	
Bi	Hex ⊥c	.11	...	...	...	...	...	...	14
	‖c	.15							
	vol	.37							
C, diamond	Cub vol	.031	.091	.268	.489.	.747	1.038	1.236	40, 65
C, graphite	Hex ⊥c	-.014	-.020	-.020	-.020	-.004	...	...	42
	‖c	.223	.490	1.057	1.636	2.228	...	...	
	vol	.193	.450	1.018	1.596	2.221	...	...	
Co	Cub vol	.301	.690	1.507	2.378	...	...	...	44
Cr	Cub vol	.159	.360	...	...	...	...	...	69
Cu	Cub vol	.425	.976	2.110	3.338	4.661	...	...	21
Fe, pure (inversions at 916° C and 1388° C. See Table 6-3)	Cub vol	.326	.747	1.645	2.560	3.523	4.039	2.986	5
Fe, steel, 1.2% C	Cub vol	.27	.60	1.47	2.43	3.45	...	...	11
Ge	Cub vol	.11	.32	.75	1.17	1.66	...	...	43
Hg	Liquid	1.458	3.307	...	...	...	...	...	58
Mg	Hex ⊥c	.187	.462	1.068	1.808	...	...	...	8, 48
	‖c	.187	.471	1.096	1.866	...	...	...	
	vol	.592	1.432	3.298	5.614	...	...	...	

Material									Ref.
Ni	Cub vol	.337	.776	1.812	2.891	:	:	:	46
(Curie point at 370° C, See Table 6-4)									
Pb	Cub vol	.724	1.698	:	:	:	:	:	68
Pt	Cub vol	.216	.494	1.074	1.689	2.339	3.026	3.750	9
Sb	Hex ⊥c	.08	:	:	:	:	:	:	15
	∥c	.17	:	:	:	:	:	:	
	vol	.33	:	:	:	:	:	:	
Si	Cub vol	.066	.171	.398	.631	.875	1.109	:	40
Sn (metallic)	Tet ⊥c	.13	.30	:	:	:	:	:	38
	∥c	.28	.66	:	:	:	:	:	
	vol	.54	1.27	:	:	:	:	:	
Ti	Hex ⊥c	.065	.163	.391	.642	:	:	:	7
	∥c	.111	.240	.529	.791	:	:	:	
	vol	.240	.567	1.316	2.095	:	:	:	
W	Cub vol	.095	.228	.513	.789	1.104	1.438	1.774	35
Zn	Hex ⊥c	.115	.273	.718	:	:	:	:	45
	∥c	.486	1.104	2.225	:	:	:	:	
	vol	.717	1.656	3.699	:	:	:	:	
CARBIDES									
NbC	Cub vol	.141	.329	.740	1.172	1.626	2.088	2.565	39
TaC	Cub vol	.121	.297	.709	1.122	1.530	1.945	2.369	39
TiC	Cub vol	.125	.326	.771	1.232	1.736	2.270	2.869	39
WC	Hex ⊥c	.038	.086	.182	.282	.385	.499	.616	39
	∥c	.028	.063	.141	.229	.328	.427	.525	
	vol	.104	.236	.507	.796	1.103	1.431	1.768	
ZrC	Cub vol	.141	.326	.711	1.103	1.509	1.923	2.344	39
NITRIDES									
BN	Hex ⊥c	-.022	-.046	-.082	-.103	-.109	:	:	47
	∥c	.329	.741	1.564	2.387	3.210	:	:	
	vol	.286	.649	1.398	2.176	2.986	:	:	
SILICIDES									
Cr_3Si	Cub vol	.191	.468	1.077	1.761	2.516	3.368	:	39
Fe_3Si	Cub vol	.362	.735	1.668	2.822	:	:	:	13

TABLE 6-1. *Continued*

Symmetry and orientation	Expansion from 20° C to indicated temperature, in per cent							Ref.
	100° C	200° C	400° C	600° C	800° C	1000° C	1200° C	
	SILICIDES. *Continued*							
MoSi₂ Tet ⊥c	.047	.119	.278	.440	.602	.765	.927	39
∥c	.073	.162	.340	.533	.743	.954	1.164	
vol	.166	.400	.899	1.420	1.960	2.503	3.048	
Mo₃Si Cub vol	.141	.314	.659	1.011	1.444	1.947	2.508	40
WSi₂ Hex ⊥c	.044	.109	.261	.414	.573	.731	.903	40
∥c	.077	.146	.342	.536	.729	.950	1.212	
vol	.164	.364	.868	1.370	1.886	2.432	3.047	
	HALIDES							
CaF₂, fluorite Cub vol	.47	1.12	:	:	:	:	:	59
KBr Cub vol	.951	2.265	5.116	:	:	:	:	41
KBr:RbBr, 1:1 solid solution Cub vol	.934	2.174	:	:	:	:	:	41
KCl, sylvite Cub vol	.887	1.994	4.850	8.085	:	:	:	41
KCl:KBr, 1:1 solid solution Cub vol	.934	2.211	:	:	:	:	:	41
KI Cub vol	.90	2.04	4.92	:	:	:	:	12
LiF Cub vol	.912	2.086	4.759	:	:	:	:	41
NaCl, halite Cub vol	.963	2.288	5.256	8.932	:	:	:	41
RbBr Cub vol	.925	2.171	:	:	:	:	:	41
RbBr:RbCl, 1:1 solid solution Cub vol	.921	2.180	:	:	:	:	:	41
RbCl Cub vol	.891	2.079	:	:	:	:	:	41
RbCl:KCl, 1:1 solid solution Cub vol	.922	2.163	:	:	:	:	:	41
	SULFIDES							
CuFeS₂, chalcopyrite Tet vol	.42	:	:	:	:	:	:	16
FeS₂, pyrite Cub vol	.219	.529	1.291	:	:	:	:	66
Fe₁₋ₓS, pyrrhotite Hex ⊥c	.25	:	:	:	:	:	:	16
∥c	.03	:	:	:	:	:	:	
vol	.53	:	:	:	:	:	:	
PbS, galena Cub vol	.490	1.099	2.402	3.878	:	:	:	66
ZnS, sphalerite Cub vol	.156	.386	.898	1.440	1.996	2.559	:	66

Mineral	System								Ref.
ZnS, wurtzite	Hex ⊥c	.058	.141	.322	.528	.759	.994	…	66
	‖c	.056	.130	.283	.452	.628	.802	…	
	vol	.163	.395	.919	1.505	2.146	2.839	…	
SELENIDES									
PbSe, clausthalite	Cub vol	.474	1.110	2.420	3.716	…	…	…	66
ZnSe, stilleite	Cub vol	.151	.380	.902	1.635	2.059	…	…	66
OXIDES									
Al₂O₃, corundum	Hex ⊥c	.044	.112	.278	.455	.632	.815	.998	1, 10
	‖c	.055	.130	.302	.490	.685	.885	1.088	
	vol	.143	.354	.858	1.400	1.949	2.515	3.084	
BeO, bromellite	Hex ⊥c	.047	.120	.288	.500	.663	.910	…	20
	‖c	.050	.114	.251	.425	.618	.835	…	
	vol	.144	.354	.829	1.377	1.956	2.678	…	
CaO	Cub vol	.225	.571	1.402	2.246	3.107	3.975	5.078	20
3CaO·Al₂O₃	Cub vol	.18	.41	.97	1.58	2.23	2.94	3.66	50
5CaO·3Al₂O₃	Cub vol	.13	.29	.71	1.16	1.65	2.19	2.79	50
CaO·Al₂O₃	Mono? vol	.12	.28	.63	1.05	1.49	2.00	2.37	50
CaO·Fe₂O₃	? vol	.27	.60	1.28	1.98	2.71	3.43	…	50
2CaO·Fe₂O₃	? vol	.17	.42	1.00	1.58	2.28	3.02	3.68	50
4CaO·Al₂O₃·Fe₂O₃	? vol	.14	.37	.96	1.52	2.14	2.86	…	50
Cr₂O₃, eskolaite	Hex vol	.15	.36	.78	1.23	1.68	2.13	2.61	52
FeO, wustite	Cub vol	.30	.63	1.32	2.10	3.06	…	…	51
62.7FeO:37.3MgO, solid solution	Cub vol	.33	.69	1.47	2.25	…	…	…	53
35.9FeO:64.1MgO, solid solution	Cub vol	.33	.75	1.53	2.34	3.15	…	…	53
15.8FeO:84.2MgO, solid solution	Cub vol	.33	.72	1.53	2.34	3.15	…	…	53
FeO·Al₂O₃, hercynite	Cub vol	.15	.33	.75	1.20	1.80	2.49	…	52
FeO·Cr₂O₃, chromite	Cub vol	.09	.21	.48	.84	1.26	1.74	…	52
FeO·Fe₂O₃, magnetite (*See* Table 6-5)	Cub vol	.212	.513	1.328	2.285	3.24	4.26	…	52, 59
Fe₂O₃, hematite	Hex ⊥c	.068	.165	.406	…	…	…	…	60
	‖c	.066	.155	.358	…				
	vol	.202	.485	1.175	…				

TABLE 6-1. *Continued*

Symmetry and orientation		Expansion from 20° C to indicated temperature, in per cent							Ref.
		100° C	200° C	400° C	600° C	800° C	1000° C	1200° C	
OXIDES. *Continued*									
HfO_2	Mono ‖a	.054	.119	.253	.388	.534	.742	...	20
	‖b	.000	.000	.020	.050	.090	.164	...	
	‖c	.090	.200	.422	.644	.869	1.167	...	
	vol	.144	.319	.696	1.085	1.499	2.085	...	
$Li_2O \cdot Al_2O_3$	Tet? vol	.2	.5	1.2	2.0	2.8	3.7		23
$Li_2O \cdot 5Al_2O_3$	Cub vol	.1	.3	.7	1.3	1.8	2.4		23
MgO, periclase	Cub vol	.219	.588	1.386	2.256	3.150	4.050	...	1, 65
$MgO \cdot Al_2O_3$, spinel	Cub vol	.18	.39	.90	1.41	2.01	2.61	3.24	52
$MgO \cdot Cr_2O_3$, picrochromite	Cub vol	.15	.33	.72	1.17	1.71	2.28	2.85	52
$MgO \cdot Fe_2O_3$, magnesioferrite	Cub vol	.21	.48	1.14	1.95	2.79	3.72	4.68	52
ThO_2, thorianite	Cub vol	.234	.517	1.100	1.668	2.249	2.833	...	20
TiO	Cub vol	.187	.432	.944	1.509	2.163			40
TiO_2, rutile	Tet ⊥c	.059	.137	.298	.457	.629	.819		35
	‖c	.064	.159	.368	.578	.791	1.020		
	vol	.182	.434	.968	1.500	2.063	2.681		
$TiO_{1.97}$, oxygen deficient rutile	Tet ⊥c	.054	.128	.278	...	...	...		35
	‖c	.078	.183	.399	...	...	...		
	vol	.187	.440	.959	...	...	...		
$UO_{2.03}$, uraninite	Cub vol	.199	.468	1.045	1.678	2.368	3.115		27
ZrO_2, baddeleyite	Mono ‖a	.058	.130	.276	.421	.584	.792		20
	‖b	.015	.035	.070	.080	.085	.155		
	‖c	.100	.222	.470	.720	.975	1.270		
	vol	.209	.423	.854	1.262	1.688	2.267		
CARBONATES									
$CaCO_3$, aragonite	Ortho ‖a	.05	.13	.33	...	...	...	...	28
	‖b	.11	.29	.74	...	...	...	...	
	‖c	.20	.58	1.39	...	...	...	...	
	vol	.36	1.00	2.48	...	...	...	...	
$CaCO_3$, calcite	Hex ⊥c	.189	.476	1.115	1.843	...	...	...	56
	‖c	-.042	-.096	-.175	-.224	...	...	...	
	vol	.105	.285	.765	1.395	...	...	...	

									Ref.
SrCO₃, strontianite	Ortho ∥a	.049	.129	.317	.530	.747	:	: :	66
	∥b	.101	.228	.485	.750	1.052	:	
	∥c	.312	.743	1.656	2.659	3.970	:	
	vol	.541	1.168	2.473	3.975	5.726	:	
SULFATES									
BaSO₄, barite	Ortho ∥a	.116	.274	.646	:	:	:	: :	61
	∥b	.198	.459	1.039	:	:		
	∥c	.120	.286	.677				
	vol	.434	1.023	2.381				
CaSO₄·5H₂O, gypsum	Mono vol	.58	*Inverts to hexagonal form at 586° C.*						14
K₂SO₄	Ortho ∥a	.095	.398	1.386					6
	∥b	.099	.794	1.221				
	∥c	.349	.912	2.252				
	vol	.544	2.118	4.935				
NITRATES									
NaNO₃, soda niter	Hex ⊥c	.093	.203	:	:		:	: :	4
	∥c	.89	2.34					
	vol	1.076	2.74					
SILICATES									
Akermanite	Tet vol	.21	.48	1.08	1.71	2.32	3.03	3.73	49
Andalusite	Ortho ∥a	.092	.218	.476	.741	1.046	1.348	:	67
	∥b	.042	.113	.284	.486	.774	1.071	:
	∥c	.054	.148	.367	.612	.885	1.171	:
	vol	.151	.417	1.071	1.833	2.681	3.606	:
Beryl	Hex ⊥c	.027	.034	:	:	:	:	: :	17
	∥c	.007	.011					
	vol	.061	.079					
Calcium silicate									
Ca₃Si₂O₇	? vol	.30	.66	1.40	2.19	3.02	3.89	5.06	49
β-Ca₂SiO₄	? vol	.30	.68	1.46	2.39	3.39	4.23	5.22	49
Ca₃SiO₅	? vol	.24	.52	1.11	1.93	2.76	3.73	:	49
Cancrinite	Hex ⊥c	.06	.16	.42	:	:	:	: :	36
	∥c	.13	.36	.91				
	vol	.25	.68	1.76				

TABLE 6-1. *Continued*

Mineral	Symmetry and orientation	Expansion from 20°C to indicated temperature, in per cent							Ref.
		100°C	200°C	400°C	600°C	800°C	1000°C	1200°C	
		SILICATES. *Continued*							
Coesite	Mono ‖a, ‖c	.020	.048	.116	.194	.284	.383	..	66
	‖b	.022	.050	.114	.193	.283	.381	..	
	vol	.059	.145	.345	.580	.849	1.150	..	
Cordierite (synthesized 1420°C)	Hex? vol	.01	.03	.11	.25	.43	.64	..	49
Cristobalite (inversion at 218°C See Table 6-6)	Tet ⊥c	.221	.503	..	..	..	..	..	24
	‖c	.346	.779	..	..	..	..	..	
	vol	.791	1.795	6.271	6.414	6.499	6.575	6.651	
β-Eucryptite	Hex ⊥c	.050	.124	.284	.465	.663	..	..	18
	‖c	-.143	-.321	-.669	-1.026	-1.375	..	..	
	vol	-.044	-.074	-.105	-.104	-.062	..	..	
Feldspars Celsian	Mono vol	.07	.17	.39	..	..	..	..	17
Adularia $Or_{88.3}$, $Ab_{9.3}$, $An_{2.4}$	Mono ‖a	.109	.269	.609	.989	1.379	1.779	..	29
	‖b	.000	.000	.020	.070	.110	.130	..	
	⊥(001)	.000	.000	.014	.032	.070	.145	..	
	vol	.109	.269	.643	1.091	1.559	2.054	..	
Microcline $Or_{83.5}$, $Ab_{16.5}$	Tri ‖a	.120	.294	.628	.979	1.337	1.755	..	55
	‖b	.004	.004	.000	.000	.013	.117	..	
	‖c	.004	.010	.016	.050	.088	.120	..	
	vol	.128	.398	.644	1.029	1.438	1.992	..	
Orthoclase $Or_{66.6}$, $Ab_{32.8}$, $An_{0.6}$	Mono ‖a	.049	.140	.480	.900	1.455	1.910	..	29
	‖b	.000	.010	.040	.130	.265	.380	..	
	⊥(001)	.000	.005	.065	.155	.210	.320	..	
	vol	.049	.155	.585	1.185	1.910	2.610	..	
Plagioclase $Ab_{99}An_1$	Mono ‖a	.09	.22	.50	.83	1.17	1.53	..	32
	‖b	.03	.06	.16	.29	.43	.61	..	
	⊥(010)	.03	.08	.19	.32	.47	.62	..	
	vol	.14	.36	.85	1.44	2.07	2.75	..	

Mineral	Orientation	1	2	3	4	5	6	7	Ref
Plagioclase $Ab_{77}An_{23}$	⊥(001)	.04	.12	.29	.49	.72	.95	⋮	32
		.02	.04	.12	.21	.31	.43	⋮	
		.03	.07	.18	.30	.44	.58	⋮	
	vol	.09	.23	.59	1.00	1.47	1.96	⋮	
Plagioclase $Ab_{56}An_{44}$	⊥(001)	.04	.11	.28	.48	.69	.90	⋮	32
		.02	.06	.13	.22	.30	.40	⋮	
		.04	.07	.16	.25	.33	.45	⋮	
	vol	.10	.24	.55	.95	1.32	1.75	⋮	
Plagioclase $Ab_{5}An_{95}$	⊥(001)	.05	.14	.24	.34	.46	.60	⋮	32
		.02	.04	.07	.12	.19	.29	⋮	
		.06	.15	.26	.33	.45	.57	⋮	
	vol	.12	.32	.57	.78	1.10	1.45	⋮	
Garnets									
Almandite	Cub vol	.137	.337	.800	1.326	1.906		⋮	64
Andradite	Cub vol	.169	.396	.880	1.399	1.948		⋮	64
Grossularite	Cub vol	.141	.342	.794	1.292	1.829		⋮	64
Pyrope	Cub vol	.168	.398	.900	1.439	2.007		⋮	64
Spessartite	Cub vol	.157	.396	.940	1.528	2.142		⋮	64
Gehlenite	Tet vol	.20	.45	.93	1.45	1.97	2.50	3.07	49
Hornblende	Mono ⊥(100)	.05	.12	.29	.48	.70	.90	⋮	34
	∥b	.06	.17	.39	.64	.89	1.15	⋮	
	∥c	.05	.13	.29	.46	.63	.79	⋮	
	vol	.16	.42	.97	1.58	2.22	2.84	⋮	
Keatite (SiO_2)	Tet vol	−.06	−.11	−.11	⋮	⋮	⋮	⋮	26
Kyanite	Tri ∥a	.046	.177	.295	.505	.713	.922	⋮	67
	∥b	.052	.122	.279	.449	.647	.821	⋮	
	∥c	.039	.118	.320	.549	.779	1.007	⋮	
	vol	.127	.360	.890	1.478	2.081	2.687	⋮	
Merwinite	Mono vol	.20	.49	1.19	2.03	2.84	3.79	4.61	49
Mullite	Ortho ⊥c	.024	.058	.147	.242	.347	.442	⋮	1
	∥c	.032	.072	.177	.302	.427	.555	⋮	
	vol	.070	.188	.471	.786	1.121	1.439	⋮	
Nephelines Ne_{78}, Ks_{22}	Hex ⊥c	.090	.230	.560	.980	1.470		⋮	57
	∥c	.072	.167	.358	.561	.824		⋮	
	vol	.248	.634	1.488	2.535	3.751		⋮	

TABLE 6-1. *Continued*

	Symmetry and orientation	Expansion from 20° C to indicated temperature, in per cent							Ref.
		100° C	200° C	400° C	600° C	800° C	1000° C	1200° C	
		SILICATES. *Continued*							
$Ne_{59}Ks_{41}$	Hex ⊥c	.170	.370	.730	1.120	1.530	⋮	⋮	57
	∥c	.178	.355	.592	.782	.924	⋮	⋮	
	vol	.523	1.101	2.053	3.033	4.013	⋮	⋮	
Olivine									
Fa_{100}	Ortho vol	.21	.48	1.08	1.71	2.34	2.64	⋮	51
$Fa_{80}Fo_{20}$	Ortho vol	.21	.48	1.11	1.80	2.49	3.18	⋮	53
$Fa_{41}Fo_{59}$	Ortho vol	.21	.51	1.11	1.80	2.55	3.24	⋮	53
$Fa_{15}Fo_{85}$	Ortho vol	.21	.51	1.14	1.83	2.55	3.34	⋮	53
$Fa_{10.1}Fo_{89.9}$	Ortho ∥a	.04	.10	.26	.43	.58	.76	⋮	37
	∥b	.08	.18	.43	.74	1.04	1.36	⋮	
	∥c	.07	.18	.42	.68	.92	1.20	⋮	
	vol	.19	.46	1.11	1.85	2.54	3.32	⋮	
Fo_{100}	Ortho ∥a	.06	.15	.34	.56	.80	1.04	1.32	66
	∥b	.07	.19	.47	.78	1.10	1.43	1.78	
	∥c	.07	.18	.42	.69	1.00	1.34	1.71	
	vol	.20	.52	1.24	2.05	2.92	3.86	4.88	
Monticellite	Ortho vol	.26	.59	1.30	2.08	2.83	3.64	4.50	49
Fe-monticellite	Ortho vol	.21	.48	1.05	1.77	2.55	3.30	⋮	51
$Mont_{50}Fa_{25}Fo_{25}$	Ortho vol	.21	.51	1.14	1.89	2.64	3.39	⋮	53
Pseudo-wollastonite	? vol	.24	.52	1.12	1.76	2.52	3.28	4.03	49
Pyroxenes									
Augite	Mono ⊥(100)	.03	.06	.16	.29	.44	.63	⋮	35
	∥b	.08	.19	.44	.72	1.03	1.37	⋮	
	∥c	.04	.10	.23	.36	.51	.67	⋮	
	vol	.15	.35	.83	1.37	1.98	2.67	⋮	
Clinoenstatite	Mono vol	.19	.42	.96	1.61	2.28	2.95	3.68	49
Diopside	Mono ⊥(100)	.03	.08	.20	.33	.47	.62	⋮	33
	⊥(010)	.10	.25	.57	.90	1.27	1.67	⋮	
	∥c	.02	.08	.18	.30	.43	.57	⋮	
	vol	.15	.41	.95	1.53	2.17	2.86	⋮	
Enstatite	Ortho vol	.18	.45	1.05	1.74	2.28	⋮	⋮	57a

Mineral									Ref.
Jadeite	Mono vol	.166	.401	.930	1.543				71
Protoenstatite	Ortho vol	.13	.36	.87	1.47	2.07			57a
Quartz (inversion 573° C see Table 7)	Hex ⊥c	.14	.30	.73	1.75	1.72	1.70	⋮	30, 54
	∥c	.08	.18	.43	1.02	.98	.89	⋮	
	vol	.36	.78	1.89	4.52	4.42	4.29	⋮	
Sillimanite	Ortho ∥a	.019	.040	.094	.187	.306	.437	⋮	67
	∥b	.039	.104	.263	.452	.654	.915	⋮	
	∥c	.042	.092	.196	.314	.454	.617	⋮	
	vol	.088	.215	.531	.931	1.414	1.979	⋮	
Spodumene	Mono vol	.07	.20	.50	.86	1.20	⋮	⋮	22
Topaz	Ortho ∥a	.03	.09	.20	.35	.50	.67	⋮	31
	∥b	.03	.07	.16	.27	.40	.53	⋮	
	∥c	.04	.11	.27	.46	.65	.85	⋮	
	vol	.10	.27	.65	1.08	1.56	2.06	⋮	
Tridymite (inversions at 117° C, 163° C, 210° C, 300° C, 475° C)	Ortho vol	.63	2.40	3.33	3.48	3.66	3.75	3.60	3, 25
Wollastonite-ferrosilite solid solutions									
Wo69Fs31	Tri vol	.12	.30	.69	1.08	⋮	⋮	⋮	51
Wo45Fs55	Tri vol	.12	.30	.72	1.20	⋮	⋮	⋮	51
Zircon	Tet ⊥c	.02	.05	.11	.19	.28	⋮	⋮	1
	∥c	.03	.08	.20	.34	.48	⋮	⋮	
	vol	.07	.17	.42	.73	1.05	⋮	⋮	

REFERENCES FOR TABLE 6-1

1. Austin, Jour. Am. Ceram. Soc. 14, 795, 1931
2. —— Physics 3, 240, 1932
3. —— Jour. Am. Chem. Soc. 76, 6019, 1954
4. Austin and Pierce, Jour. Am. Chem. Soc. 55, 661, 1933
5. Basinski, Hume-Rothery, and Sutton, Proc. Roy. Soc. A229, 459, 1955
6. Bernard and Hocart, Bull. Soc. Franc. Min. Crist. 84, 396, 1961
7. Berry and Raynor, Research 6, 21, 1953
8. Busk, Jour. Metals 4, 207, 1952
9. Campbell, U.S. Bur. Mines, Inform. Circ. 8107, 1962
10. Campbell and Grain, U.S. Bur. Mines Rep. Invest. 5757, 1961
11. Draisin, Ferum 11, 129, 1914
12. Euken and Dannohl, Zeit. Electrochemie 40, 814, 1934
13. Farquhar, Lipson and Weill, Jour. Iron and Steel Inst. 152, 457, 1945
14. Fizeau, Compt. rend. 66, 1172, 1866
15. —— Compt. rend. 68, 1125, 1869
16. —— Bur. d. Long. Annuaire pour l'an 1888

REFERENCES FOR TABLE 6-1. *Continued*

17. Geller and Insley, Bur. Standards Jour. Research **9**, 35, 1932
18. Gillery and Bush, Jour. Am. Ceram. Soc. **42**, 175, 1959
19. Gordon, Jour. Appl. Phys. **20**, 908, 1949
20. Grain and Campbell, U.S. Bur. Mines Rep. Invest. 5982, 1962
21. Hume-Rothery and Andrews, Jour. Inst. Met. **68**, 19, 1942
22. Hummel, Foote Prints **20**, 3, 1948
23. ——— Jour. Am. Ceram. Soc. **34**, 235, 1951
24. Johnson and Andrews, Trans. Brit. Ceram. Soc. **55**, 227, 1956
25. Kainarskii and Degtyareva, *quoted in* Berezhnoi, "Silicon and its binary alloys," 275 p., 1958
26. Keat, Science **120**, 328, 1954
27. Kempter and Elliott, Jour. Chem. Phys. **30**, 1524, 1959
28. Kozu and Kani, Proc. Imp. Acad. Japan **10**, 222, 1934
29. Kozu and Saiki, Sci. Rep. Tohoku Univ. Ser. 3, **2**, 203, 1925
30. Kozu and Takane, Sci. Rep. Tohoku Univ. Ser. 3, **3**, 239, 1929
31. Kozu and Ueda, Sci. Rep. Tohoku Univ. Ser. 3, **3**, 161, 1929
32. ——— Proc. Imp. Acad. Japan **9**, 262, 1933
33. ——— Proc. Imp. Acad. Japan **9**, 317, 1933
34. ——— Proc. Imp. Acad. Japan **10**, 25, 1934
35. ——— Proc. Imp. Acad. Japan **10**, 87, 1934
36. Kozu, Ueda, and Tsurumi, Proc. Imp. Acad. Japan **9**, 13, 1933
37. ——— Proc. Imp. Acad. Japan **10**, 83, 1934
38. Lee and Raynor, Proc. Phys. Soc. **B67**, 737, 1954
39. Mauer and Bolz, W. A. D. C. Tech. Rept. **55–473**, 1955
40. ——— W. A. D. C. Tech. Rept. **55–473**, Supp. 1, 1957
41. McKinstry, H. A., Ph.D. thesis, Penn. State Univ., 1960
42. Nelson and Riley, Proc. Phys. Soc. **57**, 477, 1945
43. Nitka, Phys. Zeit. **38**, 896, 1937
44. Owen and Jones, Proc. Phys. Soc. **B67**, 456, 1954

45. Owen and Yates, Phil. Mag. **17**, 113, 1934
46. ——— Phil. Mag. **21**, 809, 1936
47. Pease, Acta Cryst. **5**, 356, 1952
48. Raynor and Hume-Rothery, Jour. Inst. Met. **65**, 379, 1939
49. Rigby and Green, Trans. British Ceram. Soc. **41**, 123, 1941
50. ——— Trans. British Ceram. Soc. **42**, 95, 1941
51. Rigby, Lovell, and Green, Trans. British Ceram. Soc. **44**, 37, 1945
52. ——— Trans. British Ceram. Soc. **45**, 137, 1946
53. ——— Trans. British Ceram. Soc. **45**, 237, 1946
54. Rosenholtz and Smith, Am. Mineral. **26**, 103, 1941
55. ——— Am. Mineral. **27**, 344, 1942
56. ——— Am. Mineral. **34**, 846, 1949
57. Sahama, Jour. Petrology **3**, 65, 1962
57a. Sarver and Hummel, Jour. Am. Ceram. Soc. **45**, 152, 1962
58. Sears, Proc. Phys. Soc. London **26**, 95, 1913
59. Sharma, Proc. Ind. Acad. Sci. **31A**, 261, 1950
60. ——— Proc. Ind. Acad. Sci. **32A**, 285, 1950
61. ——— Proc. Ind. Acad. Sci. **33A**, 283, 1951
62. ——— Proc. Ind. Acad. Sci. **34A**, 72, 1951
63. Simmons and Balluffi, Phys. Rev. **119**, 600, 1960
64. Skinner, Am. Mineral. **41**, 428, 1956
65. ——— Am. Mineral. **42**, 39, 1957
66. ——— U.S. Geol. Surv. Prof. Paper **450D**, 109, 1962
67. Stokes and Wilson, Proc. Phys. Soc. **53**, 658, 1941
68. Clark and Appleman, Am. Jour. Sci. **259**, 651, 1961
69. Sully, Brandes and Mitchell, Jour. Inst. Met. **81**, 585, 1953
70. Wilson, Proc. Phys. Soc. **54**, 487, 1942
71. Yoder and Weir, Am. Sci. **249**, 683, 1951

TABLE 6-2. THERMAL EXPANSIONS OF THE RARE-EARTH OXIDES

Reference: Stecura and Campbell, U.S. Bur. Mines Rep. Invest. 5847

| | Symmetry and orientation | Expansion from 20° C to indicated temperature, in per cent | | | | | | |
		100° C	200° C	400° C	600° C	800° C	1000° C	1200° C
CeO_2	Cub vol	.255	.595	1.281	2.027	2.810	3.700	4.613
Dy_2O_3	Cub vol	.180	.417	.904	1.400	1.933	2.481	3.115
Er_2O_3	Cub vol	.162	.370	.810	1.288	1.777	2.362	2.970
Eu_2O_3	Cub vol	.150	.347	.739	1.219	1.740	2.414	2.992
Gd_2O_3	Cub vol	.188	.417	.906	1.398	1.940	2.733	3.147
Ho_2O_3	Cub vol	.175	.408	.896	1.392	1.918	2.472	3.080
La_2O_3	Hex ⊥ c	.069	.155	.351	.572	.810	1.049	..
	‖ c	.114	.271	.594	.932	1.299	1.723	..
	vol	.252	.582	1.300	2.088	2.947	3.868	..
Lu_2O_3	Cub vol	.153	.359	.794	1.277	1.796	2.323	2.923
Nd_2O_3	Hex ⊥ c	.068	.159	.353	.554	.768	.985	1.201
	‖ c	.118	.284	.610	.939	1.284	1.679	2.085
	vol	.254	.603	1.321	2.060	2.845	3.691	4.552
Pr_6O_{11}	Cub vol	.262	.619	1.409	2.566	4.267	5.859	..
Sc_2O_3	Cub vol	.140	.354	.831	1.381	1.939	2.591	3.331
Sm_2O_3	Cub vol	.206	.465	.982	1.526	2.082	2.638	..
Tm_2O_3	Cub vol	.157	.378	.861	1.368	1.897	2.455	3.028
Y_2O_3	Cub vol	.170	.391	.871	1.404	1.962	2.551	3.180
Yb_2O_3	Cub vol	.161	.380	.848	1.340	1.875	2.424	2.989

TABLE 6-3. THERMAL EXPANSION OF Fe

Reference: Basinski, Hume-Rothery and Sutton, Proc. Roy. Soc. **A229**, 459, 1955

Temperature ° C	Volume change from 20° C in per cent
100	.326
200	.747
400	1.645
600	2.560
800	3.523
916	4.039
Transition from δ(bcc) to γ(fcc) at 916° C	
916	2.986
1000	3.573
1200	5.046
1388	6.428
Transition from γ(fcc) to δ(bcc) at 1388° C	
1388	6.995
1400	7.105
1534	8.052
Melts at 1534° C	

TABLE 6-4. THERMAL EXPANSION OF Ni
(The Curie point is at 370° C.) Reference: Owen
and Yates, Phil. Mag. **21**, 809, 1936

Temperature ° C	Change of volume from 20° C, in per cent
100	.337
200	.776
300	1.239
350	1.497
360	1.582
370	1.659
380	1.716
390	1.764
400	1.812
500	2.348
600	2.891

TABLE 6-5. THERMAL EXPANSION OF MAGNETITE (Fe$_3$O$_4$)
(The Curie point is at 570° C.) References: Rigby,
Lovell and Green, Trans. British Ceram. Soc. **45**,
137, 1946; Sharma, Proc. Ind. Acad. Sci. **31A**,
261, 1950

Temperature °C	Change of volume from 20° C, in per cent
100	.212
200	.513
400	1.328
500	1.894
570 (below)	2.373
570 (above)	2.083
600	2.285
800	3.24
1000	4.26

TABLE 6-6. THERMAL EXPANSION OF CRISTOBALITE
Reference: Johnson and Andrews, Trans. British Ceram. Soc. **55**,
227, 1956

Temperature, ° C	Change of dimensions, per cent		
	‖a	‖c	Volume
100	.221	.346	.791
200	.503	.779	1.795
218 below	.563	.851	1.990
At 218° C the tet. form inverts to a cubic modification			
218 above			5.772
300			6.039
400			6.271
500			6.360
600			6.414
700			6.459
800			6.499
900			6.539
1000			6.575
1100			6.615
1200			6.651

TABLE 6-7.   THERMAL EXPANSION OF QUARTZ

Expansions referred to dimensions at 20° C. Reference: Kozu and Takane, Sci. Rep. Tohoku Univ. Ser. 3, **3**, 239, 1929. Measurements by Jay, Proc. Roy. Soc. **A142**, 237, 1933; Rosenholtz and Smith, Am. Mineral. **26**, 103, 1941; Chevenard and Portevin, Bull. Soc. Franc. de Min. **66**, 131, 1943; and others do not significantly change the measurements reported.

Temperature ° C	Change of length, per cent $\perp$c	Change of length, per cent $\parallel$c	Change of volume per cent
50	.07	.03	.17
100	.14	.08	.36
150	.22	.12	.56
200	.30	.18	.78
250	.40	.23	1.03
300	.49	.29	1.27
350	.60	.36	1.56
400	.72	.43	1.87
450	.87	.51	2.25
500	1.04	.62	2.70
525	1.15	.67	2.97
550	1.29	.75	3.33
560	1.36	.80	3.52
570	1.46	.84	3.76
Transition, α to β quartz, 573° C			
580	1.76	1.03	4.55
590	1.76	1.03	4.55
600	1.76	1.02	4.54
650	1.76	1.02	4.54
700	1.75	1.01	4.51
750	1.74	1.00	4.48
800	1.73	.97	4.43
850	1.72	.94	4.38
900	1.71	.92	4.34
950	1.70	.89	4.29
1000	1.69	.88	4.26

TABLE 6-8. COEFFICIENTS OF VOLUME EXPANSION, $\alpha_V = \frac{1}{V}\left(\frac{dV}{dT}\right)$,

OF SELECTED SILICATES AT ATMOSPHERIC PRESSURE

Compositions, where stated, are in mole per cent. The coefficients were derived by analytically differentiating polynomial functions fitted to the volume-temperature data by the method of least squares. Most sets of measurements commence at room temperature giving poor control of the derived functions at 20° C, compared to the control at higher temperatures, and leading to an uncertain estimate of α_V at 20° C. The values enclosed in parentheses were derived by extrapolating from temperatures where adequate control on the functions could be established. Less credence should be given the values at 20° C than those at 400° C or 800° C.

Compound	$\alpha_V \times 10^6$ °C^{-1}			Ref.
	20° C	400° C	800° C	
Akermanite	(26)	30	33	11
Andalusite	16	29	43	19
Coesite	8	11	14	18
Cordierite (synthesized at 1420° C)	(14)	18	22	11
Feldspars				
Adularia $Or_{88.3}Ab_{9.3}An_{2.4}$	14	20	24	3
Microcline $Or_{83.5}Ab_{16.5}$	(7)	17	23	15
Plagioclase $Ab_{99}An_1$	18	27	33	6
Plagioclase $Ab_{77}An_{23}$	12	19	24	6
Plagioclase $Ab_{56}An_{44}$	13	17	20	6
Plagioclase Ab_5An_{95}	12	12	20	6
Garnets				
Almandine	15	25	30	17
Andradite	21	25	29	17
Grossularite	18	23	28	17
Pyrope	19	26	30	17
Spessartite	15	28	34	17
Gehlenite	(23)	25	26	11
Hornblende	23	28	33	8
Kyanite	11	28	30	19
Merwinite	(29)	38	42	11
Mullite	9.5	15	17	1
Nepheline				
$Ne_{78}Ks_{22}$	(31)	53	72	16
$Ne_{59}Ks_{41}$	(66)	51	49	16
Olivine				
Fa_{100}	(27)	30	31	12
$Fa_{80}Fo_{20}$	(26)	32	34	13
$Fa_{41}Fo_{59}$	(27)	32	35	13
$Fa_{15}Fo_{85}$	(25)	32	39	13
$Fa_{10.1}Fo_{89.9}$	(23)	31	39	10
Fo_{100}	24	38	44	18
Monticellite	(32)	36	39	11
Fe-Monticellite	(25)	32	38	12
Pseudo-wollastonite	(30)	32	36	11
Pyroxenes				
Augite	18	25	32	9
Clinoenstatite	(25)	29	33	11
Diopside	24	28	32	7
Jadeite	(20)	29	(38)	20
Quartz	34	69	−3	2, 4, 14
Sillimanite	10	18	26	19
Topaz	14	20	25	5
Zircon	9.3	13.7	17.7	1

REFERENCES FOR TABLE 6-8

1. Austin, Jour. Am. Ceram. Soc. **14**, 795, 1931
2. Jay, Proc. Roy. Soc. **A142**, 237, 1933
3. Kozu and Saiki, Sci. Rep. Tohoku Univ. Ser. 3, **2**, 203, 1925
4. Kozu and Takane, Sci. Rep. Tohoku Univ. Ser. 3, **3**, 239, 1929
5. Kozu and Ueda, Sci. Rep. Tohoku Univ. Ser. 3, **3**, 161, 1929
6. —— Proc. Imp. Acad. Japan **9**, 262, 1933
7. —— Proc. Imp. Acad. Japan **9**, 317, 1933
8. —— Proc. Imp. Acad. Japan **10**, 25, 1934
9. —— Proc. Imp. Acad. Japan **10**, 87, 1934
10. Kozu, Ueda, and Tsurmuri, Proc. Imp. Acad. Japan **10**, 83, 1934
11. Rigby and Green, Trans. British Ceram. Soc. **41**, 123, 1941
12. Rigby, Lovell, and Green, Trans. British Ceram. Soc. **44**, 37, 1945
13. —— Trans. British Ceram. Soc. **45**, 237, 1946
14. Rosenholtz and Smith, Am. Min. **26**, 103, 1941
15. —— Am. Min. **27**, 344, 1942
16. Sahama, Jour. Petrology **3**, 65, 1962
17. Skinner, Am. Min. **41**, 428, 1956
18. ——U.S. Geol. Survey, Prof. Paper **450D**, 109, 1962
19. Skinner, Clark, and Appleman, Am. Jour. Sci. **259**, 651, 1961
20. Yoder and Weir, Am. Jour. Sci. **249**, 683, 1951

TABLE 6-9. DENSITY AT HIGH TEMPERATURE: LIQUID AND CRYSTALLINE STATES
m.p. = melting point

	Temperature °C	Density		Density difference,* per cent	Volumetric thermal expansion of liquid	Ref.
		Crystal	Liquid			
ROCKS						
Diabase	1200	..	2.614	..	44×10^{-6}	1
Diabase, Palisades	1200	2.89	2.603	9.9	160?	5
Diabase, Vinal Haven	1250	2.88	2.64	8.6	38	4, 9
Diabase, Olonetze	1200	..	2.79	..	279	14
Basalt, Transcaucasia	1250	..	2.63	..	82	14
Diorite	1250	..	2.60	..	140	14
MINERALS						
Akermanite (synthetic)	1458 (m.p.)	..	2.724	4.4	56	4, 12
Diopside (synthetic)	1391 (m.p.)	3.14	2.671	14.9	64	4, 10
Plagioclase ($Ab_{30}An_{70}$)	1480	2.63	2.519	4.2	56	4, 9
OTHER MATERIALS						
Copper	1083 (m.p.)	8.29	7.96	3.9	143	3
Iron, pure	1535 (m.p.)	7.30	7.25	1.?	144	2, 13
LiF	870 (m.p.)	2.027	1.789	11.8	147	6, 8
NaCl	804 (m.p.)	1.904	1.549	18.6	367	6, 7
$NaNO_3$	308 (m.p.)	2.122	1.909	10.1	363	11, 8
KCl	776 (m.p.)	1.766	1.524	13.6	402	6, 8
KBr	730 (m.p.)	2.473	2.122	14.2	391	6, 8
K_2SiO_3	1050	..	2.24	..	205	14

* Density difference = difference in density between crystal and liquid at indicated temperature, in per cent.

REFERENCES FOR TABLE 6-9

1. Barus, U.S. Geol. Surv. Bull. 103, 1891
2. Benedicks, Ericsson, and Ericsson, Archiv. Eisenhuttenwesen 3, 473, 1929
3. Borneman and Sauerwald, Zeit. Metallkunde 14, 145, 1922
4. Dane, Am. Jour. Sci. 239, 809, 1941
5. Day, Sosman, and Hostetter, Am. Jour. Sci. 37, 1, 1914
6. Eucken and Dannohl, Zeit. Electrochemie 40, 814, 1934
7. Hanlein, Glastech. Ber. 10, 126, 1932
8. Jaeger, Zeit. anorgan. Chemie 101, 1, 1917
9. Kozu and Ueda, Proc. Imp. Acad., Japan 9, 262, 1933
10. —— Proc. Imp. Acad., Japan 9, 317, 1933
11. Kracek, Jour. Am. Chem. Soc. 53, 2609, 1931
12. Rigby and Green, Trans. British Ceram. Soc. 41, 123, 1941
13. Schmidt, Ergeb. d. Röntgenkunde, Leipzig, 1933
14. Wolarowitsch and Leontjewa, Zeit. anorgan. Chemie 225, 327, 1935

TABLE 6-10. THERMAL EXPANSION OF ROCKS
Temperature interval, 20–100° C

Rock type	Number of determinations	Average linear expansion coefficient $\dfrac{1}{L}\dfrac{\Delta L}{\Delta T}$
Granites and rhyolites	21	8 $\pm 3 \times 10^{-6}$
Andesites and diorites	4	7 ± 2
Basalts, gabbros, and diabases	10	5.4 ± 1
Sandstones	10	10 ± 2
Quartzites	2	11
Limestones	20	8 ± 4
Marbles	9	7 ± 2
Slates	3	9 ± 1

The limits include nearly all the determined values. Data from the following sources were used in making these averages:

Wheeler, Trans. Roy. Soc. Canada 3, 19, 1910
Souder and Hidnert, U.S. Bur. Stands. Sci. Paper 352, 1919
Griffith, Iowa Eng. Exp. Sta. Bull. 131, 1937

TABLE 6-11. THERMAL EXPANSIONS OF A FEW COMMERCIAL GLASSES
Reference: Morey, Properties of glass, 2d ed., Reinhold, 1954

Name	Composition, weight per cent									Density, g/cc	Average linear thermal expansion $\frac{1}{L_0} \cdot \frac{\Delta L}{\Delta T} \times 10^6$	Temperature range °C
	SiO_2	B_2O_3	Na_2O	K_2O	CaO	BaO	ZnO	Al_2O_3	PbO			
Silica	100	..	..	..	..	..	..	..	..	2.203	0.54	0–1000
Vycor	96.3	2.9	..	..	..	..	..	0.4	..	2.18	0.8	0– 300
Pyrex, chemical resistant	80.5	12.9	3.8	0.4	..	..	..	2.2	..	2.23	3.2	19– 350
Wine glass	73	..	18	..	9	..	..	..	..	..	9.8	0– 400
Thermometer, 59III	72	12	11	..	..	..	..	5	..	2.37	5.90	0– 100
Crown	64.6	2.7	5.0	15.0	..	10.2	2.0	..	..	2.49	8.83	19– 90
Borosilicate crown	68.2	10.0	10.0	9.5	..	..	2.0	..	..	2.47	7.97	17– 95
Light barium crown	48.1	4.5	1.0	7.5	..	28.3	10.1	..	..	3.21	7.90	19– 93
Heavy flint	20.0	..	..	..	..	..	..	..	80.0	5.94	9.33	25– 84

TABLE 6-12. COMPRESSION AND THERMAL EXPANSION AT HIGH PRESSURE
OF THE ALKALI METALS

Reference: Bridgman, Proc. Am. Acad., **60**, 385, 1925; Proc. Am. Acad., **70**, 71, 1935

	Li		Na		K	
Pressure kg/cm^2	$-\Delta V/V_0$ at 0° C	Mean linear thermal expansion 0°–95° C	$-\Delta V/V_0$ at 0° C	Mean linear thermal expansion 0°–95° C	$-\Delta V/V_0$ at 0° C	Mean linear thermal expansion 0° C
0	..	56×10^{-6}	..	71×10^{-6}	..	83×10^{-6}
2.000	.0164	51.5	.0295	62.2	.0571	67.0
4.000	.0320	47.3	.0552	55.3	.1002	53.8
6.000	.0466	43.4	.0779	49.5	.1347	42.7
8.000	.0606	40.0	.0981	45.0	.1640	33.6
10.000	.0739	37.0	.1165	40.8	.1890	26.0
12.000	.0866	34.5	.1332	37.0	.2108	22.0
14.000	.0984	32.5	.1488	33.7	.2300	18.3
16.000	.1094	30.6	.1632	30.0	.2472	15.5
18.000	.1198	28.8	.1767	26.5	.2626	13.8
20.000	.1296	27.3	.1894	23.3	.2767	12.5

TABLE 6-13. EFFECT OF PRESSURE ON THERMAL EXPANSION

Reference: Bridgman, Proc. Am. Acad. **74**, 21, 1940; Phys. Rev. **57**, 237, 1940

	Volume decrement per cm^3 on cooling from 20° C to −80° C		Ratio of column 3 to 2
	At 1 atm.	At 50,000 kg/cm^2	
NaCl	.0107	.0048	.45
NaBr	.0117	.0092	.79
NaI	.0120	.0130	1.08?
KCl*	.0101	.0	0?
KBr*	.0110	.0012	.11
KI*	.0123	.0038	.31
RbCl*	.0186	.0132	.71
RbBr*	.0110	.0036	.33
RbI*	.0165	.0070	.47
CsCl	.0200	.0118	.59
CsBr	.0140	.0081	.58
CsI	.0146	.0039	.27

* The volume change of a polymorphic transition is included.

SECTION 7

COMPRESSIBILITY; ELASTIC CONSTANTS

(See also Section 9)

by Francis Birch

Contents

Density and specific volume depend on stress as well as temperature. A stress consisting of uniform pressure in all directions is known as "hydrostatic" pressure, and the relationship between change of volume or density and hydrostatic pressure may be expressed in terms of a single coefficient, the compressibility β, defined by

$$\beta = -\frac{1}{V}\left(\frac{\partial V}{\partial P}\right)_T = \frac{1}{\rho}\left(\frac{\partial \rho}{\partial P}\right)_T,$$

where V is the specific volume, and ρ the density, at pressure P. Since $\partial V/\partial P$ is intrinsically negative, β is a positive number having the dimensions of the reciprocal of a pressure or stress. Its reciprocal K is known as the bulk modulus; K and β depend in general upon pressure and temperature. For small compressions, the volume change is often related to the specific volume V_0 or density ρ_0 at $P = 0$ (or 1 atmosphere) instead of to the volume or density at pressure P; the difference is proportional to the total change of volume between the pressures 0 and P.

Compressibility may be determined directly as a volume change under pressure, or volume changes may be computed from changes of linear dimensions under pressure. If the material is not isotropic, measurements of linear changes in as many as three mutually perpendicular directions may be required to determine the volume change. Unless specified as linear, the tabulated data refer to volume changes. The directions of linear measurements are specified as "parallel" or "perpendicular" with reference to the axis of highest symmetry for crystals of the hexagonal, tetragonal, and trigonal classes; for the others, the directions are the usual crystallographic axes. The initial compressibility (compressibility at $P = 0$) may also be computed from the elastic constants, most readily from the quantities S_{pq} (see below); the general relationship is

$$\beta = S_{11} + S_{22} + S_{33} + 2(S_{23} + S_{13} + S_{12}).$$

Most modern techniques furnish values of the "adiabatic" elastic constants, and the corresponding compressibility will be the adiabatic compressibility β_S, rather than the isothermal compressibility β_T defined above. The thermodynamic relationship between these two quantities is: $\beta_T = \beta_S + T\alpha^2/(\rho C_P)$, where T is the absolute temperature, α the volume thermal expansion, and C_P the specific heat per gram at constant pressure. The difference does not exceed a few per cent for most solids at ordinary temperature. Values obtained from elastic constants are distinguished by an asterisk.

Many of the measurements of compression have been reduced to the form, $-\Delta V/V_0 = aP - bP^2$, where a and b depend upon the temperature and $\Delta V = V - V_0$. Then a is the initial compressibility, while compressibility at pressure P, referred to V_0, is $a - 2bP$. In addition to constants fitted to the data by the original authors, a few constants have been computed from tabulated compressions (Tables 7-2, 7-8, 7-11) by plotting the quantity $(-\Delta V/V_0)/P$ against the pressure, and, where this plot is reasonably linear, by taking the intercept at $P = 0$ as a, and the slope as $-b$. Where this plot is decidedly nonlinear, the notation "nl" has been entered in the "b" column; the corresponding value of a will then be somewhat arbitrary.

While for larger compressions it is generally satisfactory to record only the compressions as a function of pressure, it is often useful, as well as economical of space, to have an analytical expression relating pressure and volume. An expression suggested by the theory of finite strain [45] has proved to be efficient for this purpose. Putting $y = (V_0/V)^{2/3} - 1$, we have $P = (3K_0/2)y(1 + y)^{5/2}[1 - \xi y + 0(y^2)]$; here K_0 may be identified with $1/a$ and ξ is a dimensionless parameter related to a and b: $2b/a^2 = 5 - 4\xi/3$. The parameter ξ is given instead of b where this form has been adopted by the author.

The stress will be strictly hydrostatic only when applied through a fluid medium of low viscosity; this condition is satisfied for most of the measurements at pressures below 12 kb, and for Bridgman's measurements to 30 kb. At higher pressures, and at low temperatures, the pressure medium has usually been a weak solid, in which the stress is only approximately uniform, and furthermore, increasingly uncertain as to absolute magnitude as the pressure increases.

Data at the highest pressures are obtained by the observations of shock waves produced by explosives. Observed quantities are the velocity of propagation of the shock front U_s and the particle velocity U_p. For a plane shock proceeding into material having an initial density ρ_0 at zero pressure, the conditions of conservation of mass and momentum lead to the relationships,

$$P = \rho_0 U_s U_p$$
$$\rho = \rho_0 U_s/(U_s - U_p).$$

The pressure-density function obtained in this way is known as the Hugoniot or shock equation of state and differs from the isothermal or adiabatic equations of state; the shock compression is irreversible, and the rise of temperature is greater than the rise along the adiabatic compression curve having the same starting point. Reduction to isothermal curves have been given for many of the materials. Most of the published work refers to metals, but preliminary results are now available for a number of rocks and single crystals. Because of the importance of these measurements for geophysics, some unpublished material has been included, but should be used with reserve. Virtually all rocks give indications of irregularities, probably associated with phase changes, below a few hundred kilobars. The measurements at the highest pressures probably refer to assemblages of high-pressure phases.

Stress in general requires for its complete specification six independent quantities, the components of stress, here denoted by T_i ($i = 1$ to 6). Similarly, the most general (pure) strain requires for its complete specification the six components of strain, e_i. For small strains, the stress components are linearly related to the strain components, by equations of the form

$$T_i = \sum_{j=1}^{6} C_{ij} e_j \quad \text{or} \quad e_i = \sum_{j=1}^{6} S_{ij} T_j$$

(See, for example, Voigt [234], Huntington [135], Hearmon [126]. The two latter references include comprehensive accounts of experimental methods, as well as much valuable discussion.) The quantities C_{ij} are known as elastic constants or stiffness coefficients, the S_{ij} as elastic moduli or compliances. They are functions of temperature and pressure (or more generally, of stress). In the following tabulations, the C_{ij} are expressed in megabars, or (10^{12} dyn/cm^2); the S_{ij} in reciprocal megabars.

The maximum number of independent C_{ij} or S_{ij} is 21 for a medium without symmetry elements (triclinic system); there are no examples of a complete determination of all 21 constants for a triclinic mineral. Several twinned triclinic minerals have been treated as if they were elastically monoclinic, with 13 independent constants [12b]; the significance of the results is not clear. Similarly, several monoclinic minerals have been treated as if they were elastically hexagonal [12a]. Determination of all the constants in crystals of low symmetry is difficult, especially for natural crystals often of small size and subject to many kinds of imperfection.

A greater number of elastic constants has been proposed [See ref. 135, 126], partly on theoretical grounds, and partly in explanation of various experimental discrepancies.

Careful studies of these supposed discrepancies have failed to support the new proposals. The differences reported for nominally identical materials show that substantial experimental errors frequently appear, especially for crystals of relatively low symmetry.

Even the conversion of the C_{ij} to S_{ij}, or vice versa, a purely arithmetical procedure, has sometimes introduced errors; in the following tables this conversion has been checked by a computer program designed by S. P. Clark. Corrections of one or two digits in the last significant figure have not been recorded. The number of determinations of single-crystal constants has increased rapidly in recent years, with the introduction of convenient methods for measuring the velocities of propagation of elastic waves. In the following tabulations advantage has been taken of the compilations by Hearmon [126], Huntington [135], Alexandrov and Ryzhova [13] and others. Where many concordant determinations exist for a single material some have been arbitrarily omitted; a few obviously erroneous measurements have also been left out.

In most of the applications of the theory of elasticity the medium is assumed to be elastically isotropic, and the elastic properties are defined in terms of two independent elastic constants, either the Lamé constants, λ and μ, or, more commonly in engineering, Young's modulus E, the rigidity modulus G, or Poisson's ratio σ. The relationships among these constants, are shown below in tabular form, with the expressions for the velocities of propagation of the two kinds of elastic body waves. While the only strictly isotropic materials are well-annealed glasses and similar noncrystalline materials, many polycrystalline materials with random orientation of individual grains are found to be effectively isotropic in samples of adequate size. Among such quasi-isotropic materials are many of the metals of technology, sintered ceramics, and even rocks; however,

CONNECTING IDENTITIES FOR ELASTIC CONSTANTS OF ISOTROPIC BODIES

K = bulk modulus; E = Young's modulus; μ = shear modulus;
β = compressibility = $1/K$; λ = Lamé's constant; σ = Poisson's ratio;
ρ = density; $R_1 = V_P/V_S$; $R_2^2 = K/(\rho V_S^2)$; $R_3^2 = K/(\rho V_P^2)$.

K	E	λ	σ	ρV_P^2	$\rho V_S^2 = \mu$
$\lambda + 2\mu/3$	$\mu\dfrac{3\lambda + 2\mu}{\lambda + \mu}$	..	$\dfrac{\lambda}{2(\lambda + \mu)}$	$\lambda + 2\mu$	..
..	$9K\dfrac{K - \lambda}{3K - \lambda}$	..	$\dfrac{\lambda}{3K - \lambda}$	$3K - 2\lambda$	$3(K - \lambda)/2$
..	$\dfrac{9K\mu}{3K + \mu}$	$K - 2\mu/3$	$\dfrac{3K - 2\mu}{2(3K + \mu)}$	$K + 4\mu/3$	..
$\dfrac{E\mu}{3(3\mu - E)}$	..	$\mu\dfrac{E - 2\mu}{3\mu - E}$	$E/(2\mu) - 1$	$\mu\dfrac{4\mu - E}{3\mu - E}$	..
..	..	$3K\dfrac{3K - E}{9K - E}$	$\dfrac{3K - E}{6K}$	$3K\dfrac{3K + E}{9K - E}$	$\dfrac{3KE}{9K - E}$
$\lambda\dfrac{1 + \sigma}{3\sigma}$	$\lambda\dfrac{(1 + \sigma)(1 - 2\sigma)}{\sigma}$	..	..	$\lambda\dfrac{1 - \sigma}{\sigma}$	$\lambda\dfrac{1 - 2\sigma}{2\sigma}$
$\mu\dfrac{2(1 + \sigma)}{3(1 - 2\sigma)}$	$2\mu(1 + \sigma)$	$\mu\dfrac{2\sigma}{1 - 2\sigma}$	..	$\mu\dfrac{2 - 2\sigma}{1 - 2\sigma}$	..
..	$3K(1 - 2\sigma)$	$3K\dfrac{\sigma}{1 + \sigma}$	..	$3K\dfrac{1 - \sigma}{1 + \sigma}$	$3K\dfrac{1 - 2\sigma}{2 + 2\sigma}$
$\dfrac{E}{3(1 - 2\sigma)}$	..	$\dfrac{E\sigma}{(1 + \sigma)(1 - 2\sigma)}$	..	$\dfrac{E(1 - \sigma)}{(1 + \sigma)(1 - 2\sigma)}$	$\dfrac{E}{2 + 2\sigma}$
$\rho(V_P^2 - \tfrac{4}{3}V_S^2)$	$\dfrac{9\rho V_S^2 R_2^2}{3R_2^2 + 1}$	$\rho(V_P^2 - 2V_S^2)$	See below.	..	..

$$2\sigma = (R_1^2 - 2)/(R_1^2 - 1) = (3R_2^2 - 2)/(3R_2^2 + 1) = 2(3R_3^2 - 1)/(3R_3^2 + 1).$$

unless examination of directional properties has been made, the assumption of isotropy is always open to question. Appreciable differences have been found for velocities or for E or G in different directions in rocks; in spite of this, the simplified expressions for the ideal elastic medium have frequently been employed for derivation of unmeasured constants. If the medium is not quasi-isotropic, two independent constants will not suffice for specifying the elastic properties, and the relationship for the ideal isotropic medium will not be valid.

The elastic constants of structural metals are nearly independent of stress within the "proportional" limits, but much research has shown that the elastic constants of rocks may vary with stress, particularly at low stresses where the relationship between stress and strain often departs markedly from linearity. This behavior is caused by porosity or intercrystalline spaces which may be changed by stress; thus the effective constants of a rock are determined, not only by the constants of the solid components, but also by the shape and distribution of the spaces between them. These spaces may be greatly reduced by the application of pressure to the solid components, and are often virtually eliminated by pressures of the order of 1 kb; thus a substantial increase of such constants as Young's modulus, bulk modulus, rigidity modulus, and corresponding wave velocities, is often found to occur within the first 1 or 2 kb. These changes are of most importance for studies concerned with considerable depths in the Earth, but they also affect the interpretation of experimental work at lower pressures [46, 289].

In the sections on the elastic constants of rocks, a fair sampling of the literature, rather than exhaustive coverage, has been sought, with emphasis on recent studies. Because of the great variety of composition, texture, grain size and so on, the number of entries is still large and of somewhat questionable utility. Sampling is inadequate for furnishing valid estimates of the degree of variation in any geological or lithological unit, although enough has been done to demonstrate uniformity on a small scale (a few cubic feet). Users should be cautioned against uncritical application of any measurements on rocks to conditions greatly different from those under which the measurements were made.

In many recent studies, the elastic constants have been derived from directly measured velocities of propagation by use of the formulas for the isotropic medium, but there are few demonstrations that these formulas are applicable. Most of the data available for a test are collected in Table 7-16, where the compressibility β as derived from velocities is compared with β obtained from measurements of change of length under hydrostatic pressure. The comparison is for a pressure of 4 kb, sufficient to suppress most of the abnormal low-pressure behavior. [For further discussion of this subject, see Ref. 46.] With several notable exceptions, the fair agreement between the two independent values of β justifies the use of the classical formulas at moderately high pressures. Very compact fine-grained rocks (certain diabases, dolomites, pyroxenites) may show a close approach to isotropic elasticity even at low pressures [136]. The distinct anisotropy of many rocks should be noticed (Table 7-15).

The relationship between the elastic constants of a polycrystalline material and those of its individual constituents has been approached in a number of ways. For the monomineralic aggregate, two methods of averaging the single-crystal constants proposed by Voigt and Reuss yield upper and lower limits, respectively, for the two elastic constants of the quasi-isotropic aggregate of zero porosity. The treatment of multicomponent systems has proceeded by way of introducing inclusions (or pores) in an otherwise isotropic continuum. None of these methods yields exact results, but the limiting values are sometimes of interest. A few theoretical values have been included for comparison with experimental determinations on monomineralic aggregates.

The Voigt and Reuss schemes [126] for obtaining the elastic constants of quasi-isotropic aggregates of a single material lead to the following relationships, where C_{pq} and S_{pq} refer to the individual crystal, and K and G are the bulk modulus and modulus of rigidity, respectively, of the aggregate:

Voigt	Reuss
$K = (A + 2B)/3$	$K = 1/(3a + 6b)$
$G = (A - B + 3C)/5$	$G = 5/(4a - 4b + 3c)$

with

$3A = C_{11} + C_{22} + C_{33}$	$3a = S_{11} + S_{22} + S_{33}$
$3B = C_{23} + C_{31} + C_{12}$	$3b = S_{23} + S_{31} + S_{12}$
$3C = C_{44} + C_{55} + C_{66}$	$3c = S_{44} + S_{55} + S_{66}.$

Other coefficients for the aggregate may be obtained from K and G by use of the relationships for the isotropic medium given above.

REFERENCES FOR SECTION 7

1. Adams, F. D., and Coker, Carnegie Inst. Washington, Pub. 46, 1906
2. Adams, L. H., Jour. Wash. Acad. Sci. **11**, 45, 1921
3. —— Beitr. Zur Geophys. **31**, 315, 1931
4. Adams, L. H., and Gibson, Proc. Nat. Acad. Sci. **12**, 275, 1926
5. —— Nat. Acad. Sci. Proc. **15**, 713, 1929
6. —— Jour. Wash. Acad. Sci. **21**, 381, 1931
7. Adams, L. H., and Williamson, Jour. Franklin Inst. **195**, 475, 1923
8. Adams, L. H., Williamson, and Johnston, Jour. Am. Chem. Soc. **41**, 12, 1919
9. Alers, Phys. Rev. **119**, 1532, 1960
10. Alers, and Neighbours, Jour. Phys. Chem. Solids **7**, 58, 1958
11. Alers, Neighbours, and Sato, Jour. Phys. Chem. Solids **9**, 21, 1959
12. Alexandrov and Ryzhova, Bull. (Izvestiya) Acad. Sci. USSR, Geophys. Ser. 9, 871 (English) 1961
12a. —— Bull. (Izvestiya) Acad. Sci. USSR, Geophys. Ser. **12**, 1165, 1961
12b. —— Bull. (Izvestiya) Acad. Sci. USSR, Geophys. Ser. **2**, 129, 1962
13. —— Soviet Phys. Cryst. **6**, 228, 1961
14. Altschuler and Kormer, Bull. (Izvestiya) Acad. Sci. USSR, Geophys. Ser. **1**, 18, 1961
15. Altschuler, Krupnikov, and Brazhnik, Soviet Phys. JETP, **34**, 886, 1958
16. —— Soviet Phys. JETP **34**, 614, 1958
17. Altschuler, Kormer, Brazhnik, Vladimirov, Speranskaya, and Funtikov, Soviet Phys. JETP **11**, 766, 1960
18. Altschuler, Kormer, Bakanova, and Trunin, Soviet Phys. JETP **11**, 573, 1960
19. Altschuler, Kuleshova, and Parlovskii, Soviet Phys. JETP **12**, 10, 1961
20. Arenberg, Jour. Appl. Phys. **21**, 941, 1950
21. Armstrong, Carlson, and Smith, Jour. Appl. Phys. **30**, 36, 1959
22. Atanasoff and Hart, Phys. Rev. **59**, 85, 1941
23. Bacon and Smith, Phys. Rev. **98**, 1553, 1955(A)
24. —— Acta Met. **4**, 337, 1956
25. Bancroft, Peterson, and Minshall, Jour. Appl. Phys. **27**, 291, 1956
26. Barnes and Hiedemann, Jour. Acoust. Soc. **28**, 1218, 1956
27. Bass, Rossberg, and Ziegler, Zeits. Phys. **149**, 199, 1957
28. Bateman, Mason, and McSkimin, Jour. Appl. Phys. **32**, 928, 1961
29. Bechmann, Phys. Rev. **110**, 1060, 1958
30. Bender, Ann. Phys. **34**, 359, 1939
31. Bergmann, Der Ultraschall, 6th ed., Verlag S. Herzel, Stuttgart and Zurich, 1954
32. Bhagavantam, Proc. 33d Indian Sci. Congr. Part II, Pres. Address to Section III, Physics, 1946
33. —— Proc. Indian Acad. Sci. **A41**, 72, 1955
34. Bhagavantam and Bhimasenachar, Nature **154**, 546, 1944
35. —— Proc. Indian Acad. Sci. **A20**, 298, 1944
36. —— Proc. Roy. Soc. (London) **A187**, 381, 1946
37. Bhagavantam and Seshagiri Rao, Nature **168**, 42, 1951
37a. Bhagavantam and Suryanarayana, Proc. Indian Acad. Sci. **A20**, 304, 1944
38. Bhimasenachar, Proc. Indian Acad. Sci. **A22**, 199, 1945

39. —— Proc. Indian Acad. Sci. **A22**, 209, 1945
40. —— Curr. Sci. **18**, 372, 1949
41. Bhimasenachar and Venkata Rao, Jour. Acoust. Soc. Am. **29**, 343, 1957
42. Birch, Jour. Appl. Phys. **8**, 129, 1937
43. —— Bull. Geol. Soc. America **54**, 263, 1943
44. —— Phys. Rev. **71**, 809, 1947
45. —— Jour. Geophys. Res. **65**, 1083, Pt. I, 1960
46. —— Jour. Geophys. Res. **66**, 2199, Pt. II, 1961
47. Birch and Bancroft, Jour. Geol. **46**, 59 and 113, 1938
48. —— Jour. Geol. **48**, 752, 1940
49. —— Am. Jour. Sci. **240**, 457, 1942
49a. —— Am. Jour. Sci. **237**, 2, 1939
50. Simmons and Birch, Jour. Appl. Phys. **34**, 2736, 1963
50a. Birch and Bancroft, Bull. Seismol. Soc. America **28**, 243, 1938
51. Birch and Dow, Bull. Geol. Soc. America **47**, 1235, 1938
52. Birch and Law, Bull. Geol. Soc. America **46**, 1219, 1935
53. Bolef, Jour. Appl. Phys. **32**, 100, 1961
53a. Bolef and de Klerk, Jour. Appl. Phys. **33**, 2311, 1962; Phys. Rev. **129**, 1063, 1963
54. Bolef and Menes, Jour. Appl. Phys. **31**, 1010, 1960
55. Bond, Mason, McSkimin, Olsen, and Teal, Phys. Rev. **78**, 176, 1950
56. Bozorth, Mason, and McSkimin, Bell Syst. Tech. Jour. **30**, 970, 1951
57. Bridgman, Am. Jour. Sci. **7**, 81, 1924
58. —— Am. Jour. Sci. **10**, 359, 1925
59. —— Am. Jour. Sci. **10**, 483, 1925
60. —— Am. Jour. Sci. **15**, 287, 1928
61. —— Am. Jour. Sci. **237**, 7, 1939
62. —— Jour. Appl. Phys. **30**, 214, 1959
63. —— Phys. Rev. **6**, 100, 1915
64. —— Phys. Rev. **38**, 182, 1931
65. —— Phys. Rev. **47**, 393, 1935
66. —— Phys. Rev. **57**, 235, 1940
67. —— Phys. Rev. **57**, 237, 1940
68. —— Phys. Rev. **60**, 351, 1941
69. —— Proc. Am. Acad. **47**, 347, 1912
70. —— Proc. Am. Acad. **58**, 166, 1923
71. —— Proc. Am. Acad. **59**, 109, 1923
72. —— Proc. Am. Acad. **60**, 305, 1925
73. —— Proc. Am. Acad. **60**, 385, 1925
74. —— Proc. Am. Acad. **62**, 297, 1927
75. —— Proc. Am. Acad. **63**, 347, 1928
76. —— Proc. Am. Acad. **64**, 33, 1929
77. —— Proc. Am. Acad. **64**, 39, 1929
78. —— Proc. Am. Acad. **64**, 51, 1929
79. —— Proc. Am. Acad. **66**, 255, 1931
80. —— Proc. Am. Acad. **67**, 29, 1932
81. —— Proc. Am. Acad. **67**, 345, 1932
82. —— Proc. Am. Acad. **68**, 27, 1933
83. —— Proc. Am. Acad. **70**, 71, 1935
84. —— Proc. Am. Acad. **70**, 285, 1935
85. —— Proc. Am. Acad. **72**, 207, 1938
86. —— Proc. Am. Acad. **74**, 11, 1940
87. —— Proc. Am. Acad. **74**, 21, 1940
88. —— Proc. Am. Acad. **74**, 425, 1942
89. —— Proc. Am. Acad. **76**, 1, 1945
90. —— Proc. Am. Acad. **76**, 9, 1945
91. —— Proc. Am. Acad. **76**, 89, 1948
92. —— Proc. Am. Acad. **76**, 71, 1948
93. —— Proc. Am. Acad. **76**, 55, 1948
94. —— Proc. Am. Acad. **77**, 187, 1949
95. Briscoe and Squire, Phys. Rev. **106**, 1175, 1957
96. Bruckshaw and Mahanta, Petroleum **17**, 14, 1954
97. Clark and Strakna, Jour. Appl. Phys. **32**, 1172, 1961
98. Chandrasekhar and Rayne, Phys. Rev. **124**, 1011, 1961
99. Daniels, Phys. Rev. **119**, 1246, 1960
100. Daniels and Smith, Phys. Rev. **111**, 713, 1958
101. de Klerk and Bolef, Bull. Am. Phys. Soc. **6**, 76(A), 1961
102. de Klerk and Musgrave, Proc. Phys. Soc. (London) **B68**, 81, 1955
103. Doraiswami, Proc. Indian Acad. Sci. **A25**, 413, 1947
104. Durand, Phys. Rev. **50**, 449, 1936

105. Dremin and Adadurov, Doklady **128**, 261, 1959: Adadurov, Balashov and Dremin, Bull. (Izvestiya) Acad. Sci. USSR, Geophys. Ser. **5**, 463, 1961
106. Druyvesteyn, Physica **8**, 439, 1941
107. Ebert, Phys. Zeits. **36**, 388, 1935
108. Eckstein, Lawson, and Reneker, Jour. Appl. Phys. **31**, 1543, 1960
109. Enck, Phys. Rev. **119**, 1873, 1960
110. Eros and Reitz, Jour. Appl. Phys. **29**, 683, 1958
111. Fai, Bull. (Izvestiya) Acad. Sci. USSR, Geophys. Ser. **10**, 1004, 1961
112. Fine, Jour. Appl. Phys. **24**, 338, 1953
113. Fisher and McSkimin, Jour. Appl. Phys. **29**, 1473, 1958
114. Garland and Dalven, Phys. Rev. **111**, 1232, 1958
115. Garland and Silverman, Phys. Rev. **119**, 1218, 1960
116. Gassmann, Weber and Vögtli, Verh. Schweiz. Naturforsch. Ges., Bern, 1952
117. Goens, Ann. Phys. **17**, 233, 1933
118. Goens and Schmid, Naturwiss. **19**, 521, 1931
119. —— Phys. Zeits. **37**, 385, 1936
120. Goens and Weerts, Phys. Zeits. **37**, 321, 1936
121. Gold, Phys. Rev. **77**, 390, 1950
122. Green and Mackinnon, Jour. Acoust. Soc. America **28**, 1292, 1965
123. Gruneisen and Goens, Zeits. Phys. **26**, 235, 1924
124. Gruneisen and Sckell, Ann. Phys. **19**, 387, 1934
125. Gutsche, Naturwiss. **45**, 566, 1958
126. Hearmon, Rev. Mod. Phys. **18**, 409, 1946
     —— Phil. Mag. Suppl. **5**, 323, 1956
127. House and Vernon, Brit. Jour. Appl. Phys. **11**, 254, 1960
128. Hughes and Jones, Bull. Geol. Soc. America **61**, 843, 1950
129. Hughes and Cross, Geophysics **16**, 577, 1951
129a. Hughes and Kelly, Phys. Rev. **92**, 1145, 1953
130. Hughes and Maurette, Geophysics **21**, 277, 1956
131. —— Geophysics **22**, 23, 1957a
132. —— Rev. de l'Inst. Francais du Pétrole **12**, 730, 1957b
133. Hughes and McQueen, Trans. Am. Geophys. Union **39**, 959', 1958
134. Hunter and Siegel, Phys. Rev. **61**, 84, 1942
135. Huntington, Solid State Physics **7**, 213, 1958
136. Ide, Proc. Nat. Acad. Sci. **22**, 81 and 482, 1936
136a. —— Jour. Geol. **45**, 689, 1937
137. Jaffe and Smith, Phys. Rev. **121**, 1604, 1961
138. Jain, Phys. Rev. **123**, 1234, 1961
139. Jona and Scherrer, Helv. Phys. Acta **25**, 35, 1952
140. Kabalkina and Vereshchagin, (Doklady) Akad. Sci. USSR **131**, 300, 1960
141. Kammer, Pardue, and Frissell, Jour. Appl. Phys. **19**, 265, 1948
142. Kimura and Ohne, Sci. Rev. **23**, 359, 1934
143. Knopoff, Trans. Am. Geophys. Union **35**, 969, 1954
144. Koga, Aruga, and Yoshinaka, Phys. Rev. **109**, 1467, 1958
145. Koppelmann and Landwehr, Zeit. Angew. Phys. **11**, 164, 1959
146. Koppelmann and Ermakova, Sov. Phys. Solid State 643, 1960, and Fiz. Tuer. Tela **2**, 697, 1960
147. Koptsik and Kobyakov, Cryst. **4**, 201, 1959
148. Krishnan, Sekharan, and Rajagopal, Nature **182**, 518, 1958
149. Laquer, McGee, and Kilpatrick, Trans. A.S.M. **42**, 771, 1950
150. Lazarus, Phys. Rev. **76**, 545, 1949
151. Lombard, The Hugoniot equation of state of rocks, Univ. Calif. Radiation Lab. **6311**, 28, 1961
152. Long and Smith, Acta Met. **5**, 200, 1957
153. Madelung and Fuchs, Ann. Phys. **65**, 289, 1921
154. Marshall, Phys. Rev. **121**, 72, 1961
155. Mason, Bell Syst. Tech. Jour. **22**, 179, 1943
156. Mason, Piezoelectric crystals and their application to ultrasonics, Van Nostrand, New York, 1950
157. Mason and Bömmel, Jour. Acoust. Soc. America **28**, 930, 1956
158. Mayer and Hiedemann, Jour. Acoust. Soc. America **32**, 1699, 1960
159. McQueen and Marsh, Jour. Appl. Phys. **31**, 1253, 1960
160. McSkimin, Jour. Appl. Phys. **24**, 988, 1953
161. —— Jour. Appl. Phys. **26**, 406, 1955
162. —— Jour. Acoust. Soc. America **29**, 1185, 1957
162a. —— Jour. Acoust. Soc. America **30**, 314, 1958
163. McSkimin and Bond, Phys. Rev. **105**, 116, 1957
164. McSkimin and others, Phys. Rev. **83**, 1951
165. McSkimin and Fisher, Jour. Appl. Phys. **31**, 1627, 1960
166. Nash and Smith, Jour. Phys. Chem. Solids **9**, 113, 1959
167. Neighbours and Alers, Phys. Rev. **111**, 707, 1958

168. Neighbours, Bratten, and Smith, Jour. Appl. Phys. **23**, 389, 1952
169. Norwood and Briscoe, Phys. Rev. **112**, 45, 1958
170. Obert, Windes, and Duvall, Bur. Mines Rep. Inv. 3891, 1946
171. Overton and Swim, Phys. Rev. **84**, 758, 1951
172. Overton and Gaffney, Phys. Rev. **98**, 969, 1955
173. Perrier and de Mandrot, C. R. **175**, 622 and 1006, 1922
174. Peselnick and Outerbridge, Jour. Geophys. Res. **66**, 581, 1961; Geophysics **24**, 285, 1959
175. Prasad and Wooster, Acta Cryst. **8**, 682, 1955
176. —— Acta Cryst. **8**, 361, 1955
177. —— Acta Cryst. **9**, 169, 1956
178. Prince and Wooster, Acta Cryst. **4**, 191, 1951
179. —— Acta Cryst. **6**, 450, 1953
180. Quimby and Siegel, Phys. Rev. **54**, 293, 1938
181. Ramachandra Rao, Proc. Indian Acad. Sci. **A22**, 194, 1954
182. Ramachandran and Wooster, Acta Cryst. **4**, 335, 1951
183. Rayne, Phys. Rev. **115**, 63, 1959
184. —— Phys. Rev. **118**, 1545, 1960
185. Rayne and Chandrasekhar, Phys. Rev. **122**, 1914, 1961
186. Reddy and Subrahmanyam, Acta Cryst. **13**, 493, 1960
186a. —— Proc. Ind. Acad. Sci. **A50**, 380, 1959
187. Reinitz, Phys. Rev. **123**, 1615, 1961
188. Reitzel, Simon, and Walker, Rev. Sci. Instr. **28**, 1957
189. Rice, McQueen, and Walsh, Solid State Physics **6**, 1, 1958
190. Richards, Jour. Am. Chem. Soc. **37**, 1646, 1915
191. Richards and Boyer, Jour. Am. Chem. Soc. **43**, 274, 1921
192. Richards and Jones, Jour. Am. Chem. Soc. **31**, 158, 1909
193. Richards and Speyer, Jour. Am. Chem. Soc. **36**, 491, 1914
194. Richards and White, Jour. Am. Chem. Soc. **50**, 3290, 1928
195. Rohl, Ann. Phys. **16**, 887, 1933
196. Saerens, Bull. Soc. Chim. de Belgique **33**, 17, 1924
197. Seeger and Buck, Zeits. Naturf. **15**, 1056, 1960
198. Schmunk and Smith, Jour. Phys. Chem. Solids **9**, 100, 1959
199. —— Acta Met. **8**, 396, 1960
200. Seshagiri Rao, Proc. Indian Acad. Sci. **A33**, 251, 1951
201. Slater, Phys. Rev. **23**, 488, 1924
202. —— Proc. Am. Acad. **61**, 135, 1926
203. Slutsky and Garland, Phys. Rev. **107**, 972, 1957
204. Smith and Arbogast, Jour. Applied Phys. **31**, 99, 1960
205. Smith and Gjevre, Jour. Applied Phys. **31**, 645, 1960
206. Spangenberg and Haussühl, Zeit. Krist. **109**, 422, 1957; Haussühl, Zeit. Phys. **159**, 223, 1960
207. Stein, Einspruch, and Truell, Jour. Applied Phys. **30**, 820, 1959
208. Stepanov and Eidus, Soviet Phys. (JETP) **2**, 377, 1956
209. Stephens, Advances in Phys. **7**, 266, 1958
210. Stewart, Phys. Rev. **97**, 578, 1955
211. —— Phys. and Chem. Solids **1**, 146, 1956
212. Stewart and Swenson, Phys. Rev. **94**, 1069, 1954
213. Sundara Rao, Proc. Indian Acad. Sci. **A29**, 352, 1949
213a. —— Proc. Indian Acad. Sci. **A31**, 365, 1950
213b. —— Proc. Indian Acad. Sci. **A28**, 475, 1948
214. —— Proc. Indian Acad. Sci. **A32**, 275, 1950
215. —— Proc. Indian Acad. Sci. **40**, errata 150, 1954
216. Susse, Jour. Phys. Radium **16**, 348, 1955
217. —— Jour. Rech., Centre National de Rech. Sci. (France) **54**, 23, 1961
218. Sutton, Phys. Rev. **91**, 816, 1953
219. Swenson, Phys. Rev. **99**, 423, 1955
220. —— Phys. Rev. **100**, 1607, 1955
221. —— Phys. Rev. **111**, 82, 1958
222. Swift and Tyndall, Phys. Rev. **61**, 359, 1942
223. Tannhauser, Bruner, and Lawson, Phys. Rev. **102**, 1276, 1956
224. Tomashevskaya, Bull. (Izvestiya) Acad. Sci. USSR, Geophys. Ser. 3, 281, 1961
225. Turner, Phys. Rev. Letters **5**, 100, 1960
226. U.S. Bur. Reclamation, Concrete Lab. Rept. No. SP-39, 1953
227. Verma, Jour. Geophys. Res. **65**, 757, 1960; Birch, idem. **65**, 3855, 1960
228. Voigt, Wied. Ann. **35**, 642, 1888
229. —— Wied. Ann. **39**, 412, 1890a
230. —— Wied. Ann. **41**, 712, 1890b
231. —— Ann. Phys. **22**, 129, 1907
232. —— Ann. Phys. **24**, 290, 1907
233. —— Gottinger, Nachr. **424**, 1918

234. Voigt, Lehrbuch der Kristallphysik, Leipzig, B. G. Teubner, 1928
235. Volarovich, Balashov, and Pavlogradsky, Bull. (Izvestiya) Acad. Sci. USSR, Geophys. Ser. 5, 486, 1959
236. Volarovich and Stakhovskaya, Bull. (Izvestiya) Acad. Sci. USSR, Geophys. Ser. 5, 329, 1958
237. Voronov, Vereshchagin, and Goncharova, Sov. Phys. (Doklady) 5, 1280, 1961
238. Wachtman, Tefft, Lam, and Stinchfield, Jour. Res. Nat. Bur. Stand. **64A**, 213, 1960
238a. —— Bull. Am. Phys. Soc. **5**, 278, 1960
239. Walsh, Rice, McQueen, and Yarger, Phys. Rev. **108**, 196, 1957
240. Waterman, Jour. Appl. Phys. **29**, 1190, 1958
241. Wert and Tyndall, Jour. Appl. Phys. **20**, 587, 1949
242. Windes, U.S. Bur. Mines, Rep. Inv. 4459, 1949
243. Winder and Smith, Jour. Phys. Chem. Solids **4**, 128, 1958
244. Wright, Proc. Roy. Soc. **126**, 613, 1929
245. Yoder and Weir, Am. Jour. Sci. **258A**, 420, 1960
246. —— Am. Jour. Sci. **249**, 683, 1951
247. —— Carnegie Inst. Washington, Year Book No. **53**, 139, 1953
248. Zisman, Proc. Nat. Acad. Sci. **19**, 653 and 666, 1933
249. —— Proc. Nat. Acad. Sci. **19**, 680, 1933
250. Zubov and Firsova, Kristallografiya **1**, 546, 1956
251. Peselnick and Robie, Jour. Appl. Phys. **34**, 2495, 1963
252. Weir, Jour. Res. N.B.S. **52**, 247, 1954
253. —— Jour. Res. N.B.S. **56**, 187, 1956
254. Boyle and Sproule, Canadian Jour. Res. **5**, 601, 1931
255. Breyer, Zeit. Geophys. **6**, 98, 1930
256. Drude and Voigt, Wied. Ann. **42**, 537, 1891
257. Ewing, Crary, and Thorne, Physics **5**, 165, 1934
258. Koch, Ann. d. Phys. **45**, 237, 1914
259. Müller, Geol. Jb. **70**, 127, 1954
260. Regula, Zeit. Geophys. 1640, 1940
261. Richards, Proc. Phys. Soc., London **45**, 70, 1933
262. Weatherby, Born, and Harding, Bull. Am. Assoc. Petr. Geol. **19**, 9, 1935
263. Horton, Phil. Trans. Roy. Soc. London, A204, 407, 1905 also, Iida, Bull. Earthquake Res. Inst. 13, 665, 1935
264. Hermann, Stocke, and Udluft, Beitr. z. angew. Geophys. **6**, 206, 1937
265. Wackerle, Jour. Appl. Phys. **33**, 922, 1962
266. McQueen and Marsh, unpublished
267. Robertson, unpublished
268. Serata, Reactor fuel waste disposal project. Development of design principle for disposal of reactor fuel waste into underground salt cavities. Univ. Texas, Sanitary Engineering Res. Lab. A.E.C. Contract AT(11-1)-490, 173 p., 1959
269. LeComte, Creep and internal friction in rock salt, thesis, Harvard Univ. 1960; Jour. Geol. **73**, 469, 1965
270. Ahrens and Gregson, Jour. Geophys. Res. **69**, 4839, 1964
271. Aleksandrov and Ryzhova, Bull. (Izvestiya) Acad. Sci. USSR. No. 6, 43, 1961
272. Bateman, Jour. Appl. Phys. **33**, 3309, 1962
273. Bartels and Smith, unpublished
274. Bernstein, Jour. Appl. Phys. **34**, 169, 1963
275. Brace, Jour. Geophys. Res. **70**, 391, 1965
276. Brugger, Jour. Appl. Phys. **36**, 768, 1965
277. Chung, Swica and Crandall, Jour. Am. Ceram. Soc. **46**, 452, 1963
278. Einspruch and Manning, Jour. Appl. Phys. **35**, 560, 1964
279. Ferris, Shepard, and Smith, Jour. Appl. Phys. **34**, 768, 1963
280. Huffman and Norwood, Phys. Rev. **117**, 709, 1960
281. Kamm and Alers, Jour. Appl. Phys. **35**, 327, 1964
282. McSkimin and Andreatch, Jour. Appl. Phys. **34**, 651, 1963
283. —— Jour. Appl. Phys. **35**, 2161, 1964
284. —— Jour. Appl. Phys. **35**, 3312, 1964
285. Ryzhova and Aleksandrov, Bull. (Izvestiya) Acad. Sci. USSR, Geophys. Ser. No. 11, 1125, 1962
286. Ryzhova, Bull. (Izvestiya) Acad. Sci. USSR, Geophys. Ser. No. 7, 633, 1964
287. Somerton, Ward and King, Jour. Geophys. Res. **68**, 849, 1963
288. Waldorf and Alers, Jour. Appl. Phys. **33**, 3266, 1962
289. Walsh, Jour. Geophys. Res. **70**, 381 and 399, 1965
290. Wasilik and Wheat, Jour. Appl. Phys. **36**, 791, 1965
291. Stephens, Jour. Geophys. Res. **69**, 2967, 1964
292. Peselnick, Jour. Geophys. Res. **67**, 4441, 1962
293. Usher, Geophys. Prosp. **10**, 119, 1962
294. Simmons, Jour. Geophys. Res. **69**, 1117, 1123, 1964
295. Anderson and Schreiber, Jour. Geophys. Res. **70**, 5241, 1965
296. Birch, unpublished

TABLE 7-1. ELEMENTS: COMPRESSIBILITY

$(V_0 - V)/V_0 = aP - bP^2$, with pressure P in megabars (mb), for indicated temperatures, and pressures below P_{max}. $a = \beta_0 =$ initial compressibility, in reciprocal megabars. When marked "linear", the same form has been used for $(L_0 - L)/L_0$. * denotes values of initial volume compressibility calculated from elastic constants (Table 7-6). For the significance of ξ, see introduction.

Element	Temp. °C	a (mb^{-1})	b (mb^{-2})	P_{max} (kb)	Ref.
A	−208	63.7	$\xi = -4.9$	19	211
	−196	93.8	$\xi = -6.5$	19	211
Ag	30	1.002	3.7	12	70, 84
	25	.985	3.0	30	94
			*3.5	10	100
		*.966			24
		*.9635			167
Al	30	1.365	4.9	12	70, 84
	25	1.387	5.1	30	94
				see Table 7-2	
	23	1.378	7.2	10	52
	163	1.438	5.4		
	435	1.601	4		
	20	1.37	3.1	5	107
		1.285	4.1	10	150
			5.1	6.5	198
		*1.29			117
	0	*1.212			218
	100	1.272			
	300	1.452			
	500	1.680			
As (trig.)	30	3.16		12	78, 82, 93
linear ∥		2.7			
linear ⊥		.23		see Table 7-2	
Au	25	.577	.83	30	94
		*.579	1.3	10	100
		*.578			167
B (tetr.)	30	.558	.8		78
Ba	30	10.4	nl	see Table 7-2	74
Be (hex.)	30	.795	2.2	12	74, 82
linear ∥		.223	.2		
linear ⊥		.287	1.2		
linear ∥		.327	1	30	94
linear ⊥				see Table 7-2	
	27	*.875			204
linear ∥		.272			
linear ⊥		.302			
Bi (trig.)	30	2.970	22	12	70, 72
linear ∥		1.622	11		
linear ⊥		.674	4.1	see Table 7-2	
		*3.08			108
linear ∥		1.82			
linear ⊥		.63			

Handbook of Physical Constants

TABLE 7-1. *Continued*

Element	Temp. °C	a (mb^{-1})	b (mb^{-2})	P_{max} (kb)	Ref.
C, diamond		.18		12	2, 7
		*.226			163
		*.174			36
C, graphite (hex.)		3.0		*see* Table 7-2	190
linear ‖		2.8	45	16	140
Ca	30	5.81	65	12	70, 84
				see Table 7-2	
Cd (hex.)	20	2.25	nl	*see* Table 7-2	70, 72
linear ‖		1.83		12	
linear ⊥		.21			
	27	*2.048			115
linear ‖		1.588			
linear ⊥		.2299			
Ce	30	4.649	−169	4	74
		(Transition at 7600 Kg/Cm². *see* Table 7-2, also Ref. 237)			
Co (hex.)	25	.517	nl	30	94
		*.525			161
linear ‖		.181			
linear ⊥		.172			
Cr	30	.525	.9	12	74, 82
Cs	50	71	nl	*see* Table 7-2	73
	−269	43.5	$\xi = +.6$	10	219
	−196	48.7	$\xi = +.4$	10	
Cu	25	.727	1.46	30	94
			*1.9	10	100
		*.717	1.3	10	150
		*.723			120
		*.720			172
		*.730			199
D_2	−269	308	$\xi = -1.6$	20	211
Fe(α)	24	.5941	.83	30	66, 86, 94
		*.595			185
Ga (orth.)	20	2.0			191
	30 (liquid)	4.0			
Ge	25	1.293	3.6	30	94
				see Table 7-2	
		*1.327	5.02	12	145
		*1.319			55
		*1.338			160
		*1.284			112
H_2 (hex.)	−269	500	$\xi = -1.9$	20	211
He (hex.)	−269	1168	$\xi = -2.3$	?	211
Hf	30	.915	1.1	12	75

TABLE 7-1.   *Continued*

Element	Temp. °C	a (mb^{-1})	b (mb^{-2})	P_{max} (kb)	Ref.
Hg(α)	−190	*3.1			124
Hg(α) (trig.)	−273	2.60		12	221
	−223	2.67			
	−173	2.89			
	−123	3.16			
	−73	3.48			
	−39	(3.70)			
Hg(β)	−273	2.17			221
	−223	2.17			
Hg (liquid)	0°	3.86		7	69
	20	4.04	68.8	12	
In (tetr.)		2.43	13.3	50 *see* Table 7-2	67, 87
		*2.419			243
linear ‖		.679			
linear ⊥		.870			
		*2.357			98
linear ‖		.583			
linear ⊥		.887			
Ir	25	.278	nl	30	94
K	45	36.35	nl	*see* Table 7-2	70
		24.9			30
	−269	28.4	$\xi = 0$	10	219
	−196	29.2	$\xi = 0$	10	
Kr	−196	56	$\xi = -5.1$	20	211
La	30	3.58	13.9	12 *see* Table 7-2	70, 74
Li	30	8.859	100	12 *see* Table 7-2	73
	−269	7.7	(228) $\xi = -2.0$	10	219
	−196	8.7	(315) $\xi = -2.5$	10	
Mg (hex.)	30	3.008	27.5	12	70, 79, 80
linear ‖		1.003	6.3		
linear ⊥		1.003	9.1		
	20	2.967	27.2	5	107
linear ‖		.984	6.7	*see* Table 7-2	
linear ⊥		.999	8.8		
	25	2.81	13.5	30	91
		*2.838			203
		*2.893			117
		*2.909			152
linear ‖		1.011			
linear ⊥		.949			
Mn	30	.803	4.2	12	78, 93
Mo	25	.365	nl	30	94
		*.372			106
		.386			101

Table 7-1. *Continued*

Element	Temp. ° C	a (mb^{-1})	b (mb^{-2})	P_{max} (kb)	Ref.
N_2	−208 (hex.)	80.1	$\xi = -2.3$	<10.2	211
	(cub.)	54.5	$\xi = -.7$	>10.2 to 19	
		Phase change at $10,200 \pm 800$ Kg/cm²			
Na	−269	13.7	$\xi = 0$	10	219
	−196	15.4	$\xi = -0.9$	10	
	30	15.93	nl	12	70
				see Table 7-2	
	26	15.11	525	10	92, 93, 88, 99
Nb(Cb)	30	.577	.9	12	82
	25	.58	nl	30	94
		*.584			53
Nd		3.2	20	40	92
				see Table 7-2	
Ne	−269	100.6	$\xi = -4.0$	20	211
Ni	30	.535	.9	12	70, 84, 94
		*.534			56
		*.537			168
		*.558			102
P (white)	20	20.5			190
(black)		2.96		see Table 7-2	74
(red)		5.56			74
Pb	30	2.415	19.6	12	70, 84
				see Table 7-2	
	20	2.354	14	10	52
	143	2.504	13	10	
	221	2.624	16	10	
	20	2.448	14.5	5	107
		2.34	10	25	90
		*2.28			117
Pd	30	.534	.9	12	70, 84
		.512	nl	30	94
		*.510			184
Pr	30	3.45	12.2	12	74
				see Table 7-2	
Pt	25	.359	nl	30	70, 84, 94
Pu	25	1.98	nl	40	62
				see Table 7-2	
Rb	50	53	nl	see Table 7-2	73
	−269	34.4	$\xi = -.15$		219
	−196	38.3	$\xi = -.3$		
Rh	25	.367	nl	30	71, 82, 94
Ru	25	.32		30	94
	30	.348	1.7	12	82
S (orth.)	30	13.5	nl	see Table 7-2	74
	75	14.7	nl	12	
		*5.6	?		214, 215
Sb (trig.)	30	2.748	31.3	12	70, 72
linear ‖		1.679	20.8		
linear ⊥		.535	4.3	see Table 7-2	
	25	2.63	18	30	94

TABLE 7-1. *Continued*

Element	Temp. ° C	a (mb^{-1})	b (mb^{-2})	P_{max} (kb)	Ref.
Se	crystalline	11.3	nl	see Table 7-2	252
	glassy	17.3	nl		
Si	25	1.012	2.5	30	93, 94
				see Table 7-2	
		*1.023			160
Sn (β)	30	1.909	12.8	12	70, 72
linear ∥		0.684	3.7		
linear ⊥		0.613	3.8		
				see Table 7-2	
	25	1.86	9.0	30	94
		*2.31			157
		*1.65			127
Sr	30	8.278	103	12	70, 84
				see Table 7-2	
Ta	25	.497	(0.2)	30	94
		*.509			53
Te	30	5.178	103.6	12	70, 72
linear ∥		−.423	−10.5		
linear ⊥		2.801	54.3		
	25	4.3	(38)	30	94
				see Table 7-2	
Th	25	(2.0)	nl	30	93, 94
	30	1.85	12.0	12	74
		*1.74			21
Ti (hex.)	25	.94	nl	30	94
				see Table 7-2	
Tl (hex.)	30	3.55		12	70
U (orth.)	30	.981	1.9	12	70, 84
		1.02	5	40	92, 93
				see Table 7-2	
		*.901			113
		*.794			149
V	30	.617	1.35	12	74
		*.6446			9
		*.6438			53
W	25	.32		30	70, 72, 94
		*.321			101
Y (hex.)		*2.414			205
Zn (hex.)	30	1.693	−8.6	12	65, 70, 72
linear ∥		1.376	7.5		
linear ⊥		.159	.26	see Table 7-2	
		1.64	7.3	40	92
	25	1.63	nl	30	94
		*1.692			241
	22	*1.624			10
	127	1.671			
	227	1.718			
	327	1.766			
	397	1.798			
Zr (hex.)	30	1.115	6.3	12	75
				see Table 7-2	

Handbook of Physical Constants

TABLE 7-2. ELEMENTS: STATIC COMPRESSION
$(V_0 - V)/V_0$ as function of pressure above 12 kilobars; room temperature.

P kg/cm²	Ag	Al	As	Au	Ba	Be	Bi
5,000	.00473	.00668	.0119	.00281		.0047	
10,000	.00938	.01312	.0221	.00558	.086	.0094	.028
15,000	.01385	.01932	.0309	.00831	(a)	.0139	
20,000	.01820	.02520	.0385	.01101	.159	.0181	.052
25,000	.02236	.03090	.0447	.01367		.0219	(c)
30,000	.02619	.03642	.053	.01626	.211	.0256	.158
35,000						.0294	
40,000		.042	.067		.253	.0329	.174 (d)
50,000		.049	.079		.288		.192
60,000		.056	.089		.318 (b)		.205 (e)
70,000		.063	.097		.361		.222
80,000		.071	.104		.382		.232
90,000		.078	.110		.402		.240 (f)
100,000		.085	.116		.420	.055	.261
Ref.	94	93, 94	88, 90, 93	94	85, 88	92, 93	88

P kg/cm²	C (graphite)	Ca	Cd	Ce	Co	Cs	Cu
5,000	.0138		.0100	.0234	.00253	.1585	.00353
10,000	.0260	.058	.0194	.0549 (h)	.00504	.2392	.00696
15,000	.0366		.0283	.1655	·.00760	.2981	.01039
20,000	.0458	.103	.0368	.1864	.01006	.3442 (i)	.01370
25,000	.0535		.0449	.2027	.01253	.3908	.01695
30,000	.060	.139	.060	.2154	.01492	.4261	.02010
35,000				.2257		.4559	
40,000	.071	.168	.076	.2342		.4816	
50,000	.081	.195	.091	.244		.569	
60,000	.089	.220 (g)	.104	.256		.591	
70,000	.097	.252	.116	.268		.608	
80,000	.104	.268	.127	.278		.619	
90,000	.110	.284	.138	.286		.625	
100,000	.115	.298	.148	.292		.632	
Ref.	90, 93	85, 88	88, 90	92, 93	94	85, 92, 93	94

P kg/cm²	Fe	Ge	In	Ir	K	La
5,000	.00289	.00623	.0127	.00137	.1152	.0194
10,000	.00575	.01237	.0241	.00272	.1862	.0370
15,000	.00856	.01826	.0347	.00408	.2374	.0526
20,000	.01133	.02394	.0445	.00545	.2772	.0665 (j)
25,000	.01407	.02950	.0537	.00683	.3093	.0827
30,000	.01676	.03488	.0619	.00818	.3360	.0952
35,000					.3584	.1072
40,000		.044	.0781		.3774	.1189
50,000		.051	.0932		.405	.137
60,000		.058	.1072		.432	.154
70,000		.065	.1202		.454	.168
80,000		.071	.1324		.472	.181
90,000		.077	.1439		.487	.192
100,000		.083	.1549		.500	.202
Ref.	94	92, 93, 94	85, 87, 88, 89, 90	94	85, 88, 92, 93	92, 93

TABLE 7-2. *Continued*

P kg/cm²	Li	Mg	Mn	Mo	Na	
5,000	.0389	.01343		.00179	.0624	
10,000	.0715	.02634		.00357	.1115	
15,000	.1005	.03834		.00536	.1511	
20,000	.1261	.04990		.00714	.1836	
25,000	.1485	.06062	.039	.00891	.2111	.211
30,000	.1689	.07056	.044	.01064	.2350	.230
35,000	.1872				.2559	
40,000	.2040	.081	.053		.2740	.263
50,000	.227	.096	.061			.292
60,000	.252	.110	.068			.317
70,000	.273	.122	.074			.339
80,000	.293	.134	.078			.359
90,000	.311	.144	.082			.377
100,000	.328	.153	.085			.394
Ref.	85, 88, 92, 93	91, 93	93	94	92	93

P kg/cm²	Nb	Nd	Ni	P black	P violet	Pb	Pd
5,000	.00283	.0152	.00277			.0110	.00267
10,000	.00562	.0289	.00479 (k)			.0215	.00517
15,000	.00839	.0416	.00750			.0315	.00761 (n)
20,000	.01114	.0536	.01001			.0411	.01015
25,000	.01386	.0650	.01262	.065	.097	.0504	.01273
30,000	.01649	.0757	.01515	.073	.115	.0587	.01522
35,000		.0858					
40,000	(mean)	.0955		.088	.147	.0747	
50,000		.111		(l)	.171	.0892	
60,000		.127		.163	.191	.1024	
70,000		.142		.175	.207	.1145	
80,000		.155		.184	.220 (m)	.1255	
90,000		.167		.193	.333	.1356	
100,000		.178		.201	.340	.1449	
Ref.	94	92, 93	94	93	93	89, 90	94

P kg/cm²	Pr	Pt	Pu	Rb		Rh	Ru
5,000	.0174	.00176	.0092	.1224		.00180	.00154
10,000	.0329	.00351	.0175	.1982		.00361	.00312
15,000	.0471	.00526	.0250	.2506		.00540	.00477
20,000	.0604	.00701	.0318	.2920		.00719	.00645
25,000	.0729	.00877	.0380	.3254	.325	.00896	.00818
30,000	.0848	.01048	.0437	.3530	.348	.01071	.00989
35,000	.0961		.0492	.3760			
40,000	.1069		.0543	.3954	.388		
50,000	.122		.0665		.422		
60,000	.137		.0758		.449		
70,000	.151		.0839		.472		
80,000	.164		.0908		.493		
90,000	.177		.0968		.511		
100,000	.189		.1019		.527		
Ref.	92, 93	94	62	92	93	94	94

TABLE 7-2. *Continued*

P kg/cm²	S	Sb	Se	Si	Sn	Sr
5,000		.01248		.00491	.00889	
10,000	.083	.02414	.089	.00965	.01732	.075
15,000		.03486		.01433	.02530	
20,000	.131	.04459	.149	.01888	.03283	.122
25,000		.05384		.02332	.04004	(p)
30,000	.163	.06243	.187	.02755	.04691	.172
35,000						
40,000	.188	.083	.208	.032		.209
50,000	.208	.098	.227	.038		.239
60,000	.225	.112	.243	.043		.266 (q)
70,000	.240	.124	.258	.048		.298
80,000	.253	.136 (o)	.271	.052		.317
90,000	.264	.185	.283	.056		.235
100,000	.274	.197	.295	.060		.352
Ref.	89	88, 94	88	93, 94	88, 94	85,88

P kg/cm²	Ta	Te		Th	Ti	Tl
5,000	.00243	.02011		.00933	.00449	.0130
10,000	.00485	.03915	.045	.01733	.00900	.0251
15,000	.00726	.05551		.02472	.01332	.0367
20,000	.00967	.06943	.079	.03188	.01810	.0476
25,000	.01208	.08234		.03882	.02174	.0577
30,000	.01448	.09346	.111	.04555	.02581	.061
35,000						
40,000			.138 (r)	.063	.0332	.079 (t)
50,000			.214	.076		.103
60,000			.225	.087		.119
70,000			.234 (s)	.096		.132
80,000			.250	.103		.145
90,000			.258	.109		.157
100,000			.267	.114	.063	.169
Ref.	94	94	88	93, 94	92, 93, 94	88,90

P kg/cm²	U	W	Zn	Zr	
5,000	.0048	.00152	.00794	.0054	
10,000	.0095	.00301	.01575	.0111	
15,000	.0139	.00458	.02293	.0168	
20,000	.0181	.00612	.02967	.0220	
25,000	.0219	.00765	.03618	.0267	.026
30,000	.0255	.00917	.04242	.0312	.033
35,000	.0290			.0356	
40,000	.0324		.061	.0399	.044
50,000	.040		.075		.054
60,000	.045		.088		.063
70,000	.049		.100		.071
80,000	.053		.111		.078
90,000	.056		.122		.084
100,000	.059		.132		.090
Ref.	92, 93	94	88, 92, 94	92	93

		Transition pressure kg/cm²	Compressions at transition	
a	Ba	17,000	.135	.141
b	Ba	60,000	.318	.337
c	Bi	∼25,000 (two transitions)	.064	.150 (extremes)
d	Bi	45,000	.180	.186
e	Bi	65,000	.211	.216
f	Bi	90,000	.240	.252
g	Ca	64,000	.229	.242
h	Ce	12,430	.0736	.1504
i	Cs	23,300	.3716	.3776
j	La	23,370	.0755	.0781
k	Ni	10,500 (cusp)		
l	P (black)	50,000 (reversible)	.101	.151
m	P (violet to black)	85,000 (irreversible)	.227	.330
n	Pd	16,500 (cusp)		
o	Sb	85,000	.142	.179
p	Sr	25,000	.143	.152
q	Sr	65,000	.279	.287
r	Te	45,000	.152	.207
s	Te	70,000	.234	.241
t	Tl	40,000	.079	.086

TABLE 7-3. METALS: SHOCK COMPRESSION

Relative Volume, $10^3(V/V_0)$, for pressure P_H on Hugoniot Curve

See also Tables 7-4, 7-5.

P_H (mb)	Ag	Al (24 ST)	Au	Be	Bi	Cd	Co	Cr	Cu	Fe	In	Mg	Mo	Nb	Ni
0	1000	1000	1000	1000	1000	1000	1000	1000	1000	1000	1000	1000	1000	1000	1000
.1	929	905.3	953	927.7		877	956	955	940		870.1	830.0	966	947.6	954
.2	881	844.1	917	873.5		815	920	920	897		797.9	743.2	937	906.7	919
.3	845	800.8	888	829.9		774	890	891	864		747.8	686.1	912	873.0	889
.4	817	766.1	864			745	865	867	836	801	708.7		890	844.9	865
.5	794	740.8	843		651	722	843	846	814		677.4		870	819.7	843
.6	775	714.3	825			704	823	827	794				852		825
.7	759	694.7	810			688	806	811	777				836		808
.8	744	677.8	796			675	791	797	762	729			821		794
.9	731	663.0	783			664	776	784	749				807		780
1.0	720	649.8	772		576	654	764	772	737				795		768
1.1	710		762			646	752	761	726				783		757
1.2	700		752			638	741	751	716				772		747
1.3	692		743			631	731	742	707	688			762		738
1.4	684		735			624	721	733	698				752		729
1.5	677		728		538		712		690				743		721
1.6	670		720				704						734		
1.7			714										726		
1.8			708												
1.9			702												
2.0			696												
Ref.	159	189	159	189	159	159	159	159	159	159	189	189	159	189	159

Table 7-3. Continued

P_H (mb)	Pb	Pd	Pt	Rh	Sb	Sn	Ta	Th	Ti	Tl	V	W	Zn	Zr
0	1000	1000	1000	1000	1000	1000	1000	1000	1000	1000	1000	1000	1000	1000
.1	865	952.0	967.9	968.3		871	951.0	870	919	853	945	970	895	909.8
.2	796	917.0	941.2	941.9		802	912.2	795	860	781	902	944	834	842.1
.3	751	890.3	919.0	919.1		757	880.3	744	814	736	867	921	793	789.4
.4	718	869.2	899.3	899.2		724	852.4	707	777	703	838	901	762	746.7
.5	693	851.3	881.9	881.2	651	698	828.4	677	746	678	812	882	737	710.4
.6	673					677		652	719	658	790	866	717	
.7	656					659		632	696	642	770	851	700	
.8	642					644		614	675	628	753	836	686	
.9	630					631		599	657	616	737	824	673	
1.0	619				590	620		585	640	605	723	812	662	
1.1	609					610		573	625	596	709	800	652	
1.2	600					601		562		587	697	790	643	
1.3	593					593		553		580	686	780	635	
1.4	586					585		544		573		771	628	
1.5								535		567		762	621	
1.6												754		
1.7												746		
1.8												738		
1.9												731		
2.0												725		
Ref.	159	189	189	189	159	159	189	159	159	159	159	159	159	189

Handbook of Physical Constants

TABLE 7-4. METALS: SHOCK COMPRESSION
P_H in megabars

ρ/ρ_0	Ag	Al	Au	Bi	Cd	Cu	Pb	Sn	Zn
1.1	.12	.090	.25		.07	.167	.053	.05	.09
1.2	.34	.211	.56		.17	.413	.134	.14	.21
1.3	.63	.374	1.01		.32	.755	.250	.27	.38
1.4	1.04	.582	1.63	.29	.52	1.225	.423	.43	.61
1.5	1.61	.861	2.45	.43	.79	1.858	.655	.65	.91
1.6	2.40	1.217	3.57	.59	1.15	2.714	.955	.92	1.32
1.7	3.51	1.652	5.06	.80	1.64	3.880	1.330	1.26	1.85
1.8	5.01	2.160		1.06	2.30		1.765	1.65	2.57
1.9				1.39	3.22		2.255	2.09	
2.0				1.80	4.49		2.776	2.57	
2.1				2.31			3.355	3.10	
2.2				2.95			4.010	3.77	
2.3				3.76					
Ref.	15	18	15	15	15	18	18	15	15

TABLE 7-5. SHOCK COMPRESSION OF IRON
$\rho_0 = 7.84$ g/cc
$C_H = (\partial P/\partial \rho)^{1/2}$, the derivative taken along the Hugoniot curve

P_H megabars	ρ/ρ_0	Ref.	P_H megabars	ρ/ρ_0	Ref.	C_H Km/s	Ref.
.106	1.054	25	1.040	1.375	18		
.132	1.069		1.850	1.496			
			3.560	1.664			
			4.020	1.678			
.147	1.100		.689	1.3		6.91	17
.165	1.121		1.190	1.4		7.83	
.188	1.140		1.881	1.5		8.70	
.200	1.148		2.849	1.6		9.54	
			4.230	1.7		10.40	
.25	1.153	159					
.50	1.248						
.75	1.318						
1.00	1.372						
1.25	1.416						
1.50	1.453						
1.75	1.486						

TABLE 7-6. ELEMENTS: ELASTIC CONSTANTS

All measurements at about 20° C unless otherwise noted;
S_{pq} in reciprocal megabars; C_{pq} in megabars; i = isothermal; a = adiabatic.

CUBIC

$S_{11} = S_{22} = S_{33}$; $S_{23} = S_{31} = S_{12}$; $S_{44} = S_{55} = S_{66}$; all others zero.

Element	Temp.	S_{11}	$-S_{12}$	S_{44}	C_{11}	C_{12}	C_{44}		Ref.
Ag		2.32	.993	2.29	1.199	.897	.437	i	195
		2.306	.9923	2.168	1.2399	.9367	.4612	a	167
		2.288	.983	2.168	1.240	.934	.461	a	23
Al		1.59	.580	3.516	1.082	.622	.2844	i	117
		1.583	.573	3.531	1.0732	.6094	.2832	a	198
		1.5940	.5780	3.545	1.0678	.6074	.2821	a	281
	0° C	1.554	.575	3.557	1.140	.670	.2812	a	218
	100	1.654	.615	3.745	1.082	.641	.2670		
	300	1.924	.720	4.192	.941	.563	.2385		
	500	2.320	.880	4.847	.803	.491	.2063		
Au		2.33	1.065	2.38	1.863	1.568	.420	i	120, 195
		2.347	1.077	2.384	1.9234	1.6314	.4195	a	167
C diamond	300° C	.147	.045	.24	9.3	4.1	4.2	a	34
		.138	.040	.232	9.5	3.9	4.3	a	36
		.105	.024	.23	11.0	3.3	4.4	a	179
		.0953	.00993	.174	10.76	1.25	5.76	a	163
Cr	77° K	.280	.052	.969	3.91	.896	1.032	a	53a
	298° K	.305	.049	.992	3.50	.678	1.008		
	500° K	.314	.057	1.013	3.46	.762	.987		
	(inversions at 120° K, 310° K)								
Cu	300° K	1.491	.625	1.328	1.698	1.226	.753	i	120
		1.495	.628	1.323	1.710	1.239	.756	a	150
		1.498	.628	1.326	1.684	1.214	.754	a	172
		1.512	.634	1.331	1.681	1.215	.7511	a	199

TABLE 7-6. *Continued*

Element	Temp.	S_{11}	$-S_{12}$	S_{44}	C_{11}	C_{12}	C_{44}		Ref.
Fe(α)		.757	.282	.862	2.369	1.406	1.160	i	118
		.765	.289	.895	2.415	1.466	1.117	i	142
	300° K	.7488	.2751	.8487	2.331	1.3544	1.1783	a	185
Ge	25° C	.97867	.26716	1.49703	1.28528	.48260	.66799	a	284
K	83° K	82.3	37.0	38.0	.0457	.0374	.0263	i	30
Li	195° K	31.62	14.42	10.42	.1342	.1125	.0960	a	166
	300° K	32.7	14.9	11.4	.131	.110	.088	a	138
Mo		.28	.078	.91	4.6	1.76	1.10	i	106
	300° K	.262	.069	.936	4.696	1.676	1.068	a	53a
	500° K	.272	.073	.955	4.580	1.682	1.047		
Na	−183° C	42.0	19.0	16.2	.0945	.0779	.0618	i	30
	−183° C	48.61	21.02	17.05	.0603	.0459	.0586	a	180
	26° C	60.16	27.56	23.87	.0738	.0624	.0419	a	99
Nb		.660	.233	3.48	2.46	1.34	.287	a	53
Ni		.750	.286	.816	2.526	1.561	1.226	a	56
		.721	.271	.808	2.528	1.52	1.238	a	168
		.734	.274	.802	2.465	1.473	1.247	a	102
		.737	.273	.813	2.507	1.507	1.230	a	11
Pb		9.28	4.26	6.94	.488	.414	.1441	i	120, 222
		9.46	4.36	6.71	.4953	.4229	.1490	a	288
Pd		1.206	.518	1.404	2.341	1.761	.712	a	184
Si	25° C	.76809	.21376	1.2560	1.65773	.63924	.79619	a	284
Ta		.686	.258	1.212	2.67	1.61	.825	a	53
Th		2.72	1.07	2.09	.753	.489	.478	a	21
V		.6438	.2343	2.347	2.28	1.19	.426	a	53
		.6818	.2335	2.350	2.2795	1.1870	.4255	a	9
W	298° K	.2573	.0729	.6604	5.01	1.98	1.514	i	72, 244
	500° K	.2445	.0682	.6234	5.215	2.017	1.604	a	101
		.2520	.0714	.6301	5.113	2.021	1.587	a	53a

HEXAGONAL

$S_{11} = S_{22}$; $S_{13} = S_{23}$; $S_{44} = S_{55}$; $S_{66} = 2(S_{11} - S_{12})$; all others zero except S_{33}.

Element	Temp.		11	33	44	12	13		Ref.
Be	300° K	C	2.923	3.364	1.625	.267	.14	a	204
		S	.3455	.2984	.615	−.031	−.013		
		C	3.08	3.57	1.10	−.58	.87	a	121
		S	.3775	.3373	.909	.104	−.117		
Cd		C	1.21	.513	.185	.481	.442	i	123
		S	1.23	3.55	5.40	−.15	−.93		
		C	1.10	.460	.156	.398	.376	i	72
		S	1.29	3.69	6.40	−.15	−.93		
Co	300° K	C	1.152	.5122	.2025	.3972	.4053	a	115
		S	1.213	3.332	4.938	−.112	−.872		
		C	3.071	3.581	.755	1.650	1.027	a	161
		S	.473	.319	1.324	−.231	−.069		
Mg	293° K	C	.585	.610	.166	.250	.208	i	119
		S	2.215	1.975	6.03	−.77	−.493		
	298° K	C	.5974	.617	.1639	.2624	.217	a	152
		S	2.200	1.971	6.101	−.786	−.497		
	298° K	C	.5943	.6164	.1642	.256	.214	a	203
		S	2.191	1.966	6.090	−.765	−.495		
Tl	300° K	C	.4080	.5280	.0726	.354	.29	a	279
Y	300° K	C	.779	.769	.2431	.285	.21	a	205
		S	1.539	1.458	4.113	−.485	−.288		

TABLE 7-6. *Continued*

Element	Temp.		11	33	44	12	13		Ref.
Zn	295° K	C	1.6368	.6347	.3879	.364	.530	a	10
	400	C	1.5590	.6168	.3573	.358	.515		
	500	C	1.4648	.5982	.3261	.351	.508		
	600	C	1.3843	.5793	.2933	.365	.504		
	670	C	1.3395	.5661	.2667	.408	.502		
	295° K	S	.841	2.823	2.578	.0553	−.749		
	400	S	.889	2.940	2.799	.0567	−.790		
	500	S	.974	3.185	3.066	.0757	−.891		
	600	S	1.064	3.462	3.409	.0826	−.997		
	670	S	1.120	3.601	3.749	.0465	−1.035		

TETRAGONAL

$S_{11} = S_{22}$; $S_{13} = S_{23}$; $S_{44} = S_{55}$; all others zero except S_{66}, S_{33}, S_{12}.

Element	Temp.		11	33	44	66	12	13		Ref.
In	300° K	C	.444	.443	.0653	.122	.394	.404	a	243
		S	14.94	18.70	15.31	8.20	−5.07	−9.03		
	300° K	C	.4535	.4515	.0651	.1207	.4006	.4151	a	98
		S	14.96	20.83	15.36	8.29	−3.95	−10.12		
Sn		C	.839	.967	.175	.0741	.487	.281	i	72
		S	1.85	1.18	5.70	13.5	−.99	−.25		
		C	.735	.876	.220	.2265	.239	.249	a	157
		S	1.61	1.34	4.55	4.42	−.41	−.34		
		C	.86	1.33	.49	.53	.35	.30	a	175
		S	1.46	.85	2.04	1.90	−.53	−.21		
	15° C	C	.753	.955	.219	.234	.617	.442	a	127
		S	4.16	1.49	4.56	4.28	−3.12	−.48		
	105° C	C	.734	.981	.198	.218	.638	.507	a	127
		S	5.83	1.65	5.05	4.59	−5.62	−.69		
	195° C	C	.762	1.162	.170	.198	.711	.677	a	127
		S	10.56	1.85	5.87	5.05	−9.10	−.85		

TRIGONAL

$S_{11} = S_{22}$; $S_{13} = S_{23}$; $S_{44} = S_{55}$; $S_{66} = 2(S_{11} - S_{12})$; all others zero except S_{33}, S_{14}.

Element	Temp.		11	33	44	12	13	14	Ref.
Bi		C	.628	.440	.108	.350	.211	−.042	72
		S	2.69	2.87	10.48	−1.40	−.62	1.60	
	301° K	C	.635	.381	.1130	.247	.245	+.0723	108
		S	2.57*	4.08	11.62	−.81	−1.13	−2.17	
Hg	83° K	C	.360	.505	.129	.289	.303	.047	124
		S	15.4	4.5	15.1	−11.9	−2.1	−10.0	
Sb		C	.792	.427	.285	.248	.261	.105	72
		S	1.77	3.38	4.10	−.38	−.85		
Te		S	4.87	2.34	5.81	−.69	−1.38	−.80	72

ORTHORHOMBIC

Element	Temp.		11	22	33	44	55	66	12	13	23	Ref.
S		C	.240	.205	.483	.043	.087	.076	.133	.171	.159	214, 215
		S	7.1	8.3	3.0	23.2	11.5	13.2	−3.6	−1.3	−1.5	
U(α)	25° C	C	2.147	1.986	2.671	1.2444	.7342	.7433	.465	.218	1.076	113
		S	.491	.673	.479	.804	1.362	1.346	−.118	+.008	−.261	

* (These values of S_{pq} differ appreciably from those published in reference 108)

TABLE 7-7. EFFECT OF PRESSURE ON ELASTIC CONSTANTS, ELEMENTS, AND COMPOUNDS

$$C' = (C_{11} - C_{12})/2; \quad C_H = C_{11} + C_{12} + 2C_{33} - 4C_{13}; \quad K = (C_{11} + 2C_{12})/3$$

Single crystals	$\dfrac{dK}{dP}$	$\dfrac{dC_{11}}{dP}$	$\dfrac{dC_{12}}{dP}$ (all dimensionless numbers)	$\dfrac{dC_{44}}{dP}$	$\dfrac{dC'}{dP}$	Ref.
Al	3.95	8.4	(2.2)	2.1		150
Al	5.19			2.31	1.62	198
Ag	6.18			2.31	.64	100
Au	6.43			1.79	.44	100
Ce (curves only)						237
Cu	5.59			2.35	.58	100
Cu	3.91			.85	.58	150
Ge*		(5.0)	(4.4)	(1.4)		162a, 282
Ge	4.71	5.24	4.54	1.34		145
Li				1.03	.08	138
Na	3.60			1.63	.23	99
Mg		6.11		1.58	1.36	198
		$(dC_{33}/dP = 7.22; \; dC_H/dP = 13.7)$				
Si	4.24	4.33	4.19	.80		283
KCl	4.8	12.2	1.0	−.5	5.36	150
NaCl	6.04	12.2	2.7	2.7	4.7	150
LiF				1.41	3.60	217
MgO				1.025	3.34	217
SiO$_2$ (α quartz)				2.9		216
		$(dC_{14}/dP = -1.7; \; dC_{66}/dP = -2.7)$				

Polycrystalline aggregates	$\dfrac{dK}{dP}$	$\dfrac{dG}{dP}$	Ref.
Al	3.9	2.2	197
Cu	4.9	1.4	See also 42,
Fe	4.0	1.9	77, 129a
Ni		1.5	
MgO	3.91	2.6	295

*Complete sets of third-order elastic constants have been found for Ge and Si (284):

	C_{111}	C_{112}	C_{123}	C_{144}	C_{166}	C_{456}	
Si	−8.25	−4.51	−.64	.12	−3.10	−.64	megabars
Ge	−7.10	−3.89	−.18	−.23	−2.92	−.53	

(for notation and theory, *see* 44, 276, 278)

TABLE 7-8. SIMPLE CHEMICAL COMPOUNDS: COMPRESSION

The tabulated quantity is $(V_0 - V)/V_0$; pressure in kg/cm². (Refs. 61, 87 to 50,000 kg/cm²; ref. 89 to 100,000 kg/cm², unless noted)

	10,000	20,000	30,000	40,000	50,000	60,000	70,000	80,000	90,000	100,000	Ref.
					P(kg/cm²)						
LiF	.01406	.02696	.03861								94
CHLORIDES											
NaCl	.0365	.0664	.0919	.1130	.1309						
	.038	.068	.093	.115	.135	.152	.168	.183	.197	.210	90
KCl	.0366	.0664	.0924	.1160							
	.0478	.0841 (a)	.2225	.2419	.2579						
	.048	.084	.223	.244	.262	.277	.290	.302	.312	.321	92
RbCl (b)	.1882	.2184	.2422	.2612	.2768						
	.188	.219	.246	.270	.292	.311	.327	.341	.353	.364	
CsCl	.0479	.0850	.1146	.1387	.1596						
	.048	.086	.118	.144	.166	.184	.199	.212	.223	.233	
AgCl	.0216	.0401	.0562	.0704	.0838						
	.021	.040	.058	.074	.090	.104	.117	.129	.140	.165	
TlCl	.0383	.0688	.0936	.1139	.1313						
	.038	.071	.099	.123	.144	.162	.177	.191	.202	.213	
NH₄Cl	.0489	.0818	.1070	.1278	.1462						
	.049	.082	.109	.133	.154	.172	.188	.202	.215		
BROMIDES											
NaBr	.0430	.0771	.1047	.1274	.1464						
	.043	.078	.107	.132	.153	.171	.186	.199	.211	.222	
KBr	.0547 (c)	.1989	.2267	.2479	.2650						
	.055	.199	.229	.254	.274	.291	.305	.317	.327	.336	
RbBr (d)	.1879	.2207	.2462	.2670	.2848						
	.188	.221	.250	.275	.297	.315	.330	.343	.354	.364	
CsBr	.0537	.0949	.1274	.1532	.1748						
	.053	.095	.130	.160	.186	.208	.227	.243	.258	.272	
AgBr	.0215	.0404	.0584	.0743	.0890						
	.022	.041	.059	.075	.091	.106	.120	.133 (e)	.157	.169	
TlBr	.0426	.0763	.1026	.1224	.1377						
	.043	.077	.106	.131	.152	.170	.186	.200	.212	.223	
NH₄Br	.0487	.0880	.1203	.1465	.1676						
	.049	.088	.120	.147	.170	.189	.205	.219	.232	.244	

TABLE 7-8. *Continued*

	P(kg/cm²)										Ref.
	10,000	20,000	30,000	40,000	50,000	60,000	70,000	80,000	90,000	100,000	
IODIDES											
NaI	.0553	.0974	.1294	.1538	.1728						
	.056	.098	.132	.160	.184	.205	.223	.239	.253	.266	
KI	.0648 (f)	.1970	.2296	.2532	.2715						
	.065	.197	.230	.257	.279	.298	.314	.327	.338	.348	
RbI(g)	.1918	.2315	.2609	.2831	.3009						
	.192	.235	.271	.301	.326	.346	.362	.376	.388	.398	
CsI	.0647	.1120	.1485	.1781	.2025						
	.065	.113	.151	.182	.208	.230	.249	.266	.281	.294	
AgI(h)	.1896	.2095	.2257	.2396	.2525						
	.189	.209	.228	.246	.263	.278	.292	.305	.317	.328	
TlI	.0510	.0891	.1173	.1387	.1554						
	.050	.090	.123	.152	.177	.198	.216	.232	.245	.256	
NH₄I(i)	.192	.230	.258	.282	.302	.320	.335	.350	.363	.376	90
NITRATES (See also ref. 90)											
NaNO₃	.0339	.0611	.086	.107	.127 (j)	.154	.167	.180	.191	.201	
	.034	.062									
KNO₃(k)	.138	.169	.196	.219	.238	.255	.268	.280	.289	.297	
RbNO₃	.043	.079	.109	.135	.157	.175	.190	.202	.211	.219	
CsNO₃	.045	.083	.115	.142	.165	.183	.198	.210	.219	.226	
AgNO₃(l)	.044	.077	.103	.126	.146	.162	.176	.188	.198	.206	
TlNO₃	.037	.068	.095	.118	.137	.152	.165	.176	.185	.194	
NH₄NO₃	.050	.086	.115	.140	.162	.180	.194	.206	.215	.222	
SULFIDES											
CaS	.0240	.0421	.0555	.0658	.0740						
SrS	.0309	.0516	.0658	.0754	.0830						
BaS	.0251	.0450	.0612	.0747	.0861						
ZnS	.0123	.0231	.0328	.0414	.0495						
HgS	.0427	.0682	.0854	.0980	.1085						93
			.032	.039	.046	.053	.060	.066	.071	.076	
PbS	.0200	.0383 (m)	.0752	.0885	.0988						93
				.084	.088	.094	.101	.108	.115	.121	
galena	*See Table 7-10*		.072	.082	.091	.100	.108	.114	.119	.124	93

Note: In the formula labels above, subscripts are written as NH_4I, $NaNO_3$, KNO_3, $RbNO_3$, $CsNO_3$, $AgNO_3$, $TlNO_3$, NH_4NO_3.

Compound		Compression values at successively increasing pressure	Ref.
FeS$_2$ pyrite	*See* Table 7-10		
CoAsS cobaltite	*See* Table 7-10		

SELENIDES

Compound	Compression values at successively increasing pressure	Ref.
CaSe	.0190 .0345 .0482 .0605 .0718 .079 .088 .096 .105 .113	93
SrSe	.0213 .0380 .0525 .0653 .0775 .195 .205 .212 .218 .223	93
BaSe	.0251 .0449 .0610 .0745 .0882	
ZnSe	.0224 .0392 .0506 (o) .0617 .0693 .070	
HgSe	.1152 .1378 .1555 .1692 .1804 .184	93
PbSe	.0289 .0523 .0711 .0855 (n) .1183 .112 .123 .133 .142 .151 .159	93

TELLURIDES

Compound	Compression values at successively increasing pressure	Ref.
CaTe	.0210 .0377 .0519 .0650 .0773	
SrTe	.0269 .0490 .0675 .0833 .0971	
BaTe	.0293 .0531 .0730 .0898 .1049 (p)	
ZnTe	.0226 .0413 .0581 .0740 (q) .0931 .078	
HgTe	(s) .056 .137 .168 .183 .197 .210 .223 .235	93
PbTe	.0255 .0469 .0650 .0802 (r) .0998 .116 .131 .145 .158 .169 .180	93

	Transition pressure Kg/cm²	Compressions at transition	
a	20,060	.0847	.1980
b	5,000	.0295	.1701
c	18,430	.0886	.1938
d	4,600	.0330	.1655
e	86,000	.141	.152
f	18,200	.1049	.1899
g	4,050	.0349	.1614
h	3,020	.011	.174
i	560	.003	.143
	55,000	.136	.147

	Transition pressure Kg/cm²	Compressions at transition	
k	3,650	.023	.113
l	9,500	.030	.043
m	24,680	.0464	.0663
n	43,320	.0903	.1067
o	38,470	.0568	.0607
p	50,000	$-\Delta V/V_0 \approx$ .01+	
q	41,270	.0763	.0812
r	41,200	.0818	.0912
s	7,650	.0130	.1090

Handbook of Physical Constants

TABLE 7-9. ALKALI HALIDES.
ELASTIC CONSTANTS AND THEIR TEMPERATURE COEFFICIENTS AT 0° C
$d \log C_{ij}/dT = -10^{-6}A_{ij}$ (Ref. 206)

(22° C)	C_{11}	C_{12} megabars	C_{44}	A_{11}	A_{12} deg^{-1}	A_{44}
LiF	1.136	.476	.635	660	−10	280
LiCl	.494	.228	.246	930	150	420
LiBr	.394	.187	.193	1020	140	455
NaF	.970	.243	.281	637	−180	210
NaCl	.494	.129	.127	800	−170	266
NaBr	.401	.109	.099	845	−100	200
NaI	.303	.088	.074	937	−100	220
KF	.656	.146	.125	721	−270	207
KCl	.408	.069	.063	835	−560	212
KBr	.348	.057	.051	852	−770	234
KI	.276	.045	.037	918	−890	206
RbF	.553	.140	.093	773	−145	190
RbCl	.363	.062	.047	867	−570	234
RbBr	.316	.050	.038	881	−700	234
RbI	.258	.037	.028	940	−870	206

TABLE 7-10. MINERALS. COMPRESSIBILITY

$(V_0 - V)/V_0 = aP - bP^2$, P in megabars. Asterisk denotes values from elastic constants

Mineral	Ideal composition	a mb^{-1}	b mb^{-2}	Remarks	Ref.
Acanthite	Ag_2S	3.0		Compressed slug	153
		3.265	49.5		84
Actinolite	$Ca_2(Mg, Fe)_5Si_8O_{22}(OH)_2$	1.3		mean, 2 to 12 kb	7
Aegirite	$NaFeSi_2O_6$	*.94		$\rho = 3.50$	12
Albite	$NaAlSi_3O_8$	2.02	21.6	$\rho = 2.641$, 2 to 10 kb	246
Varuträsk, Sweden				See note A	
Ammonium niter	NH_4NO_3	6.689	138.6	See Table 7-8	6
Analcite	$NaAlSi_2O_6.H_2O$				245
Golden, Col.		1.970	−277?	$\rho = 2.252$. trans. at 8400?	
Nova Scotia		2.485	−99?	$\rho = 2.234$	
Seisser Alp, Austria		2.641	−125?	$\rho = 2.198$	
Fassa Thal, Austria		3.673	−1?	$\rho = 2.093$. See note A	
Anglesite	$PbSO_4$	1.94			153
Anhydrite	$CaSO_4$	1.84			153
Apatite	$Ca_5(F, Cl)(PO_4)_3$	1.091	4.1		60
linear, ∥ c axis		.245	−.12		
linear, ⊥ c axis		.423	1.91		
		1.08	2.4	See Table 7-11	94
		*1.182			39
Aragonite	$CaCO_3$	1.55			153
		*2.24			232
Arcanite	K_2SO_4	3.32	38		6
Argentite	Ag_2S	2.51	33.8	75° C; trans. at 9000 at 30°	59
Arsenopyrite	FeAsS	.99			153
Augite	$Ca(Mg, Fe, Al)(Al_2Si)_2O_6$	1.02		mean, 2 to 12 kb; $\rho = 3.373$	7
Barite	$BaSO_4$	1.77–1.81			153
		1.760	11.9		60
		1.71	7.6	to 30 kb	94
		*1.70			200
		*1.88			31
		*1.91			234

TABLE 7-10. *Continued*

Mineral	Ideal composition	a mb^{-1}	b mb^{-2}	Remarks	Ref.
linear, ∥ a axis		.5026	3.22	*See also* Table 7-11	60
linear, ∥ b axis		.6816	4.03		
linear, ∥ c axis		.5760	3.48		
Beryl	$Be_3Al_2Si_6O_{18}$	.5403	.94	*See also* Table 7-11	60
linear, ∥ c axis		.2075	.24		
linear, ⊥ c axis		.1664	.24		
		.516	(−0.5)	to 30 kb	94
		.57			153
		*.736			234
		*.699			213
Bismuthinite	Bi_2S_3	3.32			153
Bromellite	BeO (compressed powder)	.27			253
Bromyrite	AgBr	2.74			192
		*2.37		synthetic	223
Calcite	$CaCO_3$	1.367	3.9		59
linear, ∥ c axis		.822	2.9	*See also* Table 7-11	153
linear, ⊥ c axis		.273	.24		8
		1.35			229
		1.39		mean, 2 to 12 kb	38
		*1.55			186
		*1.53			251
		*1.22			153
		*1.41			153
Cassiterite	SnO_2	.49			59
Celestite	$SrSO_4$	1.57–1.63			
		1.55	7.61	*See also* Table 7-11	
linear, ∥ a axis		.6380	3.33		94
linear, ∥ b axis		.4553	2.20		31
linear, ∥ c axis		.4615	1.28	to 30 kb	
		1.51	5.9		
		*1.218			

Name	Formula			Notes	
Cerargyrite	AgCl	2.4		synthetic, *See also* Table 7-8	192
Cerussite	PbCO₃	*2.28			20
Chalcopyrite	CuFeS₂	1.91			153
Chromite	FeCr₂O₄	1.29			153
		+.49	1.9		103
Cobaltite	CoAsS	.767		to 30 kb, Table 7-11	59
		.72			94
Corundum	Al₂O₃	.38			153
		.336		mean to 12 kb	82
		.363		to 30 kb, Table 7-11	94
		+.404			158
		+.399			238
Cotunnite	PbCl₂	3.4			196
Crocoite	PbCrO₄		3.44		59
linear, ∥ c axis		.5065			
Cuprite	Cu₂O	1.94	19	mean, 2 to 12 kb; ρ = 3.257	81
Diopside, Alaska	CaMgSi₂O₆	1.07		to 40 kb, Table 7-11; ρ = 3.260	7
DeKalb, N.Y.		.93	3.1		92
Dolomite	CaMg(CO₃)₂	1.22			153
Enstatite	MgSiO₃	1.01		mean, 2 to 12 kb, ρ = 3.254	7
(En₈₈Fs₁₂)		*2.29		*See* Table 7-12	214
Epsomite	MgSO₄·7H₂O	.91		mean, 2 to 12 kb, ρ = 4.068	3
Fayalite	Fe₂SiO₄	1.22–1.26			153
Fluorite	CaF₂	1.226			59
		1.21	6.5	to 30 kb (Table 7-11)	94
		*1.179	3.95		228
		*1.164			31
Forsterite	Mg₂SiO₄	.79		mean, 2 to 12 kb, ρ = 3.288	34
Olivine (Dunite)		.82	1	to 40 kb, Table 7-11; ρ = 3.364	92
Peridot, Red Sea		*.77		ρ = 3.324	227
Peridot, Burma	(Fo₉₂)	1.96			153
Galena	PbS	1.869	7.43	to 30 kb	59
		1.96		*See also* Table 7-11	94
		*1.626			37

TABLE 7-10. *Continued*

Mineral	Ideal composition	a mb^{-1}	b mb^{-2}	Remarks	Ref.
Garnet (note B)					
Almandite		.57		$\rho = 4.160$	5
		.558	.59	to 30 kb, *see also* Table 7-11	94
		.545	.91	mislabelled "pyrope"	60
Almandite-spessartite		*.567		$\rho = 4.122$	227
Grossularite		*.571		$\rho = 4.183$	227
		.60		$\rho = 4.247$	5
		.673	.86	$\rho = 3.544$	60
				$\rho = 3.482$ mislabelled "andradite"	
Yttrium-iron (YIG)	$Y_3Fe_5O_{12}$	.671	1.7	to 30 kb, Table 7-11	94
Goslarite	$ZnSO_4 \cdot 7H_2O$	*.621		synthetic	97
Gypsum	$CaSO_4 \cdot 2H_2O$	*.68			214
		2.5			153
Halite	NaCl	4.26	51	*See* Table 7-11	76, 201, 202
		*4.065		*See* Tables 7-9, 7-12	171
		*3.97		for other values	206
Hanksite		2.457	24.5		60
linear, $\parallel$ *c* axis		1.187	12.4		
linear, $\perp$ *c* axis		.635	5.0		
Hematite	Fe_2O_3	2.72	20.8	to 30 kb Table 7-11	94
Hornblende		.6			153
		*1.03			231
Hydrophilite	$CaCl_2$	*1.1-1.2		questionable sample	12
Hypersthene	$(Mg, Fe)SiO_3$	4.36			196
	$En_{70}Fs_{30}$				
Labrador		.99		mean, 2 to 12 kb, $\rho = 3.415$	7
Labrador		1.08	5.2	to 40 kb, Table 7-11; $\rho = 3.421$	92
Ice	H_2O	12.0		$-7°$ C	193
		*11.1		$-16°$ C	139
		*12.5		$-16°$ C	27
				See Table 7-12	

					Ref.
Ilmenite	$FeTiO_3$	.56			153
Iodyrite	AgI	4.11			192
Jadeite	$NaAlSi_2O_6$				
Burma		.75	−2.1?	Mean, 2 to 12 kb, $\rho = 3.328$	5
Burma		.747	15?	See note A, $\rho = 3.328$	246
Japan		1.11		$\rho = 3.189$	246
Jeffersonite		.909	3.94		60
linear, a axis		.314	1.61		
linear, b axis		.399	1.32		
linear, c axis		.313	2.12		
linear, Y axis		.197	.24	Y direction normal to b and c	
Labradorite					
Labrador	An_{52}	1.50	9.8	$\rho = 2.696$	5, 7
Labrador,	An_{48}	1.39	3.1	to 40 kb, $\rho = 2.681$	92
Lime	CaO	.88			253
Magnetite	Fe_3O_4	.54–.57			153
		.547	.82		59
		.587	.8	to 30 kb, Table 7-11	94
		*.62			103
Marcasite	FeS_2	.82			153
Mica, phlogopite		2.34	18.2	$\rho = 2.877$	7
muscovite		1.2		See Table 7-11	94
Microcline	$KAlSi_3O_8$	1.92	13	$\rho = 2.557$	7
($Or_{91}Ab_9$)					
Nantokite	CuCl	2.51	13	See note A	81
Nepheline	$NaAlSiO_4$	2.05	5.2	See Table 7-8	246
Niter	KNO_3				
Oldhamite	CaS	2.321	39		81
Oligoclase	$Ab_{78}An_{22}$	1.74	9.1	$\rho = 2.638$	7
		1.79	13.4	See Note A	246
Olivine	$(Mg, Fe)_2SiO_4$			See fayalite, forsterite	
Orthoclase	$KAlSi_3O_8$	2.123	14.5		60
linear, a axis		1.013	4.8		
linear, b axis		.559	4.9		
linear, c axis		.468	1.3	$\perp$ b and c	
linear, Y axis		1.097	6.9		

TABLE 7-10. *Continued*

Mineral	Ideal composition	a mb^{-1}	b mb^{-2}	Remarks	Ref.
(Sanidine), Madagascar		1.78	4.2		92
Spain		1.86	7.3		92
Periclase	MgO	.598	1	to 40 kb, Table 7-11. $\rho = 2.568$	81
		.596	.83	to 40 kb, Table 7-11. $\rho = 2.556$	94
		*.654		to 30 kb, Table 7-11	33
		*.644			104
		.59			253, 295
Pyrite	FeS_2	.680	.87	See also Table 7-12	59
		.686			
		.71		$\rho = 4.992$	7, 153
		.676	1.35	to 30 kb, Table 7-11	94
		*1.131			234
		*.907			33
		*.705			50
Quartz, α	SiO_2	2.706	24.0		60
linear, c axis		.718	6.2		7
linear, $\perp c$ axis		.995	7.6		94
		2.697	20.4		155
		2.77			22
		*2.767		to 30 kb, Table 7-11	29
		*2.556			144
		*2.668			
		*2.671			
Quartz, β	SiO_2	*1.776		600° C	141
Rhodocrosite	$MnCO_3$	1.3			153
Rutile	TiO_2	.483	.92		60
linear, c axis		.105	.24		153
linear, $\perp c$ axis		.190	.24		238a
		.59			227
		*.373			
		*.473			

Mineral	Formula				Ref.
Salammoniac	NH$_4$Cl	5.60			64
Siderite	FeCO$_3$	1.0			153
Soda niter	NaNO$_3$	3.92		See Table 7-8	78
linear, c axis		2.48	39		
linear, $\perp$ c axis		.72	24		
		*3.40	5.6		38
Sphalerite	ZnS	1.303	1.28	transition above 9 kb	59
		1.29–1.22		See Table 7-8	153
		*1.2–1.44			
Spinel					
Ceylon,	MgAl$_2$O$_4$	.41		mean to 10 kb, $\rho = 3.58$	247
Artificial, composition		*.493		$\rho = 3.63$	227
about MgO·3.5(Al$_2$O$_3$)					59, 60
Spodumene	LiAlSi$_2$O$_6$	.703	1.5		94
linear, a axis		.183	.24		41
linear, b axis		.250	.24		153
linear, c axis		.203	.24		153
linear, Y axis		.251	.84	$\perp$ b and c	201, 202
		.693	1.24	Table 7-11, to 30 kb	150
Staurolite	FeAl$_5$Si$_2$O$_{12}$(OH)	*.80			169
Stibnite	Sb$_2$S$_3$	1.50			110
Strontianite	SrCO$_3$	1.75			206
Sylvite	KCl	5.62	75	See Tables 7-8, 7-9, 7-12	6
		*5.43			
		*5.58			
		*5.625			
		*5.50			
Thenardite	Na$_2$SO$_4$	2.37	23.7		60
Topaz					
Japan,	Al$_2$SiO$_4$(F, OH)$_2$	.611	1.1	$\rho = 3.544$ (mean)	94
linear, a axis		.2176	.24		234
linear, b axis		.1504	.24		
linear, c axis		.2429	.24	Table 7-11, to 30 kb	
		.58			
		*.602			

TABLE 7-10. *Continued*

Mineral	Ideal composition	a mb⁻¹	b mb⁻²	Remarks	Ref.
Tourmaline	WX₃B₃Al₃(AlSi₂O₉)₃(O, OH, F)₄			black, ρ = 3.091	59, 60
linear, c axis		.816	1.95		
linear, ⊥ c axis		.486	1.17		
		.165	.24	Table 7-11, to 30 Kb	94
		.889			230
		*1.15			156
	I	*1.026			33
	II	*.974			
		*.905			
Villiaumite	NaF	2.11	17		79
		*2.06			206
Witherite	BaCO₃	2.03			153
Wurtzite	ZnS	1.36			153
Zincite	ZnO	.78			153
		*.70			
Zircon	ZrSiO₄	.86			153

A. In these references, the volume change is given in the form, $(V_{2000} - V)/V_0 = a(P - .002) - b(P - .002)^2$, where V_{2000} is the volume at 2000 bars (.002 mb), and P is in megabars.

B. Natural garnets are silicate solid solutions having the general formula $M_3N_2(SiO_4)_3$, where M is commonly Mg, Fe, Mn, Ca, and N is Al, Fe, Cr. Names given to the ideal end members are often applied to garnets in which one of these components predominates, but pure end members are not found in nature and satisfactory description requires a chemical analysis. The names of the principal end members are as follows:

	M	N
Pyrope	Mg	Al
Almandite	Fe	Al
Spessartite	Mn	Al
Grossularite	Ca	Al
Andradite	Ca	Fe
Uvarovite	Ca	Cr

Silicon is not essential, however, as a large number of synthetic compounds having the general formula $A_3B_5O_{12}$ crystallize with the garnet structure; A may be one of the rare-earth elements, B may be Fe, Al, Ga, *etc*, as in yttrium iron garnet, $Y_3Fe_5O_{12}$. Almost unlimited substitution of similar ions may be effected within the garnet structure.

TABLE 7-11. MINERALS: COMPRESSION ABOVE 12 KB

$(V_0 - V)/V_0$ or $(L_0 - L)/L_0$ (For halides, sulfides, selenides, tellurides, and nitrates, *see also* Table 7-8) (Refs. 92, 93, 94).

Mineral	\multicolumn{7}{c}{$P(\text{kg/cm}^2)$}
	5,000	10,000	15,000	20,000	25,000	30,000	40,000
Apatite							
linear, ‖ c	.00121	.00240	.00362	.00484	.00603	.00716	
linear, ⊥ c	.00203	.00398	.00592	.00779	.00963	.01139	
volume	.00525	.01032	.01539	.02028	.02508	.02964	
Barite							
linear, a	.00247	.00478	.00696	.00895	.01076	.01243	
linear, b	.00323	.00634	.00934	.01222	.01495	.01748	
linear, c	.00251	.00498	.00740	.00973	.01204	.01427	
volume	.00819	.01601	.02351	.03058	.03728	.04354	
Beryl							
linear, ‖ c	.00100	.00199	.00299	.00398	.00496	.00585	
linear, ⊥ c	.00077	.00155	.00242	.00320	.00404	.00486	
volume	.00254	.00509	.00781	.01033	.01297	.01550	
Calcite							
volume		.0134		.0725		.0887	.1019
volume (Ref. 61)	.0066	.0130	.0192	.077	.082	.087	.096
(*See also* marble)							
Celestite							
linear, a	.00296	.00588	.00861	.01134	.01377	.01623	
linear, b	.00215	.00418	.00612	.00795	.00973	.01151	
linear, c	.00215	.00423	.00629	.00825	.01017	.01198	
volume	.00725	.01423	.02088	.02729	.03330	.03920	
Cobaltite							
volume	.00353	.00702	.01087	.01444	.01753	.02050	
Corundum							
linear, 90° C	.00060	.00119	.00179	.00238	.00297	.00355	
linear, 10° C	.00059	.00118	.00179	.00239	.00300	.00360	
volume	.00178	.00355	.00537	.00704	.00891	.01067	
Diopside,							
volume $\rho = 3.260$		.0088		.0169		.0245	.0318
Fluorite							
volume	.00585	.01147	.01695	.02213	.02735	.03234	
Galena							
volume	.00936	.01792	.02602	.03363	.04074		
Garnet							
volume	.00272	.00538	.00807	.01071	.01333	.01588	
$\rho = 4.090$		.0071		.0138		.0200	.0257
Grossularite							
volume	.00325	.00636	.00947	.01248	.01542	.01852	
$\rho = 3.475$		.0072		.0140		.0204	.0264
Halite							
volume		.0366		.0664		.0924	.1160
Hanksite							
linear, ‖ c	.00523	.01020	.01455	.01843	.02196	.02522	
linear, ⊥ c	.00369	.00738	.01073	.01379	.01662	.01927	
volume	.01256	.02476	.03558	.04531	.05419	.06241	
Hypersthene							
volume		.0101		.0191		.0272	.0347
$\rho = 3.421$							
Labradorite							
volume		.0133		.0260		.0381	.0495
$\rho = 2.681$							
Magnetite							
volume	.00286	.00564	.00845	.01118	.01394	.01670	
Mica							
linear, par. cleavage	.0013	.0028	.0042	.0058	.0070	.0082	
volume	.0049	.0092	.0165	.0227	.0311	.0353	
Olivine							
volume		.0079		.0156		.0231	.0304
$\rho = 3.364$							

TABLE 7-11. *Continued*

Mineral	5,000	10,000	15,000	$P(\text{kg/cm}^2)$ 20,000	25,000	30,000	40,000
Orthoclase, volume							
Madagascar $\rho = 2.568$		.0171		.0333		.0488	.0634
Spain $\rho = 2.556$		.0175		.0335		.0484	.0625
Periclase							
volume	.00290	.00571	.00859	.01139	.01410	.01674	
Pyrite							
volume	.00328	.00645	.00963	.01282	.01575	.01869	
Quartz							
linear, ∥ c	.00334	.00642	.00920	.01170	.01406	.01622	
linear, ⊥ c	.00480	.00909	.01308	.01688	.02056	.02411	
volume	.01289	.02440	.03495	.04478	.05418	.06308	
volume		.0236		.0441		.0625	.0792
volume	(meas. to 100,000 kg/cm²)				.054	.061	.074
Spodumene							
linear, a	.00088	.00176	.00265	.00353	.00442	.00529	
linear, b	.00128	.00252	.00375	.00495	.00610	.00719	
linear, c	.00095	.00189	.00283	.00375	.00466	.00556	
linear	.00114	.00225	.00338	.00448	.00557	.00663	
volume	.00337	.00663	.00993	.01312	.01624	.01925	
Sylvite	*See* Table 7-8						
Topaz							
linear, a	.00106	.00210	.00317	.00421	.00525	.00622	
linear, b	.00072	.00144	.00218	.00291	.00366	.00448	
linear, c	.00108	.00217	.00331	.00443	.00555	.00658	
volume	.00285	.00570	.00863	.01150	.01439	.01718	
Tourmaline							
linear, ∥ c	.00245	.00484	.00715	.00937	.01147	.01336	
linear, ⊥ c	.00094	.00185	.00273	.00359	.00444	.00525	
volume	.00431	.00851	.01257	.01647	.02023	.02368	

TABLE 7-12.   MINERALS: ELASTIC CONSTANTS

C_{pq} in megabars; S_{pq} in reciprocal megabars. Room temperature unless otherwise noted.

CUBIC

Mineral	Temp.	S_{11}	S_{44}	$-S_{12}$	C_{11}	C_{44}	C_{12}	Ref.
Bromyrite, AgBr	26° C	3.13	13.9	1.17	.563	.0720	.323	223
	100	3.423	14.5	1.272	.521	.0691	.308	
	200	4.271	15.3	1.646	.453	.0653	.284	
	300	6.24	16.3	2.53	.359	.0612	.245	
	400	14.51	18.2	6.32	.210	.0550	.162	
	410	13.54	18.5	5.69	.189	.0542	.137	
Cerargyrite, AgCl		3.04	16.0	1.14	.601	.0625	.362	20
Chromite, $FeCr_2O_4$		.427	.857	.132	3.225	1.167	1.437	103
Diamond, C		.147	.24	.045	9.3	4.2	4.1	34
		.138	.232	.040	9.5	4.3	3.9	36
	300° C	.105	.23	.024	11.0	4.4	3.3	179
		.0953	.174	.0099	10.76	5.76	1.25	162
					9.49	5.21	1.51	148
Fluorspar, CaF_2		.691	2.96	.149	1.64	.338	.448	228
		.694	2.77	.153	1.646	.361	.466	31
		.710	2.88	.166	1.644	.347	.502	32
		.724	2.97	.176	1.64	.337	.53	280
Galena, PbS		1.2	4.0	.3	1.02	.25	.38	182
		.87	4.03	.164	1.270	.248	.298	37
Garnet (See Note B, Table 7-10)								
Almandite, $\rho = 4.183$		.409	1.06	.110	3.048	.944	1.123	227
Almandite-spessartite $\rho = 4.247$		.401	1.050	.1054	3.073	.952	1.097	227
Yttrium-iron (YIG) $\rho = 5.17$		.483	1.31	.138	2.69	.764	1.077	97
(?) Almandite $\rho = 4.320$		.387	1.12	.11	3.27	.89	1.24	181

(For other garnets, of unknown composition, *see* Ref. 181)

TABLE 7-12. *Continued*

CUBIC *(Continued)*

Mineral	Temp.	S_{11}	S_{44}	$-S_{12}$	C_{11}	C_{44}	C_{12}	Ref.
Halite, NaCl	17° C	2.301	7.841	.473	.4864	.1275	.1258	171
		2.26	7.79	.45	.4911	.1284	.1225	150
	300° K	2.280	7.809	.450	.4857	.1281	.1194	134
	400° K	2.523	8.014	.546	.4502	.1248	.1243	
	500° K	2.818	8.237	.649	.4116	.1214	.1232	
	600° K	3.185	8.487	.758	.3688	.1178	.1152	
	700° K	3.595	8.779	.885	.3315	.1139	.1082	
	800° K	4.114	9.108	1.068	.2972	.1098	.1042	
	900° K	4.786	9.474	1.342	.2674	.1056	.1042	
	1000° K	5.637	10.00	1.724	.2428	.1000	.1070	
	1050° K	6.160	10.35	1.967	.2318	.0966	.1087	

(For additional independent measurements *see* Ref. 208. A comprehensive tabulation for the alkali halides is given by 206, Spangenberg and Haussuhl)

Mineral	Temp.	S_{11}	S_{44}	$-S_{12}$	C_{11}	C_{44}	C_{12}	Ref.
Magnetite, Fe_3O_4		.459	1.047	.126	2.75	.955	1.04	103
		.480	1.013	.137	2.70	.987	1.08	
Periclase, MgO		.408	.676	.095	2.86	1.48	.87	33
	80° K	.3839	.6380	.0855	2.987	1.5673	.856	104
	170° K	.3888	.6399	.0878	2.963	1.5627	.866	
	270° K	.3991	.6447	.0922	2.910	1.5516	.874	
	370° K	.4109	.6502	.0972	2.852	1.5382	.883	
	470° K	.4243	.6564	.1027	2.788	1.5234	.891	
	560° K	.4383	.6626	.1085	2.725	1.5092	.896	
	25° C	.403	.647	.094	2.892	1.5461	.8795	277
	20° C	.3983	.6349	.100	2.998	1.575	.991	217
	100° C	.4080	.6395	.103	2.924	1.564	.968	
	200° C	.4206	.6456	.108	2.846	1.549	.954	
	300° C	.4341	.6520	.113	2.762	1.534	.934	
	400° C	.4486	.6589	.118	2.678	1.518	.912	
	500° C	.4636	.6658	.123	2.598	1.502	.894	
	600° C	.4792	.6730	.129	2.530	1.486	.887	
	700° C	.4959	.6806	.135	2.444	1.469	.859	

Material / Temp							Ref.
PbF₂							
800° C	.5136	.6880	.141	2.368	1.453	.841	290
900° C	.5321	.6959	.147	2.289	1.437	.818	234
1000° C	.5519	.7040	.155	2.217	1.420	.802	50
1100° C	.5727	.7125	.163	2.152	1.404	.792	36
1200° C	.5947	.7216	.172	2.091	1.386	.787	271
Pyrite, FeS₂	1.784	4.074	.619	.888	.2454	.472	271
	.289	.948	−.044	3.61	1.054	−.474	177
	.265	.914	+.020	3.818	1.094	+.310	33
Sample 1	.287	.950	−.042	3.62	1.052	−.464	
Sample 2	.293	.925	+.024	3.46	1.081	+.31	
	.280	.951	+.024	3.63	1.052	+.34	
	.269	.92	+.021	3.77	1.09	+.32	
28° C	.2623	.9361	−.020	3.854	1.068	−.273	233
100° C	.2651	.9517	−.025	3.835	1.051	−.330	37a
200° C	.2696	.9745	−.030	3.794	1.026	−.380	178
300° C	.2743	.9950	−.035	3.754	1.005	−.425	227
Sphalerite, ZnS	1.94	2.29	.73	.942	.436	.568	
	2.00	2.43	.80	1.079	.412	.722	
	2.05	2.94	.81	1.00	.34	.65	
Spinel (artificial) (MgO)3.5(Al₂O₃) ρ = 3.63	.509	.631	.172	3.005	1.586	1.537	
Spinel (artificial) (MgO)3.5(Al₂O₃) ρ = 3.63	.508	.635	.173	3.028	1.560	1.576	273
Sylvite, KCl ρ = 1.987 — 25° C	2.57	15.9	.38	.4095	.0630	.0705	150
100° C	2.60	15.9	.37	.4032	.0629	.066	169
200° C	2.595	15.8	.360	.4035	.0633	.0651	110
300° C	2.600	15.86	.285	.395	.0631	.0487	109
400° C	2.762	16.20	.355	.376	.0617	.0555	
500° C	3.052	16.65	.464	.346	.0601	.0621	
600° C	3.404	17.11	.592	.317	.0584	.0667	
700° C	3.860	17.60	.766	.287	.0568	.0711	
760° C	4.430	18.14	.965	.257	.0551	.0712	
	5.120	18.72	1.224	.230	.0534	.0723	
	5.920	19.36	1.510	.205	.0517	.0701	
	6.570	19.81	1.765	.190	.0504	.0697	
Villiaumite, NaF	1.145	3.57	.229	.971	.280	.243	206

TABLE 7-12. *Continued*

HEXAGONAL

Mineral	Temp.		11	33	44	12	13	Ref.
Apatite		S	.749	1.09	1.51	.097	−.40	39
		C	1.667	1.396	.663	.131	.655	
Beryl		S	.442	.470	1.53	−.137	−.086	234
		C	2.69	2.37	.653	.964	.669	
	(II)	S	.412	.467	1.43	−.120	−.088	213b
		C	2.873	2.418	.702	.991	.729	
Cancrinite		S	2.0	1.3	4.2	−.2	−.3	146, 147
		C	.52	.826	.238	.086	.124	
Greenockite		C	2.22	2.19	7.0	−.87	−.80	125
CdS		S	.81	.80	.14	.49	.48	139
Ice, H_2O	−16° C	S	10.4	8.5	31.4	−4.3	−2.4	139
	−16° C	C	.1385	.1499	.0319	.0707	.0581	27, 122
	−5° C	S	10.13	8.28	32.65	−4.16	−1.93	
		C	.133	.142	.0306	.063	.046	
	−5° C	S	10.35	8.43	33.2	−4.27	−1.9	27
	−10° C	C	.1299	.1381	.0301	.0615	.0431	
		S	10.24	8.37	33.0	−4.22	−1.9	
	−20° C	C	.1315	.1395	.0303	.0624	.0440	
		S	10.08	8.24	32.5	−4.13	−1.9	
	−25° C	C	.1337	.1423	.0308	.0634	.0454	
		S	9.98	8.20	32.2	−4.0	−1.9	
		C	.1338	.1430	.0311	.0623	.0454	
β-quartz, SiO_2	600° C	S	.941	1.062	2.773	−.060	−.262	141
	600° C	C	1.166	1.104	.3606	.167	.328	173
					(isothermal)			
	600° C	C	.9338	1.049				
	700° C	C	.8821	1.0363				
	800° C	S	.8634	1.0310				
	900° C	S	.8526	1.0290				
	1000° C	S	.8448	1.0280				
	1100° C	S	.8386					
	1200° C	S	.8338					
Nepheline I		C	.825	1.328	.362	.417	.173	285
Nepheline II		C	.749	1.250	.346	.414	.134	285
Zincite, ZnO		C	2.097	2.109	.4247	1.211	1.051	272
(artificial)		S	.786	.694	2.355	−.343	−.221	

TRIGONAL

Mineral	Temp.		11	33	44	12	13	14	Ref.
Calcite, CaCO₃		S	1.13	1.75	4.03	-.37	-.43	.91	229
		C	1.370	.796	.342	.456	.451	-.208	
		S	1.10	1.73	3.94	-.34	-.43	.86	38
		C	1.374	.801	.342	.440	.450	-.203	
		S	1.10	1.70	3.82	-.30	-.52	1.02	186
		C	1.62	.98	.43	.45	.64	-.31	
		S	1.187	1.824	4.342	-.435	-.483	1.018	251
		C	1.445	.831	.327	.571	.534	-.205	
$10^6 \frac{1}{S}\frac{dS}{dt}$	0–200° C		370	59	510	1380	2000	1220	186
	200–300° C		560	180	430	9310	4440	3620	
Corundum, Al₂O₃ (Synthetic)		S	.228	.218	.724	-.055	-.040	.046	158
		C	4.96	5.02	1.41	1.35	1.17	-.23	
		S	.2353	.2170	.694	-.0716	-.0364	.0489	238
		C	4.968	4.981	1.474	1.636	1.109	-.235	
		C	4.902	4.902	1.454	1.654	1.130	-.232	
Hematite, Fe₂O₃		S	.441	.443	1.19	-.102	-.023	.079	274
		C	2.42	2.28	.85	.55	.16	-.13	231

(These constants lead to $\beta = 1.029$ mb⁻¹, which appears to be too high. The quality of the sample may be questioned.)

Mineral	Temp.		11	33	44	12	13	14	Ref.
Soda niter, NaNO₃		S	1.34	3.08	5.15	-.22	-.48	-.60	38
		C	.867	.374	.213	.163	.160	.082	
Quartz, α SiO₂	25° C	S	1.279	.956	1.978	-.1535	-.110	.446	155*
		C	.8605	1.071	.5865	.050	.1045	-.1825	
	35° C	S	1.236	.972	2.002	-.168	-.138	.424	22*
		C	.876	1.068	.5786	.0687	.113	-.1796	
	20° C	S	1.277	.960	2.004	-.179	-.122	.450	29
		C	.8674	1.072	.5794	.0699	.1191	-.1791	
		S	1.2776	.9718	1.9971	-.181	-.1235	.4524	144
		C	.8683	1.0594	.5826	.0709	.1193	-.1806	

* The signs of S_{14} and C_{14} have been reversed to conform with IRE 1949 Standards.

TABLE 7-12. Continued

TRIGONAL (Continued)

Mineral	Temp.	C_{11}	C_{14}	C_{44}	$C_{66} = \frac{1}{2}(C_{11} - C_{12})$	S_{11}	S_{33}	Ref.
Quartz, SiO_2	0° C	.877	.178	.559	.405	1.2714	.9711	22, 250,
	100° C	.873	.179	.550	.412	1.2762	.9881	173
	200° C	.866	.180	.537	.420	1.2827	1.0086	
	300° C	.855	.179	.518	.431	1.2974	1.0342	
	400° C	.836	.174	.492	.445	1.3261	1.0711	
	500° C	.796	.152	.441	.467	1.4162	1.1393	

Mineral	Temp.		11	33	44	12	13	14	Ref.
Tourmaline		S	.398	.624	1.51	−.103	−.016	+.058	230
		C	2.70	1.607	.668	.693	.087	−.077	
		S	.385	.636	1.54	−.048	−.071	+.045	156
		C	2.72	1.65	.65	.40	.35	−.068	
I		S	.422	.734	1.71	−.080	−.111	+.076	33
		C	2.63	1.51	.595	.61	.49	−.09	
II		S	.364	.589	1.54	−.100	−.053	+.029	33
		C	3.04	1.76	.65	.88	.35	−.04	

TETRAGONAL

Mineral	Temp.		11	33	44	66	12	13	Ref.
Rutile, TiO_2		S	.647	.259	.801	.68	−.45	−.070	238a
		C	3.6	4.8	1.26	1.47	2.7	1.7	227
		S	.655	.259	.800	.516	−.376	−.086	
		C	2.73	4.84	1.25	1.94	1.76	1.49	

ORTHORHOMBIC

Mineral	Temp.		11	22	33	44	55	66	12	13	23	Ref.
Aragonite, $CaCO_3$		S	.695	1.32	1.22	2.43	3.90	2.34	−.30	−.04	−.24	232
		C	1.60	.87	.85	.41	.26	.43	.37	.02	.168	

Mineral	Temp.		11	22	33	44	55	66	12	13	23	Ref.
Barite, BaSO₄		S	1.840	1.736	1.096	8.333	3.484	3.650	−.945	−.268	−.273	200
		C	.862	.917	1.084	.120	.287	.274	.523	.341	.356	31
		S	1.72	1.99	1.09	8.55	3.58	3.92	−.99	−.17	−.30	
		C	.880	.781	1.04	.117	.279	.255	.477	.269	.289	234
		S	1.64	1.89	1.06	8.40	3.48	3.60	−.90	−.19	−.25	
		C	.89	.78	1.05	.12	.29	.28	.46	.27	.27	186a
	35° C	S	1.657	1.906	1.067	8.212	3.682	3.698	−.865	−.362	−.173	
	105° C	S	1.702	1.936	1.087	8.288	3.868	3.710	−.796	−.209	−.703	
	185° C	S	1.750	1.983	1.111	8.419	4.061	3.895	−.936	−.026	−1.233	
Celestite, SrSO₄		S	2.197	2.185	1.142	7.408	3.584	3.759	−1.387	−.366	−.400	200
		C	1.044	1.061	1.286	.135	.279	.266	.773	.605	.619	
Epsomite, MgSO₄·7H₂O		S	2.45	3.41	1.50	9.35	4.29	4.50	−1.66	−.268	−.605	213a
		C	.698	.529	.822	.107	.233	.222	.390	.282	.283	
Goslarite, ZnSO₄·7H₂O		S	2.95	3.77	2.04	20.0	5.88	5.53	−1.08	−.349	−.610	213a
		C	.400	.322	.545	.050	.170	.181	.132	.108	.119	
Olivine (Fo₉₂Fa₈, ρ = 3.324)		S	.343	.588	.481	1.499	1.24	1.261	−.067	−.089	−.163	227
		C	3.24	1.98	2.49	.667	.810	.793	.59	.79	.78	
Staurolite		S	.318	1.370	1.730	2.17	1.43	1.09	−.0598	−.0795	−1.168	41
		C	3.43	1.85	1.47	.46	.70	.92	.67	.61	1.28	
Sulfur		S	7.1	8.3	3.0	23.2	11.5	13.2	−3.6	−1.3	−1.5	214,215
		C	.240	.205	.483	.043	.087	.076	.133	.171	.159	
Topaz		S	.443	.353	.384	.924	.754	.764	−.137	−.086	−.066	234
		C	2.81	3.49	2.94	1.08	1.32	1.31	1.26	.84	.88	

MONOCLINIC
(TREATED AS HEXAGONAL)

Mineral	Temp.		11	33	44	66	12	13	Ref.
Muscovite ρ = 2.79		C	1.78	.549	.122	.678	.424	.145	12a
		S	.6038	1.887	8.197	1.475	−.1337	−.1241	
Phlogopite, Aldan USSR ρ = 2.80		C	1.79	.517	.056	.733	.324	.258	
		S	.6104	2.2025	17.857	1.3643	−.0717	−.2688	
Phlogopite, Slyudyanka USSR ρ = 2.82		C	1.78	.510	.065	.736	.302	.152	
		S	.5894	2.0500	15.385	1.359	−.0872	−.1497	
Biotite ρ = 3.05		C	1.86	.540	.058	.768	.324	.116	
		S	.5598	1.895	17.241	1.302	−.0912	−.1007	

TABLE 7-12. *Continued*

MONOCLINIC (*Continued*)

ik	Aegirite $\rho = 3.50$		Hornblende I $\rho = 3.12$		Hornblende II $\rho = 3.15$		Ref.
	C_{ik}	S_{ik}	C_{ik}	S_{ik}	C_{ik}	S_{ik}	
11	1.858	.6693	1.160	1.0868	1.301	1.1368	
22	1.813	.6690	1.597	.7684	1.877	.6582	
33	2.344	.5164	1.916	.6929	1.984	.8637	
44	.692	1.4717	.574	1.7745	.611	1.6371	
55	.510	2.0437	.318	3.2285	.387	3.8180	
66	.474	2.1485	.368	2.7678	.450	2.2229	12
12	.685	−.2011	.449	−.1925	.614	−.2648	
13	.707	−.1454	.614	−.2786	.592	−.4126	
23	.626	−.1147	.655	−.2089	.614	−.1112	
15	.098	−.0305	.043	−.0745	.095	−.7591	
25	.094	−.0365	−.025	.1521	−.069	.0656	
35	.214	−.1676	.100	−.1966	−.406	.9875	
46	.077	−.2391	−.062	.2990	−.009	.0327	

TRICLINIC TWINNED CRYSTALS
TREATED AS IF SYMMETRY WERE MONOCLINIC

ik	Microcline Karelia, USSR $Or_{78.5}Ab_{19.4}An_{2.1}$ $\rho = 2.56$		Oligoclase Chupa, White Sea An_{15-16} $\rho = 2.64$		Labradorite Golorino, Ukraine An_{57-60} $\rho = 2.68$		Ref.
	C_{ik}	S_{ik}	C_{ik}	S_{ik}	C_{ik}	S_{ik}	
11	.664	1.9531	.806	2.3538	1.010	1.4888	
22	1.710	.7396	1.630	.7421	1.582	.8426	
33	1.215	.9491	1.242	1.3739	1.510	.7978	
44	.143	7.0236	.177	5.6585	.214	4.8656	
55	.238	4.6946	.274	5.0934	.335	3.0976	12b
66	.361	2.7822	.362	2.7667	.370	2.8142	
12	.438	-.4790	.417	-.1990	.617	-.5175	
13	.259	-.3652	.538	-1.0516	.480	-.3841	
23	.192	.0294	.374	-.1605	.260	.0071	
15	-.033	-.2281	.161	-1.5429	-.003	-.0002	
25	-.148	.4097	.171	-.3895	-.080	.1946	
35	-.131	.4900	-.074	1.0891	.096	-.2304	
46	-.015	.2918	.010	-.1563	-.056	.7364	

TABLE 7-12. *Continued*

TWINNED PLAGIOCLASE CRYSTALS (TREATED AS MONOCLINIC)

%An $\rho =$ ik	9 2.61 C_{ik}	S_{ik}	24 2.64 C_{ik}	S_{ik}	29 2.64 C_{ik}	S_{ik}	53 2.68 C_{ik}	S_{ik}	56 2.69 C_{ik}	S_{ik}	Ref.
11	.749	1.719	.818	1.588	.845	1.546	.970	1.380	.989	1.336	
22	1.375	.852	1.449	.806	1.505	.779	1.629	.742	1.720	.699	
33	1.289	.983	1.328	.953	1.325	.952	1.410	.863	1.414	.881	
44	.172	5.84	.177	5.65	.185	5.41	.196	5.13	.199	5.05	
55	.303	3.69	.312	3.52	.314	3.49	.330	3.22	.341	3.18	
66	.311	3.23	.333	3.01	.343	2.92	.370	2.72	.376	2.68	286
12	.363	−.35	.393	−.33	.417	−.34	.507	−.35	.521	−.33	
13	.376	−.39	.407	−.38	.409	−.37	.442	−.32	.441	−.32	
23	.326	−.09	.341	−.10	.330	−.09	.370	−.09	.366	−.08	
15	−.091	−.15	−.09	.15	−.087	.134	−.096	.20	−.081	.09	
25	−.104	−.13	−.079	−.05	−.069	−.03	−.051	−.03	−.051	−.02	
35	−.191	.47	−.185	.43	−.185	.44	−.150	.29	−.191	.41	
46	−.013	.24	−.008	.14	−.011	.17	−.016	.22	−.019	.26	

TABLE 7-13.   ROCKS: COMPRESSIBILITY

NOTES TO TABLE 7-13

A—Fluid pressure, β from change of length C—Fluid pressure, β from V_p, V_s
B—Axial compression, β from E and σ D—Fluid pressure, β from volume change

Rock	ρ	P bars	β mb^{-1} enclosed	unenclosed	Note	Ref.
Albitite, Sylmar, Pa.	2.615	4,000	1.52		C	46
			1.93		A	47
Andesite, Salida, Colo.	2.618	34	2.20		C	128
(glassy?)		345	2.24			
		1,030	2.08			
Anorthosite						
New Glasgow, Ont.		600		1.74	B	1
	2.708	4,000	1.22		C	46
Stillwater Complex,	2.770	4,000	1.15		C	46
Mont.						
(see also diabase, gabbro, norite)						
Basalt, altered, Chaffee,	2.586	500	2.26		C	157
Colo.		5,000	1.96			
Basalt	2.901	1	2.19		A	235
		500	1.49			
		5,000	1.25			
Basalt, Scotch Plains, N.J.	2.911	2,000	2.42		D	7
(20 per cent glass)		10,000	1.68			
Basalt, diabasic, altered	2.924	1	1.59		A	57
		10,000	1.31			
Bronzitite						
Stillwater Complex,	3.279	4,000	.97		C	46
Mont.		4,000	.96		A	47
Bushveld Complex,	3.288	4,000	.94		C	46
Transvaal		4,000	.89		A	47
Diabase						
Vinalhaven, Me.	2.96	0	1.71	1.46	A	248
		120	1.59			
		720	1.26			
	2.962	4,000	1.17		A	47
Sudbury, Ont.	3.002	2,000		1.37	D	7
(Murray Mine)		10,000		1.25		
		600		1.36	B	1
Palisade, Granton, N.J.	2.975	2,000		1.54	D	5, 7
		10,000		1.30		
Frederick, Md.	3.020	1	1.25		A	275
		1,000	1.28			
		5,000	1.22			
		9,000	1.17			
Frederick, Md.	3.033	2,000		1.23	D	5
		10,000		1.07		
Frederick, Md.	3.012	4,000	1.22		C	46
		4,000	1.16		A	47
Whin Sill, England	2.937	2,000		1.70	D	5
(quartz dolerite)		10,000		1.26		

TABLE 7-13. *Continued*

Rock	ρ	P bars	β mb^{-1} enclosed	unenclosed	Note	Ref.
Diorite, Salem, Mass.	3.025	34	1.57		C	128
		345	1.42			
		1,030	1.32			
Diorite porphyry	2.792	1	6.69		A	235
Ural Mountains		500	2.36			
		5,000	1.19			
Dolomite, Bethlehem,	2.82	0	3.71	1.19	A	248
Pa.		120	2.54	1.19		
		600	1.48	1.19		
Dolomite, Blair,	2.849	1	1.23		A	275
Martinsburg, W.Va.		1,000	1.20			
		5,000	1.14			
		9,000	1.09			
Dolomite, Webatuck,	2.867	1	19		A	275
N.Y.		500	1.36			
		1,000	1.19			
		5,000	1.05			
		9,000	1.00			
Dunite						
Balsam Gap, N.C.	3.27	0		1.12	A	248
		120		1.09		
		600		.95		
Balsam Gap, N.C.	3.288	7,000		.79	D	3, 4
Balsam Gap, N.C.	3.267	4,000	.80		C	46
		4,000	.83		A	47
Twin Sisters, Wash.	3.312	4,000	.80		C	46
Gabbro						
San Marcos, Cal.	2.993	500	1.11		C	131
		5,000	1.02			
Duluth, Minn.	2.885	500	1.24		C	131
(bytownite)		5,000	1.15			
	2.933	500	1.24		C	131
(hornblende)		5,000	1.17			
New Glasgow, Ont.	3.106	2,000	1.34		D	7
(olivine)		10,000	1.13			
		600		1.52 (mean)	B	1
Mellen, Wis.	2.931	4,000	1.05		C	46
		4,000	1.14		A	47
Granite						
Quincy, Mass.	2.59?	0	7.56	1.92	A	248
		120	4.02	1.85		
		600	2.53	1.67		
		axial 600		3.6–3.2	B	1
	2.629	500	1.81		C	130
		5,000	1.54			
	2.621	4,000	1.72		C	46
		4,000	1.92		A	47
Rockport, Mass.	2.63	0	9.17	1.95	A	248
		120	5.04	1.87		
		600	2.66			
	2.624	4,000	1.62		C	46
		4,000	1.85		A	47

TABLE 7-13. *Continued*

Rock	ρ	P bars	β mb^{-1} enclosed	β mb^{-1} unenclosed	Note	Ref.
Westerly, R.I.		1		1.95		143
		600		3.3	B	1
	2.628	34	2.31		C	128
		345	1.84			
		1,030	1.72			
	2.615	500	1.99		C	130
		5,000	1.78			
	2.616	2,000		2.12	D	7
		10,000		1.82		
		4,000	1.82		C	46
	2.646	1	8.3		A	275
		500	2.89			
		1,000	2.46			
		2,000	2.16			
		5,000	1.99			
		9,000	1.87			
Bear Mt., Texas	2.610	34	2.11		C	128
		345	1.79			
		1,030	1.68			
Washington, D.C. (granodiorite)	2.739	2,000		2.23	D	7
		10,000		1.82		
Stone Mt., Georgia	2.633	2,000		2.06	D	7
		10,000		1.80		
	2.631	1	15.6		A	275
		500	3.49			
		1,000	2.48			
		2,000	2.12			
		5,000	1.91			
		9,000	1.76			
Woodbury, Vt.	2.634	500	1.84		C	130
		5,000	1.75			
Texas, "pink"	2.636	500	1.55		C	130
		5,000	1.38?			
Texas, "gray"	2.609	500	2.05		C	130
		5,000	1.74			
Barriefield, Ont.	2.672	500	1.45		C	129
		5,000	1.35?			
Karelia, U.S.S.R. porosity = 0.4%	2.641	0	4.23		A	235
		500	1.82			
		5,000	1.07?			
Limestone Nazareth, Pa. (Carbonaceous)	2.69	0	2.92	2.47	A	248
		120	2.75	2.45		
		160	2.35	2.41		
Solenhofen, Bavaria	2.602 (mean to 12 Kb)	6,000		1.36	A	57
	2.602 (mean to 10 Kb)	5,000		1.29	6° C A	41
				1.42	100° C	
				1.63	270° C	
				1.71	476° C	
	2.656	1	1.53		C	129, 132
		500	1.54			
		5,000	1.49			

TABLE 7-13. *Continued*

Rock	ρ	P bars	β mb^{-1} enclosed	unenclosed	Note	Ref.
Limestone *Continued*						
Oak Hall Quarry, Pa.	2.712	1	1.35		A	275
		1,000	1.34			
		5,000	1.31			
		9,000	1.28			
Marble	2.71	1	18.0	1.39	A	248
Vermont		120	3.31	1.38		
		600	1.50	1.26		
Gunnison Co., Colo.	2.708	7,000	1.38	1.40	D	7
Danby, Vt.	2.704	4,000	1.28		C	46
	2.698	500	1.35		C	132
		5,000	1.21			
	2.712	1	8.7		A	275
		500	1.69			
		1,000	1.45			
		5,000	1.31			
		9,000	1.27			
Norite						
Sudbury, Ont.	2.85	0	3.15	1.65	A	248
		120	2.24	1.63		
		600	1.65	1.57		
Elizabethtown, N.Y.		34	1.35		C	128
	3.057	345	1.18			
		1,030	1.10			
French Creek, Pa.		0	5.90	1.40	A	248
(gabbro)	3.05	120	4.11	1.34		
		600	1.66	1.26		
	3.054	4,000	1.11		C	46
		4,000	1.13		A	47
Pipestone (catlinite)	2.840 (mean to 10 Kb)			1.29	A	57
Quartzite, Montana	2.647	4,000	2.18		C	46
Quartzitic sandstone,		1	5.87	2.67	A	248
Bethlehem, Pa.		120	4.28	2.65		
		600	3.09	2.60		
Quartzite, Cheshire,	2.643	1	7.6		A	275
Rutland, Vt.		500	3.04			
		1,000	2.74			
		5,000	2.48			
		9,000	2.26			
Sandstone, Caplen dome,	2.543	500	3.5		C	132
Texas		5,000	2.33			
"Serpentine"						
(Talc schist)	2.875	2,000		1.79	D	7
Alberene, Va.		10,000		1.36		
Syenite, Augite, Ont.	2.780	4,000	1.21?		C	46
		4,000	1.69		A	47
Talc, Hewitt, N.C.	2.751	1		1.86	A	57
Tonalite	2.763	4,000	1.49		C	46
Trachyte	2.712	500	2.12		C	131
		5,000	1.80			

TABLE 7-14. ROCKS AND MINERALS: SHOCK COMPRESSION

Density (ρ) and pressure (P) computed from particle velocity U_P and shock velocity U_S (see introduction). The column U_S (Std) records shock velocity in a standard material used for calibration (24 ST aluminum). Density at 1 atmosphere, ρ_0. See also 133, 151, 270, 291.

ρ_0 g/cm^3	U_S (Std) km/sec	U_P km/sec	U_S km/sec	P kilobars	ρ g/cm^3	Ref.
	ALBITITE, SYLMAR, PA.					266
2.61	8.28	2.49	6.31	410	4.31	
2.61	8.80	2.88	6.96	524	4.45	
2.61	9.42	3.35	7.75	677	4.60	
2.61	9.68	3.54	8.09	747	4.64	
2.61	9.86	3.70	8.14	786	4.78	
2.61	10.21	3.95	8.65	892	4.80	
2.61	10.25	3.98	8.69	904	4.82	
	ANDALUSITE					266
3.08	8.68	2.49	7.74	594	4.54	
3.06	8.75	2.53	7.91	613	4.50	
3.10	8.93	2.67	7.94	657	4.67	
3.07	9.02	2.76	7.94	673	4.71	
3.06	9.16	2.88	7.94	701	4.81	
3.09	9.33	2.97	8.32	763	4.80	
3.06	9.67	3.20	8.84	867	4.80	
3.08	10.08	3.50	9.20	993	4.98	
3.07	10.25	3.63	9.36	1,042	5.01	
3.06	10.27	3.65	9.39	1,049	5.01	
3.09	10.37	3.70	9.52	1,089	5.05	
3.09	10.54	3.80	9.87	1,158	5.02	
	ANORTHOSITE, TAHAWUS, NEW YORK					266
2.73	7.79	2.05	5.92	331	4.17	
2.71	7.80	2.05	5.93	330	4.14	
2.73	8.33	2.45	6.63	442	4.33	
2.73	8.33	2.47	6.46	435	4.42	
2.72	8.78	2.81	7.02	538	4.54	
2.73	8.79	2.82	7.06	542	4.54	
2.75	9.42	3.27	7.84	704	4.71	
2.76	9.68	3.44	8.25	782	4.73	
2.73	9.73	3.50	8.25	788	4.74	
2.75	9.96	3.68	8.39	849	4.90	
2.79	10.12	3.76	8.68	913	4.93	
2.73	10.13	3.84	8.49	888	4.97	
2.70	10.28	3.94	8.80	937	4.89	
2.72	10.33	3.97	8.81	952	4.96	
	BRONZITITE, BUSHVELD COMPLEX, TRANSVAAL					266
3.30	8.41	2.20	7.57	551	4.66	
3.29	8.80	2.50	7.92	649	4.80	
3.30	9.44	2.93	8.65	836	4.99	
3.30	9.73	3.14	8.90	923	5.10	
	BRONZITITE, STILLWATER COMPLEX, MONTANA					266
3.28	8.59	2.32	7.89	601	4.64	
3.27	8.61	2.33	7.93	606	4.63	
3.29	8.68	2.39	7.96	626	4.70	
3.28	8.75	2.44	8.04	643	4.71	
3.28	8.79	2.47	8.08	655	4.72	
3.28	8.93	2.57	8.20	692	4.78	
3.28	9.02	2.63	8.32	718	4.80	

TABLE 7-14. *Continued*

ρ_0 g/cm³	U_S (Std) km/sec	U_P km/sec	U_S km/sec	P kilobars	ρ g/cm³	Ref.
BRONZITITE, STILLWATER COMPLEX, MONTANA *Continued*						
3.28	9.38	2.89	8.60	817	4.95	
3.28	9.45	2.95	8.63	836	4.99	
3.28	9.67	3.10	8.93	908	5.02	
3.28	9.67	3.11	8.88	904	5.04	
3.28	9.73	3.15	8.94	922	5.06	
3.28	9.88	3.27	8.98	963	5.16	
3.28	10.13	3.42	9.40	1,055	5.16	
3.28	10.13	3.46	9.17	1,040	5.26	
3.27	10.25	3.54	9.33	1,082	5.28	
3.28	10.27	3.55	9.36	1,090	5.28	
CASSITERITE, SAN LUIS POTOSI, MEXICO						266
6.45	9.26	2.27	6.77	992	9.71	
6.52	9.33	2.31	6.77	1,021	9.90	
6.75	9.75	2.55	6.94	1,193	10.66	
6.74	10.10	2.73	7.32	1,348	10.75	
6.51	10.29	2.88	7.51	1,410	10.56	
CORUNDUM, CRYSTAL, SYNTHETIC						266
3.98	7.72	1.30	9.99	516	4.58	
3.98	8.32	1.66	10.51	693	4.73	
3.99	8.86	1.98	11.02	871	4.86	
3.99	9.18	2.20	11.17	979	4.96	
3.99	9.26	2.24	11.28	1,006	4.97	
3.99	9.29	2.27	11.24	1,016	4.99	
3.99	9.33	2.32	11.03	1,019	5.05	
3.99	10.08	2.78	11.81	1,309	5.21	
3.99	10.11	2.80	11.78	1,315	5.23	
3.99	10.29	2.95	11.69	1,376	5.33	
3.98	10.54	3.11	11.92	1,480	5.39	
CORUNDUM, CERAMIC						266
3.83	7.00	.94	8.63	310	4.30	
3.83	7.42	1.22	8.68	405	4.46	
3.83	7.67	1.37	8.92	469	4.53	
3.83	8.28	1.76	9.43	635	4.71	
3.83	8.32	1.77	9.62	653	4.70	
3.83	8.32	1.78	9.56	652	4.71	
3.83	9.01	2.21	10.26	870	4.89	
3.83	9.15	2.31	10.27	909	4.95	
3.83	10.06	2.90	11.17	1,240	5.17	
3.83	10.25	3.03	11.29	1,312	5.24	
DIABASE, CENTREVILLE, VIRGINIA						266
2.97	7.80	1.94	6.27	361	4.30	
2.97	7.79	1.94	6.21	358	4.32	
2.98	8.28	2.29	6.81	466	4.49	
2.99	8.33	2.34	6.78	475	4.57	
2.98	8.78	2.67	7.35	585	4.68	
2.98	9.42	3.15	7.96	747	4.93	
2.99	9.68	3.32	8.31	825	4.97	
2.98	10.13	3.65	8.82	961	5.09	
3.01	10.33	3.80	8.91	1,019	5.25	

TABLE 7-14. *Continued*

ρ_0 g/cm³	U_S (Std) km/sec	U_P km/sec	U_S km/sec	P kilobars	ρ g/cm³	Ref.
	DIABASE, FREDERICK, MARYLAND					266
3.02	7.58	1.74	6.22	326	4.18	
3.01	7.67	1.81	6.29	344	4.24	
3.01	7.80	1.91	6.39	368	4.29	
3.01	8.28	2.27	6.89	472	4.50	
3.01	8.33	2.31	6.90	481	4.54	
3.01	8.78	2.65	7.38	590	4.70	
3.01	8.80	2.66	7.39	593	4.71	
3.02	9.42	3.13	7.99	754	4.96	
3.02	9.45	3.14	8.08	765	4.93	
3.01	9.68	3.30	8.36	832	4.98	
3.02	10.13	3.65	8.75	963	5.17	
3.01	10.33	3.78	9.04	1,029	5.18	
	DUNITE					14
3.25				2,400	6.8	
	DUNITE, TWIN SISTERS MT., WASHINGTON					266
3.32	9.05	2.64	8.39	734	4.84	
3.32	9.05	2.65	8.31	730	4.87	
3.32	9.38	2.86	8.75	831	4.93	
3.32	9.40	2.90	8.66	832	4.98	
3.32	9.44	2.91	8.73	844	4.98	
3.32	9.45	2.93	8.69	844	5.01	
3.32	9.49	2.95	8.77	858	5.00	
3.32	9.49	2.95	8.75	857	5.01	
3.32	9.73	3.10	9.15	941	5.02	
3.32	9.73	3.10	9.12	940	5.03	
3.32	9.96	3.28	9.25	1,007	5.14	
3.32	10.13	3.37	9.55	1,070	5.13	
3.32	10.12	3.39	9.45	1,063	5.18	
3.32	10.13	3.39	9.49	1,068	5.17	
3.32	10.28	3.49	9.69	1,123	5.18	
	DUNITE (IRON-RICH), MOOIHOEK MINE, TRANSVAAL					266
3.80	8.68	2.31	7.43	653	5.51	
3.82	8.80	2.39	7.55	687	5.58	
3.80	8.79	2.39	7.52	683	5.57	
3.81	8.93	2.49	7.62	721	5.65	
3.85	9.16	2.61	7.93	798	5.74	
3.78	9.44	2.84	8.13	872	5.81	
3.84	9.54	2.89	8.22	911	5.92	
3.82	9.67	2.96	8.47	960	5.88	
3.77	9.67	2.97	8.54	957	5.78	
3.73	9.73	3.05	8.45	962	5.84	
3.68	9.73	3.06	8.48	955	5.76	
3.82	9.88	3.11	8.69	1,031	5.94	
3.75	10.12	3.32	8.79	1,094	6.02	
3.82	10.27	3.37	9.08	1,168	6.07	
3.80	10.25	3.37	9.00	1,154	6.08	
3.77	10.37	3.47	9.09	1,190	6.10	
	ECLOGITE, NORWAY					266
3.48	7.76	1.61	7.84	439	4.38	
3.52	7.80	1.61	7.99	453	4.41	
3.51	7.79	1.63	7.83	448	4.43	
3.59	8.41	2.03	8.37	609	4.74	

TABLE 7-14. *Continued*

ρ_0 g/cm³	U_S (Std) km/sec	U_P km/sec	U_S km/sec	P kilobars	ρ g/cm³	Ref.
		ECLOGITE, NORWAY *Continued*				266
3.58	8.78	2.27	8.81	718	4.83	
3.54	8.79	2.31	8.72	713	4.82	
3.56	9.12	2.55	8.88	805	5.00	
3.57	9.38	2.72	9.11	886	5.09	
3.53	9.44	2.76	9.24	902	5.04	
3.52	9.73	2.99	9.36	984	5.17	
3.56	9.73	2.99	9.22	983	5.27	
3.55	10.13	3.26	9.72	1,125	5.35	
		ECLOGITE, HEALDSBURG, CALIF.				266
3.41	9.30	2.78	8.60	817	5.04	
3.39	9.44	2.87	8.79	858	5.04	
3.40	9.51	2.94	8.79	877	5.10	
3.41	9.73	3.07	9.06	951	5.16	
3.47	10.03	3.25	9.41	1,062	5.30	
3.43	10.13	3.37	9.33	1,078	5.36	
		ENSTATITE, CERAMIC				266
2.71	7.72	2.06	5.37	300	4.40	
2.71	8.32	2.53	6.07	416	4.65	
2.71	9.00	3.07	6.74	559	4.97	
2.72	9.33	3.33	7.03	637	5.17	
		FAYALITE, ROCKPORT, MASS.				266
4.30	8.33	2.02	6.65	577	6.17	
4.29	8.76	2.30	7.06	696	6.36	
4.23	8.86	2.37	7.23	725	6.30	
4.18	9.26	2.65	7.56	839	6.45	
4.29	9.75	2.96	7.96	1,013	6.84	
4.28	10.10	3.19	8.32	1,137	6.94	
		FORSTERITE, CERAMIC				266
3.07	9.05	2.84	7.63	664	4.88	
3.03	9.40	3.10	8.07	758	4.92	
3.03	9.40	3.10	8.07	758	4.92	
3.07	9.49	3.14	8.20	788	4.97	
3.04	9.96	3.50	8.64	919	5.11	
3.06	10.28	3.70	9.14	1,035	5.15	
		GRANITE, WESTERLY, RHODE ISLAND				266
2.63	8.28	2.50	6.19	406	4.41	
2.63	8.33	2.55	6.18	414	4.47	
2.63	8.78	2.88	6.83	517	4.55	
2.63	9.42	3.37	7.58	671	4.72	
2.63	9.68	3.54	7.99	744	4.72	
2.63	10.13	3.89	8.49	868	4.85	
2.63	10.12	3.90	8.41	861	4.90	
2.63	10.33	4.05	8.62	919	4.96	
		HALITE, SINGLE CRYSTAL				19
2.16				53	2.51	
				100	2.72	
				152	2.89	
				182	3.00	
				209	3.09	
				276	3.24	
				547	3.67	
				790	4.00	

TABLE 7-14.   *Continued*

ρ_0 g/cm³	U_S (Std) km/sec	U_P km/sec	U_S km/sec	P kilobars	ρ g/cm³	Ref.
	HALITE, "ROCK SALT," LOUISIANA SALT DOME					151
2.155				89	2.66	
				226	3.10	
				620	3.73	
				709	4.01	
	HEMATITE					266
5.01	9.15	2.34	7.62	896	7.24	
4.90	9.18	2.39	7.67	900	7.13	
4.98	9.29	2.44	7.77	944	7.25	
5.01	9.33	2.45	7.86	964	7.28	
5.01	10.08	2.92	8.49	1,243	7.63	
5.02	10.08	2.92	8.47	1,243	7.67	
5.01	10.08	2.93	8.47	1,241	7.66	
5.05	10.11	2.93	8.48	1,255	7.71	
5.05	10.11	2.93	8.45	1,253	7.74	
4.97	10.54	3.23	8.84	1,421	7.84	
	JADEITE, BURMA					266
3.33	6.95	1.03	7.84	269	3.83	
3.33	6.97	1.05	7.78	271	3.85	
3.33	7.18	1.19	7.86	313	3.93	
3.33	7.58	1.46	8.22	401	4.05	
3.33	7.60	1.48	8.25	406	4.06	
3.33	7.64	1.51	8.20	413	4.09	
3.33	8.23	1.91	8.80	560	4.26	
3.33	8.33	1.99	8.78	583	4.31	
3.33	8.77	2.31	9.07	698	4.47	
3.33	8.78	2.32	9.05	701	4.49	
3.34	9.42	2.81	9.33	874	4.77	
3.33	9.68	3.02	9.39	944	4.91	
3.33	9.73	3.05	9.42	959	4.93	
3.35	10.13	3.34	9.72	1,086	5.10	
3.34	10.33	3.50	9.83	1,147	5.18	
	MAGNETITE					266
5.11	8.28	1.80	6.72	620	6.99	
5.14	8.32	1.82	6.82	637	7.00	
5.13	8.32	1.83	6.77	634	7.02	
5.14	8.32	1.83	6.74	634	7.06	
5.13	8.75	2.08	7.23	771	7.20	
5.11	9.01	2.26	7.40	853	7.35	
5.13	9.02	2.29	7.19	845	7.52	
5.13	9.15	2.35	7.43	894	7.49	
5.11	9.29	2.45	7.53	942	7.57	
5.13	9.67	2.67	7.92	1,083	7.73	
5.14	10.08	2.93	8.26	1,241	7.96	
5.01	10.06	2.93	8.37	1,227	7.70	
5.10	10.08	2.94	8.25	1,235	7.91	
5.13	10.11	2.94	8.27	1,248	7.95	
5.13	10.25	3.03	8.45	1,310	7.99	
	MARBLE (DRY)					105
2.70				50	3.00	
				103	3.19	
				125	3.27	
				166	3.40	
				208	3.54	
				326	3.78	
				508	4.13	

TABLE 7-14. *Continued*

ρ_0 g/cm³	U_S (Std) km/sec	U_P km/sec	U_S km/sec	P kilobars	ρ g/cm³	Ref.
		PERICLASE, SYNTHETIC				266
3.58	6.57	.73	7.68	202	3.96	
3.58	6.63	.78	7.63	214	3.99	
3.58	7.05	1.04	8.15	304	4.11	
3.58	7.79	1.51	8.93	484	4.31	
3.58	7.93	1.60	9.08	521	4.35	
3.58	7.98	1.64	9.01	528	4.38	
3.58	8.31	1.86	9.23	616	4.49	
3.58	8.54	2.02	9.45	683	4.56	
3.58	8.86	2.22	9.79	780	4.64	
3.58	9.12	2.40	9.93	856	4.73	
3.58	9.18	2.43	10.13	884	4.72	
3.58	9.26	2.49	10.14	904	4.75	
3.58	9.29	2.52	10.11	913	4.77	
3.58	9.40	2.59	10.21	950	4.81	
3.58	9.49	2.64	10.33	980	4.82	
3.58	9.86	2.90	10.59	1,102	4.94	
3.58	9.96	2.97	10.67	1,137	4.97	
3.58	10.25	3.18	10.92	1,244	5.06	
3.58	10.29	3.20	10.96	1,258	5.06	
		PYROLUSITE, IRONTON, MINN.				266
4.42	6.56	.81	5.11	183	5.25	
4.39	7.01	1.12	5.49	270	5.51	
4.06	7.28	1.41	5.20	298	5.57	
4.37	7.54	1.48	5.91	381	5.83	
4.33	7.55	1.48	6.00	385	5.75	
4.24	7.62	1.57	5.82	388	5.81	
4.19	7.70	1.64	5.83	402	5.84	
4.24	7.82	1.70	6.10	439	5.87	
4.37	8.33	1.98	6.85	591	6.14	
4.30	8.68	2.23	7.08	681	6.28	
4.36	8.76	2.25	7.26	713	6.32	
4.32	8.86	2.31	7.49	747	6.25	
4.26	9.00	2.45	7.39	771	6.37	
4.36	9.75	2.94	7.98	1,023	6.90	
4.34	10.10	3.16	8.37	1,149	6.97	
4.29	10.37	3.31	8.90	1,263	6.83	
4.31	10.29	3.32	8.40	1,202	7.13	
		QUARTZ, SINGLE CRYSTAL				265
2.65				50	2.92	
				100	3.08	
		Note: First break in curve at a,		144a	3.18	
		second at b. Values above 400		150	3.21	
		kilobars probably refer to sti-		200	3.43	
		shovite.		250	3.69	
				300	3.98	
				350	4.29	
				383b	4.53	
				400	4.55	
				450	4.62	
				500	4.68	
				600	4.77	
				700	4.85	

TABLE 7-14.   *Continued*

ρ_0 g/cm³	U_S (Std) km/sec	U_P km/sec	U_S km/sec	P kilobars	ρ g/cm³	Ref.
RUTILE, SYNTHETIC SINGLE CRYSTAL, EXCEPT AS INDICATED; NATURAL CRYSTAL FROM OAXACA, MEXICO						266
4.25	9.75	2.92	8.33	1,033	6.54	
4.21 Nat	9.86	2.98	8.51	1,068	6.48	
4.25	10.08	3.11	8.74	1,157	6.60	
4.25	10.10	3.13	8.77	1,165	6.60	
4.25	10.11	3.13	8.76	1,165	6.61	
4.25	10.28	3.22	9.06	1,242	6.60	
4.20 Nat	10.25	3.25	8.90	1,213	6.61	
4.25	10.29	3.25	8.94	1,235	6.68	
SERPENTINE, ITALY						
2.78	8.80	2.72	7.60	575	4.33	
2.79	9.52	3.25	8.44	766	4.54	
2.80	9.64	3.35	8.43	792	4.65	
2.76	9.70	3.40	8.63	809	4.55	
2.83	9.95	3.53	9.01	901	4.66	
2.84	10.08	3.63	9.12	940	4.72	
SILLIMANITE, DILLON, MONTANA						266
3.07	8.68	2.52	7.54	584	4.61	
3.12	8.75	2.52	7.83	616	4.60	
3.13	8.93	2.65	8.01	664	4.67	
3.13	9.00	2.70	8.05	680	4.71	
3.10	9.02	2.75	7.94	676	4.74	
3.09	9.16	2.84	8.15	715	4.74	
3.13	9.33	2.93	8.48	778	4.78	
3.13	9.67	3.16	8.89	881	4.86	
3.15	10.08	3.45	9.29	1,012	5.02	
3.13	10.25	3.59	9.42	1,060	5.06	
3.13	10.37	3.68	9.55	1,099	5.09	
SPINEL, CERAMIC						266
3.41	8.76	2.35	8.46	678	4.72	
3.42	9.00	2.53	8.54	740	4.87	
3.43	9.40	2.79	9.09	871	4.95	
3.43	9.40	2.80	9.09	871	4.95	
3.43	9.49	2.85	9.16	896	4.98	
3.43	9.49	2.86	9.13	894	4.99	
3.41	9.75	3.05	9.41	979	5.05	
3.42	9.96	3.19	9.62	1,046	5.11	
3.41	10.08	3.25	9.91	1,098	5.08	
3.40	10.10	3.29	9.76	1,093	5.14	
3.41	10.28	3.41	9.95	1,158	5.19	

TABLE 7-15. ROCKS: ELASTIC CONSTANTS

Young's modulus: E, modulus of rigidity: G, in megabars. Poisson's ratio: σ. Under "Note", the letter "d" indicates dynamical measurements, numbers, the stress or stress range, in bars, for static measurements. The notation "$P = 500$" (for example), in the first column, indicates measurements made under hydrostatic pressure of 500 bars; if not otherwise indicated the pressure is 1 atmosphere. Numbers in parentheses are obtained indirectly with the aid of the formulas for isotropic elasticity (*see* Introduction)

		ρ	E (mb)	G (mb)	σ	Note	Ref.
Albitite, Sylmar, Pa.		2.61	.69	.28		d	48
	$P = 500$			.297			47
	$P = 4,000$		(.80)	.311	(.29)	d	
	$P = 4,000$	2.615		.348		d	294
	$P = 10,000$			.364			
Amphibolite, Nundydroog Mine, Mysore, India		3.07		1.04	.46	d	242
Amphibolite, Madison County, Mont.		3.07		.467			294
	$P = 4,000$			.554			
	$P = 10,000$			.568			
Andesite							
Walkenburg, Germany			.27?			100–900	255
Palisades Damsite, Idaho (altered)		2.57	.54		.18	0–70	226
			.40		.16	0–350	
Anhydrite, Persia		3.02	.72–.74	(.28)	.295		261
Anorthosite							
Quebec			.825.	(.328)	.262	70–600	1
	$P = 4,000$	2.708		.332	(.32)	d	46
Stillwater, Mont.	$P = 1$	2.770		.353		d	48
	$P = 4,000$			.371	(.31)		
	$P = 4,000$	2.750		.389			294
	$P = 10,000$			.399			
Barite							
Clausthal, Harz			.578	.228	(.27)		256
quasi-isotropic aggregate			.61	.25	.215		234
Basalt							
Ostritz, Germany			1.115			100–900	255
Champion Mine,		2.85	.61	.27			242
Painesdale, Mich.		2.97	.85	.34			
		2.91	.70	.30		d	
Howard Prairie Dam, Oregon, altered		2.74	.63		.25	0–70	242
			.61		.22	0–350	
	$P = 1$	2.82	.764	.315	.22		111
	$P = 1,000$		.825	.330	.25		
Guadalupe Drill Site (EMT) porosity 2.06%		2.82	.485		.384	d	287
Diabase							
Olivine, Sudbury, Ont.			.949	(.370)	.284	70–600	1
Neuwerk, Germany			.793			100–900	255
Nieder Kunnersdorf, Germany			.872			100–900	255
Westfield, Mass.							
#1		2.95	.800			d	136
#2			.885				
#3			.868				
Frederick, Md.							
#1		3.017	1.074	.391		d	49a
#2		3.015	1.075	.420			
	$P = 4,000$			.442		d	47
	$P = 10,000$	3.017		.447		d	294
Noranda Mines, Ont. (2500′)		3.007	.913	.400	(.184)	d	49a
		2.989	.821	.362	(.103)		
		2.989	.982	.407	(.228)		

TABLE 7-15.　*Continued*

	ρ	E (mb)	G (mb)	σ	Note	Ref.
Olivine, Vinalhaven, Me.						
#1	2.96	1.020		.271	11	248
		1.015		.271	56	
		1.070	.421		d	136
#7	$P = 500$		.430			47
	$P = 4,000$		.439			
(Metadiabase), Noranda, Ont.						
	3.04	1.161	.481	(.217)	d	49a
	2.99	1.062	.442	(.222)	d	
Centreville, Va.	2.984		.363		d	294
	$P = 4,000$		.420			
	$P = 10,000$		.431			
Ahmeek Mine, Ahmeek, Mich.						
	2.89	.72	.28			242
	2.94	.76	.30			
Onega, USSR	$P = 1$	3.04	1.04	.43	.23	111
	$P = 1,000$		1.14	.46	.25	
Diorite						
Mineville, N.Y.		3.02	.87	.37		242
		3.03	.55	.28		
quartz, Dedham, Mass.		2.928		.336		d	294
	$P = 4,000$		.418			
	$P = 10,000$		.432			
Dolomite						
Beuthen, Silesia			.76–.81			100	264
Bethlehem, Pa.						
#1	2.83	.710	.323			136
#2		.930	.362			
#3		.916	.398			
	$P = 500$		.42			48
(Marble), Cockeysville Md.						
⊥	2.87	.493	.261			170
‖		.631	.284	(.16)		
‖		.717	.282	(.27)		
Mascot, Tenn.	2.84	.85	.35			242
Dunite						
New Zealand						
#1		1.52	.60	(.27)	d	
#2		1.62	.58	(.40)	d	
	$P = 4,000$	3.270		.647		d	294
	$P = 10,000$		.674			
Balsam Gap, N.C.						
#1	3.275	.946	.56		d	136
	$P = 500$		.64			47
	$P = 4,000$		.67			
#2		1.484	.476			136
	$P = 500$		.654			47
	$P = 4,000$		.694			
#3			.624			47
	$P = 500$		.681			
	$P = 4,000$		.706			
#4			.570			47
	$P = 500$		.612			
	$P = 4,000$		.658			
#1L		.89			d	136
#2L		1.61			d	136
Twin Sisters Mt., Wash.						
#1	3.312	1.95	.74		d	296
#2	(mean)	1.4	.66			
#3			.72			
	$P = 4,000$	3.326		.757		d	294
	$P = 10,000$		.776			

TABLE 7-15. *Continued*

	ρ	E (mb)	G (mb)	σ	Note	Ref.
Dunite *Continued*						
Mooihoek Mine,						
Transvaal	3.760		.509		d	294
	P = 10,000		.572			
Eclogite						
Healdsburg, Calif.						
#1	3.441	1.42			d	296
#2		1.23				
	3.444		.625		d	294
	P = 4,000		.707			
	P = 10,000		.723			
Eclogite, Norway	3.578		.490		d	294
	P = 4,000		.751			
	P = 10,000		.777			
Epidosite,						
Mt. Weather, Va.	3.26	.91	.41			242
Essexite,						
Mt. Johnson, Que.		.671	(.267)	.258	70-600	1
Fluorite						
Stolberg, Harz		1.025	.420	(.22)		256
quasi-isotropic aggregate		1.13	.44	.275		234
Gabbro (*See also* diabase,						
norite)						
New Glasgow, Que.		1.08	(.438)	.219	70–600	1
Neurode, Germany		.914			100–900	255
Harzburg, Germany		.960			100–900	255
Gabbro, hypersthene,						
French Creek, Pa.						
#1	3.05	.727		.162	11	248
		.767		.169	56	
		.781	.348		d	136
	P = 500		.446		d	47
	P = 4,000		.480		d	
#2		.584		.114	11	248
		.615		.136	56	
		.711	.307		d	136
	P = 500		.443			47
	P = 4,000		.480			
#3		.672	.149		11	248
		.703	.154		56	
		.871	.354		d	136
Mellen, Wis.						
#1	P = 1	2.90		.332		d	47
	P = 500		.386			
	P = 4,000		.395			
#2	P = 1		.325		d	47
	P = 500		.393			
	P = 4,000		.405			
"greenstone", Mt.						
Weather, Va.		3.02	1.051	.421	(.25)	d	170
		2.96	.81	.35			
altered, Mineville, N.Y.	2.93	.85	.34		d	242
"San Marcos", California						
mean of 5	2.874		.370		d	294
	P = 4,000		.413			
	P = 10,000		.424			
Gneiss, (Granitic),						
Pelham, Mass.						
⊥	(2.64)	.033		.03	0	248
		.043			?	
		.284	.145		d	136
	P = 1		.079			47
	P = 500		.262			
	P = 4,000		.334			

TABLE 7-15. *Continued*

	ρ	E (mb)	G (mb)	σ	Note	Ref.
Gneiss (Granitic), *Continued*						
‖		.142			11	248
		.220			56	
		.220			d	136
‖		.168		.086	11	248
		.255		.146	56	
	$P = 1$	.288	.090		d	136
	$P = 500$		.277			47
Gneiss, Maggio, Tessin		.30			d	116
Gneiss, syenite, Mineville, N.Y.	(2.81)	.55	.24		d	242
Gneiss, granitic, Star Lake, N.Y. (*See* ref. 242 for other samples)	(2.64)	.50	.24		d	242
Gneiss, diorite, Montezuma quadrangle, Colo.	(2.87)	.68		.08	0–70	226
		.70		.11	0–140	
Gneiss, biotite	$P = 1$	2.91	.340			48
	$P = 500$		.359			
Gneiss, Hell Gate, N.Y.		(2.65)				48
‖	$P = 1$		.164		d	
	$P = 500$		.287			
⊥	$P = 1$		.182		d	
	$P = 500$		.308			
	$P = 4,000$		.338			
Granite						
biotite, Peterhead, Scotland		.571	(.234)	.211	70–600	1
biotite, Lily Lake, N.B.		.563	(.233)	.198	70–600	1
quartz monzonite, Westerly, R.I.		.509	(.208)	.220	70–600	1
coarse gray, Quincy, Mass.		.464	(.192)	.215	70–600	1
biotite, Baveno, Italy		.471	(.188)	.253	70–600	1
biotite muscovite, Stanstead, Quebec		.392	(.156)	.259	70–600	1
coarse gray, Quincy, Mass.		.568	(.237)	.198	70–600	1
Jannowitz, Germany		.415			100–900	255
Dresden, Germany		.435			100–900	255
Quincy, Mass. surface						
#1	2.66	.271			3	248
		.508			78	
		.416	.197	(.055)	d	136
#2	2.67	.239			28	248
		.473			78	
		.376	.180	(.045)	d	136
#7	2.63	.213			11	248
		.398			56	
		.325	.155	(.048)	d	136
#8	2.63	.238			11	248
		.465			56	
		.370			d	136
Quincy, Mass., from 100 ft. depth						
#1	2.67	.518			11	248
		.582			56	
		.598	.278	(.073)	d	136
#2	2.67	.495			11	248
		.566			56	
		.593	.277	(.069)	d	136
#3	2.66	.485			11	248
		.577			56	
		.605	.270	(.118)	d	136

TABLE 7-15. *Continued*

	ρ	E (mb)	G (mb)	σ	Note	Ref.
Granite *Continued*						
Quincy, Mass., from 235 ft. depth						
#4	2.66	.348			11	248
		.470			56	
		.467	.207	(.130)	d	136
#5	2.66	.345		.097	11	248
		.463		.137	56	
		.434	.187	(.180)	d	136
Quincy, Mass., from 75 ft. depth	2.65	.470	.209	(.124)		50a
Rockport, Mass., from 100 ft. depth						
H	2.65	.354		.096	11	248
		.426		.116	56	
		.434	.171	(.180)	d	136
E	2.64	.348		.084	0	248
		.410		.093	22	
		.460		.111	67	
		.510		.129	112	
		.560		.149	157	
		.610		.172	202	
		.510	.200	(.144)	d	136
Westerly, R. I.	(2.64)	.399	.180	(.065)	d	136
Westerly, R. I.	(2.66)	.705	.277	.271		143
$P = 1$	(2.61)	.55	.25	.13		111
$P = 1,000$		.66·	.39	.22		
$P = 4,000$			.325		d	294
$P = 10,000$			.338			
Arbuckle Mts.	(2.65)	.437–.472			d	262
Barre, Vt.						
$\perp$	(2.66)	.304	.168	−.04?	d	170
‖		.273	.152	−.10?		
‖		.442	.169	.31?		
Soevik, Sweden		.54			d	116
Stone Mt., Ga.						
$P = 1$	2.639		.15		d	294
$P = 4,000$			.369			
$P = 10,000$			.381			
Granodiorite,						
Weston, Mass.	(2.63)	.600	.253	(.187)	d	48
$P = 500$			.313			47
$P = 4,000$			.366			
Halite (*see also* Table 7-12)						
Upper Zechstein series		.28			d	259
artificial aggregates		.33			d	269
quasi-isotropic aggregate (Voigt)		.373	.15			
Grand Saline Dome, mean		.01?				268
Hematite ore						
Ishpeming, Mich.	4.22	1.42	.55		d	242
Soudan, Mich.	5.07	2.00	.78		d	
Bessemer, Ala.	3.78	.69	.27		d	
Ice (*see also* Table 7-12)						
−5°C	.917	.0917	.0336	(.365)	d	257
−9°C		.0929			d	254
−35°C		.109			d	
Limestone						
Knoxville, Tenn.		.621	(.248)	.251	70–600	1
Montreal		.635	(.250)	.252	70–600	1
Solenhofen, Bavaria	2.60	.577	.231	(.25)		296
		.627				136
$P = 1$			.196			47
$P = 500$			.220			
$P = 4,000$			.247			

TABLE 7-15. *Continued*

	ρ	E (mb)	G (mb)	σ	Note	Ref.
Limestone *Continued*						
Solenhofen (dry)	2.480	.547	.215	.27		292
	2.500	.567	.222	.28		
(smoothed values)	2.550	.616	.239	.29		
	2.600	.666	.256	.30		
	2.650	.720	.275	.31		
	2.700	.775	.294	.32		
(extrapolated)	2.712	.789	.299	.32		
(water-saturated)	2.570	.553	.213	.30		
	2.632	.648	.248	.31		
	2.669	.709	.270	.31		
Pennsylvania, carbonaceous						
#1	2.71	.337		.156	11	248
		.457		.193	56	
		.592			d	136
#2		.760		.270	11	248
		.750		.302	56	
		.801			d	136
#3		.606		.177	11	248
		.722		.193	56	
		.701	.267		d	136
	$P = 500$		.288			47
	$P = 4,000$		.300			
Persia	2.64–2.70	.53–.64		.23–.26		261
Bedford, Indiana						
$\perp$	2.37	.334	.142	(.18)		170
‖		.410	.159	(.29)		
‖		.372	.153	(.22)		
Redwall Formation, Marble Canyon Dam, Ariz.						
	2.71	.67		.25	0–70	226
por. = 3.4%		.68		.25	0–245	
		.71	.28		d	
	2.44	.17		.18	0–14	
por. = 13.9%		.19		.20	0–70	
		.21		.22	0–100	
		.28	.12		d	
	2.68	.34		.19	0–70	
por. = 4.7%		.36		.23	0–175	
		.52	.20	(.31)	d	
Limestone	$P = 1$	2.64	.55	.22	.27	111
	$P = 1,000$		.64	.24	.32	
Magnesite	$P = 1$	2.848		.47		d	294
	$P = 10,000$			.52			
Magnetite						
massive, Noranda Mines, Ontario	4.74	1.038	.447	(.160)	d	49a
quasi-isotropic aggregate	5.18	2.27	.98			
Mineville, N.Y.	4.23	.31	.19		d	242
Ishpeming, Mich.	4.01	1.09	.44		d	242
Marble (*See also* Dolomite, Limestone)						
Proctor, Vt.						
#1	2.71	.343		.141	11	248
		.460		.190	56	
		.495	.217		d	136
#2		.232		.104	11	248
		.399		.189	56	
		.280			d	136
#3		.383		.150	11	248
		.495		.220	56	
		.509	.223		d	136
	$P = 500$		.318			47
	$P = 4,000$	(.87)	.333	(.305)		

TABLE 7-15. *Continued*

	ρ	E (mb)	G (mb)	σ	Note	Ref.
Marble *Continued*						
Dinant, Belgium (fine, black)		.724	(.298)	.278	70–600	1
Carrara, Italy		.554	(.217)	.274	70–600	1
Rutland, Vt.		.524	(.207)	.263	70–600	1
"Gray"	2.74	.587	.229	(.28)		260
"White"	2.76	.378	.17	(.11)		260
Star Lake, N.Y.	2.72	.54	.23			242
Calcite quasi-isotropic aggregate (Voigt)		.95	.37	.27		
Monticellite, Crestmore, Calif.	$P = 1$	2.975			.441	d	294
	$P = 10,000$				.490		
Norite (*See also* Gabbro, Diabase)						
Sudbury, Ont.						
#1		2.87	.807		.224	36	248
			.906	.287		d	136
	$P = 4,000$			.404			47
#2		2.86	.796		.236	36	248
			.880	.285		d	136
	$P = 4,000$			.381			47
#3		2.92	.805			36	248
			.886	.360		d	136
#4		2.84	.936			36	248
			.940	.389		d	136
Norite, Bushveld Complex, Transvaal	$P = 1$	2.984		.378		d	294
	$P = 10,000$			.463			
Obsidian, Modoc, Calif.		2.446	.656	.303	.08		49a
Opal			.38	.18	.06		234
Phyllite							
Sly Park Dam, Calif., graphitic	por. = 15.3%	2.35	.10			0–35	226
			.27	.07		d	
quartzose,	por. = 22%	2.18	.09		.06	0–35	226
			.19	.05			
sericitic,	por. = 17%	2.34	.17			0–35	226
Pyrite, massive, Noranda Mines, Ont.		4.85	1.649	.702	(.175)	d	49a
	$P = 4,000$			.78		d	48
Pyrrhotite, massive, Noranda Mines, Ont.		4.59	.892	.341	(.309)	d	49a
Pyroxenite							
Bronzitite, Stillwater Complex, Montana							
#1		3.27	1.513	.654	(.156)	d	49a
	$P = 500$			.681		d	48
	$P = 4,000$			.692			
#2			1.526	.648	(.177)	d	49a
	$P = 500$			.666		d	48
	$P = 4,000$			.680			
	$P = 1$	3.287		.660		d	294
	$P = 10,000$			.714			
Bronzitite, Bushveld Complex, Transvaal		3.28	1.557	.628	(.239)	d	49a
	$P = 500$			.665		d	47
	$P = 4,000$			.680			
Bronzitite, Star Lake, St. Lawrence Co., New York, fresh (moderately altered)		3.43	1.24	.50		d	242
		3.31	1.13	.41			

TABLE 7-15. *Continued*

		ρ	E (mb)	G (mb)	σ	Note	Ref.
Sandstone, quartzite							
quasi-isotropic aggregate							
(Voigt)		2.65	1.00	.47	.07		234
Quartzite, Mont.	$P = 4,000$	2.647	.975	.424	.15		46
Quartzitic, Penna.							
#1		2.66	.636		.115	11	248
			.665		.110	56	
			.715	.324		d	136
#2			.635	.310		d	136
	$P = 500$			.398		d	47
	$P = 4,000$			.442		d	
#3			.570	.262		d	136
	$P = 500$			.382		d	47
	$P = 4,000$		.96	.43	.12	d	
Flint, Rugen			.745	.345	(.08)		234
Feldspathic, Ohio			.158	(.061)	.290	70–600	1
Ten Sleep formation,							
Wyoming		2.28–2.37	.14		.06	0–35	226
	por. $= 11$–16%		.17		.08	0–70	
			.22		.17	0–280	
Waterford, Ohio							
$\perp$		2.17	.071	.040			170
$\parallel$			.106	.048			
			.112	.045			
Amherst, Ohio							
$\perp$		2.06	.060	.032			170
$\parallel$			.067	.032			
			.088	.044			
Schist							
Chlorite-epidote,							
Framingham, Mass.		2.95	.705	.315	(.117)	d	48
	$P = 4,000$			.413			
Quartz-muscovite,							
Framingham, Mass.		2.70	.544	.230	.181	d	48
	$P = 4,000$			.379			
Idaho Springs Formation,							
Colo., Biotite		2.68–2.71	.40		.01	0–35	226
			.59	.25		d	
Biotite-chlorite		2.7	.68		.20	0–140	226
Shale, siltstone		2.63	.44 dry			200	264
			.19 wet				
arenaceous		2.60	.23–.41 dry			100	264
			.19 wet				
calcareous, Mauv Formation,							
Marble Canyon, Ariz.		2.67	.12		.04	0–70	226
	por. $= 1.8\%$		.25	.16		d	
quartzose		2.67	.14		.07	0–70	226
	por. $= 6.6\%$		.22	.12		d	
siltstone, Chico Formation		2.50	.13		.12	0–140	226
Monticello Dam, Colo.			.27	.12		d	
Serpentinite							
California	$P = 1$	2.718		.264		d	294
	$P = 10,000$			.292			
Ludlow, Vt.	$P = 1$	2.806		.366		d	294
	$P = 10,000$			.412			
Thetford, Que.	$P = 1$	2.602		.191		d	294
	$P = 10,000$			.219			
Shonkinite,							
Lyon Mtn., N.Y.		3.35	.35	.19		d	242
Sillimanite, Williamstown,							
Australia	$P = 1$	3.187		.774		d	294
	$P = 10,000$			.845			

TABLE 7-15. *Continued*

	ρ	E (mb)	G (mb)	σ	Note	Ref.
Slate						
Penna. ‖	2.78	1.129	.465		d	136
Everett, Mass.	2.67	.487	.218	(.115)	d	48
P = 4,000			.272			
Argillite, Brookline, Mass.	2.76	.769	.348	(.105)	d	48
P = 4,000			.368			
Bangor, Penna. ‖	2.74	.942	.275	(.71 ?)		170
‖		.835	.256	(.63 ?)		
Ishpeming, Mich. "White"	2.93	.76	.33			242
Syenite						
nepheline, Montreal, Que.		.629	(.251)	.256	70–600	1
Dresden, Germany		.671			100–900	255
Freital, Germany		.678			100–900	255
Riesa-Groba, Germany		.863			100–900	255
Ontario						
#1 P = 1	2.79		.171			47
P = 500			.300			
P = 4,000			.319			
#2 P = 1			.158			47
P = 500			.291			
P = 4,000			.310			
porphyry, Noranda						
Mines, Ont.	2.65	.755	.329	(.180)	d	49a
porphyry, Kirkland Lake,						
Ont.	2.70	.71	.30		d	242
mafic, Kirkland Lake,						
Ont.	2.82	.74	.28		d	242
Tuff						
Kirkland Lake, Ont.	2.78	.87	.32			242
"lithic", Howard Prairie						
Dam, Oregon	1.45	.014		.11		226
por. = 42%						
"Bedded", Oak Spring						
Formation, Nevada	1.6	.042	.021		d	267
por. = 37%		.049	.017	.08	tension	
		.076	.034	.11	compression	
P = 1,500		.023			compression	
welded, por. = 14%	2.2	.102	.041		d	
		.116	.054	.12	tension	
"silicified", Noranda						
Mines, Ont.	2.74	.815	.377	(.07)	d	49a

TABLE 7-16.   ROCKS: ELASTIC PARAMETERS AT 4 KILOBARS (46). *See* also 294

Terms σ, E, G, β calculated from velocities according to the formulas for isotropic bodies. (*See* introduction.) β (obs) from ref. 47.

Rock	ρ	Observed V_ρ Km/s	V_s Km/s	σ	E (mb)	G (mb)	β calc mb^{-1}	β obs mb^{-1}
Granite								
Westerly, R.I.	2.619	6.10	3.49	.26	.80	.32	1.82	(1.98)
Quincy, Mass.	2.621	6.30	3.62	.25	.86	.34	1.72	1.92
Rockport, Mass.	2.624	6.39	3.59	.27	.86	.34	1.62	1.85
Albitite, Pa.	2.615	6.40	3.45	.29	.80	.31	1.52	(1.93)
Anorthosite								
New Glasgow, Que.	2.708	6.82	3.50	.32	.88	.33	1.22	(1.4)
Stillwater Complex, Mont.	2.770	7.04	3.68	.31	.98	.38	1.15	
Syenite, Augite, Ontario	2.780	6.70	3.36	.33	.83	.31	1.21	1.69
Tonalite, Calif.	2.763	6.48	3.64	.27	.93	.37	1.49	
Diabase, Md.	3.012	6.84	3.83	.27	1.12	.44	1.22	1.16
Gabbro, Mellen, Wis.	2.931	7.13	3.71	.31	1.06	.40	1.05	1.14
Gabbro, French Creek, Pa.	3.054	7.11	3.98	.27	1.23	.48	1.11	1.13
Bronzitite, Mont.	3.279	7.71	4.59	.23	1.70	.69	.97	.96
Transvaal	3.288	7.75	4.55	.24	1.69	.68	.94	.89
Dunite								
Balsam Gap, N.C.	3.267	8.13	4.57	.27	1.73	.68	.80	.83
Twin Sisters Mt., Wash.	3.312	8.32	(4.86)	(.24)	(1.94)	(.78)	(.80)	
Marble, Danby, Vt.	2.704	6.72	3.49	.31	.86	.33	1.28	(1.39)
Quartzite	2.647	6.22	4.00	.15	.97	.42	2.18	(2.51)

TABLE 7-17. ROCKS: ELASTIC PARAMETERS AS FUNCTION OF PRESSURE AND TEMPERATURE

(Calculated from velocities, ref. 132)

	T, °C	P (bars)	E (mb)	G (mb)	σ	β mb⁻¹
Limestone, Solenhofen,	25°	500	.633	.237	.336	1.56
Bavaria		5000	.655	.245	.337	1.49
ρ = 2.656	200°	500	.605	.228	.327	1.72
		5000	.623	.234	.332	1.62
Marble, Danby, Vt.	25°	500	.705	.263	.341	1.35
ρ = 2.698		5000	.762	.283	.346	1.21
	200°	500	.586	.221	.325	1.79
		5000	.705	.261	.350	1.28
Sandstone,	25°	500	.457	.185	.234	3.50
Caplen Dome, dry		5000	.573	.224	.278	2.33
ρ = 2.543	200°	500	.404	.172	.175	4.83
porosity = 5.1%		5000	.570	.224	.272	2.40
Granite, biotite,	25°	500	.792	.315	.257	1.84
Woodbury, Vt.		5000	.887	.357	.242	1.75
ρ = 2.644	200°	500	.774	.307	.260	1.86
		5000	.868	.351	.237	1.82
Granite, (gray), Texas,	25°	500	.804	.328	.225	2.05
Llano County, Texas		5000	.852	.340	.253	1.74
ρ = 2.609	200°	500	.751	.304	.236	2.11
		5000	.836	.337	.240	1.87
Granite, (pink),	25°	500	.752	.288	.306	1.55
Llano County, Texas		5000	.795	.302	.317	1.38
ρ = 2.636	200°	500	.670	.258	.300	1.79
		5000	.781	.298	.312	1.45
Basalt, hornblende,	25°	500	.675	.271	.246	2.26
Chaffee County, Colo.		5000	.708	.279	.269	1.96
ρ = 2.586	300°	500	.637	.257	.240	2.45
		5000	.697	.273	.276	1.93
Gabbro, "San Marcos,"	25°	500	.960	.363	.322	1.11
Escondido, Calif.		5000	.998	.375	.331	1.02
ρ = 2.993	300°	500	.883	.334	.322	1.21
		5000	.983	.370	.329	1.04
Gabbro, bytownite,	25°	500	.901	.343	.314	1.24
Duluth, Minn.		5000	.953	.362	.317	1.15
ρ = 2.885	300°	500	.781	.303	.289	1.62
		5000	.901	.344	.309	1.27
Gabbro, hornblende	25°	500	.981	.378	.297	1.24
ρ = 2.933		5000	1.054	.407	.295	1.17
	300°	500	.878	.345	.272	1.56
		5000	1.037	.403	.287	1.23

TABLE 7-18. ROCKS: RELATIVE CHANGES OF YOUNG'S MODULUS AND MODULUS OF RIGIDITY UNDER PRESSURE. (Refs. 224, 236) E_0 and G_0 refer to 1 atmosphere.

Rock	Sample numbers		$P(Kg/cm^2)$ 300	900	1000	2000	4000
Basalt	43–9	E/E_0	1.25	1.5		1.7	
	43	G/G_0			1.18	1.19	
Basalt	4–2	E/E_0	1.4	1.6		1.8	1.95
		G/G_0			1.15	1.28	
Diabase	3	G/G_0			1.09		
Gabbrodiorite	38	G/G_0			1.12	1.15	
Gabbro	15–1	E/E_0	1.1	1.4		1.8	2.1
Gabbro	15–5	E/E_0	1.5	2.1		2.6	3.2
Labradorite	44–3	E/E_0	1.3	1.45			
Marble	26	E/E_0	1.2	1.4		1.5	1.5
		G/G_0			1.19	1.32	
Sandstone		E/E_0	1.1	1.3		1.5	
Syenite	42–3	E/E_0	1.5	2.1			
Syenite	31	G/G_0			1.10		

TABLE 7-19. ROCKS: EFFECT OF FREQUENCY ON ELASTIC CONSTANTS. (ROOM TEMPERATURE). *See also* Ref. 96.

Rock	f (cps)	E (mb)	G (mb)	Ref.
Granite, Quincy, Mass.				
1 atmosphere, $\rho = 2.65$				
Flexural vibrations	139	.465		50a
	372	.468		
	693	.465		
	1081	.461		
	1536	.469		
mean		.466		
Longitudinal vibrations	854	.466		
	1714	.469		
	2566	.467		
	3437	.471		
	4300	.472		
mean		.469		
Torsional vibrations	569		.211	
	1130		.209	
	1707		.211	
	2243		.205	
	2825		.208	
	3411		.211	
	4000		.213	
	4540		.210	
mean			.209	
Limestone, Solenhofen, Bavaria,	3.89	.258		174
(evacuated), $\rho = 2.67$	6.52	.259		
	8200	.266		
	9500	.268		
	16,400	.266		
	18,600	.261		
	28,500	.269		
$\rho = 2.66$	10×10^6	.26		
$\rho = 2.59$	9×10^6	.22		

Increases of the order of a few percent have been reported for Young's modulus as frequency increases from 40 to 120 cps (96) or from 2 to 40 cps (293).

TABLE 7-20. GLASS AND GLASSY ROCKS: COMPRESSIBILITY
$(V_0 - V)/V_0 = aP - bP^2$, P in megabars

	T, °C	a	b	P_{max} (kb)	Ref.
Silica	25	2.689	−20.8	12	6
	30	2.696	−19.7	12	58
	14	2.61	−32	10	42
	283	2.47	−17		
	11	2.54	−38	10	41
	100	2.56	−29		
	247	2.42	−19		
	390	2.45	−7		
	0	2.695	−22.7	4	188
	30	2.680	−21.4		
	100	2.645	−18.5		
	200	2.595	−14.3		
	300	2.545	−10.1		
		2.727		dynamic	26
Pyrex	25	3.045	−7.1	12	6
	30	3.037	−8.6	12	57, 58
	5	3.10	−2.2	10	41
	100	3.01	−2.4		
	217	2.79	−8.3		
	313	2.78	−8.1		
Obsidian					
Lipari, Italy	25	3.01		0.6	248
	15	2.76⎫			
	139	2.79⎬	mean to ⟶ 10		42
	294	2.75⎭			
	25	2.78–2.89		dynamic	49
Ascension Island	30	2.56	mean to ⟶ 10		58
Yellowstone Park, Wyoming	25	2.85	4.8	12	6, 7
Modoc, Calif.	25	2.76		dynamic	49
Pitchstone, Meissen, Germany	30	2.54	4.3	12	58
Tachylite, Torvaig, Skye	30	1.906	10	12	58
	75	1.945	10		
Kilauea, Hawaii	30	1.348		12	58
	75	1.397	8		
	25	1.44		12	4
Diabase glass	0	1.59	6.5	12	84
artificial	100	1.61	.4		
	12	1.60⎫			
	140	1.65⎬	mean to ⟶ 10		42
	300	1.62⎭			
Melts of natural diabase	25	1.36–1.53		dynamic	49

TABLE 7-21. GLASS AND GLASSY ROCKS:
ELASTIC CONSTANTS: EFFECT OF PRESSURE ON G

	E (mb)	G (mb)	σ	$\dfrac{1}{G}\dfrac{\Delta G}{\Delta P}$ (mb^{-1})	Ref.
Silica glass	.721	.305	(.181)	−10.3	42
(fused quartz)		.300			263
	.722				136a
Pyrex glass	.630				136a
	.621	.252	(.232)	−8.5	42
	.56	.231	(.22)	−8.6	77
Opal	.38	.18	(.06)		256
Obsidian					
Modoc, Calif.	.656	.303	(.08)	−5.3	47
Lipari, Italy	.652	.278	(.17)		256
Lipari, Italy	.695				136a
Arnafels, Iceland	.718	.303	(.18)		256
Feldspar glass	.899				49
An$_{70}$					
Diabase glass	.90–.96	.35–.38	.26–.30		49

TABLE 7-22. GLASS: EFFECT OF TEMPERATURE ON ELASTIC CONSTANTS

$T,°C$	Silica glass E/E_0	G/G_0	σ	Pyrex glass E/E_0	Obsidian Lipari E/E_0	Diabase glass E/E_0
0	1.000	1.000	.187	1.000	1.000	1.000
100	1.019	1.010	.198	1.027	1.003	.991
200	1.035	1.019	.205	1.044	1.005	.983
300	1.044	1.029	.205	1.059	1.007	.973
400	1.057	1.037	.210	1.068		.961
500	1.073	1.044	.220			.945
600	1.084	1.051	.225			.924
700	1.089	1.057	.222			
800	1.090	1.060	.220			
Ref.	136a	263	136a	136a	136a	49

SECTION 8

INTERNAL FRICTION IN ROCKS

by James J. Bradley and A. Newman Fort, Jr.

Contents

Handbook of Physical Constants—*Revised Edition*
THE GEOLOGICAL SOCIETY OF AMERICA MEMOIR 97, 1966

Studies of the propagation of stress waves in solid bodies demonstrate that the transmission of elastic energy is accompanied by a dissipation of energy even when the waves have small amplitudes. This dissipation results from imperfections of elasticity within the body and cannot be attributed to loss by radiation, geometrical spreading, or other effects. In a perfectly elastic, homogeneous solid the strain at any point is directly proportional to the instantaneous stress; a pulse or sine wave of infinitesimal amplitude traveling through such a material would have constant energy, and the medium once set into vibration would continue to vibrate indefinitely. Actual materials do not exhibit such ideal behavior; elastic vibrations subside even when the material is isolated from its surroundings.

The study of attenuation of stress waves in solids has demonstrated that Hooke's law does not hold even for extremely small strains. Fortunately, the deviations from perfectly elastic behavior are small, and the usual approximations of elastic wave theory are sufficiently accurate for most materials if the pressure, temperature, and frequency are not varied too widely.

The term "internal friction" has been frequently used for the nonelastic mechanisms that convert strain-energy into heat, thereby damping or attenuating the stress waves in a solid. The accumulation of experimental results seems to indicate that the damping of solids does not satisfy any simple general formula. There have been a number of mechanisms suggested to explain the dissipation of energy in a vibrating solid. These can be grouped into four main types:

(1) Thermal losses arising because of the direct conversion of mechanical energy into thermal energy, and the subsequent conduction of heat during the compression and expansion of the solid;

(2) Scattering losses arising because of the elastic anisotropy of the grains even in a chemically homogeneous, polycrystalline material. The grains will have varied orientations causing an impedance mismatch between adjacent grains and resulting in the scattering of vibrational energy. This effect becomes very important in inhomogeneous, coarsely crystalline materials when the wave length approaches the grain size;

(3) Ferromagnetic losses resulting from the interaction of matter in adjacent crystalline domains due to magnetostrictive or electrostrictive effects. If the solid is ferromagnetic or ferroelectric there will be dimensional changes along the direction of polarization which will result in strains along the boundaries of crystals having different polarization vectors. Thus, mechanical energy can be transformed into electrical energy and finally into thermal energy. This effect is relatively minor in most rocklike materials.

(4) Frictional losses arising from the sliding or movement of one surface past another within the solid. It is widely acknowledged that this mechanism probably accounts for most of the energy loss by elastic waves traveling through solid material.

What is not agreed upon is the proper phenomenological theory for non-Hookean solids. Birch and Bancroft [5], Ricker [38], Förtsch [13], Collins and Lee [9], Mason [28], Knopoff and MacDonald [21, 22, 23], and Zener [50, 51, 52], as well as others, have suggested and discussed physical and mathematical theories for such anelastic behavior but there has been no wholly satisfying model as yet postulated. Several mathematically convenient models have been developed such as the Voigt solid, the Maxwell solid, the Jeffreys-Ricker model, the Coulomb friction models, but none of these fits the experimental data at all frequency ranges.

From reviewing the literature and experimental data on rocks, several generalizations can be made:

(1) The specific dissipation constant $(1/Q)$ is essentially independent of frequency

(Birch and Bancroft [5], Collins and Lee [9], McDonal [29], Knopoff and MacDonald [22]) over a range of $\approx 10^6$ cps;

(2) Little has been done on the amplitude dependence of the specific dissipation constant, but the data available indicate that for strain below 10^{-4} the factor is independent of strain amplitude (Mason [28]);

(3) Observations made on crystalline materials (quartz, etc.) indicate that the dissipation is less for a single crystal than for an aggregate;

(4) The rate of dissipation of energy decreases with increased pressure. This indicates that, at least in porous materials such as rocks, the losses are closely associated with intercrystalline spaces; when these are decreased by compression the dissipation is decreased;

(5) The data are scanty but the experimental evidence that is available indicates that dissipation is relatively insensitive to temperature changes. The effect of temperature on attenuation is one area that needs additional experimental work.

In summary, an adequate theory of anelasticity must account for the variation of attenuation with the nature of stress (its frequency, magnitude, and direction) *and* with the physical conditions affecting the material (pressure, temperature, water saturation, etc.). A knowledge of the variation of wave attenuation with frequency, temperature, and pressure is required to extrapolate laboratory data to the conditions within the earth. Such understanding is particularly important in geophysics since much of the information about the earth's layering is derived from the study of the transmission and mechanical response of solids to stress waves.

This phenomenon has more than academic interest because much of the decrease in amplitude of a seismic wave with distance is caused by internal friction in earth materials. The change in shape of the seismic wave with distance is also, in part, a result of this anelastic character.

The references given here were selected to provide the reader with the source material for the attenuation data given in the table as well as a representative cross section of general references on anelastic theory.

In using the tabulated values of attenuation, careful attention should be given to the sample descriptions, frequencies, and the environmental conditions under which the measurements were made. In compiling the table of data on attenuation, preference was given to data upon reasonably well described materials and to studies showing the dependence of attenuation upon frequency, pressure, temperature, porosity, saturation, grain size, type of wave, and the direction of propagation. If available these parameters were indicated.

As yet there has been no general agreement as to the best means of determining or expressing the amount of damping taking place in a vibrating solid, and so several measures of attenuation or internal friction are in common use. In preparing this table, all values were converted to the equivalent "100b" value, the per cent of stored energy lost per cycle. The symbols for and brief definitions of some of the other internal friction parameters are:

$1/Q$ = specific dissipation constant—the tangent of the phase angle by which the strain lags behind the applied stress in the case of sinusoidal excitation. It is related to the rate at which the mechanical energy of vibration is converted irreversibly into thermal energy and thus does not depend on the detailed mechanism by which the energy is dissipated

δ = logarithmic decrement—the natural logarithm of the ratio of the amplitudes of two successive maxima or minima in an exponentially decaying free vibration

a = damping amplitude coefficient in the expression for a free vibration:

$$e^{-at} \sin 2\pi ft$$

α = attenuation coefficient in the expression for plane harmonic waves in an infinite medium: $e^{-\alpha x} \sin 2\pi f\left(t - \dfrac{x}{c}\right)$ where c = wave velocity

D = damping ratio, defined by analogy with simple second-order systems

$\Delta f/f$ = relative bandwidth of resonance curve between the half-power or 0.707 amplitude points for a solid undergoing forced vibrations—is a measure of the sharpness of the response curve

$\Delta E/E$ = fraction of strain energy lost per stress cycle.

By using the analogy of a simple linear second-order vibrating system b, the specific damping capacity, may be related to the other parameters as indicated:

$$b = 2\pi/Q = 2\delta = 2\frac{a}{f} = 2c\frac{\alpha}{f} = 4\pi D = 2\pi\frac{\Delta f}{f} = \frac{\Delta E}{E}$$

The numbers in the "Notes" column of the table refer to the sample and experimental conditions listed immediately after the table. Unless otherwise indicated in the "Notes" column, the measurements were made with longitudinal forced vibrations. The values in parentheses following "Notes" numbers 3, 16, 31, and 19 indicate, respectively, percentage water saturation, probable deviation of the measurement, temperature of the sample in degrees centigrade, and pressure on the sample in pounds per square inch.

TABLE 8-1. INTERNAL FRICTION IN ROCKS

Material	Frequency kilocycles/ sec.	100b per cent energy- loss/cycle	Ref.	Notes
Igneous Rocks				
Basalt				
Berestovetsk (U.S.S.R.)	3–4	1.57	46	31 (20°)
	3–4	1.319	46	31 (100°)
	3–4	1.130	46	31 (200°)
	3–4	.943	46	31 (300°)
	3–4	1.005	46	31 (400°)
	3–4	.943	46	31 (500°)
	3–4	.628	46	31 (600°)
	3–4	.690	46	31 (700°)
	3–4	1.068	46	31 (800°)
	3–4	1.885	46	31 (900°)
fine-grained (Ahmeek, Mich.)	10.56	3	48	14, 16 (50%)
	9.67	4	48	14, 16 (50%)
Kutaisi (U.S.S.R.)	3–4	1.256	46	31 (20°)
	3–4	1.130	46	31 (100°)
	3–4	1.256	46	31 (200°)
	3–4	1.256	46	31 (300°)
	3–4	1.130	46	31 (400°)
	3–4	.880	46	31 (500°)
	3–4	1.005	46	31 (600°)
	3–4	1.035	46	31 (700°)
	3–4	1.005	46	31 (800°)
	3–4	2.26	46	31 (900°)
sample of 2.85 gm/cm³ density (Painesdale, Mich.)	9.12	4	48	14, 16 (80%)
sample of 2.86 gm/cm³ density (U.S.S.R.)	1,000	1.08	47	..

TABLE 8-1.   *Continued*

Material	Frequency kilocycles/ sec.	100b per cent energy- loss/cycle	Ref.	Notes
Deccan trap				
sample of 0.30 mm grain size (India)	2,100	17.42	25	29
	3,500	35.9	25	29
	6,300	39.0	25	29
Diabase				
altered, amygdular, calcitized (Mich.)	9.9	5	62	14, 16 (50%)
altered (Lyon Mountain, N.Y.)	11.2	1.0	48	14, 16 (50%)
coarse-grained, mottled (Ahmeek, Mich.)	9.29	4	48	14, 16 (50%)
	10.32	3	48	14, 16 (50%)
fine-grained (Ahmeek, Mich.)	10.00	4	48	14, 16 (50%)
	10.28	3	48	14, 16 (80%)
	10.61	3	48	14, 16 (80%)
	9.72	4	48	14, 16 (80%)
Olivine (Vinal Haven, Me.)	..	2.62	5	6, 8
	..	1.74	5	6, 9
	..	1.07	17	..
Onega (U.S.S.R.)	3–4	.503	46	31 (20°)
	3–4	.565	46	31 (100°)
	3–4	.628	46	31 (200°)
	3–4	.628	46	31 (300°)
	3–4	1.005	46	31 (400°)
	3–4	1.381	46	31 (500°)
	3–4	2.64	46	31 (600°)
Diorite				
Augite porphyry, white (Utah)	10.7	2	62	14, 16 (80%)
	9.7	5	62	14, 16 (50%)
gneissic-diorite-gabbro	8.4	4	48	14, 16 (80%)
(Mineville, N.Y.)	10.59	1	48	14, 16 (50%)
sample (U.S.S.R.)	3–4	1.896	46	31 (20°)
	3–4	3.64	46	31 (100°)
	3–4	1.57	46	31 (200°)
	3–4	1.06	46	31 (300°)
	3–4	1.192	46	31 (400°)
	3–4	2.39	46	31 (500°)
	3–4	4.72	46	31 (600°)
sample	0.04	4.5	8	6
	0.05	4.8	8	6
	0.06	4.3	8	6
	0.07	4.6	8	6
	0.08	3.9	8	6
	0.09	4.8	8	6
	0.10	4.6	8	6
	0.11	4.8	8	6
	0.12	4.8	8	6
Dolerite				
sample (Clee Hills, England)	0.002–0.04	3.49±0.15	10	20
	16–96	3.14±0.25	10	20
sample	0.04	6.0	8	6
	0.05	6.2	8	6
	0.06	6.3	8	6
	0.07	6.9	8	6
	0.08	7.2	8	6
	0.09	7.8	8	6
	0.10	7.1	8	6
	0.11	8.2	8	6
	0.12	8.1	8	6

TABLE 8-1. *Continued*

Material	Frequency kilocycles/ sec.	100b per cent energy- loss/cycle	Ref.	Notes
Dolerite *Continued*				
sample of 0.28 mm grain size (India)	2,100	28.9	25	29
	3,500	41.6	25	29
	6,300	29.3	25	29
Gabbro				
altered, gray, massive	10.57	1.0	48	14, 16 (80%)
(Lyon Mountain, N.Y.)				
coarse-grained sample of 2.90 gm/cm³	..	1.85	5	6, 8
density (Mellen, Wis.)	..	0.37	5	6, 9
French Creek Norite, coarse-grained,	..	3.7	17	..
holocrystalline (French Creek, Pa.)	..	1.57	5	6, 8
	..	0.45	5	6, 9
sample of 1.6-mm grain size, $\lambda/d = 3.0$	500	2.57	26	33
at 1500 kc (U.S.S.R.)	1,000	2.00	26	33
	1,500	1.33	26	33
sample of 2.9 gm/cm³ density	1,000	1.54	47	..
sample (U.S.S.R.)	3–4	2.95	46	31 (20°)
	3–4	2.26	46	31 (100°)
	3–4	1.005	46	31 (200°)
	3–4	.628	46	31 (300°)
	3–4	.816	46	31 (400°)
	3–4	1.508	46	31 (500°)
	3–4	1.885	46	31 (600°)
	3–4	1.508	46	31 (700°)
	3–4	1.381	46	31 (800°)
	3–4	1.822	46	31 (900°)
	3–4	6.16	46	31 (1000°)
Sudbury Norite (Sudbury, Ontario)	..	2.14	17	..
	..	2.62	5	6, 8
	..	1.9	5	6, 9
Granite				
Biotite, medium- to fine-grained	8.7	2	48	14, 16 (50%)
(Lincoln Co., Nev.)				
coarse-grained, pink-red (Ukr.S.S.R.)	20–200	1.61	42	25
	20–200	2.76	42	26
fine-grained, dark gray (Ukr.S.S.R.)	20–200	1.38	42	33
gneissic (Lithonia, Ga.)	5.35	3	63	14, 16 (75%)
medium-grained, unweathered	20–200	1.61	42	..
(Ukr.S.S.R.)	20–200	1.15	42	18
medium-grained, weathered	20–200	3.69	42	..
(Ukr.S.S.R.)	20–200	3.69	42	18
medium-grained, pink-red	20–200	3.46	42	..
(Ukr.S.S.R.)	20–200	2.53	42	18
medium-grained, mottled, white	4.8	6	48	14, 16 (50%)
(Mount Airy, N.C.)				
medium- to coarse-grained, massive	6.65	4	48	11, 14, 16 (80%)
(Barre, Vt.)	..	5	48	12, 16 (50%)
	..	2	48	12, 16 (50%)
Quincy, moderately coarse-grained,				
holocrystalline (Quincy, Mass.)				
depth 75 ft.	0.86	4.2–6.3	6	..
	0.14–1.6	4.2–3.1	6	6
depth 100 ft.	7.0	3.5	5	6, 8
	7.0	0.53	5	6, 9

TABLE 8-1. *Continued*

Material	Frequency kilocycles/ sec.	100b per cent energy- loss/cycle	Ref.	Notes
Granite *Continued*				
depth 235 ft.	8.0	6.28	17	..
Quartzsyenite and granite (Lyon Mountain, N.Y.)	7.03	2	48	14, 16 (80%)
Rockport, coarse-grained, holocrystalline	..	4.84	17	..
(Rockport, Mass.)	..	3.5	5	6, 8
	..	.37	5	6, 9
sample (Kamýk, Bohemia)	200–2500	5.03	19	..
sample, medium-grained, 2.78 gm/cm³ density (U.S.S.R.)	1,000	4.0	47	..
sample of 2.5 mm grain size,	500	10.6	26	33
$\lambda/d = 2$ at 1500 kc (U.S.S.R.)	1,000	7.06	26	33
sample at depth of 200 m (U.S.S.R.)	.01	4.0	45	18, 34
	.01	6.0	45	34
sample (U.S.S.R.)	3–4	3.14	46	31 (20°)
	3–4	1.130	46	31 (100°)
	3–4	.753	46	31 (200°)
	3–4	1.130	46	31 (300°)
	3–4	1.130	46	31 (400°)
	3–4	1.319	46	31 (500°)
	3–4	2.69	46	31 (600°)
	3–4	2.32	46	31 (700°)
	3–4	2.39	46	31 (800°)
	3–4	5.33	46	31 (900°)
black-gray, speckled, holocrystalline, granitoid (Grants, N.M.)	10.7	2	63	14, 16 (75%)
Unaweep, light gray to pink, plutonic	6.24	4	64	14, 16 (75%)
(Grand Junction, Colo.)	7.38	4	64	14, 16 (75%)
	7.74	4	64	14, 16 (75%)
	6.24	5	64	14, 16 (75%)
Westerly, blue white, fine-grained, fresh,	100	7.68	65	23
1.0 mm grain size, 2.66 gm/cm³	200	7.86	65	23
density (Westerly, R.I.)	300	7.93	65	23
	400	8.23	65	23
	500	9.11	65	23
	650	9.95	65	23
	700	11.6	65	23
	750	11.6	65	23
	800	14.3	65	23
Westerly, gray, finely crystalline (Westerly, R. I.)	100–600	8.16±1.13	18	22
Woodstock, medium- to coarse-grained (Woodstock, Md.)	8.89	2.0	48	14, 16 (80%)
Yaitsen (U.S.S.R.)	3–4	1.570	46	31 (20°)
	3–4	1.255	46	31 (100°)
	3–4	.565	46	31 (200°)
	3–4	.565	46	31 (300°)
	3–4	.880	46	31 (400°)
	3–4	1.068	46	31 (500°)
	3–4	2.32	46	31 (600°)
	3–4	1.256	46	31 (700°)
	3–4	1.885	46	31 (800°)
	3–4	6.60	46	31 (900°)

TABLE 8-1. *Continued*

Material	Frequency kilocycles/ sec.	100b per cent energy- loss/cycle	Ref.	Notes
Labradorite				
sample of 2.75 gm/cm³ density (U.S.S.R.)	1,000	6.0	47	..
sample (U.S.S.R.)	3–4	3.58	46	31 (20°)
	3–4	2.83	46	31 (200°)
	3–4	1.885	46	31 (300°)
	3–4	1.885	46	31 (400°)
	3–4	2.03	46	31 (500°)
	3–4	2.52	46	31 (600°)
	3–4	1.885	46	31 (700°)
	3–4	2.52	46	31 (800°)
	3–4	4.53	46	31 (900°)
Pegmatite				
(Star Lake, N.Y.)	9.6	4	48	14, 16 (50%)
Peridotite				
Dunite, medium-grained, sugary,	..	1.57	5	6, 8
holocrystalline (Balsam Gap, N.C.)	..	1.26	5	6, 9
Pyroxenite, altered heavily (Star Lake, N.Y.)	4.8	9	48	14, 16 (50%)
Pyroxenite, altered moderately (Star Lake, N.Y.)	11.45	3	48	14, 16 (50%)
Pyroxenite, coarse-grained (Lyon Mountain, N.Y.)	3.90	7	48	14, 16 (50%)
Pyroxenite, garnet (Star Lake, N.Y.)	11.6	5	48	14, 16 (50%)
Syenite				
Augite, coarse-grained (Peninsula Station, Ontario)	..	0.314	5	6, 9
mafic (Kirkland Lake, Ontario)	10.05	2	48	14, 16 (50%)
sample of 2.71 gm/cm³ density (U.S.S.R.)	1,000	3.8	47	..
sample of 1.5-mm grain size	500	6.21	26	33
$\lambda/d = 2.5$ at 1500 kc (U.S.S.R.)	1,000	4.44	26	33
	1,500	4.08	26	33
Shonkinite, gneissic, medium-grained, dark (Lyon Mountain, N.Y.)	8.65	1	48	14, 16 (50%)
Shonkinite and pyroxenite, coarse-grained (Lyon Mountain, N.Y.)	6.36	3	48	14, 16 (80%)
Shonkinite to syenite, fine-grained (Star Lake, N.Y.)	9.83	3	48	14, 16 (50%)
Metamorphic Rocks				
Amphibolite				
fine-grained (Mysore State, India)	11.4	2	48	14, 16 (50%)
schistose (Mysore State, India)	7.75	3	48	10, 14, 16 (50%)
siliceous (Mysore State, India)	10.88	3	48	10, 14, 16 (50%)
	10.73	2	48	10, 14, 16 (50%)
Epidosite				
sample (Mount Weather, Va.)	10.39	2.0	48	14, 16 (80%)
Gneiss				
Augite, hornblende (N.J.)	10.9	2	62	14, 16 (80%)
Biotite, granitic (Star Lake, N.Y.)	8.4	3	48	14, 16 (80%)
Biotite, hornblende (N.J.)	9.4	2	62	14, 16 (80%)

TABLE 8-1. *Continued*

Material	Frequency kilocycles/ sec.	100b per cent energy- loss/cycle	Ref.	Notes
Gneiss *Continued*				
foliated, granitic (Pelham, Mass.)	..	11.3	17	..
	..	6.28	5	6, 8
	..	1.21	5	6, 9
granitic and pegmatitic (Star Lake, N.Y.)	8.10	4	48	14, 16 (50%)
Hornblende, syenitic (Star Lake, N.Y.)	7.92	3	48	14, 16 (80%)
Magnetite, granitic (Star Lake, N.Y.)	9.18	4	48	14, 16 (50%)
Pyroxene-biotite, syenitic (Star Lake, N.Y.)	8.94	3	48	14, 16 (50%)
Pyroxene, granitic (Star Lake, N.Y.)	8.76	3	48	14, 16 (80%)
Pyroxene, syenitic (Star Lake, N.Y.)	9.3	3	48	14, 16 (50%)
Quartz-magnetite (Mineville, N.Y.)	6.72	3	48	14, 16 (80%)
Syenite, quartzitic (Mineville, N.Y.)	5.60	4	48	14, 16 (80%)
	7.75	2	48	14, 16 (80%)
	8.69	1	48	14, 16 (80%)
Greenstone				
amygdaloidal (Pen Mar, Pa.)	7.85	5	63	14, 16 (75%)
amygdaloidal, epidote-rich (Mount Weather, Va.)	11.5	2	48	14, 16 (50%)
	10.26	3	48	14, 16 (50%)
Phyllite and quartz-oligoclase (Ishpeming, Mich.)	9.54	1–2	48	14, 16 (50%)
schistose (Ishpeming, Mich.)	10.3	1	48	14, 16 (50%)
Hornstone				
fine-grained (Lincoln Co., Nev.)	10.8	1	48	14, 16 (50%)
Marble				
coarsely crystallized (Star Lake, N.Y.)	8.70	3	48	14, 16 (50%)
Danby, coarse-grained (Danby, Vt.)	..	31.4	17	..
dolomitic (Cockeysville, Md.)	8.2	4	48	11, 14, 16 (80%)
	..	5	48	12, 16 (50%)
	..	4	48	12, 16 (50%)
Gazgan (U.S.S.R.)	3–4	0.816	46	31 (20°)
	3–4	1.005	46	31 (100°)
	3–4	.628	46	31 (200°)
	3–4	.565	46	31 (300°)
	3–4	.565	46	31 (400°)
	3–4	.816	46	31 (500°)
	3–4	3.64	46	31 (600°)
metamorphic limestone-calcite with brucite (Oro Grande, Calif.)	9.66	1	63	14, 16 (75%)
sample of 0.20-mm grain size (India)	2,100	13.8	25	29
	3,500	33.8	25	29
	6,300	24.0	25	29
sample of 2.68 gm/cm³ density	1,000	1.32	47	..
sample of 0.03-mm grain size, $\lambda/d = 85$ at 1500 kc (U.S.S.R.)	500	2.76	26	..
	1,000	2.16	26	..
	1,500	1.99	26	..
Tennessee	..	1.4	60	..
Vermont, white, 0.4-mm grain size (Proctor, Vt.)	..	4.5	5	6, 8
	..	0.63	5	6, 9
white, fine-grained (Lincoln Co., Nev.)	9.96	4	48	14, 16 (50%)
Quartzite				
magnetite-bearing taconite (Minn.)	10.9	1	63	14, 16 (50%)

TABLE 8-1. *Continued*

Material	Frequency kilocycles/ sec.	100b per cent energy- loss/cycle	Ref.	Notes
Quartzite *Continued*				
sample of 0.02-mm grain size,	500	2.76	26	33
$\lambda/d = 50$ at 1500 kc (U.S.S.R.)	1,000	2.39	26	33
	1,500	1.84	26	33
sample (U.S.S.R.)	3–4	1.82	46	31 (20°)
	3–4	1.258	46	31 (100°)
	3–4	.89	46	31 (200°)
	3–4	.628	46	31(300°)
	3–4	1.07	46	31 (400°)
	3–4	1.113	46	31 (500°)
	3–4	2.20	46	31 (550°)
	3–4	4.91	46	31 (575°)
	3–4	2.20	46	31 (600°)
	3–4	1.35	46	31 (625°)
	3–4	1.26	46	31 (650°)
	3–4	.942	46	31 (700°)
	3–4	.816	46	31 (800°)
	3–4	1.07	46	31 (900°)
	3–4	2.52	46	31 (1000°)
Schist				
Sericite, fine-grained (Superior, Ariz.)	9.3	5	48	14, 16 (50%)
Skarn				
calcareous, pyroxenite (Star Lake, N.Y.)	..	2	48	14, 16 (50%)
Garnet-pyroxene (Star Lake, N.Y.)	..	4	48	14, 16 (50%)
Slate				
black, calcareous, very fine-grained,	..	2.3	33	..
2.74 gm/cm³ density (Bangor, Pa.)	..	4.2	33	3 (100%)
	..	4.2	33	3 (93.3%)
	..	2.9	33	3 (26.1%)
	..	2.4	33	3 (3.3%)
	..	2.1	33	2
	.·.	1.7	33	1
	11.5	2.0	48	12, 14, 16 (50%)
	..	4.0	48	12, 16 (50%)
	..	2.39	17	..
	..	2.37	33	12
	..	3.81	33	12
sample	.002	1.2	61	6
	.040	2.6	61	6
white, extremely fine-grained (Ishpeming, Mich.)	10.1	1	48	14, 16 (80%)
Sedimentary Rocks				
Cap Rock				
Gypsum and anhydrite (Orchard, Tex.)	.12	11.8	7	6
	.35	11.0	7	6
	.65	11.5	7	6
	1.00	12.1	7	6
	1.50	12.5	7	6
	2.00	13.0	7	6
	1.10	10.8	7	..
	2.20	14.4	7	..
	3.30	14.4	7	..
	4.40	15.8	7	..
	5.50	15.4	7	..
	6.60	17.8	7	..

TABLE 8-1. *Continued*

Material	Frequency kilocycles/ sec.	100b per cent energy- loss/cycle	Ref.	Notes
Conglomerate				
Jelm, porosity 23.5 per cent	7.5	2.6	60	19 (4500)
	7.5	6.0	60	18, 19 (4500)
porphyritic rhyolite in cryptocrystalline phyllite matrix (Kirkland Lake, Ontario)	10.6	1	48	14, 16 (50%)
Dolomite				
gray, fine-grained (Jefferson City, Tenn.)	10.44	3.0	48	14, 16 (50%)
gray, fine-grained, brecciated (Mascot, Tenn.)	10.74	2.0	48	14, 16 (80%)
gray, medium- to coarse-grained, siliceous (Jefferson City, Tenn.)	10.31	3.0	48	14, 16 (50%)
massive, fine-grained (Bethlehem, Pa.)	..	1.63	17	..
sample of 0.05-mm grain size,	500	5.93	26	33
$\lambda/d = 50$ at 1500 kc (U.S.S.R.)	1,000	3.96	26	33
	1,500	3.27	26	33
Limestone				
Bedford, richly fossiliferous, medium- to coarse-grained (Bedford, Ind.)	..	1.5	33	3 (0.0%) (initial)
	..	9.0	33	3 (70%), 13
	..	3.8	33	3 (12%)
	..	3.8	33	3 (8%)
	..	3.0	33	3 (4%)
	..	2.2	33	3 (0.0%) (final)
	..	1.1	33	2
	..	3.14	33	11
	..	.94	33	12
	..	1.14	33	12
	..	1.7	33	1, 4
	..	2.4	33	1, 4
	..	3.4	33	1, 4
Chalk	.002	3.5	61	6
	.040	5.7	61	6
Chalk, hard (Flamborough Head Pebble, England)	.002–.04	5.71±.57	10	20
	11–66	8.98±1.02	10	20
coarse, white (Bessemer, Ala.)	8.52	4	48	14, 16 (50%)
fine-grained, richly fossiliferous (Barberton, Ohio)	9.24	4	48	14, 16 (80%)
fossiliferous (Bedford, Ind.)	7.44	3	48	11, 14, 16 (80%)
	..	1	48	12, 16 (50%)
	..	1	48	12, 16 (50%)
Georgian (U.S.S.R.)	3–4	.503	46	31 (20°)
	3–4	.565	46	31 (100°)
	3–4	.440	46	31 (200°)
	3–4	.314	46	31 (300°)
	3–4	.377	46	31 (400°)
	3–4	.628	46	31 (500°)
	3–4	2.14	46	31 (600°)
Hunton, white-to-limy marlstone (Okla.)	10.55	10.6	7	1
	2.82	8.8	7	1, 15
limonitic (Bessemer, Ala.)	9.36	3	48	14, 16 (50%)
Marble and limestone (Nev.)	10.4	1	48	14, 16 (50%)
mineralized limestone, shale (Utah)	9.35	2	48	14, 16 (80%)
Neva	..	1.43	34	6, 16 (80%)
	..	.91	34	6, 16 (80%)
	..	1.23	34	16 (80%)
	..	2.7	34	6, 16 (80%)

TABLE 8-1. *Continued*

Material	Frequency kilocycles/ sec.	100b per cent energy- loss/cycle	Ref.	Notes
Limestone *Continued*				
oölitic	.002	2.0	61	6
	.040	4.2	61	6
	.04	14.7	8	6
	.05	15.5	8	6
	.06	15.9	8	6
	.07	16.0	8	6
	.08	16.2	8	6
	.09	16.3	8	6
	.10	15.7	8	6
	.11	16.2	8	6
	.12	15.8	8	6
sample (Colo.)	2.79	9.6	27	7, 3 (100%)
	2.85	8.85	27	7, 3 (60%)
	2.85	1.2	27	7, 3 (7%)
	3.48	0.6	27	7
sample of 0.05-mm grain size (India)	2,100	27.4	25	29
	3,500	16.7	25	29
	6,300	9.4	25	29
sample (Pa.)	..	4.2	17	..
sample of 2.72 gm/cm³ density,	3,100	1.19	37	20
1.0 per cent porosity	4,900	1.20	37	20
	6,100	1.21	37	20
	8,700	1.30	37	20
	10,200	1.27	37	20
	15,000	1.33	37	20
	5,000	3.59	37	..
	7,700	3.66	37	..
	10,000	3.88	37	..
sample of nonuniform limestone with	5,000	3.5	37	..
2.71 gm/cm³ density, 0.0 per cent	7,000	3.33	37	..
porosity	10,000	3.49	37	..
sample of limestone core, 100 per cent	.125	4.8–10.2	9	..
water-saturated, 10 per cent porosity	.320	7.6–9.6	9	..
	2.810	9.0–9.6	9	..
	4.320	7.4–8.0	9	..
shelly	.04	10.0	8	6
	.05	10.7	8	6
	.06	10.8	8	6
	.07	10.7	8	6
	.08	11.2	8	6
	.09	11.2	8	6
	.10	10.9	8	6
	.11	11.1	8	6
	.12	10.7	8	6
	.002	1.0	61	6
	.040	2.4	61	6
Solenhofen (Bavaria)	.00389	.68–.82	36	20
	.00652	.8	36	20
	8.2	1.0	36	20
	16.4	1.0	36	20
	9.5	1.0	36	20
	18.6	1.0	36	20
	9,000	3.4	36	20

TABLE 8-1.   *Continued*

Material	Frequency kilocycles/ sec.	100b per cent energy- loss/cycle	Ref.	Notes
Limestone *Continued*				
Solenhofen	..	2.3	5	6, 8
	..	1	5	6, 9
Solenhofen, very pure, homogeneous	3,000	3.13	37	20
sample, 2.59 gm/cm³ density,	4,000	3.18	37	20
2.86 per cent porosity	4,500	3.20	37	20
	5,500	3.17	37	20
	6,100	3.30	37	20
	7,000	3.35	37	20
	7,800	3.27	37	20
	9,000	3.21	37	20
	3,000	6.45	37	..
	4,500	5.74	37	..
	5,000	5.72	37	..
	6,000	6.47	37	..
	7,700	5.71	37	..
	9,000	5.74	37	..
	15,000	5.60	37	..
Upper oölite (Portland, England)	.002–.04	3.49±.35	10	20
	10–80	2.02±.10	10	20
interbedded limestone and shale	9.75	3	62	14, 16 (50%)
(Huntington, Utah)	5.65–8.25	8–10	62	14, 16 (50%)
Marlstone				
calcareous, dolomitic (Colo.)	6.7	14	62	14, 16 (80%)
	7.7	7	62	14, 16 (80%)
kerogenaceous (Colo.)	4.6–6.7	11–16	62	14, 16 (50%)
sample (Rifle, Colo.)	4.68	22	48	14, 16 (50%)
	6.12	18	48	12, 14, 16 (50%)
light buff to dark brown, dolomitic,	3.66	16	63	14, 16 (75%)
kerogenaceous (Rifle, Colo.)				
Sandstone				
Amherst	.93	12.4	7	1
	1.26	11.4	7	1
	2.55	12.2	7	1
	3.83	12.0	7	1
	1.20	16.0	7	3 (.25%)
	2.40	21.0	7	3 (.25%)
	3.60	25.0	7	3 (.25%)
	.55	31.0	7	3 (.4%)
	1.10	50.0	7	3 (.4%)
	1.65	70.0	7	3 (.4%)
Amherst, medium-grained, porous,	..	13.4	33	11
weakly cemented (Amherst, Ohio)	..	11.6	33	12
	..	12.3	33	12
Berea, porosity 19.4 per cent	20	2.0	60	19 (6,000)
	20	7.6	60	18, 19 (6,000)
Connoquenessing (Franklin, Pa.)	4.8	11	4	14
ferruginous (Bessemer, Ala.)	7.97	11	48	14, 16 (50%)
	6.12	7	48	14, 16 (80%)
fossiliferous red (Bessemer, Ala.)	7.31	7	48	14, 16 (50%)
gray, fine-grained, silty (Tulsa, Okla.)	5.64	9	64	14, 16 (75%)

TABLE 8-1. *Continued*

Material	Frequency kilocycles/ sec.	100b per cent energy- loss/cycle	Ref.	Notes
Sandstone *Continued*				
Homewood (Franklin, Pa.)	3.06	14	14	14, 16 (50%)
	2.68	12	14	14
	4.26	10	14	14
	4.31	10	14	14, 16 (80%)
	3.90	12	4	14
	4.20	7	4	14
	3.90	7	4	14
	4.92	6	4	14
	4.86	7	4	14
	4.62	7	4	14
	4.20	8	4	14
micaceous	.002	3.5	61	6
	.040	7.4	61	6
Old Red	.002	5.0	61	6
	.040	8.5	61	6
Oriskany, porosity 3.3 per cent	25	.0088	60	19 (7,000)
	25	.0076	60	18, 19 (7,000)
quartzitic (Allentown, Pa.)	..	4.83	17	..
quartzitic sample of 2.84 gm/cm³ density	1,000	3.4	47	..
quartzitic sample of .04-mm grain	500	4.15	26	33
size, $\lambda/d = 70$ at 1500 kc	1,000	3.09	26	33
	1,500	2.72	26	33
sample (U.S.S.R.)	3.44	3.83	46	31 (20°)
	3–4	1.57	46	31 (100°)
	3.39	1.13	46	31 (200°)
	3–4	1.13	46	31 (300°)
	3–4	1.07	46	31 (400°)
	3–4	1.26	46	31 (500°)
	3–4	3.20	46	31 (550°)
	3–4	4.52	46	31 (575°)
	3–4	1.76	46	31 (600°)
	3–4	2.70	46	31 (650°)
	3–4	3.01	46	31 (700°)
	3–4	2.70	46	31 (800°)
	3–4	3.64	46	31 (900°)
	3–4	4.55	46	31 (1000°)
sample (U.S.S.R.)	3–4	2.39	46	31 (20°)
	3–4	1.885	46	31 (100°)
	3–4	.377	46	31 (200°)
	3–4	.565	46	31 (300°)
	3–4	.880	46	31 (400°)
	3–4	1.005	46	31 (500°)
	3–4	1.381	46	31 (550°)
	3–4	5.03	46	31 (575°)
	3–4	1.508	46	31 (600°)
	3–4	1.130	46	31 (625°)
	3–4	1.068	46	31 (650°)
	3–4	1.005	46	31 (700°)
	3–4	.943	46	31 (800°)
	3–4	1.256	46	31 (900°)
Navajo, fine-grained, massive, homogeneous, eolian, buff-colored (Huntington, Utah)	5.8	10	62	14, 16 (50%)

TABLE 8-1. *Continued*

Material	Frequency kilocycles/ sec.	100b per cent energy- loss/cycle	Ref.	Notes
Navajo *Continued*				
light-gray, fine-grained, interbedded with coal (Monongalia Co., W. Va.)	7.75	6	62	12, 14, 16 (80%)
sandstone, shale, and siltstone (Ala.)	7.5	10	48	14, 16 (50%)
soft	.04	29.5	8	6
	.05	30.5	8	6
	.06	31.5	8	6
	.07	32.2	8	6
	.08	32.5	8	6
	.09	32.9	8	6
	.10	33.0	8	6
	.11	33.3	8	6
	.12	32.9	8	6
Teapot, porosity, 29.7 per cent	7.5	8.6	60	19 (7,000)
	7.5	10.8	60	18, 19 (7,000)
Tensleep, porosity 15.3 per cent	10	1.2	60	19 (6,000)
	10	3.6	60	18, 19 (6,000)
Waterford, medium- to coarse-grained,	..	7.22	33	11
weakly cemented, porous (Waterford,	..	6.28	33	12
Ohio)	..	6.22	33	12
Shale				
Pierre, depth 300–600 ft. (Eastern Colo.)	..	.079f	38	17
Pierre (Limon, Colo.),	.075	20.0	29	27, 34
depth 260–750 ft.	.145	16.6	29	27, 34
	.200	16.8	29	27, 34
	.265	16.28	29	27, 34
	.325	17.38	29	27, 34
	.385	17.01	29	27, 34
	.440	18.8	29	27, 34
	.500	18.3	29	27, 34
	.555	17.25	29	27, 34
depth 500 ft.	.37	54.4	29	28, 34
	.50	54.9	29	28, 34
	.66	50.8	29	28, 34
	.79	52.2	29	28, 34
	.95	68.8	29	28, 34
	.110	66.7	29	28, 34
	.125	60.2	29	28, 34
	.138	56.6	29	28, 34
100–4000 ft.	.05	6.4 ± 3.2	29	34
silicified (Utah)	9.7	3	62	14, 16 (80%)
sample of 0.30-mm grain size (India)	2,100	31.4	25	29
	3,500	18.25	25	29
	6,300	27.1	25	29
light gray, finely laminated, very fine- grained (Ophir, Utah)	9.0	5	62	14, 16 (80%)
dark gray to black, very fine-grained, laminated (Monongalia County, W. Va.)	8.2	9	62	12, 14, 16 (80%)
Sylvan	12.80	9.0	7	1
	6.58	8.4	7	1, 15
	3.36	8.6	7	1, 15
dark, gray black, semigritty, silty	4.68	12	64	14, 16 (75%)
(Smithville, Tenn.)	4.68	13	64	14, 16 (75%)

TABLE 8-1. *Continued*

Material	Frequency kilocycles/ sec.	100b per cent energy- loss/cycle	Ref.	Notes
Siltstone				
interbedded with shale (Bessemer, Ala.)	8.65	5	48	14, 16 (80%)
interbedded with sandstone and shale (Bessemer, Ala.)	7.5	10	48	14, 16 (50%)
dark gray fine-grained, semigritty (Bakerton, Pa.)	3.18	17	64	14, 16 (75%)
Miscellaneous Materials				
Air, dried, 76 cm Hg	20	.026	58	31 (26.5°)
Air, undried, 76 cm Hg, relative humidity = 37 per cent	20	.26	58	31 (26.5°)
Aluminum, cold-rolled	..	.68	55	..
Alundum 7919, porosity 25.7 per cent	12	4.8	60	19 (8,000)
	12	6.6	60	18, 19 (8,000)
Brass, cold-rolled	..	.96	55	..
Cooper, cold-rolled	..	1.00	55	..
Glass, Pyrex	10	.338	59	..
Glass, soda-lime	10	0.47–0.55	59	..
Monel, cold-rolled	..	.286	55	..
Nickel, cold-rolled	..	.64	55	..
Polystyrene	20–60	2.6	57	..
Quartz	..	.52	54	..
Steel	..	.12	54	..
Water, salt, salinity 36 parts/million	150	.01	53	31 (15°)
Water, fresh	100	.003	53	31 (17°)

TABLE 8-2. INTERNAL FRICTION IN THE EARTH

Material	Period, sec.	100b	Reference	Notes
Earth's crust	4	0.483	15	32
	2	0.251	15	32
	12	1.57	15	32
	12	0.897	15	32
	24	1.57	15	32
	100	8.97	15	5
	20	3.14	15	5
	0.4	2–4	45	5
	20.0	1.80	45	5
	250	4.98	41	5
	250–350	2.3	12	5
	140	4.22	11	5
	215	4.18	11	5
	20	4.65	13	5
	10	1.4	6	5
	1	2.0	35	5
	22–24	2.01	3	5
	200–300	4.40	3	5
	300–320	4.28	3	5
	T = several min.	1.26–1.89	22	5, 21
	50–250	5.03–6.28	22	5
	72	5.02	40	5
	108	6.91	40	5
	215	7.55	40	5
	360	11.92	40	5
	43.2	2.51	40	5
	54	3.77	40	5
	72	5.02	40	5
	108	5.65	40	5
	215	5.34	40	5
	360	8.50	40	5
Earth's mantle 0– 56.5 km.	10–1800	3–6	2	30
56.5– 156.5 km.	10–1800	6–10	2	30
156.5– 396.5 km.	10–1800	8	2	30
396.5– 446.5 km.	10–1800	3–6	2	30
446.5– 696.5 km.	10–1800	1.5–2	2	30
696.5– 996.5 km.	10–1800	0.7–0.8	2	30
996.5–2896.5 km.	10–1800	0.3–0.4	2	30

NOTES

1. Oven dry
2. Desiccator dry
3. Saturated with water to the indicated percentage of pore space
4. Oven drying produced erratic effects, often irreversible
5. Calculated from damping of earthquake surface waves
6. Forced vibrations, torsional and flexural
7. Free vibrations
8. Pressure 200 kg/cm², temperature 30°C
9. Pressure 4000 kg/cm², temperature 30°C
10. Core parallel to foliation
11. Core cut perpendicular to bedding
12. Core cut parallel to bedding
13. For most fully saturated rocks the damping was too high to measure with available apparatus
14. Frequency calculated from the given velocity and an assumed length of 10 inches, which is given as the standard length in an earlier report (33) on testing procedure

15. Fabricated bars obtained by cementing short lengths of cores end to end
16. The value in parentheses after the note number approximates the statistical reliability that the recorded value is within 20 per cent of the population mean
17. Obtained by comparing observed wave forms from dynamite charges with wave shapes calculated from the Voigt viscoelastic theory, in which stress is a linear combination of strain and strain rate and b is found to be proportional to frequency in the low frequency range
18. Shear vibrations
19. The value in parentheses after the note number indicates the pressure in pounds per square inch when the measurements were made
20. Shear vibrations. Atmospheric conditions
21. The term T, the period of 1 cycle of a wave, is equal to $1/f$, where f is the frequency
22. Rayleigh waves
23. The observed Rayleigh pulse waveforms were Fourier analyzed, power spectra were computed, and ratios of the spectral amplitudes were calculated. From these ratios at varying radial distances from the source the attenuation at each frequency was determined
24. The difference in this value for 100b and the one immediately above it in the table can quite probably be attributed to differences in frequency used in testing
25. Measured parallel to flattened plane of microcline crystals
26. Measured perpendicular to flattened plane of microcline crystals
27. Vertically traveling compressional waves generated by charge of 1 pound of dynamite at a depth of 260 ft
28. Horizontally traveling shear waves generated by a weight dropped on the bottom of a 500-foot borehole
29. Values obtained from this reference are considerably higher than other data for corresponding rock types. Peselnick and Zietz [37] have noted this disagreement but made no attempt to explain the differences
30. Calculated from damping of earthquake surface waves and the earth's free oscillations. Shallower data are most sensitive to short-period vibrations, deeper data to long-period
31. The value in parentheses following the note number indicates the temperature of the specimen in degrees Centigrade at which the measurements were made
32. Calculated from earthquake body waves
33. Term λ/d is the symbol for the wave length (λ) to grain size (d) ratio
34. *In situ*

REFERENCES FOR SECTION 8

1. Alfrey, Mechanical behavior of high polymers, New York, Interscience Publishers, Inc., 1948
2. Anderson and Archambeau, Jour. Geophys. Research **69**, 2071, 1964
3. Arkhangel'skaya and Fedorov, Bull. Acad. Sci. U.S.S.R., Geophys. Ser., No. 8, 738, 1961
4. Atchison and Duvall, Bur. Mines Rept. E6-2, 1951
5. Birch and Bancroft, Jour. Geol. **46**, 59 and 113, 1938
6. —— Bull. Seismol. Soc. America **28**, 243, 1938
7. Born, Geophysics **6**, 132, 1941
8. Bruckshaw and Manhanta, Petroleum **17**, 14, 1954
9. Collins and Lee, Geophysics **21**, 16, 1956
10. Donata, O'Brien, and Usher, Nature **193**, 764, 1962
11. Ewing and Press, Bull. Seismol. Soc. America **44**, 127, 1954
12. —— Bull. Seismol. Soc. America **44**, 471, 1954
13. Förtsch, Z. Geophys. **16**, 57, 1940; *see also* Iiada, Bull. Earthquake Res. Inst. **16**, 391, 1938; **17**, 79, 1939
14. Grant, Duvall, Obert, Rough, and Atchison, Bur. Mines RI-4714, 1950
15. Gutenberg, Bull. Seis. Soc. America **48**, 269, 1958
16. Howell and Kaukonen, Bull. Seismol. Soc. America **44**, 481, 1954
17. Ide, Jour. Geol. **45**, 689, 1937
18. Institute of Geophysics, Univ. Calif., Seismic Scattering Project, Third Annual Report, p. 235, 1958
19. Klíma, Pros, and Vaněk, Jour. Geophys. Research **67**, 2078, 1962
20. Knopoff, Jour. Acoust. Soc. America **26**, 183, 1954
21. —— Bull. Seismol. Soc. America **46**, 175, 1956
22. Knopoff and MacDonald, Rev. Mod. Phys. **30**, 1178, 1958
23. —— Jour. Geophys. Research, **65**, 2191, 1960
24. Kolsky, Stress waves in solids, Oxford, Clarendon Press, 1953
25. Krishnamurthi and Balakrishna, Geophysics **22**, 268, 1957

26. Levykin, Bull. Acad. Sci. U.S.S.R., Geophys. Ser., No. 3, 259, 1962
27. Martin, John L., Dallas, Texas, Some of Martin's results are given in reference 9
28. Mason, Physical acoustics and the properties of solids, Princeton, N.J., Van Nostrand Co., Inc., 1958
29. McDonal, Angona, Mills, Sengbush, Van Nostrand, and White, Geophysics 23, 421, 1958
30. Menzel, Geophys. Pros. 2, 139, 1954
31. Nyborg and Rudnick, Jour. Acoust. Soc. Am. 20, 597, 1948
32. Obert and Duvall, Bur. Mines RI-4683, 1950
33. Obert, Windes, and Duvall, Bur. Mines RI-3891, 1946
34. Oliphant, Geol. Soc. America Bull. 61, 759, 1950
35. Passechnik, Bull. Acad. Sci. U.S.S.R., Geophys. Ser., No. 12, 1161, 1960
36. Peselnick and Outerbridge, Jour. Geophys. Research 66, 581, 1961
37. Peselnick and Zietz, Geophysics 24, 285, 1959
38. Ricker, Geophysics 18, 10, 1953
39. Rinehart and Auberger, Jour. Geophys. Res. 67, 2081, 1962
40. Sato, Bull. Seismol. Soc. America 48, 231, 1958
41. Savarensky, Popov, and Lazareva, Bull. Acad. Sci. U.S.S.R., Geophys. Ser., No. 8, 744, 1961
42. Silayeva and Shamina, Bull. Acad. Sci. U.S.S.R., Geophys. Ser., No. 9, 899, 1960
43. Vaněk, Klíma, and Pros, Bull. Acad. Sci. U.S.S.R., Geophys. Ser., No. 5, 395, 1962
44. Vassilyev, Kovalev, and Parkhomenko, Bull. Acad. Sci. U.S.S.R., Geophys. Ser., No. 3, 175, 1958
45. Vassilyev, Bull. Acad. Sci. U.S.S.R., Geophys. Ser., No. 5, 390, 1962
46. Volarovich and Gurvich, Bull. Acad. Sci. U.S.S.R., Geophys. Ser., No. 4, 1, 1957
47. Volarovich, Levykin, and Sizov, Bull. Acad. Sci. U.S.S.R., Geophys. Ser., No. 8, 793, 1960
48. Windes, Bur. Mines RI-4459, 1949
49. Wuerker, Annotated tables of strength and elastic properties of rocks, AIME (Petroleum Branch), 1956
50. Zener, Phys. Rev. 52, 230, 1937
51. —— Phys. Rev. 53, 90, 1938
52. —— Elasticity and anelasticity of metals, Chicago, Illinois, Univ. Chicago Press, 1948
53. Beranek, Acoustic measurements, New York, John Wiley and Sons, Inc., 1949
54. Gemant, Frictional phenomena, Brooklyn, N.Y., Chemical Publishing Co., Inc., 1950
55. Kimball, Vibration prevention in engineering, New York, John Wiley and Sons, Inc., 1932
56. Kinsler and Frey, Fundamentals of acoustics, New York, John Wiley and Sons, Inc., 1950
57. Parfitt, Nature 164, 489, 1949
58. Sivian, Jour. Acoust. Soc. America 19, 914, 1947
59. Wegel and Walther, Physics 6, 141, 1935
60. Wyllie, Gardner, and Gregory, Geophysics 27, 569, 1962
61. Usher, Geophys. Pros. 10, 119, 1962
62. Windes, Bur. Mines RI-4727, 1950
63. Blair, Bur. Mines RI-5130, 1955
64. —— Bur. Mines RI-5244, 1956
65. Knopoff and Porter, Jour. Geophys. Research 68, 6317, 1963
66. McDonough, Underground effects of nuclear weapons in the close-in region, DASA 1357 (IV), Appendix F-Rock Property Data, Published by E. H. Plesset Associates, Inc., California, 1963.

SECTION 9

SEISMIC VELOCITIES

by FRANK PRESS

CONTENTS

ILLUSTRATIONS

INTRODUCTION

At best, seismic exploration reveals only the variation of elastic velocity at differing depths in the earth. It remains to interpret this variation, usually in terms of the distribution of material with depth, occasionally in terms of the vertical variation of temperature, state, porosity, and other velocity-affecting parameters. Rarely can a unique interpretation of material distribution be made from seismic data alone. This is due to the large range of velocities even for well defined materials, and the common overlapping of velocity ranges of different materials.

Velocity depends on a large number of factors. Among these are mineralogical composition, fluid content, temperature, pressure, grain size, cementation, direction with respect to bedding or foliation, and alteration. Lithologic classification is not at present fine enough to significantly reduce the velocity range for a given rock type. Sampling errors as much as 10 per cent for both laboratory and field determinations may occur. For these reasons a compilation of seismic velocities serves to provide known ranges (with no assurance that the possible extremes have been covered), and if possible, a statement of average values or typical ranges.

Many field and laboratory studies have been devoted to the determination of seismic velocities. A complete listing is not attempted here, priority in selection being given to recent measurements on well described, common rocks. Field measurements are based almost entirely on explosion-generated waves in the frequency range of 10–100 cycles/sec. Laboratory determinations are typically made on small cylindrical samples. Resonance methods using audio frequencies, and pulse techniques using frequencies as high as 10^7 cycles/sec are used. Fortunately, dispersion of seismic body waves in the frequency 10^{-1}–10^7 cycles/sec is negligible, and results from both methods may be used interchangeably [6,7] to determine velocity ranges. The agreement between ultrasonic well-logging data and seismic (explosion) hole data to within 5 per cent [79] is further support for this conclusion.

TABLE 9-1. WAVE VELOCITIES IN IGNEOUS ROCKS AT SMALL PRESSURES AND
DEPTHS AND NORMAL TEMPERATURES

These velocity data, listed according to position in the main sequence of igneous rocks, are primarily for correlation with near-surface rocks. Both laboratory and field measurements are included. It is apparent that seismic velocity alone cannot distinguish between rocks over the wide range of composition from syenite to diorite Much of the scatter in values at small depths and low pressures can be ascribed to the disturbing effect of porosity. The reader should be wary of the data in Table 9-1 because they fall in a range where the pressure effect is large. Although a gross relationship between velocity and composition is indicated, the well known systematic correlation becomes pronounced only when porosities are reduced. Reliable comparisons between seismic (field) and ultrasonic (laboratory) measurements show fairly good consistency between the two methods.

1 km/sec = 3280.8 ft/sec

Material	Velocities in km/sec V_P	V_S	Remarks*	Ref.
Nephelite syenite,				
Arkansas	5.53	..	f	2
Labradorite trachyte	5.41	3.05	l; pressure 200 bars	16
Granite				
Barriefield, Ont.	5.64	2.87	l; 20 bars	7
Quincy, Mass.	5.0	..	f	2
Quincy, Mass.	5.88	2.94	l; 90 bars	7
Westerly, R.I.	5.0	..	f	2
Westerly, R.I.	5.76	3.23	l	1
Rockport, Mass.	5.1	..	f	2
Arbuckle Mts., Okla.	5.46	..	f	11
Yosemite, Calif.	5.2	..	f	3
Bear Mtn., Tex.	5.52	3.04	l; 35 bars	6
Japan	5.12	3.03	l; 18 granites	17
Rönne, Denmark	4.8	..	f	5
New South Wales	5.6	..	f	4
U.S. and Canada	5.22	..	l; 9 rocks	82
Leningrad, USSR	5.40–5.60	..	f; V_P/V_S: 1.69–1.75	86
Ukraine, USSR	5.55–6.00	..	f; V_P/V_S: 1.6–1.8	86
Quartz Monzonite				
Westerly, R.I.	5.26	2.89	l; 35 bars	6
Granodiorite				
Lakeside, Calif.	4.88	3.16	l	8
New South Wales	4.6	..	f	4
Weston, Mass.	4.78	3.10	l	30
Diorite				
Salem, Mass.	5.78	3.06	l; 35 bars	6
Andesite				
Colorado	5.23	2.73	l; 35 bars	6
Gabbro diorite	5.4	..	..	38
Hornblende gabbro	6.60	3.56	l; 200 bars	16
Gabbro				
Escondido, Calif.	6.69	3.47	l; 200 bars	16
Duluth, Minn.	6.45	3.42	l; 200 bars	16
Johannisburg, E. Prussia	6.5	..	f; depth 1200 m	12
Diabase				
E. Siberia	5.8–6.6	..	f; V_P/V_S: 1.8–2.3	86

TABLE 9-1. *Continued*

Material	Velocities in km/sec V_P	V_S	Remarks*	Ref.
Basalt				
Germany	6.4	3.2	*l*	19
Germany	5.6	..	*f*	10
Germany	5.06	2.72	*f*; depth 710 m	13
Colorado	5.41	3.21	*l*; 200 bars	16
Gabbro-diabase-anorthosite	6.26	..	*l*; 6 rocks 18 samples	82
Norite				
Elizabethtown, N.Y.	6.18	3.24	*l*; 35 bars	6
Sudbury, Ont.	6.22	3.49	*f*	9
Eclogite				
Fichtel Mtn., Germany	8.0	4.3	*l*	19
Anorthosite				
Adirondack Mts., N.Y.	6.63	..	*f*	65
Dunite				
Jackson City, N.C.	7.40	3.79	*l*; 200 bars	16
Twin Sisters, Wash.	8.60	4.37	*l*; 70 bars	7

* *f* = field determination; *l* = laboratory determination

TABLE 9-2. COMPRESSIONAL WAVE VELOCITIES IN ROCKS
AS A FUNCTION OF PRESSURE [84, 96]

These velocities are laboratory determinations made by Birch [84] and Simmons [96] using ultrasonic pulse techniques. At low pressures, the pressure effect is large, and the velocity measurements are highly variable and of questionable significance. The intrinsic velocity of a rock is achieved at pressures of about 1 kb where porosity is reduced to the point that solid contact between grains is restored. Above 1 kb the pressure dependence is much smaller and is controlled by the intrinsic effect upon the crystalline components. The velocities are not corrected for the change in length of the specimen under pressure. The tabulated values are higher than the true values by at most 4 units in the last figure.

Birch [84] and Hughes and his collaborators [7, 77] have independently determined velocities as a function of pressure for several of the samples listed in Table 2. Such good agreement was found as to remove experimental technique as a source of uncertainty in these determinations.

Rock	Density g/cm^3	P(bars) = 10	V_P in km/sec 500	1000	2000	4000	6000	10,000
Serpentinite (chrysotile), Thetford, Que.	2.601	5.6	..	5.67	5.73	5.80	5.87	6.00
Serpentinite (antigorite), Ludlow, Vt.	2.614	4.7	6.33	6.46	6.59	6.70	6.75	6.82
Granite, Westerly, R.I. "G-1"	2.619	4.1	5.63	5.84	5.97	6.10	6.16	6.23
Granite, Quincy, Mass.	2.621	5.1	6.04	6.11	6.20	6.30	6.37	6.45
Granite, Rockport, Mass.	2.624	5.0	5.96	6.18	6.29	6.39	6.43	6.51
Granite, Stone Mtn., Ga.	2.625	3.7	5.42	5.94	6.16	6.27	6.33	6.40
Granite, Chelmsford, Mass.	2.626	4.2	5.64	5.91	6.09	6.22	6.28	6.35
Gneiss, Pelham, Mass.	2.643	⊥*3.4	5.67	5.91	6.06	6.18	6.27	6.31
Quartz monzonite, Porterville, Calif.	2.644	5.1	..	5.95	6.07	6.22	6.28	6.37
Quartzite, Montana	2.647	5.6	..	6.11	6.15	6.22	6.26	6.35
Granite, Hyderabad, India	2.654	5.4	6.26	6.31	6.38	6.44	6.49	6.56
Granite, Barre, Vt.	2.655	5.1	5.86	6.06	6.15	6.25	6.32	6.39
Sandstone, (Catskill), N.Y.	2.659	3.9	5.0	5.27	5.44	5.63	5.75	(5.85)
Pyrophyllite, ("Lava")	2.662	3.5	..	4.73	5.02	5.38	5.58	5.89
Granite, Sacred Heart, Minn.	2.662	5.9	..	6.24	6.28	6.34	6.38	6.45

TABLE 9-2. *Continued*

Rock	Density g/cm³	P(bars) = 10	500	V_P in km/sec 1000	2000	4000	6000	10,000
Granite, Barriefield, Ont.	2.672	5.7	6.21	6.29	6.35	6.42	6.46	6.51
Gneiss, Hell Gate, N.Y.	2.675	⊥5.1	6.06	6.13	6.23	6.33	6.37	6.50
Granite, Hyderabad, India (A)	2.676	5.7	..	6.42	6.46	6.51	6.55	6.61
"Granite," Englehart, Ont.	2.679	6.1	6.28	6.33	6.37	6.43	6.48	6.57
Graywacke, New Zealand	2.679	5.4	5.63	5.76	5.87	5.98	6.04	6.13
"Granite", Latchford, Ont.	2.683	5.7	6.13	6.19	6.25	6.30	6.34	6.41
Albitite, Sylmar, Pa.	2.687	6.40	..	6.62	6.65	6.68	6.72	6.76
Granodiorite, Butte, Mont. (mean)	2.705	4.4	..	6.27	6.35	6.43	6.48	6.56
Graywacke, Quebec	2.705	5.4	..	5.92	6.04	6.14	6.20	6.28
Serpentinite, Calif.	2.710	5.8	..	6.02	6.08	6.15	6.21	6.31
Slate, (Cambridge), Medford, Mass.	2.734	5.49	..	5.79	5.91	6.02	6.10	6.22
"Charnockite", Pallavaram, India	2.740	6.15	..	6.24	6.30	6.36	6.40	6.46
Granodiorite, gneiss, (Bethlehem), N.H.	2.758	⊥4.4	..	5.95	6.07	6.16	6.21	6.30
Tonalite, Val Verde, Calif.	2.763	5.1	..	6.33	6.43	6.49	6.54	6.60
Anorthosite, Tahawus, N.Y.	2.768	6.73	..	6.86	6.90	6.94	6.97	7.02
Anorthosite, Stillwater Complex, Mont.	2.770	6.5	..	6.97	7.01	7.05	7.07	7.10
Augite syenite, Ontario	2.780	5.7	..	6.58	6.63	6.70	6.73	6.79
Mica schist, Woodsville, Vt.	2.797	5.7	⊥	6.43	6.48	6.53	6.57	6.64
Serpentinite, Ludlow, Vt.	2.798	6.4	..	6.51	6.57	6.67	6.74	6.84
Quartz diorite, San Luis Rey quadrangle, Calif.	2.798	5.1	..	6.43	6.52	6.60	6.64	6.71
Anorthosite, Bushveld Complex	2.807	5.7	6.92	6.98	7.05	7.13	7.16	7.21
Chlorite schist, Chester Quarry, Vt.	2.841	4.8	..	6.75	6.82	6.92	6.98	7.07
Quartz diorite, Dedham, Mass.	2.906	5.5	..	6.46	6.53	6.60	6.65	6.71
Talc schist, Chester, Vt.	2.914	4.9	..	6.30	6.50	6.71	6.82	6.97
Gabbro, Mellen, Wis.	2.931	6.8	7.04	7.07	7.09	7.13	7.16	7.21
Diabase (Nippissing), Cobalt, Ont.	2.964	6.55	..	6.64	6.67	6.71	6.75	6.82
Diabase, Centreville, Va. "W-1"	2.976	6.14	..	6.70	6.76	6.82	6.86	6.93
Diabase, Holyoke, Mass.	2.977	6.25	6.40	6.43	6.47	6.52	6.56	6.63
Norite, Pretoria, Transvaal	2.978	6.6	7.02	7.07	7.11	7.16	7.20	7.28
Dunite (altered), Webster, N.C.	2.980	6.0	..	6.37	6.46	6.55	6.64	6.79
Diabase (Keweenawan), Sudbury, Ont.	3.003	6.4	6.67	6.72	6.76	6.81	6.84	6.91
Diabase, Frederick, Md.	3.012	6.76	..	6.77	6.80	6.84	6.88	6.92
Gabbro, French Creek, Pa.	3.054	5.8	6.74	6.93	7.02	7.11	7.17	7.23
Amphibolite, Madison Co., Mont.	3.120	6.89	..	7.17	7.21	7.27	7.31	7.35
Jadeite, Japan	3.180	7.6	..	8.21	8.22	8.23	8.24	8.28
Actinolite schist, Chester, Vt.	3.194	6.61	..	7.20	7.32	7.41	7.47	7.54
Dunite, Webster, N.C.	3.244	7.0	..	7.54	7.59	7.65	7.69	7.78
Pyroxenite, Sonoma Co., Calif.	3.247	6.8	..	7.73	7.79	7.88	7.93	8.01
Dunite, Mt. Dun, New Zealand	3.258	7.5	7.69	7.75	7.80	7.86	7.92	8.00
Dunite, Balsam Gap, N.C.	3.267	7.0	7.82	7.89	8.01	8.13	8.19	8.28
Bronzitite, Stillwater Complex, Mont.	3.279	7.42	..	7.62	7.65	7.72	7.75	7.83
Bronzitite, Bushveld Complex	3.288	..	7.40	7.49	7.60	7.75	7.85	8.02
Dunite, Addie, N.C.	3.304	7.70	..	7.99	8.05	8.14	8.20	8.28
Dunite, Twin Sisters Peaks, Wash.	3.312	7.7	8.11	8.19	8.27	8.32	8.35	8.42

TABLE 9-2. *Continued*

Rock	Density g/cm³	P(bars) = 10	500	1000	2000	4000	6000	10,000
"Eclogite", Tanganyika	3.328	6.64	7.30	7.38	7.46	7.57	7.62	7.71
Jadeite, Burma	3.331	8.45	..	8.67	8.69	8.72	8.75	8.78
Eclogite, Kimberley	3.338	6.6	7.49	7.56	7.65	7.79	7.85	7.92
Harzburgite, Bushveld Complex	3.369	6.9	7.74	7.78	7.81	7.85	7.90	7.95
Eclogite, Kimberley, South Africa	3.376	7.17	7.65	7.68	7.73	7.79	7.82	7.87
Eclogite, Sunnmore, Norway	3.376	5.2	..	7.13	7.30	7.46	7.54	7.69
Eclogite, Healdsburg, Calif.	3.441	7.31	..	7.69	7.81	7.89	7.94	8.01
Garnet (grossularite), Conn.	3.561	6.3	..	8.41	8.55	8.72	8.83	8.99
Dunite, Mooihoek Mine, Transvaal	3.744	6.7	7.13	7.16	7.21	7.27	7.30	7.36
Garnet (almandite-pyrope)	3.950	5.9	..	7.81	7.91	7.99	8.01	8.07
Microcline, Labrador	2.571	..	6.84	6.95	7.01	7.06	7.09	7.15
Serpentine, Middlefield, Mass.	2.789	..	6.71	6.74	6.79	6.84	6.90	6.97
Magnesite	2.802	..	7.06	7.11	7.19	7.27	7.33	7.45
Dolomite, Williamstown, Mass.	2.845	..	6.77	6.93	7.06	7.17	7.23	7.36
Wollastonite	2.873	..	..	7.21	7.42	7.56	7.64	7.71
Monticellite, Crestmore, Calif.	3.014	..	7.22	7.27	7.31	7.36	7.40	7.50
Idocrase, Crestmore, Calif.	3.144	..	6.10	6.54	6.95	7.27	7.40	7.54
Sillimanite, Williamstown, S. Australia	3.187	..	9.51	9.55	9.60	9.65	9.68	9.73

* The symbol $\perp$ indicates propagation normal to foliation or schistosity.

TABLE 9-3. SHEAR WAVE VELOCITIES IN ROCKS AS A FUNCTION OF PRESSURE [97]

These velocities are laboratory determinations by Simmons [97] using ultrasonic pulse techniques. At low pressures, the pressure effect is large, due to porosity effects as in the case of compressional wave velocities (Table 9-2). The velocities are not corrected for the change in length of the specimen under pressure.

Rock	Density g/cm³	P(bars) = 1	V_S in km/sec					
			500	1000	2000	4000	6000	10,000
Serpentinite (chrysotile), Thetford, Que.	2.602	2.71	2.79	2.81	2.82	2.85	2.87	2.90
Albitite, Sylmar, Pa.	2.615	3.43	3.54	3.57	3.61	3.65	3.68	3.73
Granite, Westerly, R.I.	2.635	2.77	3.27	3.36	3.44	3.51	3.54	3.58
Granite, Rockport, Mass.	2.638	3.07	3.47	3.54	3.61	3.68	3.71	3.77
Granite, Stone Mtn., Ga.	2.639	2.43	3.36	3.53	3.66	3.74	3.76	3.80
Quartz monzonite, Porterville, Calif.	2.652	3.16	3.55	3.63	3.71	3.78	3.81	3.86
Granite, Barre, Vt.	2.665	2.79	3.35	3.48	3.52	3.64	3.67	3.70
Serpentinite, Calif.	2.718	3.12	3.17	3.18	3.20	3.23	3.24	3.28
Anorthosite, Stillwater Complex, Mont.	2.750	3.56	3.65	3.69	3.72	3.76	3.77	3.81
Serpentinite, Ludlow, Vt.	2.806	3.61	3.69	3.70	3.73	3.77	3.80	3.83
Magnesite	2.848	4.05	4.08	4.11	4.14	4.19	4.23	4.29
Gabbro, San Marcos, Calif.	2.874	3.59	3.70	3.73	3.76	3.79	3.82	3.84
Quartz diorite, Dedham, Mass.	2.928	3.39	3.65	3.69	3.74	3.78	3.81	3.84
Monticellite, Crestmore, Calif.	2.975	3.85	3.90	3.94	3.97	4.00	4.02	4.06
Diabase, Centreville, Va. "W-1"	2.984	3.49	3.64	3.68	3.72	3.75	3.77	3.80
Norite, Pretoria, Transvaal	2.984	3.56	3.81	3.84	3.86	3.89	3.90	3.94
Diabase, Frederick, Md.	3.017	3.71	3.75	3.77	3.79	3.81	3.82	3.85
Idocrase, Crestmore, Calif.	3.140	3.13	3.63	3.80	3.96	4.12	4.19	4.28
Amphibolite, Montana	3.070	3.90	4.13	4.18	4.21	4.25	4.27	4.30
Sillimanite, Williamstown, S. Australia	3.187	4.93	5.04	5.06	5.08	5.11	5.13	5.15
Jadeite, Japan	3.203	4.65	4.71	4.72	4.75	4.78	4.79	4.82
Dunite, Webster, N.C.	3.264	4.01	4.25	4.28	4.30	4.33	4.36	4.40
Dunite, Mt. Dun, New Zealand	3.270	4.17	4.34	4.37	4.41	4.45	4.48	4.54
Bronzitite, Stillwater Complex, Montana	3.287	4.48	4.54	4.56	4.58	4.62	4.63	4.66
Dunite, Twin Sisters, Wash.	3.326	4.60	4.67	4.69	4.72	4.77	4.79	4.83
Hornblende-garnet granulite, Sonoma Co., Calif.	3.360	3.83	4.15	4.22	4.27	4.33	4.35	4.38
Eclogite, Healdsburg, Calif.	3.444	4.26	4.39	4.43	4.48	4.53	4.55	4.58
Eclogite 1552, Norway	3.577	4.07	4.36	4.41	4.47	4.52	4.55	4.60
Eclogite 1553, Norway	3.578	3.70	4.38	4.46	4.52	4.58	4.61	4.66
Dunite, Mooihoek Mine, Transvaal	3.760	3.68	3.76	3.77	3.80	3.83	3.86	3.90

TABLE 9-4. VELOCITIES IN SEDIMENTARY AND METAMORPHIC ROCKS

These are field and laboratory measurements as indicated. Faust [36] concludes that shale and sandstone show systematic correlation with depth and age. Faust's average velocity data based on 1 million feet of section in 500 Canadian and American well surveys are summarized in Figure 9-1. Average sand velocity exceeds average shale velocity by about 0.1 km/sec. Limestone velocity does not show as definite a correlation with depth and age but is very sensitive to the extent of crystallization. Because of porosity effects, the velocity in sedimentary rocks never reaches the intrinsic value of the components. Unlike the case of igneous rocks, it is virtually impossible to eliminate porosity effects by application of pressure [84].

Material	Velocities in km/sec V_P	V_S	Remarks*	Reference
Sandstone–Shale, U.S. and Canada				
Tertiary	2.1–3.5	..	f; see Fig. 9-1; Average	36
Cretaceous	2.4–3.9	..	sand velocity exceeds	..
Pennsylvanian	2.9–4.4	..	shale by about 0.1 km/sec.	..
			Velocity range for depth	
			range 0.3–3.6 km.	..
Ordovician	3.3–4.5	..	depth 0.3–2.1 km.	
Sandstone	1.4–4.3	..	..	13, 20, 21, 22, 23, 25, 27, 85
Sandstone conglomerate				
Australia	2.4	..	f	4
Limestone				
Soft	1.7–4.2	..	f and l	22, 32, 33, 31, 34, 35, 39, 87
Hard	2.8–6.4	..	f and l	14, 20, 21, 86, 35, 37, 41, 87
Solenhofen, Bavaria	5.97	2.88	l	7
Solenhofen, Bavaria	..	2.75	l	30
U.S. Midcontinent and Gulf Coast	3.4–6.1	..	f	29, 31
Argillaceous; Texas	6.03	3.03	l; 50 bars; ‖ to bedding	29
Argillaceous; Texas	5.71	3.04	$\perp$ to bedding	..
Dolomitic; Pennsylvania	5.97	..	f	14
Cement rock; Pennsylvania	7.07	..	f	14
Crystalline; Texas, New Mexico, Oklahoma	5.67–6.40	..	f; depth 1–3 km	36
Dense; Sochi, USSR	5.90–7.00	3.03–3.59	f	86
Salt, cornallite, sylvite	4.4–6.5	..	f	13, 24, 29, 35, 39
Caprock (salt, anhydrite, gypsum, limestone)	3.5–5.5	..	f	35, 39, 40, 41
Anhydrite				
U.S. midcontinent and Gulf Coast	4.1	..	f	29
Bashkir and Tatar, USSR	5.00	2.67–2.99	f	86
Gypsum				
U.S. and Germany	2.0–3.5	..	f	29, 41, 42
Chalk	2.1–4.2			
U.S., Germany and France	2.1–4.2	..	..	..
Austin, Tex.	2.58	1.07 SV	f; $\perp$ bedding	34, 35, 44, 86
Austin, Tex.	3.05	1.13 SH	f; ‖ bedding	..
Slate				
Everett, Mass.	4.27	2.86	l	30
Shale and slate	2.3–4.7	..	f	4, 20, 22, 24, 32, 34, 45
Hornfels slate	3.5–4.4	..	f	4
Taconite				
Minnesota	4.3–6.3	..	f	28

TABLE 9-4.   *Continued*

Material	Velocities in km/sec V_P	V_S	Remarks*	Reference
Magnetite ore				
Ukraine [USSR]	5.50	..	f; $V_P/V_S \sim 1.67$–1.72	86
Dolomite	3.5–6.9	..	f and l	28, 38, 6
Marble				
Japan, Korea, Italy	3.75–6.94	2.02–3.86	l; range 46 samples	17
	5.78	3.22	average 46 samples	..
Danby, Vt.	5.87	2.82	l; 70 bars	..
Quartzite				
West Virginia	6.1	..	f	15
Cheshire	6.0	..	l; 90 bars	7
Chlorite schist				
Framingham, Mass.	4.89	3.27	l	30
Amphibolite schist				
Ukraine, USSR	4.2	2.5	f	86
Gneiss				
Wisconsin	6.71	..	f	28
New Hampshire	3.54–4.60	..	f	85
Ukraine, USSR	3.50	..	f; $V_P/V_S \sim 1.75$–1.94	86
Spain	5.15–7.50	..	f	39
New York, Massachusetts, Quebec	..	3.43–3.61	l; 4000 bars, 5 samples	74
Wet clay				
USSR (6 locations)	1.50–1.65	..	f; $V_P/V_S \sim 4.5$–13.7	86
Clay				
Baltic Shield (Leningrad)	1.20–2.50	..	f; V_P/V_S 2.08–8.5	86
Impermeable argillaceous clay	2.00	.59	f	..
Sand				
Baltic Shield and Caucasus	.60–1.85	..	f; $V_P/V_S \sim 3.0$–3.5	86
Soil	.11–.20	..	f; $V_P/V_S \sim 1.7$–2.0	86
Volcanic tuff				
New Zealand	2.16	.83	f	88

* f = field determination; l = laboratory determination

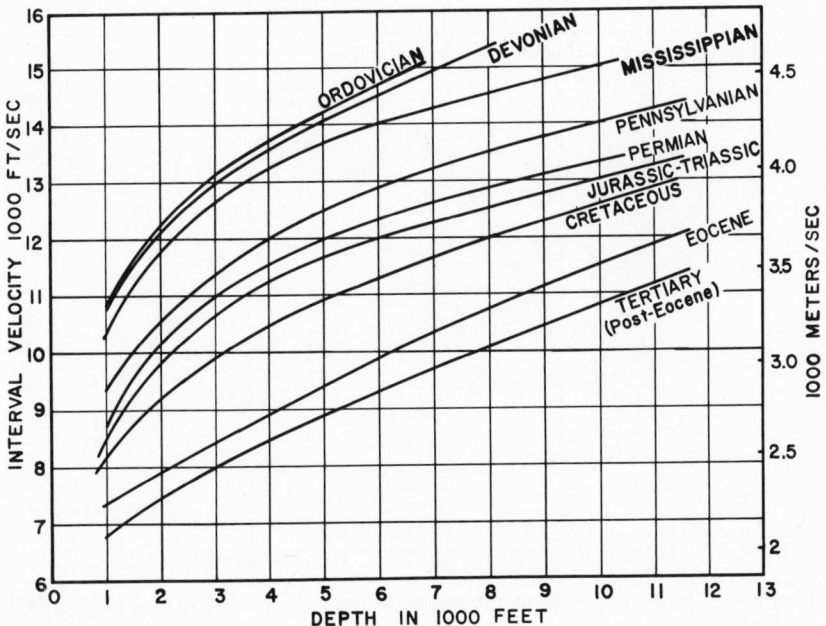

Figure 9-1. Compressional velocities from bore holes in sandstone-shale sections for depth intervals of 1000 feet [*after* Faust, **36**]

TABLE 9-5. WAVE VELOCITIES IN UNCONSOLIDATED SEDIMENTS

Water saturation is a significant factor influencing compressional velocity but having no effect on shear velocity. Nafe and Drake [78] have developed theoretical-empirical velocity depth curves (Fig. 9-2) which fit a wide variety of laboratory and field measurements on submarine sediments.

Material	Velocity in km/sec V_P	V_S	Remarks*	Ref.
Alluvium	.5 –2.0	..	f; near surface	3, 39, 45
	3.0 –3.5	..	f; depth 2000 meters	..
Clay	1.1 –2.5	..	f	4, 26, 34, 46, 47
Diluvium	.7 –1.8	..	f	23, 34, 39
Embankments and fill	.4	..	f	39
Loam	.8 –1.8	..	f	4, 21
Loess	.3 – .6	..	..	19, 46
Sand				
loose	.2 –2.0	..	f	3, 10, 19, 23, 29, 32, 34, 39, 41
loose	1.0	.4	f; above water table	43
loose	1.8	.5	f; below water table	43
calcareous	.8	..	f	42
wet	.75–1.5	..	f	41, 68
Weathered layer	.3 – .9	..	f	29
Glacial				
till	.43–1.04	..	f; unsaturated	28
till	1.73	..	f; saturated	28
sand and gravel	.38– .50	..	f; unsaturated	28
sand and gravel	1.67	..	f; saturated	28
River, Bay	1.1 –1.8	..	..	48, 49
Suboceanic	over 1.6	over .6	f and l; see Figure 2	78
Shallow water fine-grained; off San Diego, Calif.	1.46–1.68	..	in situ ultrasonic measurement sea water	50

* f = field determination; l = laboratory determination

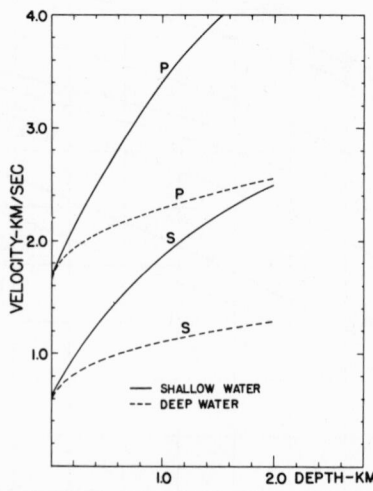

Figure 9-2. Wave velocities in submarine sediments [after Nafe and Drake, 78]

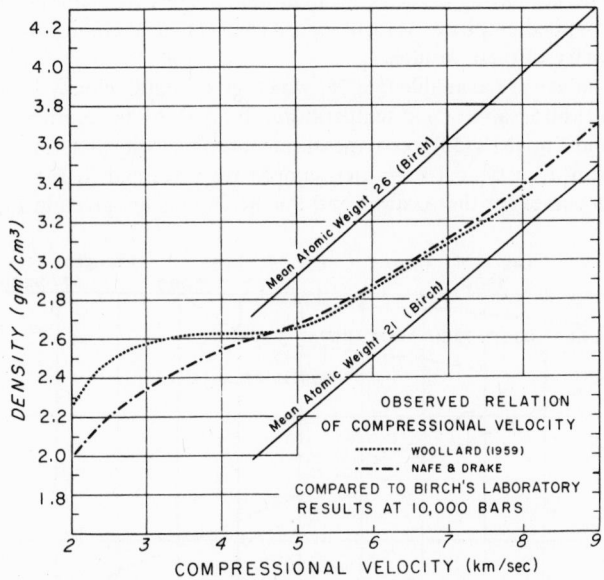

Figure 9-3. Empirical velocity dependence on density and mean atomic weight [**84, 89, 94, 95**]

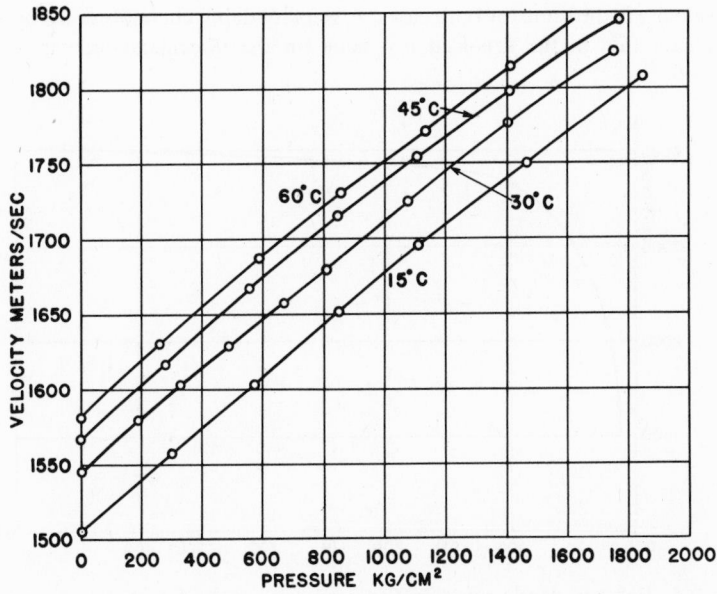

Figure 9-4. Sound velocity in sea water [*after* Carnevale and Litovitz, **53**]

Birch [84] found experimentally that velocity is an approximately linear function of density for materials having the same mean atomic weight. Woollard [94] and Nafe and Drake [95] compiled empirical velocity-density curves for common rocks. Figure 9-3 [89] is a summary of these results.

Extensive tables are available [56, 76] which give sound velocity in sea water as a function of pressure, salinity and temperature, to an absolute accuracy of 0.2 per cent. Carnevale's and Litovitz's [53] recent measurements of velocity as a function of pressure and temperature in a typical sea-water sample are presented in Figure 9-4. Typical velocity-depth curves for the Atlantic and Pacific Oceans are given in Figure 9-5.

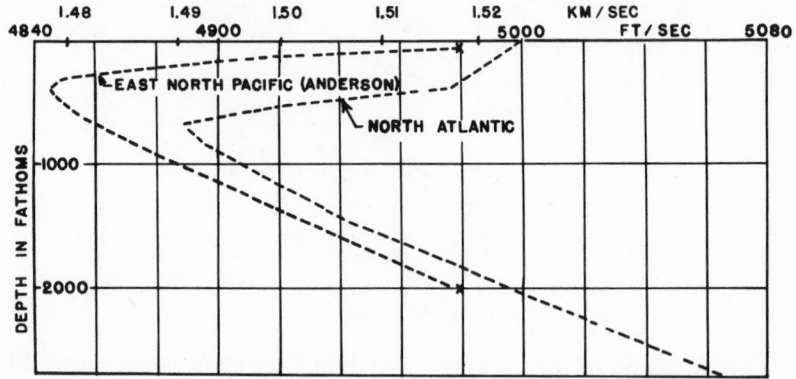

Figure 9-5. Typical velocity-depth curves in Atlantic and Pacific oceans

In ice it is necessary to distinguish between the longitudinal plate velocity usually measured in sheets and the higher compressional velocity in media of infinite extent. Shear velocity is the same for both cases. A velocity-depth curve observed by Joset and Holtzscherer [60] in the firn–iced firn zone on the Greenland ice cap is given in Figure 9-6.

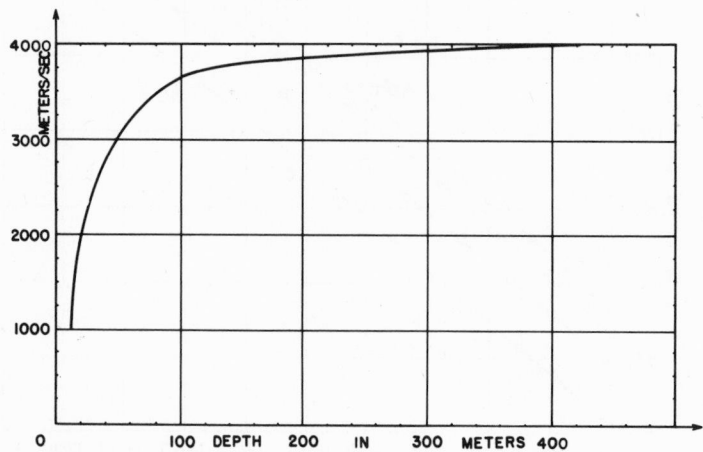

Figure 9-6. Velocity-depth curve in firn–iced firn zone of Greenland ice cap [*after* Joset and Holtzscherer, **60**]

TABLE 9-6. WAVE VELOCITIES IN WATER, ICE, AND PETROLEUM

Material	V_P	V_S	Ref.
Fresh water			
0° C	1.404	..	51, 52
5°	1.439	..	..
13°	1.470	..	..
15°	1.477	..	..
18.5°	1.485	..	..
25°	1.509	..	..
35°	1.534	..	..
Sea water	*See* Figure 9-4	..	53
Function of pressure, temperature and salinity	*See* Reference	..	56, 76
Atlantic and Pacific Ocean—typical vertical profiles	*See* Figure 9-5	..	54, 55
Arctic pack ice	2.59 –2.79*	1.49–1.56	59
	3.01 –3.49	..	..
Glacier Ice (Fig. 9-5)			
firn to iced-firn	1.0 –4.0	..	60
iced-firn and blue ice;			
$T = 0°$ C	3.6 –3.8	1.6 –1.7	60
$T = 30°$ C	4.0	1.8 –1.9	60
Permafrost	3.50	1.66–2.02	86
Lake ice	3.3 –3.5	..	61
Petroleum	1.326–1.395	..	57
23° C	1.275	..	58

* This is longitudinal plate velocity as distinct from compressional wave velocity in infinite medium.

Compressional and shear velocities in various materials have been compiled by Molotova and Vassil'ev [86]. Their results are reproduced in Table 9-7.

TABLE 9-7. COMPRESSIONAL AND SHEAR VELOCITIES IN VARIOUS METALS AND MATERIALS [86]
(σ is Poisson's ratio)

Material	Values of V_P/V_S and σ in materials		
	V_P, m/sec	V_P/V_S	σ
Aluminum	7050	2.35–2.50	.39–.40
Window glass	6790	2.08	.350
Aluminum	6320	2.04	.344
Steel	6150–6300	2.17–2.32	.36–.386
Steel	5940	1.84	.29
Iron	5920	1.83	.287
Iron	5837	1.79	.274
Copper	4820–5960	2.1–2.6	.35–.41
Glass	5800	1.73	.25
Magnesium	5780	1.89	.30
Birch (lengthwise)	5000	6.6	.486
Copper (sheet M-1)	4660	2.01	.336
Lead	..	3.34	.45
Bakelite	3460	1.73–1.75	.25–.26
Cellulose	3590	2.10	.358
Concrete	3560	1.65	.21
Fused quartz glass	..	1.55–1.62	.14–.19
Plexiglas	2550	2.0	.33
Resin	2443	2.4	.395
Plastic	2340	1.5–1.6	.10–.18
Rubber	1040	38.6	.5
Agar-agar	100	3.3	.45

VELOCITY VARIATION WITH PRESSURE AND TEMPERATURE
IN THE EARTH

In general, velocity increases with pressure and decreases with temperature. The pressure effect can be estimated from Table 9-2. It is difficult to determine the effect of temperature on velocity due to damage to samples heated at low pressures. Birch [82] gives $-40 \cdot 10^{-6}$ per degree and $-60 \cdot 10^{-6}$ per degree as velocity coefficients for shear waves in granites and gabbros respectively. When applied to compressional waves in the crust, these coefficients may have an uncertainty as high as 50 per cent, according to Birch.

Table 9-2 together with Birch's estimate of temperature-velocity coefficients and temperature gradient in the crust leads to an estimate of velocity as a function of depth presented in Figure 9-7 [82]. These results reflect uncertain assumptions about temperature gradients and velocity coefficients.

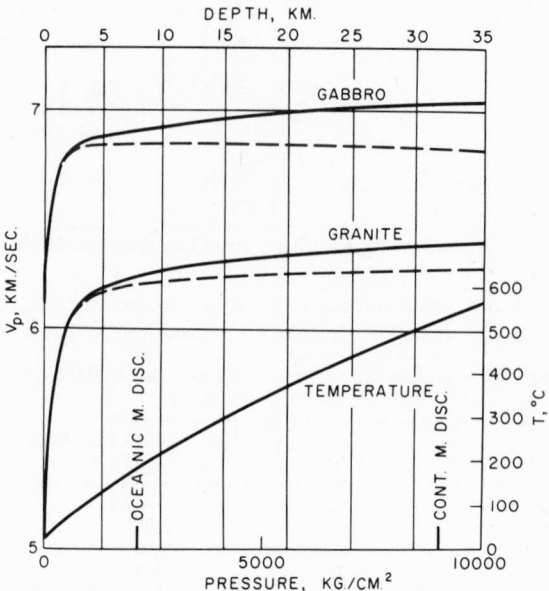

Figure 9-7. Compressional velocity variation with depth in the continental crust. Solid line, effect of pressure only; dashed line, effect of pressure and temperature combined [82]

VELOCITY IN CRUST AND UPPER MANTLE

Table 9-8 compiled by Steinhart and Meyer [89] summarizes field determinations of crustal structure. Typical values for P and S velocities in the upper continental crust are 6.1 and 3.5 km/sec respectively. These values are representative of a great variety of common metamorphic rocks, as well as granite, at pressures corresponding to depths of a few kilometers [74, 81]. Velocity variation with depth is uncertain. Many investigators infer a major discontinuity within the crust (Conrad discontinuity). A wide range of values (6.4–7.6 km/sec) is reported for the P velocity in the layer below the Conrad discontinuity, which poses a difficult problem as to composition of this layer. Upper mantle P and S velocities of 7.9–8.2 and 4.7–4.8 km/sec are typical, except in Japan and the Western U.S. where lower velocities are reported. The oceanic crust is composed of less than 1 km of sediments, 0.2 km of silicic or volcanic rock, and a layer approximately 5 km thick with a velocity consistent with a gabbroic composition. Occasionally a mantle velocity between 7.5 and 8 km/sec is reported for an oceanic station under a ridge or an inland sea.

TABLE 9-8. CRUSTAL STRUCTURE MEASUREMENTS BY SEISMIC REFRACTIONS [89]

Location	V_1 km/sec	h_1 Thickness km	V_2 km/sec	h_2 Thickness km	V_3 km/sec	h_3 Thickness km	V_4 km/sec	h_4 Thickness km	V_n Velocity below M	D Depth to M	$\bar{V}$ Mean velocity above M, km/sec	B Bouguer Anomalies mgals	I_1 Isostatic Anomalies local mgals	I_2 Isostatic Anomalies 1° squares (Tanni) mgals	R Isostatic Anomalies 5° squares	E Elevation, meters
Europe																
Northern Germany	3.6	6.0	5.4	7.5	6.5	13.9			8.2	27.4	5.564	-5	+5	+6	+10	50
Haslach, Germany	5.63	2.4	5.97	17.7	6.54	10.1			8.15	30.2	6.134	-25	+25	+20	+10	610
Prague, Czechoslovakia	5.62	10.9	6.35	19.9	6.65				8.15	30.8	6.092	-20	+10	+11	+13	305
Hungary	2.4	2.0	5.90	17.1	6.65	4.6			8.10	23.7	5.750	+10	+20	+27	+15	90
Central Asia																
Black Sea	4.5	10.0	[6.0]	13.0	6.5	[24.0]			[8.1]	23.0	5.348	+50?	0?	0	+15	-500?
Caucasus	4.3	7.0	5.6	17.0	6.6	15.0			[8.0]	[48.0]	5.860	-30?		+40	+25	400
Caspian Sea	4.8	15.0	6.0	10.0	5.5	9.0			8.0	40.0	5.775	-50?		-5	-20	-150
Transcaspian Depression	3.5	8.3	5.0	10.0	6.3	16.0			8.0	46.3	5.362	-75		-30	-20	300
Great Balkhan Range	3.5	3.9	5.5	9.9	6.3	19.0			8.0	28.8	5.865	-10		-30	-20	450
Margin of Kopet Dag Mts.	4.0	6.4	5.5	13.6			6.3	19.0	8.0	39.0	5.645	-30		-15	-20	1400
Stalinabad	5.8	30.0	6.4	20.0					7.9	50.0	6.040	-110		-35	-25	3000
38° 30'–70° 20'	5.5	33.0	6.4	18.0					8.1	51.0	5.818	-300		-80	-30	5000
Academy Sci. Mts.	5.5	43.0	6.4	29.0					8.1	72.0	5.863	-410		-90	-50	4000
Zaalaisk Mts.	5.5	32.0	6.4	25.0					8.1	57.0	5.895	-390		-65	-50	1150
Osh	5.5	20.0	6.4	24.0					8.1	44.0	5.991	-190		-35	-50	1830
Lake Issk Kul, Tien Shan	5.5	10.5	6.4	41.0					8.1	51.5	6.217	-210		-40	-35	3300
Zailisk Mts.	5.5	15.0	6.4	23.0					8.1	38.0	6.045	-160		-50	-35	600
East Lake Balkhash	5.5	11.0	6.4	36.0					8.1	47.0	6.189	-80		-30	-15	400
West Lake Balkhash	5.5	16.0	6.4	27.0					8.1	43.0	6.065	-30		-50	-15	500
Ural Mts. (9 layers, increasing from 2.1–7.6 km/sec)									8.0	41.2	6.411	-75?		+20	0	
Southern Africa																
South Africa	5.65	4.5	6.09	22.7	6.83	15.5			8.27	38.2	6.312	-130	-10		+20	1600
South Africa	5.4	1.3	6.20	36.6					8.21	37.9	6.173	-70	0		+20	1400
South Africa	6.03	28.2	7.19	8.4					7.96	36.6	6.296	-130	+20		+20	1500
South Africa	5.4	1.3	6.09	34.7					8.42	36.0	6.065	-140	+10		+20	1300
Australia–New Zealand																
Western Australia	6.03	37.4							8.32	37.4	6.03	-45	-30		-35	300
Eastern Australia	[4.5]	1.5	6.04	34.8					8.03	37.0	5.863	-40	-15		-20	625
Wellington NE, New Zealand	3.5	.6	5.5	3.1	6.07	3.3	6.22	10.6	8.02	18.1	5.807					100
South America																
Peru, Altiplano	5.3	4.1	6.2	21.2	6.7	39.6			8.0	64.9	6.448				+10	4300
Peru, (flank of plateau)	5.3	4.1	6.2	21.2	6.7	26.4			8.0	51.7	6.384				+30	1520
Altiplano, Chile	5.5	6.0	6.35	28.4	7.0	35.9			8.0	70.3	6.609					4500
Chile (flank of plateau)	5.5		6.35	28.4	7.0	22.2			8.0	56.5	6.526					1520

Seismic crustal-structure compilation (rotated table). Columns are given in reading order left-to-right; region headers (Japan, Iceland, North America) appear in the mean-velocity column. Some readings are approximate owing to the density of the original table.

Location			V	H	V	H	Pn	Depth	V̄					Elev.
Japan														
Sakhalin Is.	1.74	1.0	5.5	4.3	6.2	21.7	7.7	27	5.923	+125	+15		+35	25
Sea of Okhotsk	2.51	.53	5.8	9.0	6.15	15.5	7.75	25	5.951	+50	+50		0	200
Pacific Margin	5.8	1.5	6.15	22.5			7.75	24	6.128	+125	−47		−20	360
	5.5	12.0	6.3–6.7	23.0			8.0	35.0	6.157	+140		+30	0	0
	1.5	3.0	6.3–6.7	17.0			8.0	20.0	5.750	+170		+50		−3000
	1.5	5.0	6.3–6.7	9.5			8.0	14.5	4.776	+410			+50	−5000
Iceland														
Western Iceland	3.69	2.12	6.71	15.70	7.38	10.02	[8.0]	27.8	6.731	−10		+25	+15	150
North America														
Alaska: Prince William Sd.	5.7	9.1	6.6	15.0	7.3	22.0	8.3	46.1	6.756	+10	+25		+20	0
Southern Alaska	5.7	6.1	6.6	10.6	7.3	32.2	8.3	48.9	6.948	−70	0		+20	850
Alaska: Skagway area	5.5	4.0	6.1	10.0	6.7	24.0	[8.1]	38.0	6.416	−75	−12		0	1000
Alberta, Canada	3.6	2.0	6.1	1.0	6.2	26	8.2	43.0	6.402	−115	−18		0	900
Washington: Puget Sound	6.0 increasing to 7.0 km/sec at base of crust				7.2		8.0	30.0	6.5	−45	+10		−15	300
Western Montana North	5.0	3.72	5.95	26.16	7.44	5.48	7.94	35.36	6.081	−160	+3		+10	1500
Western Montana South	5.0	2.29	5.95	19.89	7.44	23.91	7.94	46.09	6.676	−200	+5		+10	1850
Northern Montana	[3.6]	.7	5.63	14.77	6.70	13.51	7.87	54.7	6.691	−135	+15		+10	1500
Southern Montana	[3.6]	2.78	6.08	12.93	6.88	24.61	8.15	40.32	6.397	−170	+8		+10	1700
East Montana North	3.50	2.09	6.08	15.13	6.97	16.91	8.07	56.92	6.854	−105	+20		+20	900
East Montana South	3.58	3.38	6.08	19.62	6.97	16.86	8.07	49.97	6.512	−105	+20		+20	950
Northeast Wyoming	[3.6]	3.06	6.14	13.62	6.87	11.02	7.97	46.02	6.588	−100	+27		+25	800
Central Minn.	5.6	1.0	6.0 increasing to 7.0 km/sec		7.25		8.1	42.5	6.5	−8	−15		+10	430
N.W. Wisconsin	5.40	3.67	6.11	12.17	6.51	26.50	8.03	42.34	6.300	−53	+10		+10	300
Keweenaw	4.75	1.85	6.44	13.84	6.67	22.57	8.15	38.27	6.492	+3	−23		0	200
Central Wisconsin	5.40	.98	6.11	11.25	6.51	25.17	8.03	37.40	6.361	−63	−15		−10	300
Central Wisconsin	4.16	2.7	6.03 increasing at (1 + .0038Z) to 6.9			37.95	8.17	40.65	6.317	−45	−26		−10	200
Central Wisconsin	4.58	1.44	5.74	6.05	6.22	30.0	8.17	37.5	6.078	−45	−11		0	195
Central Wisconsin	4.5	.63	5.94 increasing at (1 + .0049Z) to 7.09			42.95	[8.17]	43.6	6.488	−37	−18		−10	170
Ontario	6.23	28.1	7.09	12.1			[8.17]	40.2	6.489	−45			−20	305
St. Laurence River Basin	5.9	?	6.08	12.1			[8.17]	32.5					−5	−40
Adirondacks	6.3 (increasing by 2.5 × 10⁻⁴ km/sec/km to 7.2 km/sec)						8.07	36.0	6.750	−40	−10		−10	315
Pennsylvania	5.6	1.4	6.01	31.3			8.21	32.7	5.992	−50	−20		−10	270
Chesapeake Bay	5.6	.7	6.15 increasing to 7.0 at base of crust				8.1	32.5	6.5	−5	−10		010	30
East Tennessee	6.01	5.3	6.33	8.42	6.73	31.58	8.06	45.3	6.572	−75	−25		−15	760
Arkansas	4.64	2.03	5.18	8.19	6.64	30.98	8.16	41.2	6.251	+13	+22		0	87
Arizona—New Mexico	4.8	4.3	6.1	21.7	7.34	22.1	8.15	48.1	6.563	−210	−20		−10	2000
Utah	5.2	5.9	5.8	11.7	7.34	21.3	8.18	47.7	6.215	−193			+10	1000
Nevada	3.8	2.5	6.15	33.5			8.15	36.0	5.987	−130	−20		−10	1830
S. Calif. (inland)	6.11	23.0	7.66	26.0			8.11	49.0	6.932	−105	−25		−20	920
S. Calif.	5.68	11.3	7.18	32.6			8.10	43.9	6.794	−50	−55		−20	450
S. Calif. (near coast)	5.9	1.0	6.1	5.0	6.85	10.0	8.20	40.0	6.645	−50	−55		−20	200
Central Calif.	5.0	.5	5.9	5.5	7.0	20.0	8.2	32.0	6.198	−20	−60		−20	100
	5.5	10.0	6.5	21.5	7.63	28.46	7.98	31.5	6.183	−3	−27		−15	200
Mexico	3.0	.80	4.95	3.40	6.01	10.69	8.38	43.36	6.269	−210	−20		−20	2200

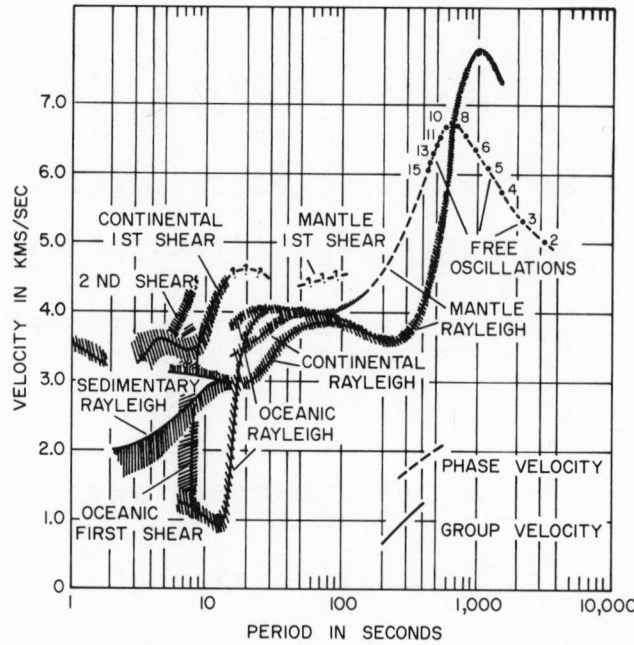

Figure 9-8. Observed velocities for Rayleigh waves. Shading indicates the approximate regional variation to be expected [*after* Oliver, **98**]

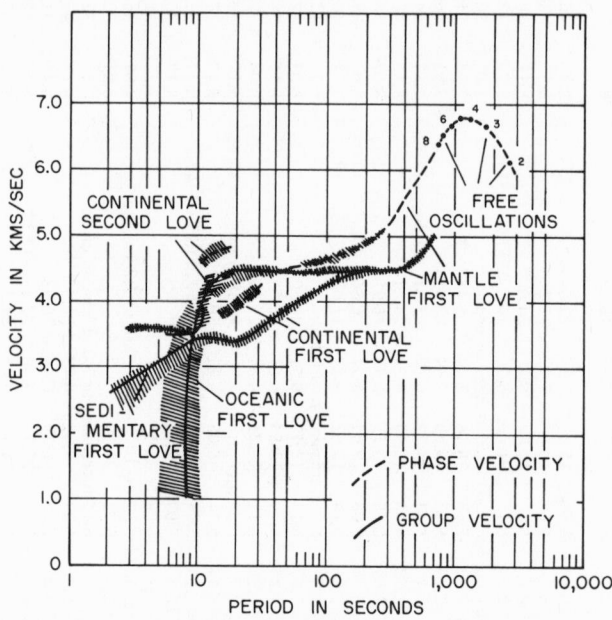

Figure 9-9. Observed velocities for Love waves. Shading indicates the approximate regional variation to be expected [*after* Oliver, **98**]

SURFACE WAVES, GUIDED WAVES, AND FREE OSCILLATIONS

Earthquake-excited surface waves and guided waves are useful for determining crustal and mantle structure. Surface waves are always dispersed because of the variation of velocity with depth in the earth. Observed velocity curves for Rayleigh and Love waves over a period range where they are fairly well known are presented in Figures 9-8 and 9-9, after Oliver [98]. Guided waves are usually described as body waves confined over large horizontal distances to one or more channels associated with particular variations in elastic properties. Actually, surface waves and guided waves are inseparable, the latter being associated with stationary values of group velocity curves of the former [90]. A definite velocity can be assigned due to the impulsive initiation. Guided waves are summarized in Table 9-9.

TABLE 9-9. GUIDED WAVES

P = compressional wave
SH = horizontally polarized shear wave
SV = vertically polarized shear wave

Wave type	Velocity km/sec	Remarks	Ref.
Lg	3.5–3.6	Short-period SH and SV in upper crust	80
Rg	3.0–3.1	Short-period Rayleigh wave in upper crust	80
Πg	6.0–6.2	Short-period P wave in upper crust	81
Pa	7.9–8.2	Intermediate-period P wave in upper mantle	80
Sa	4.4–4.6	Intermediate-period SV and SH wave in upper mantle	80
G	4.38	Long-period SH wave in upper mantle	83

TABLE 9-10. PERIODS OF FREE OSCILLATIONS OF THE EARTH PERIODS IN MINUTES

Mode*	Theoretical†				Experimental** Mean
	JB-A	JB-B	GB-A	GB-B	
$_0S_2$	53.43	53.72	53.50	53.78	53.95
$_0S_3$	35.25	35.52	35.32	35.58	35.62
$_0S_4$	25.50	25.75	25.53	25.78	25.82
$_0S_5$	19.62	19.85	19.65	19.88	19.86
$_0S_6$	15.90	16.17	15.92	16.15	16.07
$_0S_7$	13.42	13.65	13.43	13.67	13.52
$_0S_8$	11.73	11.97	11.73	11.97	11.76
$_0S_9$	10.53	10.77	10.53	10.77	10.57
$_0S_{10}$	9.650	9.883	9.650	9.883	9.629
$_0S_{11}$	8.950	9.183	8.950	9.183	8.917
$_0S_{12}$	8.383	8.617	8.383	8.617	8.362
$_0S_{13}$	7.887	8.105	7.887	8.108	7.875
$_0S_{14}$	7.473	7.680	7.475	7.683	7.465
$_0S_{15}$	7.107	7.300	7.108	7.305	7.102
$_0S_{16}$	6.780	6.962	6.782	6.967	6.778
$_0S_{17}$	6.488	6.658	6.492	6.663	6.492
$_0S_{18}$	6.227	6.383	6.230	6.390	6.231
$_0S_{19}$	5.988	6.133	5.993	6.142	5.998
$_0S_{20}$	5.772	5.907	5.778	5.915	5.778
$_0S_{21}$	5.575	5.698	5.582	5.708	5.595
$_0S_{22}$	5.392	5.505	5.402	5.515	5.410
$_0S_{23}$	5.225	5.327	5.235	5.338	5.256
$_0S_{24}$	5.068	5.162	5.080	5.175	5.105

TABLE 9-10. *Continued*

Mode*	JB-A	Theoretical† JB-B	GB-A	GB-B	Experimental** Mean
$_0S_{25}$	4.923	5.007	4.937	5.022	4.959
$_0S_{26}$	4.787	4.862	4.802	4.878	4.827
$_0S_{27}$	4.660	4.727	4.675	4.743	4.694
$_0S_{28}$	4.540	4.600	4.557	4.617	4.588
$_0S_{29}$	4.427	4.478	4.445	4.498	4.469
$_0S_{30}$	4.320	4.3650	4.340	4.385	4.368
$_0S_{31}$	4.217	4.257	4.238	4.278	4.266
$_0S_{32}$	4.120	4.155	4.143	4.178	4.167
$_0S_{33}$	4.0283	4.058	4.052	4.082	4.085
$_0S_{34}$	3.942	3.965	3.967	3.990	3.992
$_0S_{35}$	3.857	3.877	3.883	3.902	3.920
$_0S_{36}$	3.777	3.792	3.803	3.818	3.829
$_0S_{37}$	3.700	3.712	3.727	3.738	3.743
$_0S_{38}$	3.652	3.633	3.653	3.662	3.671
$_0S_{39}$	3.553	3.560	3.583	3.588	3.612
$_0S_{40}$	3.485	3.488	3.515	3.518	3.475
$_0S_{41}$	3.420	3.420	3.452	3.450	3.405
$_0T_2$	43.46	44.16	43.61	..	43.78
$_0T_3$	28.13	28.60	28.23	..	28.53
$_0T_4$	21.54	21.91	21.62	..	21.76
$_0T_5$	17.77	18.07	17.84	..	17.93
$_0T_6$	15.28	15.54	15.36	..	15.36
$_0T_7$	13.37	13.72	13.57	..	13.53
$_0T_8$	12.13	12.33	12.22	..	12.25
$_0T_9$	11.05	11.23	11.15	..	11.14
$_0T_{10}$	10.20	10.34	10.28	..	10.32
$_0T_{11}$	9.50	9.59	9.55	..	9.614
$_0T_{12}$	8.86	8.95	8.93	..	8.975
$_0T_{13}$	8.33	8.40	8.39	..	8.379
$_0T_{14}$	7.86	7.92	7.93	..	7.942
$_0T_{15}$	7.43	7.50	7.51	..	7.527
$_0T_{16}$	7.07	7.12	7.15	..	7.161
$_0T_{17}$	6.73	6.78	6.81	..	6.819
$_0T_{18}$	6.45	6.48	6.52	..	6.502
$_0T_{19}$	6.18	6.20	6.24	..	6.246
$_0T_{20}$	5.93	5.95	5.99	..	6.006
$_0T_{21}$	5.70	5.72	5.77	..	5.769
$_0T_{22}$	5.50	5.50	5.55	..	5.545
$_0T_{23}$	5.30	5.31	5.36	..	5.386
$_0T_{24}$	5.12	5.12	5.18	..	5.200
$_0T_{25}$	4.95	4.95	5.01	..	5.100

* The symbol S denotes spheroidal modes, and T denotes torsional modes. Subscript preceding symbol gives number of radial nodal surfaces; subscript following symbol gives surface harmonic dependence on polar angle.

† JB-A and JB-B refer to calculations based on Jeffreys' velocities (Table 9-12) and Bullen's model A and model B density distributions [91] respectively. GB-A and GB-B refer to Gutenberg's velocities (Table 9-11) and the same density distributions. [*After* **99, 100, 101**]

** Data from Chilean earthquake of 1960 recorded at Isabella and Los Angeles, California; Ogdensberg and Palisades, New York; Nana, Peru; and Tiefenfort, Germany.

VELOCITIES IN MANTLE AND CORE

These velocities were determined by Jeffreys [73] and later by Gutenberg (*quoted by* Bullard [75]) from the travel times of earthquake-generated compressional and shear waves. Gutenberg's velocities, especially in the upper mantle, fit the data from mantle surface waves and free oscillations of the earth better than do Jeffreys' velocities [90]. Surface-wave data verify the worldwide occurrence of a low-velocity zone in the upper mantle.

TABLE 9-11.   GUTENBERG'S VELOCITIES

Depth km	Mantle		Core	
	Velocity km/sec			Velocity km/sec
	V_P	V_S	r/r_c†	
60	8.15	4.6	1.00	8.04
100	8.0	4.4	.90	8.44
150	7.85	4.35	.80	8.90
200	8.05	4.4	.70	9.31
300	8.5	4.6	.60	9.63
400	9.0	4.95	.50	9.88
500	9.6	5.3	.40	10.08
600	10.1	5.6	.38	10.11
700	10.5	5.9	.374	10.11
800	10.9	6.15	.37	10.17
900	11.3*	6.3*	.36	10.48
1000	11.4	6.35	.35	10.76
1200	11.8	6.5	.34	10.93
1400	12.05	6.6	.33	11.04
1600	12.3	6.75	.32	11.09
1800	12.55	6.85	.31	11.12
2000	12.8	6.95	.30	11.13
2200	13.0	7.0	.25	11.15
2400	13.2	7.1	.20	11.17
2600	13.45	7.2	.15	11.17
2800	13.7	7.25	.10	11.16
2900	13.7	7.2	.05	11.15
2920	13.65	7.2	.00	11.15

* Discontinuity in slope
† r_c = 3451 km.

TABLE 9-12.   JEFFREYS' VELOCITIES

r/r_M*	Depth (km)	V_P (km/sec)	V_S (km/sec)
	MANTLE		
1.00	33	7.75	4.353
.99	96	7.94	4.444
.98	160	8.13	4.539
.97	223	8.33	4.638
.96	287	8.54	4.741
.95	350	8.75	4.850
.94	413	8.97	4.962
.93	477	9.50	5.227

TABLE 9-12. *Continued*

r/r_M*	Depth (km)	V_P (km/sec)	V_S (km/sec)
.92	540	9.91	5.463
.91	603	10.26	5.670
.90	667	10.55	5.850
.88	794	10.99	6.002
.86	920	11.29	6.295
.84	1047	11.50	6.395
.82	1174	11.67	6.483
.80	1301	11.85	6.564
.78	1427	12.03	6.637
.76	1554	12.20	6.706
.74	1681	12.37	6.770
.72	1808	12.54	6.833
.70	1934	12.71	6.893
.68	2061	12.87	6.953
.66	2188	13.02	7.012
.64	2315	13.16	7.074
.62	2441	13.32	7.137
.60	2568	13.46	7.199
.58	2695	13.60	7.258
.56	2822	13.64	7.314
.55	2885	13.64	7.304

OUTER CORE

r/r_M*	Depth (km)	V_P (km/sec)	V_S (km/sec)
.548	2898	8.10	
.537	2967	8.18	
.526	3037	8.26	
.515	3106	8.35	
.504	3176	8.44	
.493	3245	8.53	
.482	3315	8.63	
.471	3384	8.74	
.460	3454	8.83	
.449	3523	8.93	
.438	3593	9.03	
.427	3662	9.11	
.416	3732	9.20	
.406	3801	9.28	
.395	3870	9.37	
.384	3940	9.44	
.373	4009	9.52	
.362	4079	9.58	
.351	4148	9.65	
.340	4218	9.72	
.329	4287	9.78	
.318	4357	9.84	
.307	4426	9.90	
.296	4496	9.97	
.285	4565	10.03	
.274	4635	10.10	
.263	4704	10.17	
.252	4773	10.23	
.241	4843	10.30	
.230	4912	10.37	
.219	4982	10.44	
.208	5051	9.92	
.197	5121	9.40	

TABLE 9-12.   *Continued*

r/r_M*	Depth (km)	V_P (km/sec)	V_S (km/sec)
	INNER CORE		
.197	5121	11.16	
.177	5246	11.19	
.158	5371	11.21	
.138	5496	11.23	
.118	5621	11.25	
.099	5746	11.27	
.079	5871	11.28	
.059	5996	11.29	
.039	6121	11.30	
.000	6371	11.31	

* r_M = 6338 km

REFERENCES FOR SECTION 9

1. Knopoff, Trans. Am. Geophys. Union **35**, 969, 1954
2. Leet and Ewing, Trans. Am. Geophys. Union **12**, 61, 1931; Physics **2**, 160, 1932
3. Gutenberg, Beitr. z. angew. Geophysik **6**, 125, 1937
4. Edge and Laby, Principles and practices of geophysical prospecting, Cambridge University Press, 1931
5. Brockamp, Zeits. f. Geophys. **11**, 39, 1935
6. Hughes and Jones, Geol. Soc. America Bull. **61**, 843, 1950; Trans. Am. Geophys. Union **32**, 173, 1951
7. Hughes and Cross, Geophysics **16**, 577, 1951
8. Press, unpublished
9. Leet, Trans. Am. Geophys. Union **14**, 288, 1933; Physics **4**, 375, 1933
10. Brockamp and Wölcken, Z. f. Geophys. **5**, 163, 1929
11. Weatherby, Born, and Harding, Am. Assoc. Petroleum Geologists Bull. **18**, 206, 1934
12. Reich, Geol. Jahrb. **64**, 243, 1950
13. Meisser and Martin, Z. f. Geophys. **3**, 106, 1927
14. Ewing and Crary, Trans. Am. Geophys. Union **15**, 91, 1934; **16**, 100, 1935
15. Leet, Seismol. Soc. America Bull. **28**, 163, 1938
16. Hughes and Maurette, Geophysics **22**, 23, 1957
17. Kubotera, Jour. Phys. Earth **2**, 33, 1954
18. Gutenberg, Beitr. z. angew. Geophysik **6**, 125, 1937
19. Baule and Müller, *in* Encyclopedia of physics **47**, Springer-Verlag, Berlin, 1956
20. Salfeld, Internat. Geol. Kong. Madrid, 1926
21. Ambronn and Cobb, Elements of geophysics, McGraw-Hill Book Co., Inc., 1928
22. Reich, Handbuch der Experimentalphysik, Angenheister, Leipzig **3**, 1930
23. Schmidt, Z. f. Geophys. **4**, 134, 1928; **8**, 378, 1932
24. Smith and Wilson, Geophysics **2**, 56, 1937
25. Heinrich, Z. f. Berg. Hutt. u. Sal. im Preuss. **81**, 347, 1933
26. Muller, Z. f. Geophys. **11**, 111, 1935
27. Devaux, Le Nature **62**, 119, 1934
28. Woollard and Hanson, Wisc. Geol. Surv. Bull. **78**, 1954
29. Person, Oil Weekly **87**, 24, 1937
30. Birch and Bancroft, Jour. Geol. **46**, 59, 1938; **48**, 752, 1940
31. Rutherford, Trans. Am. Geophys. Union **14**, 289, 1933
32. Norlund and Brockamp, Inst. Géod. de Dänemark, Ser. 3, 2, 1934
33. Reich, Beitr. z. angew. Geophysik **7**, 1, 1937
34. Barsch and Reich, Beitr. z. angew. Geophysik **1**, 168, 1930
35. Barton, A.I.M.E. Geophysical Prospecting, 572, 1929
36. Faust, Geophysics **16**, 192, 1951
37. Weatherby and Faust, Am. Assoc. Petroleum Geologists Bull. **19**, 1, 1935
38. Thoenen and Windes, U.S. Bur. Mines Rept. Inv., Progress Rept. 1, R.I. 3353, 1937
39. Siñerez, Bol. d. Inst. Geol. y Min. España, 3d ser., no. 10, 1928
40. Hanneman, Z. f. prakt. Geol. **35**, 168, 1927
41. Schweydar and Reich, Beitr. z. Geophys. **17**, 121, 1927

42. Meisser, Veröffentlechungen der Reichsanstalt Erdbebenforsch, Jena, 1–77, 1929
43. White and Sengbrush, Geophysics **18**, 54, 1953
44. Maurain and Eblé, Comptes Rendus, 181, 1077, 1925
45. Gutenberg, Wood, and Buwalda, Seismol. Soc. America Bull. **22**, 185, 1932
46. Ramspeck, Z. f. Geophys. **10**, 387, 1934
47. Kirnos, Koridalin, Masarskij, and Raiko, Seismol. Inst. Publ. No. 47, 1–70, 1934
48. Osterhoudt, Geophysics **11**, 417, 1946
49. Drake and Oliver, Geol. Soc. America Bull. **62**, 1287, 1951
50. Hamilton, Sheenway, Menard, and Shipek, Jour. Acoust. Soc. **28**, 1, 1956
51. Swainson, McIlwraith, and Dyk, U.S. Coast and Geodetic Survey, 1934
52. Litovitz and Carnevale, Jour. Appl. Phys. **26**, 816, 1955
53. Carnevale and Litovitz, Jour. Acoust. Soc. **27**, 794, 1955
54. Ewing and Worzel, Geol. Soc. America Memoir **27**, 1948
55. Anderson, Trans. Am. Geophys. Union **31**, 221, 1950
56. Tables of velocity of sound in pure water and sea water, Hydrographic Dept. Admiralty (London) 1939
57. Martini, Wied. Beibl. **12**, 566, 1888
58. Ionescu, Jour. Phys. **5**, 377, 1924
59. Oliver, Crary, and Cotell, Trans. Am. Geophys. Union **35**, 282, 1954
60. Joset and Holtzscherer, Ann. de Géophys. **9**, 330, 1953
61. Ewing, Crary, and Thorne, Physics **5**, 165, 1934; **5**, 181, 1934
62. Tatel and Tuve, Geol. Soc. America, Special Paper 62, 35, 1955
63. Hodgson, Dom. Obs. Publ. Ottawa **16**, 113–163, 169–181, 1953
64. Gane, Atkins, Sellschrop, and Seligman, Seismol. Soc. America Bull. **46**, 293, 1956
65. Katz, Seismol. Soc. America Bull. **45**, 303, 1955
66. Gutenberg, Trans. Am. Geophys. Union **33**, 427, 1952
67. Research Group for Explosion Seismology, Bull. Earthquake Res. Inst. **33**, 699, 1955
68. Rothé and Peterschmitt, Inst. Phys. Globe, Ann., Strasbourg **5**, 13, 1950
69. Fortsch, Geol. Jahrb. **66**, 65–80, 1951
70. Eiby, Nature **176**, 32, 1955
71. Ewing, Sutton, and Officer, Seismol. Soc. America Bull. **44**, 21, 1954
72. Raitt, Geol. Soc. America Bull. **67**, 1623, 1956
73. Jeffreys, Mon. Not. Roy. Astron. Soc. Geophys. Suppl. **4**, 498, 1939; **4**, 594; 1939
74. Birch, Geol. Soc. America Special Paper **62**, 101, 1955
75. Bullard, Ned. Geol. Mijnbouwk, Genoot. (Geol. Ser.) **18**, 23, 1957
76. Kuwahara, Hydrographic Review **16**, 123, 1939
77. Hughes and Maurette, Geophysics **21**, 277, 1956
78. Nafe and Drake, Geophysics **22**, 523, 1957
79. Summers and Broding, Geophysics **17**, 598, 1952
80. Ewing and Press, in Encyclopedia of physics **47**, p. 119, Springer-Verlag, Berlin, 1956
81. Press and Gutenberg, Trans. Am. Geophys. Union **37**, 754, 1956
82. Birch, Contributions in geophysics, Pergamon Press, London, p. 158, 1957
83. Benioff, Gutenberg, and Richter, Trans. Am. Geophys. Union **36**, 713, 1955
84. Birch, Jour. Geophys. Res. **65**, 1083, 1960; **66**, 2199, 1961
85. Kruger and Linchan, Geol. Soc. America Bull. **52**, 633, 1941
86. Molotova and Vassil'ev, Bull. (Izvest.) Acad. Sci. USSR, Geoph. Ser. (Eng. Ed.) **8**, 731, 1960
87. Kuiper, van Ryen, and Koefoed, Geophys. Prosp. **7**, No. 1, 1959
88. Evison, Geotechn. 6, No. 3, 1956
89. Steinhart and Meyer, Carnegie Inst. Washington Publ. **622**, 347, 1961
90. Bolt and Dorman, Jour. Geophys. Res. **66**, 2965, 1961
91. Bullen, Introduction to the theory of seismology, Cambridge Univ. Press, 3rd Ed, 1963
92. Ewing and Press, Trans. Am. Geophys. Union **37**, 213, 1956
93. Brune, Benioff, and Ewing, Jour. Geophys. Res. **66**, 2895, 1961
94. Woollard, Jour. Geophys. Res. **64**, 1521, 1959
95. *Quoted in* Talwani, Sutton, and Worzel, Jour. Geophys. Res. **64**, 1545, 1959
96. Simmons, Jour. Geophys. Res. **69**, 1117, 1964
97. Simmons, Jour. Geophys. Res. **69**, 1123, 1964
98. Oliver, Seismol. Soc. America Bull. **52**, 79, 1962
99. Pekeris, Alterman, and Jarosch, Phys. Rev. **122**, 1692, 1961
100. Sato, Landisman, and Ewing, Jour. Geophys. Res. **65**, 2399, 1960
101. Alsop, Seismol. Soc. America Bull. **53**, 483, 1963

SECTION 10

GEODETIC DATA

by GORDON J. F. MACDONALD

CONTENTS

Handbook of Physical Constants—*Revised Edition*
THE GEOLOGICAL SOCIETY OF AMERICA MEMOIR 97, 1966

TABLE 10-1. FIGURE OF THE EARTH'S SURFACE

(Numbers in parentheses refer to list at end of section 10.)

Equatorial radius $a_e = 6378.163$ km (2, 3, 6)

Polar radius $a_p = 6356.177$ km

Radius of sphere of equal volume $a_0 = 6371$ km

Flattening of surface $f = \dfrac{a_e - a_p}{a_e} = 1/298.24 = .003353$ (6, 10)

Area of surface $= 5.101 \times 10^{18}$ cm^2

Volume $= 1.083 \times 10^{27}$ cm^3

TABLE 10-2. GRAVITY AT THE SURFACE, MASS, DENSITY

Gravitational constant $G = 6.670 \times 10^{-8}$ dynes/cm^2 g^2 (4)

Gravity at the equator $g_e =$ acceleration of gravity in cm/sec$^2 =$ gals at equator of ellipsoid of dimensions given in Table 1

　　$g_e = 978.0436$ based on Potsdam Standard (6)

　　$g_e = 978.0307$ including correction of $- .0129$ to absolute gravity (6, 8)

Gravity on surface of ellipsoid g

　　$g = g_e(1 + .005302 \sin^2 \varphi - .0000058 \sin^2 2\varphi)$

　　$\varphi =$ latitude

Mass of earth $M_\oplus = 5.976 \times 10^{27}$ g

Mean density $\rho_0 = 5.517$ g/cm^3

Ratio of mass of earth to mass of moon $\dfrac{M_\oplus}{M_0} = 81.375$ (1, 11)

TABLE 10-3. ROTATION (9)

Mean solar day $d = 86400$ sec

Sidereal day $S = 86164.09$ sec

Angular velocity of rotation

　　$\Omega = 2\pi/S = 7.292116 \times 10^{-5}$ radian/sec

Ratio of centrifugal acceleration at equator to

$$g_e = m = \frac{\Omega^2 a_e}{g_e} = 1/288.4 = .003467$$

TABLE 10-4. MOMENTS OF INERTIA

Precessional constant or dynamical ellipticity

$$H = \frac{C - A}{C} = 1/305.3 = .0032755 \ (5)$$

　　$C =$ principal moment of inertia about polar axis

　　$A =$ principal moment of inertia in equatorial plane

$$J_2 = \frac{C - A}{Ma_e^2} = 1.0826 \times 10^{-3} \ (7)$$

$$J_2/H = \frac{C}{Ma_e^2} = .3305$$

$$C = 8.068 \times 10^{44} \text{ g cm}^2$$

Mean moment of inertia C_0

$$\frac{C_0}{Ma_0^2} = \frac{(1 - \tfrac{2}{3}H)}{(1 - \tfrac{2}{3}f)} \frac{C}{Ma_e^2}$$

$$C_0 = 8.014 \times 10^{44} \text{ g cm}^2$$

TABLE 10-5. EXTERNAL GRAVITATIONAL POTENTIAL (7)

Gravitational potential at a distance r from the earth center

$$= U = \frac{GM_\oplus}{r}\left[1 - \sum_{n=2}^{\infty}\left(\frac{a_e}{r}\right)^n\left\{J_nP_n(\sin\varphi)\right.\right.$$

$$\left.\left.+ \sum_{m=1}^{n}(J_n^m\cos m\lambda + K_n^m\sin m\lambda)P_n^m(\sin\varphi)\right\}\right]$$

φ = geocentric latitude

λ = longitude

$P_n = P_n^0$

P_n^m are the conventional associated Legendre functions

$$P_n^m(\sin\varphi) = \frac{\cos^m\varphi}{2^n n!}\sum_{\ell=0}^{k}\frac{(2n-2\ell)!}{(n-m-2\ell)!}\binom{n}{\ell}(-1)^\ell\sin\varphi^{n-m-2\ell}$$

$k = (n - m - 1)/2$ $n - m$ odd

$k = (n - m)/2$ $n - m$ even

$J_2 = 1082.645 \times 10^{-6}$, ± 6	$J_3 = -2.546 \times 10^{-6}$, ± 20
$J_4 = -1.649 \times 10^{-6}$, ± 16	$J_5 = -.210 \times 10^{-6}$, ± 25
$J_6 = .646 \times 10^{-6}$, ± 30	$J_7 = -.333 \times 10^{-6}$, ± 39
$J_8 = -.270 \times 10^{-6}$, ± 50	$J_9 = -.053 \times 10^{-6}$, ± 60
$J_{10} = -.054 \times 10^{-6}$, ± 50	$J_{11} = .302 \times 10^{-6}$, ± 35
$J_{12} = -.357 \times 10^{-6}$, ± 44	$J_{13} = -.114 \times 10^{-6}$, ± 84
$J_{14} = .179 \times 10^{-6}$. ± 63	

REFERENCES FOR SECTION 10

1. Delano, Astron. Jour. **55**, 129–133, 1950
2. Fischer, Jour. Geophys. Research **64**, 73–84, 1959
3. —— Jour. Geophys. Research **65**, 2067–2076, 1960
4. Heyl, and Chrzanowski, U.S. Nat'l. Bureau Standards Jour. Research **29**, 1–31, 1942
5. Jeffreys, The Earth, 4th ed., 420 p. Cambridge Univ. Press, 1959
6. Kaula, Jour. Geophys. Research **66**, 1799–1811, 1961
7. Kozai, Publ. Astron. Soc. Japan **16**, 1964
8. Morelli, Intern. Gravity Comm. I.U.G.G., Paris, 1959
9. Munk, and MacDonald, The rotation of the earth: a geophysical discussion, 323 p., Cambridge Univ. Press, 1960
10. O'Keefe, Eckels, and Squires, Astron. Jour. **64**, 245–253, 1959
11. Rabe, Astron. Jour. **55**, 112–126, 1950

SECTION 11

STRENGTH AND DUCTILITY

by JOHN HANDIN

CONTENTS

ILLUSTRATIONS

Handbook of Physical Constants—*Revised Edition*

THE GEOLOGICAL SOCIETY OF AMERICA MEMOIR 97, 1966

INTRODUCTION

Field geology provides a wealth of evidence relating to the kinematics of rock deformation. However, the origin of tectonic forces is conjectural; the state of stress in the crust can seldom be determined quantitatively, and the processes of slow deformations are never subject to direct observation in nature. The dynamics of rock deformation must be learned through controlled experiments which realistically simulate the natural environmental conditions—overburden and interstitial pressures, temperature, and time. This section outlines the results of these experiments, but includes neither the atmospheric-pressure engineering data, adequately compiled elsewhere [48, 89, 165, 166], nor a complete tabulation of the high-pressure properties of metals, which is thoroughly treated by Bridgman [30].

EXPERIMENTAL METHOD AND DEFINITION OF TERMS

In the laboratory the behavior of small samples of real rocks at high pressures and temperatures is investigated in the *triaxial compression test*. The cylindrical specimen with a diameter of about 1–3 cm is encased by the thin, impermeable, rubber or copper jacket and first subjected to the constant external fluid (hydrostatic) *confining pressure*, p_c (Fig. 11-1). The ratio of length to diameter is 2 to 3, large enough to minimize the influence of end constraint, but small enough to avoid buckling. A measured quantity of interstitial liquid is injected by the volumeter through the hollow piston into the previously evacuated sample. The internal *pore pressure*, p_p, is then raised to the desired value by thrust on the volumeter piston. The *differential pressure*, $\Delta\sigma$, is applied by a

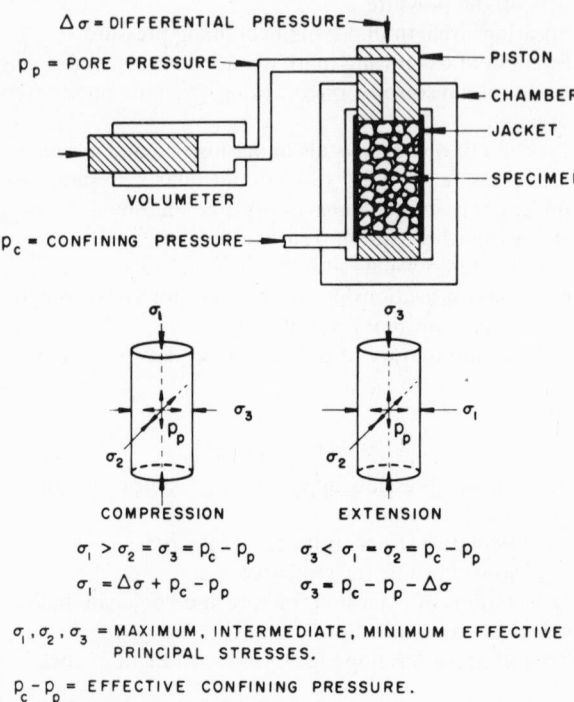

$\sigma_1, \sigma_2, \sigma_3$ = MAXIMUM, INTERMEDIATE, MINIMUM EFFECTIVE
PRINCIPAL STRESSES.

$p_c - p_p$ = EFFECTIVE CONFINING PRESSURE.

Figure 11-1. Sketch of triaxial compression apparatus and states of stress in homogeneous cylindrical jacketed specimens in compression and extension tests.

hydraulic or screw-driven press parallel to the axis of the specimen through the loading piston which enters the top of the thick-walled steel test chamber. Any change of void volume is measured by the advance or withdrawal of the volumeter piston required to maintain constant pore pressure throughout the deformation. The specimen can be heated to the temperature appropriate to the simulated depth.

Let σ_1, σ_2, and σ_3 be the maximum, intermediate, and minimum principal stresses, respectively, compressions regarded as positive. In the dry *compression test* on homogeneous material the differential pressure is superposed on the hydrostatic pressure so that σ_1 is the total axial stress, and σ_2 and σ_3 are both equal to the lateral confining pressure. The specimen shortens. In the dry *extension test* the axial stress is relieved and becomes σ_3 while σ_1 and σ_2 remain equal to the constant confining pressure. The specimen elongates. Suppose that an internal pore pressure is also applied. Then according to Terzaghi's [157] principle of *effective stress*, all normal stresses in the solid framework of the porous rock are reduced by an amount p_p. One merely substitutes *effective confining pressure*, $p_c - p_p$, for external pressure to calculate the effective principal stresses (Fig. 11-1). The normal stress σ_n and shear stress τ on any plane parallel to σ_2 and inclined at an angle θ to σ_1 can be calculated by the following set of equations.

$$\left.\begin{aligned}\sigma_n &= \frac{\sigma_1 + \sigma_3}{2} - \frac{\sigma_1 - \sigma_3}{2}\cos 2\theta \\[2mm] \tau &= \frac{\sigma_1 - \sigma_3}{2}\sin 2\theta\end{aligned}\right\} \tag{1}$$

From the records of axial differential force and relative displacements of the piston with respect to the test chamber, one can derive the *stress-strain curve* for a given effective confining pressure, temperature, and rate of deformation. The force is corrected for piston packing friction and converted to true axial differential stress by dividing by the actual cross-sectional area of the deforming specimen. The displacement is adjusted for elastic deformation of the apparatus and converted to conventional longitudinal strain, ε, the ratio of change of length to original length. The differential stress, the difference between total axial pressure and effective confining pressure, is then plotted against per cent shortening or elongation (Fig. 11-2). The stress-strain curve affords evaluations of two most important properties, strength and ductility.

Strength is qualitatively defined as resistance to failure—continuing flow or fracture. *Flow* is any deformation, not instantly recoverable, without permanent loss of cohesion. *Fracture* (or *rupture*) is used in the ordinary sense to imply complete loss of cohesion and loss of resistance to stress difference, separation into two or more parts, and release of stored elastic strain energy. Quantitative measures require more precise definitions as follows.

(1) *Yield stress* is the stress difference at the onset of permanent strain, ideally marked by a sudden break in the curve, and below which the deformation is essentially elastic (Fig. 11-2, curve E). However, this is indefinite for most rocks, so that in practice one must specify the stress at some arbitrary small strain (Fig. 11-2, curve F). The engineering "proportional limit" and "elastic limit," supposed to delimit the linear stress-strain relationship and totally recoverable deformation respectively, are even more difficult to identify. These terms are best avoided.

(2) *Ultimate strength* is the maximum ordinate of the curve, that is, the greatest stress difference that the material can withstand under given conditions of effective pressure, temperature, and strain rate. It is ambiguous only when the curve increases

monotonically because of *work* (or *strain*) *hardening* which requires an additional increment of stress for each increment of permanent strain (Fig. 11-2, curve F).

(3) *Breaking strength* is the true stress difference at fracture. This need not correspond with ultimate strength since the curves for many rocks are peaked (Fig. 11-2, curve C). *Crushing strength* is the uniaxial compressive stress required to break the material under atmospheric conditions. This is poorly reproducible because of the

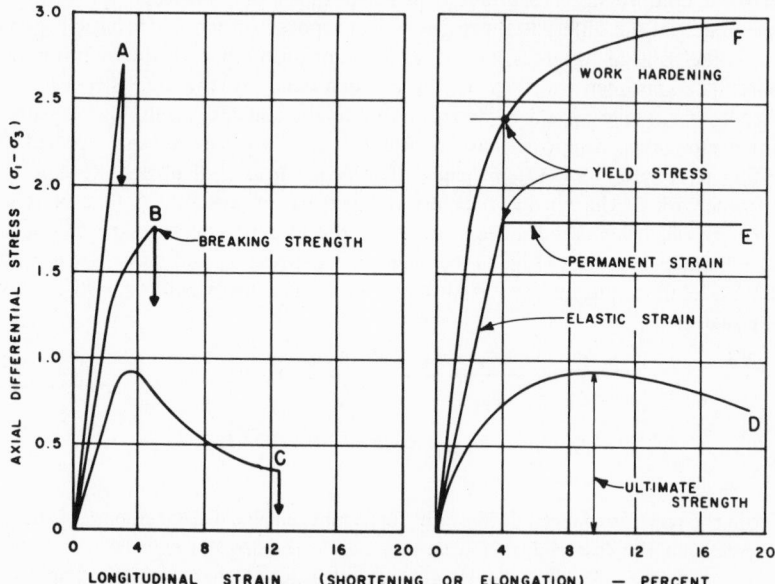

Figure 11-2. Representative stress-strain curves for rocks: *A*, Very brittle; strain essentially elastic prior to sudden rupture: *B*, Brittle; small permanent strain before rupture; *C*, Transitional; peak signals faulting without total loss of cohesion; *D*, Moderately ductile; faulting accompanied by distributed deformation: *E*, Ductile; elastic strain below well defined yield stress, permanent uniform flow beyond: *F*, Ductile; uniform flow with poorly defined yield stress and work hardening.

inherent inhomogeneities of rock samples and inconsistencies of testing procedures. Crushing strengths are tabulated for purpose of comparison only for those rocks which have also been deformed under confining pressure.

Ductility is qualitatively defined as the ability of the material to undergo large permanent deformation without fracture. Under different conditions the same material may be *brittle*; fracture ensues early in the history of the stress-strain curve (compare Fig. 11-2, curves A and F). There is no universally applicable numerical measure of relative ductility, but the following terms can be used for the purpose of discussion. The material is regarded as *very brittle, brittle, moderately brittle* (*transitional*), *moderately ductile*, and *ductile* if the total strain before fracture or faulting is less than 1, 1 to 5, 2 to 8, 5 to 10, and more than 10 per cent, respectively.

The time-dependent behaviors of rocks can be investigated in triaxial compression tests either by varying the rate of deformation (*constant strain-rate tests*) or by applying a constant differential stress of long duration and observing the ensuing strain rate (*creep test*). Strain-time curves exhibit four distinct stages (Fig. 11-3): instantaneous

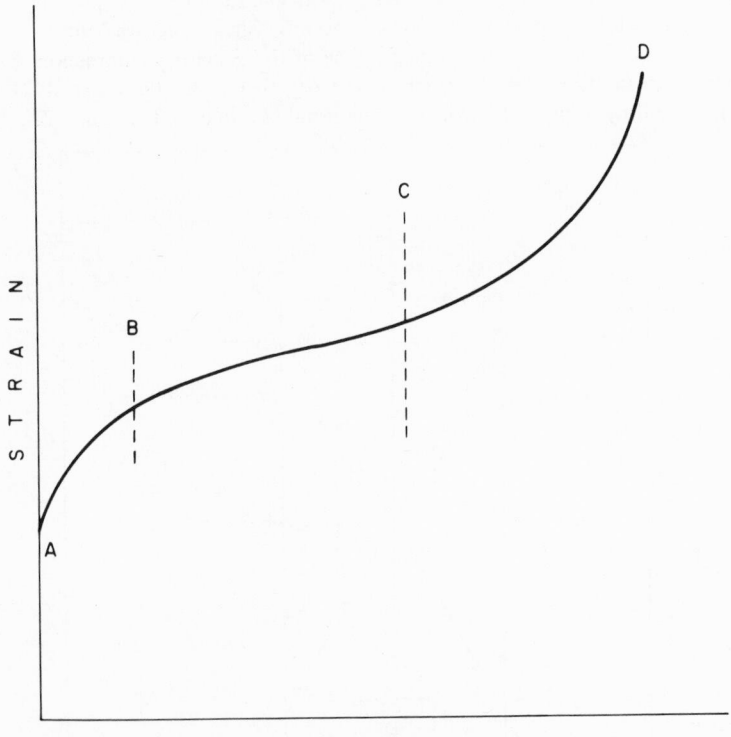

T I M E

Figure 11-3. Typical strain-time (creep) curve for a rock under constant differential stress. Instantaneous elastic strain to A; transient (decelerating) creep from A to B; pseudoviscous (steady) creep from B to C; tertiary (accelerating) creep leading to rupture at D

elastic deformation to point A; *transient* (or primary) flow at a decelerating rate from A to B; *pseudoviscous* (or secondary) flow at a constant rate over the region B to C; and *tertiary* flow at an accelerating rate beyond C and leading to rupture at D. From the steady-state pseudoviscous flow at constant stress difference, an *equivalent viscosity* can be calculated (Table 11-17).

DEFORMATION MECHANISMS

Griggs and Handin [56] believe that the macroscopic behavior of rocks and minerals as observed in the laboratory can be adequately described in terms of three fundamental phenomena.

(1) *Extension fracture* involves separation across a surface normal to the direction of least principal stress without relative displacement parallel to that surface. This can occur even though all macroscopic normal stresses are compressive. When the least stress is tensile, one may properly speak of "tension fracturing," recognizing this as merely a special case. Extension fracturing is characteristic of very brittle materials (Fig. 11-2, curve A).

(2) *Faulting* involves localized relative displacement parallel to a more or less plane surface of nonvanishing shear stress inclined at from 45° to a few degrees to the direction

of greatest principal stress in homogeneous isotropic samples. Complete loss of resistance to stress difference may or may not occur. "Shear fracture" implies complete loss of cohesion and represents a special case of the general phenomenon. Extension fracturing and faulting (Fig. 11-4) can occur together in brittle materials (Fig. 11-2, curve B). Faulting alone is typical of transitional specimens. The fault zone is sharp,

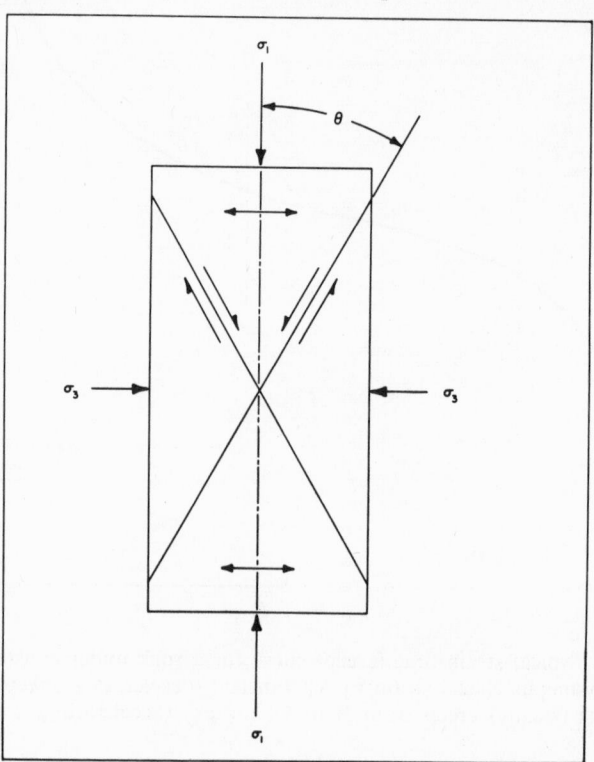

Figure 11-4. Orientations of extension fracture and conjugate faults relative to principal stress directions in homogeneous material. Fracture parallel to maximum principal compression, σ_1, normal to minimum principal compression, σ_3. Acute angle, 2θ, between pair of conjugate faults bisected by σ_1. Intersection of faults parallel to intermediate principal compression, σ_2

narrow, and comminuted. Initiation of faulting is marked by a well defined peak in the stress-strain curve (C). In moderately ductile rocks the fault zone tends to broaden, and some distributed deformation occurs throughout. The stress-strain curve commonly shows a broad maximum (D), but may also rise continuously (F).

(3) *Uniform flow* denotes the macroscopically homogeneous deformation of ductile materials. The stress-strain curve may be essentially horizontal (Fig. 11-2, curve E) or may increase monotonically when work hardening occurs (F). The curve does not always discriminate flow from faulting. Flow is accomplished by three microscopic mechanisms which cannot be distinguished by the stress-strain curve but must be identified by careful petrographic examination.

(a) *Cataclasis* is crushing, granulation, and fracture of individual grains or localized regions within the aggregate accompanied by intergranular adjustments.

(b) *Intracrystalline gliding* involves mechanical twinning and translation gliding (slip) within individual grains accompanied by minor intergranular adjustments. This process can be regarded as analogous to a simple shear by relative displacements of thin closely spaced parallel sheets over one another. The displacement is restricted to a definite crystallographic plane, T, and gliding direction, t, within that plane. The gliding system (plane, direction, and sense of shear) is determined by the particular crystal structure and not by the nature of the loading.

In twin gliding each layer must move through a constant fraction of the interionic distance so that the shear strain is fixed and the deformed portion of the crystal is in proper twinned relationship to the host. By convention [14, 133] the twin plane and direction are denoted K_1 and N_1 respectively. The deformation plane is normal to K_1 and parallel to N_1. In the strain ellipsoid, K_1 is one of the circular sections unaffected by the strain; the other is designated K_2, and its intersection with the deformation plane is N_2. These twin gliding elements of crystals are tabulated in terms of Miller indices (Table 11-2).

In translation gliding the original crystal structure is maintained. Therefore, each displacement must be through an integral number of interionic spacings, but the shear strain is not fixed. The Miller indices of translation gliding systems are listed in Table 11-1.[1]

(c) *Recrystallization* occurs on the molecular scale by solid diffusion, local melting, or through the agency of solutions. The new crystalline aggregate tends to assume the configuration of least free energy in the system. Syntectonic recrystallization in the solid phase is driven by the internal stored strain energy. The growth of strain-free crystals and polymorphic transformations are both observed. Recrystallization involving solution and redeposition occurs because grains are not uniformly stressed. Again the process tends to restore a state of equilibrium. Both mechanisms occur in the anisotropic stress field of the deforming material. New grains must, therefore, acquire some preferred orientation, but the theory is controversial [21, 86, 87, 93, 162].

EFFECTS OF CONFINING PRESSURE

The pioneering experiments of Adams and his collaborators [1–5] showed convincingly, if qualitatively, that confining pressure enhanced both ultimate strength and ductility. These effects have since been confirmed quantitatively by short-time triaxial compression tests on most rocks and rock-forming minerals to about 1 kb (Tables 11-3, 11-4) and on many to 5 kb (Table 11-3). Bridgman has tested some metals and nonmetallic crystals to 30 kb (Tables 11-5, 11-6). Space limitations prohibit reproduction of the many hundred stress-strain curves now published. The tabulation of results (Table 11-3) is a compromise. The magnitude of the differential stress at several values of strain is listed together with confining pressure, ultimate strength, and total strain. From these data one can reconstruct the stress-strain curve rather well, and the influence of pressure on ultimate strength and ductility is obvious.

Rock deformation has also been investigated for other systems of loading: indentation hardness [19, 20, 141], hollow cylinders under external (Table 11-7) and internal (Table 11-8) hydrostatic pressure, shear under high normal pressure (Table 11-9), and torsion combined with triaxial compression (Table 11-10).

Our theoretical knowledge of the effects of pressure is incomplete, but the concept of *internal friction*, first introduced by Coulomb [35] and later generalized by Mohr

---

[1] In addition slip in quartz has recently been demonstrated parallel to the basal plain along an a axis and probably parallel to a prism as well [170]

[102, 103] provides a useful qualitative explanation at low temperatures where recrystallization does not occur. The total shearing resistance τ offered by an isotropic material to failure (shear fracturing, faulting, or flow by distributed shear) is supposed to be the sum of a *cohesive strength*, τ_0, (independent of direction), and a term representing frictional resistance to slip along the potential plane of failure. This term is the product of the effective normal stress σ_n across that plane and the *coefficient of internal friction*, $n = \tan \phi$, where ϕ is an angle analogous to that of ordinary sliding friction. Thus

$$\tau = \tau_0 + \sigma_n \tan \phi. \tag{2}$$

Substituting equations 1 into 2 and solving for the angle θ for which the shear stress is as high as possible and the normal pressure is as low as possible, one finds that

$$\theta = \pm 45° \mp \phi/2. \tag{3}$$

There is a conjugate pair of potential planes of failure. The acute angle between them is bisected by the direction of maximum principal stress, σ_1, and their intersection is parallel to the intermediate principal stress, σ_2 (Fig. 11-4). In terms of the extreme principal stresses at failure, measured in the triaxial compression test,

$$\sigma_1 = 2\tau_0 \cot \theta + \sigma_3 \cot^2 \theta. \tag{4}$$

Given the value of cohesive strength, one could in principle calculate the ratio of principal stresses and the coefficient of internal friction from a measurement of the acute included angle, 2θ, between conjugate faults in the field. Alternatively, one could predict the fault angle from laboratory determinations of $\tan \phi$. The cohesive strength cannot be measured directly, but it can be read along with the friction angle from Mohr's graphical solution of equations 1–3 (Fig. 11-5). Representative values of τ_0 and $\tan \phi$ appear in Table 11-4. These parameters can also be determined from the data of Table 11-3 by plotting a series of extreme principal stress circles at ultimate strength for increasing values of confining pressure and constructing the tangent Mohr envelope curve.

The cohesive strength is of the order of 100–200 bars for sedimentary rocks and 500 bars for crystalline rocks. The friction angle ranges from about 10° to 60° for moderately ductile and brittle materials respectively. Fault angles will thus lie between 15° and 40° for most rocks; the average value is close to 30°. Since confining pressure enhances ductility, $\tan \phi$ tends to decrease with increasing normal pressure in the same material; that is, the Mohr envelopes are often concave toward the normal-stress axis (Fig. 11-5). In fact, however, the observed fault angles in homogeneous rocks cluster around 30° independently of confining pressure and despite differences in texture, composition, and degree of permanent strain. In extension tests the faults form at angles to the direction of maximum principal stress of 5°–10° less than those noted in compression tests. The criterion is evidently not independent of intermediate principal stress as assumed.

Confining pressure inhibits extension fracturing and raises internal friction. Intragranular gliding, largely insensitive to normal stress, becomes favored over rupture and faulting, and macroscopic ductility is enhanced. There is little further increase in yield stress, but work hardening tends to raise ultimate strength.

The work of Jaeger [78, 79] and of Donath (Table 11-11) demonstrates the strong influence of planar anisotropy (bedding, fissility, foliation, or cleavage) on both ultimate strength and fault inclination. When these features lie at 15°–60° with respect to the direction of maximum principal compression, faulting tends to occur parallel to them at stress differences below those predicted for a homogeneous material. For lesser or greater inclinations faulting occurs much as predicted by equations 2 and 3. However, of the theoretically equal pair of conjugate faults, only the one toward the plane of minimum cohesive strength is developed.

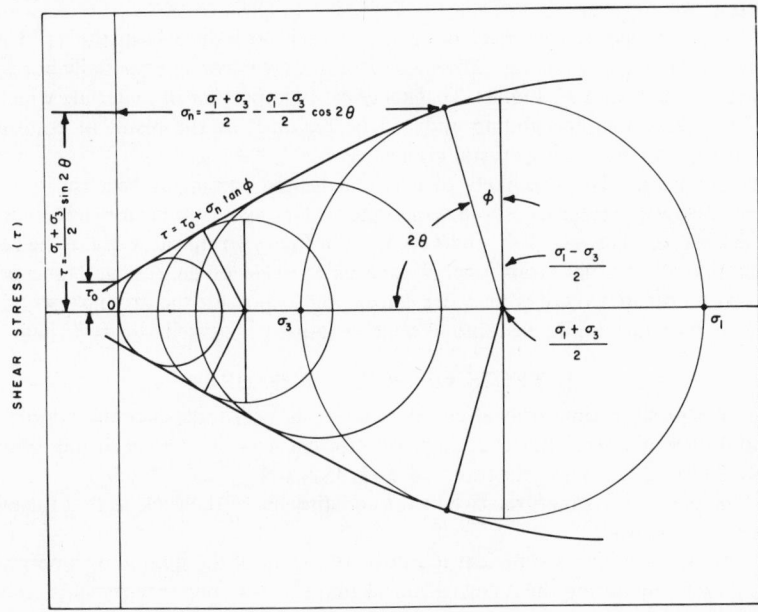

Figure 11-5. Typical Mohr envelope for ultimate strength of rock. Mohr stress circle with diameter $(\sigma_1 - \sigma_3)/2$ and center at $(\sigma_1 + \sigma_3)/2$ gives values of shear stress, τ, and normal stress, σ_n, on planes inclined at angles $\pm 2\theta$ to direction of σ_1 (equation 1). Mohr envelope tangent to series of circles from data of triaxial compression tests gives values of cohesive strength, τ_0, from zero normal stress intercept and coefficient of internal friction, tan φ, from slope (equation 2). At tangent points $\theta = \pm 45 \mp \varphi/2$ (equation 3). Envelope curves toward σ_n-axis, showing that tan φ is not necessarily constant.

Faulting appears to be largely independent of structure in crystals deformed under confining pressure. The notable exception is quartz at very high pressure in which faults occur precisely parallel to certain crystallographic planes (Table 11-12).

EFFECTS OF TEMPERATURE

With but two known exceptions, dolomite and magnesite single crystals, heating invariably lowers the yield stresses of rocks and minerals. Ductility is always enhanced, provided that no chemical changes occur. The influence of temperature on faulting is not consistent, but most commonly heating tends to increase the fault angle. Effects on ultimate strength can be generalized from the data of Table 11-3, as follows.

(1) If work hardening is largely unaffected, the enhanced ductility permits the attainment of greater strains and hence higher differential stresses previous to rupture in the heated specimen (e.g., dolomite rock).

(2) Heating may favor the mechanisms of intracrystalline gliding over those of faulting, so that, paradoxically, ultimate strength is augmented by work hardening in the high-temperature specimen (e.g., anhydrite).

(3) Heating lowers the yield stress but leaves the shape of the stress-strain curve essentially unaltered. The ultimate strength is reduced correspondingly (e.g., Yule marble).

(4) More commonly the effect of temperature is to reduce both the yield stress and work hardening (e.g., halite). The stress-strain curve becomes essentially horizontal (compare curves E and F, Fig. 11-2). This effect is important in materials which are flowing by intracrystalline gliding and can be regarded as the result of continuous annealing of work-hardening crystal grains.

Recrystallization is more likely to occur in heated specimens because its rate is negligible below a certain threshold temperature. Dry syntectonic recrystallization of calcite is observed between 400° and 600° C at ordinary strain rates where the rate of accumulation of internal strain energy exceeds the rate of annealing. None occurs above 600° C because there is no work hardening to provide the driving energy. The martensitic transformation, enstatite to clinoenstatite, is detected at 500° C [60].

EFFECTS OF PORE PRESSURE

The data of short-time triaxial compression tests with independently controllable interstitial pressures confirm the concept of effective stresses, subject to the following conditions (Table 11-3 and references 64, 142, 152, 169).

(1) The pore fluid is inert relative to the constituents of the rock so that the effects are purely mechanical.

(2) The permeability is sufficient to allow pervasion of the fluid and to permit the fluid to flow freely during the deformation so that the pore pressure remains constant and uniform throughout the aggregate.

(3) The configuration of the pore space is such that the interstitial fluid pressure is transmitted fully throughout the solid phase.

The increase of pore pressure merely reduces the effective confining pressure, completely in rocks with connected porosities of about 5 per cent or more and partially in rocks of low porosity and permeability. This tends to lower both ultimate strength and ductility.

The effect of chemically active fluids is poorly understood. The breaking strength of quartz is drastically lowered by the presence of alkaline solutions (Table 11-13). The syntectonic recrystallization of quartz seems to require an aqueous environment even at 20 kilobars and 1000° C [54]. The pressure-solution process has been studied only qualitatively, largely in sand consolidation experiments [41, 53, 100, 101].[2]

EFFECTS OF TIME

Because so few tests of long duration have been made on rocks under geologically realistic conditions, knowledge of time-dependent deformations is woefully inadequate. Griggs [51, 52] observed that under differential stresses of long duration materials generally tended to fail well below their short-time yield stresses or breaking strengths. Robertson [139] noted that the yield stress of limestone was raised about 20 per cent by very rapid, nearly impact loading. However, in shearing experiments Bridgman [30] found that a 10,000-fold change in rate of application of torque resulted in no variation in shearing resistance.

---

[2] Effective confining pressure can also be reduced by the generation of pore pressure resulting from release of a fluid phase during a hydrous-anhydrous transformation. This has been observed in gypsum [171] and serpentinite [172, 173]. Recently discovered, too, is the drastic water weakening of quartz and silicate minerals at high temperature (about 500°C), due probably to the hydrolysis of silicon-oxygen bonds [174].

From his early compression experiments on unjacketed Solenhofen limestone at 10 kb confining pressure and room temperature, Griggs [49] concluded that ultimate strength decreased with increasing duration of loading as expected, but that contrary to intuition, ductility also decreased. Recent tests on the same rock by Heard [73] at 0–1 kb, 25°–500° C, and constant strain rates of 10^{-4}–10^{-7} per second, and by Serdengecti and Boozer [152] at 0–1.4 kb, 25°–150° C, and 10^{-1}–10^{-5} per second confirm the reduction in strength, but demonstrate that ductility *increases* with decreasing strain rate.

The behavior of most materials under constant differential stress appears to be well represented by the empirical relationship

$$\varepsilon = A + B \log t + Ct, \tag{5}$$

where ε is total longitudinal strain, t is time, and A, B, and C are material "constants" which depend upon differential stress, effective confining pressure, and temperature. The first term represents instantaneous elastic strain; the second transient flow; and the third pseudoviscous flow (Fig. 11-3).

Transient flow is small and largely, if not wholly, recoverable upon release of load. The rate tends to increase with stress difference and temperature, but to decrease as confining pressure is raised (Table 11-14).

Large irreversible deformations are attainable through pseudoviscous flow. This differs from ordinary Newtonian viscous flow in that the steady strain rate $\dot{\varepsilon}$ is a non-linear function of stress difference. Nadai [130] suggested the hyperbolic sine function which was later confirmed experimentally by McVetty [94] for metals and by Griggs from creep tests on wet gypsum (Table 11-15),

$$\dot{\varepsilon} = \dot{\varepsilon}_0 \sinh \frac{(\Delta\sigma - S)}{\sigma_0}, \tag{6}$$

where $\dot{\varepsilon}_0$, σ_0, and S are empirical "constants" (about 10^{-10} per second, 45 bars, and 90 bars respectively for gypsum at atmospheric conditions). Term S is the *fundamental strength*, "the differential pressure which the body is able to withstand under given conditions of temperature and confining pressure without rupturing or deforming continuously" [Griggs, 49, p. 564]. Even if this equation should prove to be generally valid, the "constants" must still be determined for each rock under each set of experimental conditions.

Le Comte [91] has investigated the effect of temperature on the creep of rock salt, using the technique of Dorn [37] and others for metals. This is shown by

$$R \log (\dot{\varepsilon}_1/\dot{\varepsilon}_2) = E^*(1/T_2 - 1/T_1), \tag{7}$$

where $\dot{\varepsilon}_1$ is strain rate at absolute temperature T_1; $\dot{\varepsilon}_2$ is strain rate immediately following an abrupt temperature variation to T_2, all other factors assumed to remain constant; R is the gas constant (1.987 cal per deg-mole); and E^* is activation energy. At about half the absolute melting temperature (540° K), this energy amounts to 3×10^4 cal per mole, about the same as that for self-diffusion of Na in the NaCl structure [Mapother and others, 96].

Heard's constant strain rate tests on dry marble at 5 kb confining pressure reveal that a variation of 10^{-1} to 10^{-8} per second modifies the stress-strain curve very little at room temperature, but drastically reduces both yield stress and amount of work hardening at 400°–500° C where the curves become essentially horizontal for rates below about 10^{-4}, that is, the flow becomes steady (Table 11-16A). This effect is associated with the change of deformation mechanism from intracrystalline gliding at low temperatures and/or high strain rates to syntectonic recrystallization above some threshold, probably about 200° C, and at deformation rates low enough to provide time for grain growth.

The linear steady-flow regions of plots of stress difference against logarithm of strain rate can be fitted to the equation of Eyring and others [136], based on the theory of absolute reaction rates of solid diffusion and confirmed by high-temperature creep tests on metals. This relates the pseudoviscous strain rate, $\dot{\varepsilon}$, to both temperature and stress difference.

$$\dot{\varepsilon} = \dot{\varepsilon}_0 e^{-E^*/RT} \sinh \left[\frac{\Delta\sigma}{\sigma_0}\right], \tag{8}$$

where ε_0 and σ_0 are about 10^8 per second and 100 bars respectively for marble, and the activation energy, E^*, is about 6×10^4 cal per mole. The energy of self diffusion has not been measured for calcite or marble. Since no data are available for the region where the hyperbolic sine term becomes important, the fundamental strength, if any, cannot be evaluated.

By extrapolating the curves of equation 8, Heard [168] finds that the ultimate strength of marble would be of the order 2–3 kilobars, 400 bars, and less than 1 bar for temperatures of 25°, 300°, and 400° C respectively at a geologically realistic strain rate (about 10^{-14} per second).

The constant strain rate tests of Serdengecti and Boozer [152] on limestone, sandstone, and diorite show that the breaking strengths of materials in the brittle state increase with strain rate. The behavior of these rocks tends to change from brittle to ductile, that is, from fracture through faulting to uniform flow as the strain rate is reduced. In the ductile state ultimate strength decreases with strain rate (Table 11-16B).

The effect of the modest temperature change from 25° to 150° C on the sandstone and diorite is negligible, but the ultimate strength of the limestone can be specified as a function of the strain rate, temperature, and confining pressure of these experiments by an empirical equation derived from linear log-log plots of strength against $\dot{\varepsilon} \exp (E^*/RT)$,

$$\Delta\sigma = k_1 e^{\Delta p_c/k_2 p_c} [\dot{\varepsilon} e^{E^*/RT}]^{(k_3 + \Delta p_c/k_4 p_c)}, \tag{9}$$

where k_1, k_3 refer to a reference confining pressure, p_c; Δp_c is a positive increment of pressure; and k_2 and k_4 are material "constants" in the same sense as the activation energy, 2.5×10^4 cal per mole. If this relationship proves to be valid for a wide range of variables and for other rocks as well, then once the empirical constants are measured under practical laboratory conditions, the ultimate strength may be extrapolated to situations beyond the limits of the tests, especially to very high or low strain rates. However, the activation energy of the Yule marble measured by Heard [168] is more than double that of the Solenhofen limestone. The activation energies of different processes (fracture, intracrystalline slip, and recrystallization) probably differ widely. This restricts the applicability of equations like 8 and 9 to conditions under which the deformation mechanism is always the same.

For a given confining pressure and temperature one can calculate an equivalent viscosity from the steady strain rate at constant stress difference measured in both creep and constant strain rate tests. Data are available only for a few rocks under limited conditions (Table 11-17). This parameter tends to decrease nonlinearly with increasing temperature and stress difference.

The influence of confining pressure is not yet clear. An increase from atmospheric to 1 kb raises the equivalent viscosity of dry rock salt at 105° C by a factor of 3 (Table 11-17), but lowers that of wet gypsum by a factor of 4 (Table 11-15).

FUTURE WORK

Current empirical knowledge of the effects of confining pressure, pore pressure, and temperature on the short-time mechanical properties of rocks is good. The measurements of different investigators are consistent, and all specimens within each of relatively few categories are found to behave essentially similarly: (1) the unfoliated igneous and metamorphic rocks and silica-cemented sandstone, (2) schist, slate, and highly indurated and fissile shale, (3) dolomite and anhydrite, (4) moderately well cemented sandstone, (5) limestone, (6) poorly fissile shale, mudstone, and siltstone, and (7) salt and gypsum. Since the effects of the variables are approximately superimposable, one can estimate the properties of any of these rocks under a wide variety of conditions, whether tested in the laboratory or not. However, a more adequate theoretical foundation is much needed, especially for the problem of fracturing.

An understanding of the influence of time is just beginning to evolve. A vast amount of experimental work will be required to delineate the time-dependent deformational properties of all the common rocks, and this must be matched by theoretical research aimed at extrapolation of laboratory data to geologically realistic conditions. Important problems include (1) choice of proper rheological models for folded rocks, (2) speed and mode of propagation of faulting, and (3) both wet and dry syntectonic recrystallization in development of preferred grain orientations in slates, schists, and quartz tectonites.

REFERENCES FOR SECTION 11

1. Adams, Jour. Geol. **18**, 489, 1910
2. —— Jour. Geol. **20**, 197, 1912
3. Adams and Coker, Am. Jour. Sci. **29**, 465, 1910
4. Adams and Bancroft, Jour. Geol. **25**, 597, 1917
5. Adams and Nicholson, Phil. Trans. Roy. Soc. **195**, A, 363, 1901
6. Avery and Monfore, U.S. Bur. Reclamation, Concrete Lab. Rept. C-746, 1954
7. Balmer, U.S. Bur. Reclamation, Concrete Lab. Rept. SP-39, 1953
8. —— U.S. Bur. Reclamation, Concrete Lab. Rept. C-722, 1953
9. —— U.S. Bur. Reclamation, Concrete Lab. Rept. C-804, 1955
10. Balmer and Hanson, U.S. Bur. Reclamation, Structural Lab. Rept. SP-30, I, 1951
11. Balsley, Trans. Am. Geophys. Union, II, 519, 1941
12. Barrett, Structure of metals, New York, McGraw-Hill, 1952
13. Baumhauer, Zeit. deutsch. geol. Ges. **35**, 639, 1883
14. Bell, Am. Min. **26**, 247, 1941
15. Boas and Schmid, Zeits. Phys. **54**, 16, 1929
16. Böker, Mitt. Forsch. Ver. deutsch. Ing. **175**, 1, 1915
17. Borg, Friedman, Handin, and Higgs, Geol. Soc. America Mem. **79**, 133, 1960
18. Borg, Handin, and Higgs, Jour. Geophys. Res. **64**, 1094, 1959
19. Brace, Bull. Geol. Soc. America **69**, 1539, 1958
20. —— Jour. Geophys. Res. **65**, 1773, 1960
21. —— Geol. Soc. America Mem. **79**, 9, 1960
22. Bredthauer, Trans. Am. Soc. Mech. Eng. **79**, 695, 1957
23. Bridgman, Am. Jour. Sci. **45**, 243, 1918
24. —— Phys. Rev. **48**, 825, 1935
25. —— Proc. Am. Acad. **71**, 387, 1937
26. —— Proc. Am. Acad. **72**, 157, 1938
27. —— Phys. Rev. **57**, 342, 1940
28. —— Jour. App. Phys. **12**, 461, 1941
29. —— Jour. App. Phys. **18**, 246, 1947
30. —— Studies in large plastic flow and fracture, New York, McGraw-Hill, 1952
31. —— Jour. App. Phys. **24**, 560, 1953
32. Buerger, Am. Min. **13**, 1 and 35, 1928
33. —— Am. Min. **15**, 45, 174 and 226, 1930
34. Christie, Heard, and La Mori, Bull. Geol. Soc. America **71**, 1842, 1960
35. Coulomb, Acad. Sci. Paris Mem. Phys. **7**, 343, 1776

36. Donath, Bull. Geol. Soc. America **72**, 985, 1961
37. Dorn, Creep and recovery, Am. Soc. Metals, 255, 1957
38. Elam, Proc. Roy. Soc. **112**, 289, 1926
39. Ewing and Rosenhain, Phil. Trs. Roy. Soc. **193**, A, 353, 1900
40. Fahrenhorst and Schmid, Zeits. Phys. **78**, 383, 1932
41. Fairbairn, Am. Min. **35**, 735, 1950
42. Fischer, Neues Jahrb. B. B. **32**, 1, 1911
43. Florey and King, U.S. Bur. Reclamation, Concrete Lab. Rept. C-771, 1954
44. Goetze, Centralb. Min. 1919, 65
45. Goguel, Introduction à l'étude mécanique des déformations de l'écorce terrestre, Imprim. Nat., Paris, 1948
46. Goucher, Philos. Mag. **48**, p. 229, 1924
47. Gough, Proc. Roy. Soc. **118**, A, 498, 1928
48. Griffith, Iowa Eng. Exp. Sta. Bull. **131**, 1937
49. Griggs, Jour. Geol. **44**, 541, 1936
50. ——— Am. Min. **23**, 28, 1938
51. ——— Jour. Geol. **47**, 225, 1939
52. ——— Bull. Geol. Soc. America **51**, 1001, 1940
53. ——— Am. Geophys. Union, II, 526, 1941
54. ——— unpublished data, 1953–1961
55. Griggs and Bell, Bull. Geol. Soc. America **49**, 1723, 1938
56. Griggs and Handin, Geol. Soc. America Memoir **79**, 347, 1960
57. Griggs and Miller, Bull. Geol. Soc. America **62**, 853, 1951
58. Griggs, Turner, Borg, and Sosoka, Bull. Geol. Soc. America **62**, 1386, 1951
59. ——— Bull. Geol. Soc. America **64**, 1327, 1953
60. Griggs, Turner, and Heard, Geol. Soc. America Memoir **79**, 39, 1960
61. Grühn, Neues Jahrb. 1918-I, 99
62. Grühn and Johnsen, Centralb. Min. 1917, 336
63. Handin, Trans. Am. Soc. Mech. Eng. **75**, 315, 1953
64. ——— Bull. Geol. Soc. America **69**, 1576, 1958
65. ——— Jour. Petrol. Tech. **11**, 1, 15, 1959
66. ——— unpublished data, 1952–1961
67. Handin and Fairbairn, Bull. Geol. Soc. America **66**, 1257, 1955
68. Handin and Hager, Bull. Am. Assoc. Petroleum Geologists **41**, 1, 1957
69. ——— Bull. Am. Assoc. Petroleum Geologists **42**, 2892, 1958
70. Handin, Higgs, Lewis, and Weyl, Bull. Geol. Soc. America **68**, 1203, 1957
71. Handin, Higgs, and O'Brien, Geol. Soc. America Memoir **79**, 245, 1960
72. Heard, Geol. Soc. America Memoir **79**, 193, 1960
73. ——— Jour. Geophys. Res. **66**, 2534, 1961
74. ——— unpublished data, 1956–1961
75. Heide, Zeits. Kryst. **78**, 257, 1931
76. Higgs and Handin, Bull. Geol. Soc. America **70**, 245, 1959
77. Humfrey, Phil. Trans. Roy. Soc. **200**, A, 225, 1903
78. Jaeger, Geofis. Pur. App. **43**, 148, 1959
79. ——— Geol. Mag. **97**, 65, 1960
80. Johnsen, Neues Jahrb. II, 1902, 133
81. ——— Neues Jahrb. B. B. **23**, 237, 1907
82. ——— Centralb. Min. 1908, 426
83. ——— Jahrb. Rad. Elekt. **11**, 226, 1914
84. ——— Neues Jahrb. B. B. **39**, 500, 1914
85. ——— Centralb. Min. 1915, 33
86. Kamb, Jour. Geol. **67**, 153, 1959
87. ——— Jour. Geophys. Res. **66**, 259, 1961
88. Kendall, Master's thesis, A. M. Coll. Texas, 1958
89. Kessler, Insley, and Sligh, U.S. Bur. Stand. Jour. Res. **25**, 161, 1940
90. Kienow, Neues Jahrb. 1951, 39
91. Le Comte, Ph.D. thesis, Harvard Univ., 1960
92. McConnel, Proc. Roy. Soc. **48**, 259, 1890; 49, 323, 1891
93. MacDonald, Geol. Soc. America Memoir **79**, 1, 1960
94. McVetty, Trans. Am. Soc. Mech. Eng. **65**, 761, 1943
95. Mallard, Bull. Soc. Min. Paris **5**, 214, 1882
96. Mapother, Crooks, and Maurer, Jour. Chem. Phys. **18**, 1231, 1950
97. Mark and Polanyi, Zeits. Phys. **18**, 75, 1923
98. Mark, Polanyi, and Schmid, Zeits. Phys. **12**, 58, 1922
99. Masing and Polanyi, Erg. exakt. Naturwiss. **2**, 177, 1923
100. Maxwell, Geol. Soc. America Memoir **79**, 105, 1960
101. Maxwell and Verral, World Oil **138**, 5, 106; 6, 102, 1954
102. Mohr, Civilingenieure **28**, 113, 1882
103. ——— Zeits. Ver. deutsch. Ing. **44**, 1524, 1900
104. Monfore, U.S. Bur. Reclamation, Concrete Lab. Rept. C-731, 1954

105. Mügge, Neues Jahrb. 1883-I, 32
106. —— Neues Jahrb. 1883-II, 258
107. —— Neues Jahrb. 1884-I, 50
108. —— Neues Jahrb. 1884-II, 40
109. —— Neues Jahrb. 1886-I, 183
110. —— Neues Jahrb. 1886-II, 36
111. —— Neues Jahrb. 1888-I, 131
112. —— Neues Jahrb. 1889-I, 130
113. —— Neues Jahrb. 1889-II, 98
114. —— Neues Jahrb. B. B. 6, 274, 1889
115. —— Neues Jahrb. 1892-II, 91
116. —— Neues Jahrb. 1894-I, 106
117. —— Neues Jahrb. 1895-II, 211
118. —— Neues Jahrb. 1898-I, 71
119. —— Neues Jahrb. 1899-II, 55
120. —— Tech. min. petr. Mitt. **19**, 102, 1900
121. —— Neues Jahrb. B. B. **14**, 246, 1901
122. —— Neues Jahrb. 1906-I, 91
123. —— Neues Jahrb. 1914-I, 43
124. —— Centralb. Min. 1917, 233
125. —— Neues Jahrb. 1920-I, 24
126. —— Centralb. Min. 1922, 1
127. —— Zeits. anorg. Chem. **121**, 68, 1922
128. —— Zeits. Kryst. **71**, 64, 1929
129. Mügge and Heide, Neues Jahrb. B. B. **64**, 163, 1931
130. Nadai, Jour. Appl. Phys. **8**, 418, 1937
131. Obinata and Schmid, Zeits. Phys. **82**, 224, 1933
132. Ore, U.S. Bur. Reclamation, Concrete Lab. Rept. C-718, 1953
133. Pabst, Bull. Geol. Soc. America **66**, 897, 1955
134. Paterson, Bull. Geol. Soc. America **69**, 465, 1958
135. Price, Mechanical properties of non-metallic brittle materials, 122, Butterworth's London, 1958
136. Ree, Ree, and Eyring, Am. Soc. Civ. Eng., Eng. Mech. Div. Jour. **86**, 41, 1960
137. Reusch, Ann. Phys. **132**, 443 and 449, 1867
138. Ritzel, Zeits. Kryst. **52**, 238, 1912
139. Robertson, Bull. Geol. Soc. America **66**, p. 1275, 1955
140. —— Geol. Soc. America Memoir **79**, 227, 1960
141. —— Bull. Geol. Soc. America **72**, 621, 1961
142. Robinson, Colorado School Mines Quart. **54**, 177, 1959
143. Sauerwald and Sossinka, Zeits. Phys. **82**, 634, 1933
144. Schiebold and Siebel, Zeits. Phys. **69**, 458, 1931
145. Schmid and Boas, Plasticity of crystals, London, F. A. Hughes, 1950
146. Schmid and Wassermann, Zeits. Phys. **46**, 653, 1927
147. Schmidt, Zeits. angew. Mineral. **1**, 1, 1937
148. Scott, Bearden, and Howard, Am. Inst. Min. Met. Eng. **198**, 111, 1953
149. Seifert, Centralb. Min. 1920, 97
150. —— Centralb. Min. 1925A, 343
151. —— Landolt-Börnstein Phys.—Chem. Tab., 35, 1927
152. Serdengecti and Boozer, Penn. State Univ. Min. Ind. Expt. Sta. Bull. **76**, 83, 1961
153. Serata, Reactor Waste Disposal Project, Univ. Texas, 1959
154. Tarrico, Acad. Linc. 19, 278 and 508, 1910
155. Taylor and Elam, Proc. Roy. Soc. **102**, 643, 1923; **108**, 28, 1925
156. Tertsch, Festigkeitserscheinungen der Kristalle **56**, Vienna, Springer, 1949
157. Terzaghi, Theoretical soil mechanics, New York, John Wiley & Sons, 1943
158. Turner and Ch'ih, Bull. Geol. Soc. America **62**, 887, 1951
159. Turner, Griggs, and Heard, Bull. Geol. Soc. America **65**, 883, 1954
160. Turner, Griggs, Heard, and Weiss, Am. Jour. Sci. **252**, 477, 1954
161. Turner, Griggs, Clark, and Dixon, Bull. Geol. Soc. America **67**, 1259, 1956
162. Verhoogen, Trans. Am. Geophys. Union **32**, 251, 1951
163. Veit, Neues Jahrb. B. B. 45, 121, 1922
164. von Kármán, Zeits. Ver. deutsch. Ing. **55**, 1749, 1911
165. Windes, U.S. Bur. Mines Rept. Inv. 4459, 1949; 4727, 1950
166. Woolf, U.S. Bur. Pub. Roads, Washington, 1953
167. Goranson, Trans. Am. Geophys. Union **30**, 187, 1949
168. Heard, Jour. Geol. **71**, 162, 1963
169. Handin, Hager, Friedman, Feather, Bull. Am. Assoc. Petroleum Geologists **47**, 717, 1963
170. Christie, Griggs, and Carter, Jour. Geology **72**, 734, 1964
171. Heard and Rubey, Geol. Soc. America Special Paper 76, Abstracts for 1963, 77A, 1963
172. Handin, Nat. Res. Council Pub. **1188**, 126, 1964
173. Raleigh and Paterson, Jour. Geophys. Res. **70**, 3965, 1965
174. Griggs and Blacio, Science **147**, 292, 1965

TABLE 11-1.　TRANSLATION GLIDING SYSTEMS IN CRYSTALS

T = slip plane. t = slip direction in slip plane.

Crystal	Class	Gliding elements		Equivalent elements		Ref.
		t	T	t per T	T	
ISOMETRIC						
Aluminum, Al						39, 155
Copper, Cu						38, 39, 119
Gold, Au	O_h	[10$\bar{1}$]	{111}	3	4	38, 39, 119
Nickel, Ni						12
Silver, Ag						38, 39, 119
Molybdenum, Mo						12
Sodium, Na	O_h	[11$\bar{1}$]	{112}	2	12	12
Tungsten, W						46
α-iron, Fe	O_h	[11$\bar{1}$]	{101}	2	6	47
		[11$\bar{1}$]	{112}	2	12	47
		[11$\bar{1}$]	{123}	2	24	40, 47, 143
Lead, Pb	O_h	—	{111}	—	4	77
Potassium, K	O_h	[11$\bar{1}$]	{123}	2	24	12
Sylvite, KCl						33, 118
KBr						33, 80, 138
KI						33, 80, 138
NaBr	O_h	[1$\bar{1}$0]	{110}	1	6	33
		[1$\bar{1}$0]	{001}	2	3	
Halite, NaCl						33, 80, 118, 137
NaF						33
NaI						33
NH₄l (high)						80
Periclase, MgO	O_h	[1$\bar{1}$0]	{110}	1	6	125
RbCl						80
Fluorite, CaF₂						163
Altaite, PbTe	O_h	[1$\bar{1}$0]	{001}	2	3	33
Galena, Pbs	O_h	[1$\bar{1}$0]	{001}	2	3	32, 121
		[100]	{001}	1	3	123, 154
NH₄Br (low)						80
Sal ammoniac, NH₄Cl	O_h	[001]	{110}	1	6	80
Diamond, C	T_d	[10$\bar{1}$]	{111}	3	4	156
Sphalerite, ZnS	T_d	?	{111}?	?	4?	32, 163
HEXAGONAL						
Beryllium, Be						12
Cadmium, Cd						15
Magnesium, Mg	D_{6h}	[11$\bar{2}$0]	{0001}	3	1	144
Zinc, Zn						98
Graphite, C						118
Molybdenite, MoS₂	D_{6h}	[21$\bar{3}$0]	{0001}	3	1	118
Ice, H₂O	D_{6h}	?	{0001}	?	1	92, 117
Tellurium, Te	D_3	[11$\bar{2}$0]?	{10$\bar{1}$0}	1?	3	146
RHOMBOHEDRAL						
Bismuth, Bi	D_{3d}	[11$\bar{2}$0]	{0001}	3	1	99
Brucite, Mg(OH)₂	D_{3d}	?	{0001}	3?	1	107, 118
Calcite, CaCO₃	D_{3d}	[21$\bar{3}$2]	{10$\bar{1}$1}	1	3	70, 163
		[$\bar{1}$102]				
		[$\bar{1}$2$\bar{1}$2]	{02$\bar{2}$1}	2	3	163
		[10$\bar{1}$0]?	{0001}?	3?	1?	60, 71
Magnesite, MgCO₃	D_{3d}	[10$\bar{1}$1]	{0001}	3	1	80
		[21$\bar{3}$2]	{10$\bar{1}$1}	1	3	76

TABLE 11-1.   *Continued*

Crystal	Class	Gliding elements t	Gliding elements T	Equivalent elements t per T	Equivalent elements T	Ref.
RHOMBOHEDRAL *Continued*						
Rhodochrosite, $MnCO_3$						163
Siderite, $FeCO_3$	D_{3d}	$[10\bar{1}1]$	$\{0001\}$	3	1	80
Smithsonite, $ZnCO_3$						163
Pyrargyrite, $3Ag_2S\cdot Sb_2S_3$	C_{3v}	$[\bar{1}2\bar{1}0]$	$\{0001\}$	3	1	156
Dolomite, $CaMg(CO_3)_2$	C_{3i}	$[10\bar{1}0]$	$\{0001\}$	3	1	76, 80, 160
TETRAGONAL						
β-tin, Sn	D_{4h}	$[001]$	$\{110\}$	1	2	
		$[001]$	$\{100\}$	1	1	97, 131
		$[10\bar{1}]$	$\{101\}$	1	2	
		$[10\bar{1}]$	$\{121\}$	1	4	
Phosgenite, $(PbCl)_2CO_3$	D_4	$[001]$	$\{110\}$	1	2	123, 154
Chalcopyrite, $CuFeS_2$	V_d	?	$\{111\}$	?	4	32, 125
ORTHORHOMBIC						
Andalusite, Al_2SiO_5	V_h	$[10\bar{1}]$	$\{010\}$	2	1	156
Anglesite, $PbSO_4$	V_h	$[100]$	$\{001\}$	1	1	
		$[0\bar{1}1]$	$\{011\}$	2	2	75
		$[010]$	$\{102\}$	1	2	
Anhydrite, $CaSO_4$	V_h	$[100]$	$\{010\}$	1	1⎫	118, 163
		$[100]$?	$\{012\}$	1?	2⎭	
Aragonite, $CaCO_3$	V_h	$[100]$	$\{010\}$	1	1	163
Barite, $BaSO_4$	V_h	$[100]$	$\{001\}$	1	1	118
		$[0\bar{1}1]$	$\{011\}$	2	2	163
		$[100]$	$\{010\}$	1	1	75
		$[010]$	$\{102\}$	1	2	75
Bismuthinite, Bi_2S_3	V_h	$[001]$	$\{010\}$	1	1	118
Bronzite, $MgSiO_3$	V_h	$[001]$?	$\{010\}$?	1?	1?	118
Celestite, $SrSO_4$	V_h	$[100]$	$\{001\}$	1	1	
		$[100]$	$\{011\}$	1	2	75
		$[010]$	$\{102\}$	1	2	
Columbite, (Fe, Mn)$(Nb, Ta)_2O_6$	V_h	$[101]$	$\{010\}$	2	1	118
Epsomite, $MgSO_4\cdot 7H_2O$	V_h	$[1\bar{1}0]$?	$\{110\}$?	?	?	
		$[0\bar{1}0]$?	$\{100\}$?	?	?	
		$[011]$?	$\{011\}$?	?	?	83
		$[\bar{1}01]$?	$\{101\}$?	?	?	
		$[102]$?	$\{201\}$?	?	?	
Guanajuatite, Bi_2Se_3	V_h	$[001]$	$\{010\}$	1	1	118
Montroydite, HgO	V_h	$[010]$?	$\{001\}$	1?	1	156
Pseudobrookite, Fe_2TiO_5	V_h	$[001]$?	$\{010\}$?	1?	1?	156
Stibnite, Sb_2S_3	V_h	$[001]$	$\{010\}$	1	1	118
Sulfur, S	V_h	$[110]$?	$\{111\}$	2?	4	125
MONOCLINIC						
Bischofite, $MgCl_2\cdot 6H_2O$	C_{2h}	$[1\bar{1}2]$	$\{110\}$	1	1	156
$BaBr_2\cdot 2H_2O$	C_{2h}	$[001]$	$\{100\}$	1	1	118
Diopside, $CaMg(SiO_3)_2$	C_{2h}	$[001]$	$\{100\}$	1	1	60
Erythrite, $Co_3As_2O_8\cdot 8H_2O$	C_{2h}	$[001]$	$\{010\}$	1	1	118
Gypsum, $CaSO_4\cdot 2H_2O$	C_{2h}	$[001]$	$\{010\}$	1	1	119
		$[301]$	$\{010\}$	1	1	
$KClO_3$ (low)	C_{2h}	$[100]$	$\{001\}$	1	1	42

TABLE 11-1. *Continued*

Crystal	Class	Gliding elements t	Gliding elements T	Equivalent elements t per T	Equivalent elements T	Ref.
MONOCLINIC *Continued*						
Leadhillite, $4PbO \cdot SO_3 \cdot 2CO_2 \cdot H_2O$	C_{2h}	?	{001}	?	1	121
$LiSO_4 \cdot H_2O$	C_{2h}	?	{100}?	?	1?	83
		?	{301}?	?	1?	
		?	{$\bar{1}$21}?	?	2?	
		[101]?	{$\bar{1}$01}?	?	1?	
		?	{$\bar{3}$01}?	?	1?	
Lorandite, $Tl_2S \cdot As_2S_3$	C_{2h}	[010]	{10$\bar{1}$}	1	1	118
Manganite, $Mn_2O_3 \cdot H_2O$	C_{2h}	[001]	{010}	1	1	126
Miargyrite, $Ag_2S \cdot Sb_2S_3$	C_{2h}	[010]	{100}	1	1	118
Mica, $H_2KAl_3(SiO_4)_3$	C_{2h}	[100]	{001}	1	1	118
		[110]	{001}	2	1	
Orpiment, As_2S_3	C_{2h}	[001]	{010}	1	1	118
Pyroxene, $(Ca, Mg)SiO_3$	C_{2h}	[001]?	{100}?	1?	1?	118
Vivianite, $Fe_3P_2O_8 \cdot 8H_2O$	C_{2h}	[001]	{010}	1	1	118
Wolframite, $(Fe, Mn)WO_4$	C_{2h}	?	{100}	?	1	118
		?	{010}	?	1	
TRICLINIC						
$KMnCl_3 \cdot 2H_2O$	S_2	[101]	{010}	1	1	115
Kyanite, Al_2SiO_5	S_2	[001]	{100}	1	1	118

TABLE 11-2. TWIN GLIDING SYSTEMS IN CRYSTALS

(Compiled by D. V. Higgs.) K_1 = twin plane. K_2 = other "plane of no distortion." N_1 = slip direction in K_1. N_2 = intersection of K_2 and deformation plane. $2\phi = K_1 \wedge K_2$. Shear = $s = 2/\tan 2\phi$.

Crystal	Class	K_1	K_2	N_1	N_2	ϕ	s	Reference
ISOMETRIC								
Aluminum, Al	O_h	(111)		[11$\bar{2}$]				145
Copper, Cu	O_h	(111)		[11$\bar{2}$]				145
Galena, PbS	O_h	(113)	(11$\bar{1}$)					150
		(441)	(001)					
		(332)	(11$\bar{2}$)			79° 59′	.354	
		(221)?	(22$\bar{5}$)					
		(112)	(33$\bar{2}$)					
Gold, Au	O_h	(111)		[11$\bar{2}$]				145
α-iron, Fe	O_h	(112)	(11$\bar{2}$)	[111]		70° 32′	.707	119, 127
Magnetite, Fe$_3$O$_4$	O_h	(111)	(11$\bar{1}$)			70° 32′	.707	61
Silver, Ag	O_h	(111)		[11$\bar{2}$]				145
Tungsten, W	O_h	(112)		[111]				12
PSEUDO-ISOMETRIC								
Leucite, KAlSi$_2$O$_6$		(110)	(1$\bar{1}$0)	[110]				
		(101)	(10$\bar{1}$)	[101]				121
		(011)	(01$\bar{1}$)	[011]				
HEXAGONAL								
Zinc, Zn	D_{6h}	(10$\bar{1}$2)	(10$\bar{1}\bar{2}$)			85° 55′	.143	156
RHOMBOHEDRAL								
Arsenic, As	D_{3d}	?($\bar{1}$012)		[10$\bar{1}$1]		82° 42′	.256	120
			(10$\bar{1}$1)	?[$\bar{1}$012]				
Antimony, Sb	D_{3d}	($\bar{1}$012)		[10$\bar{1}$1]		85° 49′	.146	108, 109
			(10$\bar{1}$1)	[$\bar{1}$012]				
Bismuth, Bi	D_{3d}	($\bar{1}$012)		[10$\bar{1}$1]		86° 38′	.118	108, 109
			(10$\bar{1}$1)	[$\bar{1}$012]				
Calcite, CaCO$_3$	D_{3d}	(1$\bar{1}$02)	($\bar{1}$101)	[$\bar{1}$101]	[1$\bar{1}$02]	70° 52′	.694	70, 105, 163
Corundum, Al$_2$O$_3$	D_{3d}	(0001)	(02$\bar{2}$1)			72° 22′	.635	163
Dolomite, CaMg(CO$_3$)$_2$	C_{3i}	(2$\bar{2}$01)	($\bar{1}$101)	[1$\bar{1}$0$\bar{4}$]	[1$\bar{1}$02]	73° 38′	.587	67, 76, 133, 160
Hematite, Fe$_2$O$_3$	D_{3d}	(0001)	(02$\bar{2}$1)			72° 24′	.634	163
		(10$\bar{1}$1)	($\bar{1}$012)			84° 8′	.206	
Magnesite, MgCO$_3$	D_{3d}	($\bar{1}$012)?	(10$\bar{1}$1)			68° 13′	.799	156
Millerite, NiS	D_{3d}	($\bar{1}$012)	(10$\bar{1}$0)			79° 14′	.380	156
Pyrargyrite, Ag$_3$SbS$_3$	C_{3v}	(10$\bar{1}$4)?		[0001]		72° 10′	.456	156
Siderite, FeCO$_3$	D_{3d}	($\bar{1}$012)	(10$\bar{1}$1)			68° 40′	.781	156
Soda-Niter, NaNO$_3$	D_{3d}	(01$\bar{1}$2)	(0$\bar{1}$11)			69° 22′	.753	83, 156
TETRAGONAL								
Cassiterite, SnO$_2$	D_{4h}	(101)	($\bar{3}$01)			82° 27′	.265	82
Hausmanite, Mn$_3$O$_4$	D_{4h}	(101)	($\bar{1}$01)		[101]	80° 50′	.323	156
Rutile, TiO$_2$	D_{4h}	(101)	($\bar{1}$01)			65° 34′	.908	62
		(101)	(30$\bar{1}$)			84° 34′	.190	
β-tin, Sn	D_{4h}	(331)	(111)			86° 34′	.120	124
ORTHORHOMBIC								
Ammonium sulfate, (NH$_4$)$_2$SO$_4$	D_{2h}	(110)	(1$\bar{3}$0)			}88° 48′ }	.041	42
		(1$\bar{3}$0)	(110)					
Anglesite, PbSO$_4$	D_{2h}	(110)	(1$\bar{1}$0)	[1$\bar{1}$0]	[110]			75
Anhydrite, CaSO$_4$	D_{2h}	(101)	($\bar{1}$01)			83° 30′	.228	106
Aragonite, CaCO$_3$	D_{2h}	(110)	(1$\bar{3}$0)		[310]	86° 16′	.130	121
Barite, BaSO$_4$	D_{2h}	(110)?	(1$\bar{1}$0)	[1$\bar{1}$0]	[110]	78° 22′	.411	75
Bournonite, PbCuSbS$_3$	D_{2h}	(110)			[110]	86° 20′	.128	125
Carnallite, KMgCl$_3$·6H$_2$O	D_{2h}	(110)	(1$\bar{3}$0)			88° 37′	.048	81

TABLE 11-2. *Continued*

Crystal	Class	K_1	K_2	N_1	N_2	ϕ	s	Reference
		ORTHORHOMBIC	*Continued*					
Celestite, SrSO₄	D_{2h}	(110)	(1̄10)	[1̄10]	[110]			75
Chalcocite, Cu₂S	D_{2h}	(201)	(001)		[100]	73° 18′	.600	125
		(131)?			[110]			
Nickel ammonium chloride,	(?)	(110)	(1̄10)			88° 36′	.049	81
NH₄Cl·NiCl₂·6H₂O		(111)			[112]	88° 35′	.049	
Niter, KNO₃	D_{2h}	(110)	(13̄0)			88° 50′	.041	156
Potassium chromate, K₂CrO₄	D_{2h}	(110)?	(130)			89° 18′	.024	13
Potassium sulfate, K₂SO₄	D_{2h}	(110)	(13̄0)			}89° 36′ }	.014	42, 95
		(13̄0)?	(110)					
Stephanite, Ag₅SbS₄	C_{2v}	(110)	(13̄0)					156
Thallous nitrate, TlNO₃	D_2	(120)	(12̄0)			88° 46′	.043	13
		MONOCLINIC						
Aegerite, NaFeSi₂O₆	C_{2h}	(110)?						156
Barium bromide, BaBr₂·2H₂O	C_{2h}	(001)	(100)			}66° 30′ }	.870	112
		(100)	(001)					
Barium chloride, BaCl₂·2H₂O	C_{2h}	(001)	(100)			}88° 55′ }	.038	111
		(100)	(001)					
Barium iodide, BaI₂·2H₂O	$C_{2h}(?)$	(100)	(001)			67° 2′	.848	112
Bischofite, MgCl₂·6H₂O	C_{2h}		(111)	[112]		78° 35′	.404	122
Calcium chloroaluminate, (CaCl₂)Ca₃Al₂O₆·10H₂O	$C_{2h}(?)$	(110)			[310]	}87° 42′ }	.080	121
		(110)	[310]					
Cobalt chloride hexahydrate, CoCl₂·6H₂O	$C_{2h}(?)$		(111̄)	[011̄]		83° 23′	.232	122
Cryolite, Na₃AlF₆	C_{2h}		(110)	[110]?		88° 2′	.069	151
Diopside, CaMgSi₂O₆	C_{2h}	(001)			[001]	}74° 10′ }	.567	109, 123
		(100)	[100]					
Hornblende	C_{2h}	(100)?						156
		(1̄01)?						
Jordanite, Pb₄As₂S₇	C_{2h}	(101)	(3̄01)			86° 32′	.051	44
		(1̄01)	(301)			86° 5′	.137	
		(100)	(001)			89° 33′	.016	
Kernite, Na₂B₄O₇ + H₂O	C_{2h}	(011)						156
Leadhillite, PbSO₄·2PbCO₃·Pb(OH)₂	C_{2h}	(310)		[110]				121
		(310)	[110]					
Lithium sulfate monohydrate, Li₂SO₄·H₂O	C_s	(1̄21)			[012]?	76° 42′	.473	84
Nickel chloride hexahydrate, NiCl₂6H₂O	C_{2h}		(111̄)	[011̄]		83° 47′	.217	122
Potassium chlorate, KClO₃	C_{2h}	(100)	(001)		[100]	}70° 18′ }	.716	42
		(001)?	(100)					
Spodumene, LiAlSi₂O₆	C_{2h}	(100)?						156
Titanite, CaTiSiO₅	C_{2h}		(1̄31)	[11̄0]		73° 21′	.598	110
Triammonium disulfate, (NH₄)₃H(SO₄)₂	$C_{2h}(?)$	(310)			[110]	}89° 18′ }	.024	42, 122
		(310)	[110]					
Tripotassium disulfate, K₃H(SO₄)₂	$C_{2h}(?)$	(310)			[110]	}89° 40′ }	.011	42
		(310)	[110]					
		TRICLINIC						
Albite, NaAlSi₃O₈	S_2	(010)?			[010]	}85° 59′ }	.142	129
		(010)?	[010]					
Ammonium cadmium selenate, (NH₄)₂Cd(SeO₄)₂·2H₂O	(?)	(010)?			[010]	}79° 56′ }	.355	116
		(010)?	[010]					

TABLE 11-2. *Continued*

Crystal	Class	K_1	K_2	N_1	N_2	ϕ	s	Reference
		TRICLINIC	*Continued*					
Anorthite, $CaAl_2Si_2O_8$	S_2	(010)	(010)	[010]	[010]	}85° 40′	}.152	129
Barium cadmium chloride, $BaCdCl_4 \cdot 4H_2O$	(?)	(010)	(010)	[010]	[010]	}87° 16′	}.096	114
Labradorite (An_{57})	S_2	(010)	(010)	[010]	[010]	}86° 5′	}.137	18
Potassium cadmium sulfate, $K_2Cd(SO_4)_2 \cdot 2H_2O$	(?)	(010)	(010)	[010]	[010]	}88° 1′	}.069	116
Potassium manganese chloride, $KMnCl_3 \cdot 2H_2O$	(?)	(1Ī1)?	(1Ī1)?	[101]	[101]	?	?	115
Potassium manganese sulfate, $K_2Mn(SO_4)_2 \cdot 2H_2O$	(?)	(010)	(010)	[010]	[010]	}84° 36′	}.189	116

TABLE 11-3. STRESS-STRAIN RELATIONSHIPS OF ROCKS AND MINERALS FROM SHORT-TIME TRIAXIAL COMPRESSION TESTS

Tabulated in this table are data from short-time triaxial compression tests in which the important variables are confining pressure, pore pressure, temperature, and the orientation of load with respect to the fabric of anisotropic materials. Most tests were conducted at nearly constant strain rates of the order of .5-5 per cent per minute (10^{-3}–10^{-4} per second). The samples were cylinders of the order of .5-1 inch (1-3 cm) in diameter and 1-3 inch (3-8 cm) in length. Unless otherwise noted these were jacketed in thin copper or rubber tubes.

The accuracy and sensitivity of a reported determination depend on the technique and measuring devices of a particular investigator. Most values of stress and strain have an accuracy of at least .5 per cent and a sensitivity of .1 per cent. Temperatures are within ±5° C or better. Fault angles are probably good to a degree or two.

The first column of the table gives the rock type or mineral and its locality, together with the formation name, if known, or the colloquial name. In the second column is the orientation of the differential stress (load): P—parallel to; N—normal to bedding, foliation, fissility, or cleavage; U—unknown. The temperature and confining pressure of the test are listed in columns three and four. Values of the differential stress at 1, 2, 5, and 10 per cent longitudinal strain, the ultimate strength, and the total strain (per cent shortening or elongation) are picked from the stress-strain curve and listed together with the angle between faults or fractures and the direction of maximum principal stress. When results are available from two or more experiments under identical conditions, average values are recorded.

All results are from compression tests unless the entry is marked E for extension. An asterisk after the ultimate strength signifies that the test was terminated before rupture and that the stress-strain curve is still rising. If the stress-strain curve is falling, but there is no obvious macroscopic faulting, a double asterisk is entered in the fracture-angle column. Unjacketed tests are identified by a dagger. In all others the material is dry unless the pore pressure is explicitly stated.

Material	Or	Temperature (°C)	Confining pressure (bars)	Differential stress—bars Strain—per cent				Ultimate strength (bars)	Total strain (%)	Fault angle (°)	Ref.
				1	2	5	10				
Amphibolite, Hudson Highland Complex, New York	N	150	1,010	1,030	5,740	..	..	6,540	2.9	21	66
	N	500	5,050	4,720	8,290	10,400	8,400	11,380	20.1	25**	66
	P	150	1,010	1,030	2,610	..	..	6,590	3.2	30	66
	P	500	5,050	5,500	11,230	..	..	13,500	3.6	38**	66
Anhydrite (30% gypsum), Alberta, Canada	N	24	0	..	..	..	..	410	.5	18	22
	N	24	170	1,030	1,080	860	780	1,080	20.0	32**	22
	N	24	350	1,070	1,410	1,420	1,290	1,450	24.5	32	22
	N	24	520	1,380	1,700	1,880	1,820	1,880	25.0	36**	22
	N	24	690	1,400	1,890	2,030	2,080	2,080	21.0	36**	22
Anhydrite, Blaine, Oklahoma	N	24	0	1,030	..	..	..	1,280	1.2	..	68
	N	24	140	900	1,280	..	..	1,880	3.1	15	66
	N	24	470	1,060	2,040	..	..	2,750	4.0	25	66
	N	24	510	1,220	2,240	..	..	2,760	4.0	**	68

Rock	n	T									
Anhydrite, Hockley, Texas	N	24	790	1,970	3,190	3,730		3,730	6.2	**	66
	N	24	1,010	1,780	2,940	3,840		3,840	7.0	**	69
	N	150	1,010	1,710	2,400	3,220	3,110	3,320	16.5	30	69
	N	300	1,010	1,570	2,270	3,160	3,850	4,170	16.1	34	69
	N	24	1,030	1,440	2,890	3,730		3,760	7.5	**	66
	N	110	1,050	1,470	2,940	4,710		3,710	6.3	**	66
	N	24	2,020	2,420	3,560	3,790	5,170	5,170	22.2	34–42	69
	N	150	2,020	2,030	2,790	3,770	4,880	5,370	24.2		69
	N	300	2,020	1,170	2,100		4,780	6,230*	23.8		69
Anhydrite, Permian, Texas	U	24	3,140	1,260	1,800	2,110	2,430	2,520	21.3E	0	63
	U	24	3,100	2,160	3,010	4,610		5,540	9.3	35	66
	U	150	3,290	430	740	930		960*	6.1E		66
	U	300	3,170	1,360	1,430	1,580	1,770	1,820	15.3		66
Anorthosite, Marcy, New York	N	24	1,010	1,720	2,470	3,170	3,240	3,240	12.0	22	66
	U	150	1,010	2,040	2,360			5,940	2.6	29	66
	U	500	5,050	2,920	4,640	7,290	9,040	9,400	32.2	28	66
Basalt (olivine), Blairsden, California	U	24	5,050	5,880	9,650	15,300		15,400	6.6	29	60
	U	300	5,000	5,880	9,600	13,800		13,800	8.0	**	60
	U	500	5,050	6,170	8,620	10,200	10,300	10,300	14.0	**	60
	U[14]	600	2,000	3,820	5,100			5,460	3.8	**	54
	U	700	5,070	2,700	4,370	5,210	5,310	5,310	10.1	**	60
	U	800	5,070	1,850	2,160	2,400	2,630	2,630	16.2	**	60
	U	800	5,070	980	1,310	970		1,310	6.6E	**	60
Basalt, "Knippa," Texas	U	24	0	2,620				2,620	1.0	21	22
	U	24	690	4,620				4,620	1.1	29	22
	U	24	1,030	5,510				5,510	1.7	21	22
Biotite (load ∥ c)		500	5,070	30	80	50	40	80	21.4	**	66
Calcite (load ∥ c_v)		24	2,730	2,400	2,990	3,510	3,960	4,040*	11.2		70
		24	2,730	170	240	360	580	790*	12.6E		70
		24	5,070	3,630	5,580	6,350	7,900	11,900*	31.4		159
		24	5,070	200	290	430	760	1,530*	19.8E		159
		24	10,100	240	300	440	840	>1,500*	28.3E		159
		24	10,100	1,910	2,600	2,750	3,140	4,020*	17.7		57

TABLE 11-3. *Continued*

Material	Or	Temperature (°C)	Confining pressure (bars)	Differential stress—bars Strain—per cent 1	2	5	10	Ultimate strength (bars)	Total strain (%)	Fault angle (°)	Ref.
Calcite (load ‖ c_v) *Continued*											
	..	150	10,100	590	670	880	1,260	1,390*	11.8	..	58
	..	300	2,750	60	90	130	170	230*	12.5E	..	66
	..	300	2,750	410	560	960	1,520	2,380	28.8	**	66
	..	300	5,050	560	700	1,110	1,500	1,650*	18.2	..	159
	..	300	5,050	50	50	50	50	50	19.7E	0	159
Calcite (load ⊥ m)	..	24	2,750	30	60	170	390	1,300*	17.4	..	70
	..	24	2,760	640	2,010	..	..	2,110	2.3E	27	70
	..	24	10,100	90	90	110	180	550*	15.4	..	159
	..	150	10,100	130	150	230	390	980*	16.8	..	58
	..	300	5,050	50	50	50	..	50	9.6	..	159
	..	300	5,050	350	340	380	460	580	16.1E	**	159
	..	800	5,070	130	160	220	260	280	20.6	..	60
Calcite (load ⊥ e)	..	24	5,050	180	240	320	..	340*	8.5E	..	159
	..	24	5,050	4,410	4,170	3,430	..	4,410	6.3	**	159
	..	300	5,050	90	150	250	..	350*	8.3E	..	159
	..	300	5,050	690	730	870	1,270	1,730*	13.7	..	159
Calcite (load ⊥ r)	..	24	5,050	4,410	4,250	4,580	..	4,850*	9.7	..	159
	..	300	5,050	1,360	1,470	2,080	2,450	>2,500*	20.3	..	159
	..	800	5,070	230	310	330	340	340	23	..	60
	..	800	5,070	250	300	..	..	390	4.0	**	60
Calcite (load 81° to c_v, 53° to r)	..	24	5,050	3,430	..	..	..	3,460	1.9E	0	159
	..	300	5,050	460	490	..	..	490	4.7E	..	159
Calcite (load ‖ [r:r])	..	24	0	140	90	..	..	140	3.5	..	50
	..	24	4,020†	150	270	..	..	390	4.4	**	50
	..	24	5,070	3,240	4,720	4,930	..	4,960	6.4	***	60
	..	24	8,090†	230	480	1,410	..	1,850	8.3	**	50
	..	24	10,200†	290	580	2,060	580	2,750	11.0	**	50

Rock		T (°C)									
Calcite (load 81° to c_v, 35° to r)	:	250	5,070	1,480	1,470	1,400	1,510	1,980*	52		60
	:	300	5,050	940	810	1,010	1,130	1,280*	19.5E		159
	:	400	5,050	500	550	770		1,170*	9.6E		159
	:	500	4,700	560	960	1,140	1,080	1,150*	10.3E	**	159
	:	600	3,040	520	640	690		710*	9.7E		54
	:	800	5,070	300	390	480	540	980*	110E		60
	:	24	5,050	3,730	3,610	4,000		4,710*	9.6E		159
	:	300	5,050	460	490			490	4.7E		159
Calcite (load 30° to c_v, 75° to r)	:	24	5,050	4,690	4,620			4,790*	7.8		159
	:	150	5,050	1,530	1,550	1,670	1,740	1,740*	10.2		159
	:	300	5,050	740	740	740	870	870*	10.0		159
	:	400	3,040	330	370	540	1,160	1,160*	10.0		159
	:	500	3,530	270	380	800	1,040	1,130*	10.5		159
	:	600	2,740	290	560	870	900	900	11.2		54
	:	800	5,070	240	340	370		400	8.3		60
	:	800	5,070	140	170	230	350	360*	10.4E		60
Calcite (load 15° to [r:r])	:	800	5,070	240	310	350	360	370*	39		60
	:	800	5,070	200	340	400	410	620*	51E		60
Clay (dried in air)	P	24	0					10	.9	0	90
	P	24	70	15	25	25	25	25	11	35	90
	P	24	130	95	190	295	360	360	14	45	90
	P	24	290	135	225	370	430	460	18	45	90
	P	24	540	195	370	540	640	690	20	50	90
	P	24	700	295	450	690	850	880*	14	50	90
	P	24	920	295	390	590	790	930*	13	50	90
Claystone, "red beds," Wyoming	N	24	0					2,350	.9	24	22
	N	24	690	3,450	4,300	3,410	3,380	4,320	2.2	27	22
	N	24	1,030	3,450	4,140	3,630		4,380	17.0	35	22
Cryolite, Greenland (load $\perp$ c)	:	24	5,000	1,180	3,840	4,470	4,770		42.1	**	66
	:	24	5,000	1,890	3,180			5,120	21.2E	**	66
Diabase, Tishomingo, Oklahoma	U	150	1,010	1,810	2,660	3,340		5,100	1.9	28	66
	U	500	5,050	1,390			4,940	5,460	17.7	29	66
Diorite, Salem, Massachusetts	U	150	1,010	2,000	5,370	5,800		6,130	2.6	29	66
	U	500	5,050	1,210	2,160			7,100	24.0	38	66

TABLE 11-3. *Continued*

Material	Or	Temperature (°C)	Confining pressure (bars)	Differential stress—bars Strain—per cent				Ultimate strength (bars)	Total strain (%)	Fault angle (°)	Ref.
				1	2	5	10				
Dolomite crystal (load ∥ c_v)	:	24	5,000	4,170	5,960	:	:	6,320	3.0	32	76
	:	24	5,000	2,550	:	:	:	2,990	1.9E	**	76
	:	300	5,000	3,740	:	:	:	4,260	1.5	:	76
	:	300	5,000	3,200	:	:	:	3,230	1.1E	0	76
	:	350	5,000	:	:	:	:	4,950	.7	30	76
	:	375	5,000	4,970	5,150	5,350	5,500	5,550	10	**	76
	:	400	5,000	3,140	3,310	3,840	4,600	5,100	13.5	43	76
	:	400	5,000	2,980	3,450	:	:	3,500	3.0E	33	76
	:	500	5,000	1,380	1,730	2,800	4,160	5,000	16.7	**	76
	:	500	5,000	2,890	2,850	:	:	2,980	2.6E	33	76
Dolomite crystal (load ∥ a axis)	:	24	5,000	5,580	:	:	:	5,670	1.5	34	76
	:	24	5,000	2,560	:	:	:	2,850	1.7E	0	76
	:	300	5,000	5,010	:	:	:	5,070	1.1	30	76
	:	300	5,000	3,300	:	:	:	3,300	1.0E	**	76
	:	400	5,000	5,920	:	:	:	6,030	1.6	37	76
	:	400	5,000	3,000	:	:	:	3,150	1.2E	38	76
	:	450	5,000	2,050	2,180	2,500	3,000	3,040	30.0E	**	76
	:	500	5,000	3,920	4,870	5,920	:	6,220	8.9	30	76
	:	500	5,000	2,060	2,370	2,700	3,180	3,240	13.1E	33	76
Dolomite crystal (load ∥ [f:f])	:	24	5,000	1,590	1,700	2,050	2,680	2,940*	14.6	:	76
	:	24	5,000	2,160	2,190	2,350	:	2,500	7.5E	20	76
	:	300	5,000	1,960	2,090	2,490	:	2,620	6.5	32	76
	:	300	5,000	2,070	2,320	2,750	:	2,780*	5.2E	:	76
	:	400	5,000	2,230	3,000	3,320	:	3,330	5.2E	:	76
Dolomite crystal (load ⊥ r)	:	24	5,000	2,040	2,260	2,910	3,970	4,660*	16.6	:	76
	:	24	5,000	1,950	2,000	2,160	2,480	2,560*	11.9E	:	76
	:	300	5,000	3,170	3,610	4,900	:	5,980	9.7	32	76
	:	300	5,000	2,210	2,350	2,710	:	3,430*	9.2E	:	76
	:	400	5,000	2,400	2,690	2,960	:	3,200	9.1	27	76
	:	400	5,000	2,980	3,240	3,990	:	4,170	6.2E	40	76

Material											
Dolomite, "Blair," W. Virginia	:	500	5,000	1,970	3,940	5,480		5,930	9.3	37	76
	:	500	5,000	2,400	2,770	3,600		5,390*	9.0		54
	:	500	5,000	1,950	2,230	2,930		3,430*	6.0E		76
	U	24	0	2,940				3,430	1.2		139
	U	24	0	3,140				1,570	.9		68
	U	24	490	4,020	5,490			4,410	1.9		139
	U	24	980	4,110	6,880			8,340	1.9		139
	U	24	1,010	5,080	9,320			5,700	2.4	24	68
	U	24	2,020	4,610	2,930			6,940	3.7	30	68
	U	24	2,750	910	6,670			9,900	2.6		139
	U	24	5,050	3,430		15,200		4,630	3.7E	20	66
	U	24	24,500	6,130				18,140	7.0		139
	U	300	5,100					6,360	1.3	**	66
	U	300	5,100					3,900	.9E	0	66
Dolomite, Carboniferous, Russia	N	24	1,020	3,200				4,510	1.5	35	66
Dolomite, Clear Fork, Texas	N	24	0	2,110				2,330	1.1		68
	N	24	1,010	4,660	5,690			5,930	2.5	23	68
	N	24	2,020	6,570	7,210			7,330	3.8	**	68
Dolomite, Dover Plains, New York	45	24	5,070	7,350	9,720	10,800	12,450	13,700*	18.7		60
	45	300	5,070	5,120	5,970	6,960	7,040	7,280*	11.1		54
	45	380	3,000	4,470	5,220	6,140		6,570	9.3	**	160
	45	500	5,070	4,070	5,650	7,530	9,230	9,940	17.6	**	60
	45	500	5,070	2,700	4,020	4,170	3,730	4,510	>20E	**	60
	45	800	4,250	2,850	4,900	6,180		6,300	8.7	**	60
	45	800	4,250	1,620	2,830	3,750		3,920	6.9	27	60
Dolomite, Durtule, Russia	N	24	1,020	7,360				7,500	1.5	15	66
Dolomite, Fusselman, Texas	N	24	0	920				1,450	1.7	28	68
	N	24	1,010	4,730	5,590			5,840	2.6	**	68
	N	24	2,020	5,790	6,810			7,140	4.7	**	68
Dolomite, Glorieta, N. Mexico	N	24	0	640				810	1.3	28	68
	N	24	1,010	2,360	3,240			3,890	3.1	25	68
	N	24	2,020	3,460	4,360	5,540		5,690	7.1	20	68

Table 11-3. *Continued*

Material	Or	Temperature (°C)	Confining pressure (bars)	Differential stress—bars Strain—per cent 1	2	5	10	Ultimate strength (bars)	Total strain (%)	Fault angle (°)	Ref.
Dolomite, Hasmark, Montana	N	24	0					1,280	.7		68
	N	24	0†	880	270	230		1,160	9.4	29	66
	N	24	500	1,990				3,380	4.5	24	66
	N	24	1,010	2,620	3,750	3,940		4,020	7.3	27	68
	N[3]	24	1,000	3,110	2,320	3,760		3,760	5.8	**	66
	N	150	1,000	1,690	2,940			3,970	4.1	39	69
	N	300	1,000	2,730	3,710	4,020		4,020	6.0	37	69
	N[3]	24	2,020	3,590	4,560	5,270	5,350	5,440	12.8	30	68
	N[14]	24	2,000	1,200	3,540	5,760	5,800	5,900	17.3	**	66
	N[24]	24	2,000	1,090	3,500	5,580	5,470	5,650	12.6	33	66
	N[25]	24	2,000	1,100	3,500	5,400	5,330	5,500	19.2	29	66
	N	24	2,000†	1,970	3,990	5,280	5,240	5,400	16.6	**	66
	N	24	2,000	740	480			740	2.0	5	66
	N	150	2,000	3,980	4,760	5,300	5,140	5,300	12.7	35	69
	N[2]	300	2,000	2,900	4,020	5,050	5,220	5,220	13.9	36	69
	N	300	2,000	1,500	3,430	4,430		4,430	5.5	34	66
	N	24	5,050	4,560	5,690	7,110		7,650	6.5	30	67
	N	24	5,050	2,890	3,630			3,970	4.4E	20	67
	N	300	5,050	4,170	5,200	6,470		7,160	9.6	30	67
	N	300	5,000	2,750	3,190			3,780	4.0E	20	67
	N	400	5,000	3,730	4,340	5,950		6,850*	7.7		66
	N	400	5,000	3,240	3,750			3,800	2.6E	20	66
	N	500	5,000	1,380	2,600	6,140	8,060	9,220	20.2	30	66
	N	500	5,000	3,610				3,610	1.0E	30	66
	P	24	1,010	2,260	2,920			3,070	4.4	25	68
	P	24	2,020	3,430	4,220	5,200		5,290	8.9	28	68
	P	24	5,050	5,200	6,620	7,060		7,340	8.0	30	68
	P	24	5,050	3,240	4,170			4,460	4.2E	20	67
	P	300	5,050	3,920	5,850	6,570		7,260*	9.0		67
	P	300	5,050	3,160	4,120			4,210	4.0E	20	67

	P	400	5,000	4,150	4,930	6,260	8,340	9,410	19.4	30	66
	P	400	5,000	3,190	3,680	...	...	3,880	2.8*E*	20	66
	P	500	5,000	1,570	3,070	5,760	7,580	8,290	17.0	**	66
	P	500	5,000	2,830	3,550	...	...	3,920	4.4*E*		66
Dolomite, Luning, Nevada	*N*	24	0	...	...	...	...	600	.7	0	68
	N	24	1,010	3,910	4,660	...	...	4,870	4.7	22	69
	N	150	1,010	2,710	4,090	...	...	4,560	4.2	28	69
	N	300	1,010	1,750	2,170	...	...	2,220	3.4	20	69
	N	24	2,020	3,340	4,910	6,100	6,160	6,230	19.0	30	69
	N	150	2,020	3,100	4,330	5,490	...	5,650	6.8	30	69
	N	300	2,020	2,300	3,680	...	...	3,960	2.6	20	69
	N	24	5,150	3,190	4,480	...	...	4,710	3.2*E*	20	66
	N	300	5,390	...	...	...	...	4,580	.9*E*	24	66
Gabbro, Elizabethtown, New York	*U*	150	1,010	2,130	3,720	...	...	5,290	2.2	32	66
	U	500	5,050	2,480	4,000	6,520	8,090	8,170	17.0	37	66
Gneiss, biotite, Fordham, New York	*N*	500	5,050	4,900	6,650	7,630	7,460	7,650	11.3	36	66
	P	500	5,050	1,630	4,140	8,250	7,350	8,800	13.5	30	66
	22°	500	5,050	1,960	3,290	4,080	4,310	4,320	10.3	34	66
	45°	5,000	5,050	2,960	3,970	4,820	5,450	5,660	17.4	37	66
Gneiss, biotite, St. Lawrence Co., New York	*N*	150	1,010	1,130	3,330	...	...	5,890	2.5	31	66
	N	500	5,050	3,270	6,430	11,300	9,680	11,300	14.9	26	66
	P	150	1,010	1,880	2,680	...	...	7,030	3.4	26	66
	P	500	5,050	3,270	6,960	10,500	...	10,750	8.6	33	66
Gneiss, granite, "Diana," New York	*N*	150	1,010	3,910	6,150	...	...	6,320	2.9	31	66
	N	500	5,050	5,150	9,080	11,040	8,670	11,500	10.9	37	66
	P	150	1,010	1,310	5,080	...	...	6,110	2.8	32	66
	P	500	5,050	6,600	11,900	12,650	...	12,900	7.9	33	66
Granite, Barre, Vermont	*N*	24	0	...	...	...	...	1,670	.6	15	139
	N	24	490	3,140	...	...	...	4,710	1.6	20	139
	N	24	980	4,410	...	...	...	6,080	1.7	15	139
Granite, Silver Plume, Colorado	*U*	150	1,010	1,470	3,010	...	...	3,290	2.7	33	66
	U	500	5,050	2,490	5,150	8,100	7,930	8,280	17.0	32	66
Granite, Westerly, Rhode Island	*P*	24	5,070	7,250	14,700	19,800	...	20,800	6.4	32	60
	P	300	5,070	6,080	11,680	16,190	...	16,600	8.1	33	60

TABLE 11-3. *Continued*

Material	Or	Temperature (°C)	Confining pressure (bars)	Differential stress—bars Strain—per cent 1	2	5	10	Ultimate strength (bars)	Total strain (%)	Fault angle (°)	Ref.
Granite, *Continued*											
	P	500	5,070	6,030	9,000	11,250	9,950	11,290	23	31	60
	43	500	5,070	9,000	11,500	11,400	..	11,900	5.7	..	54
	P	800	5,070	2,500	4,750	6,150	6,050	6,200	15	40	60
	P	800	5,070	2,500	3,600	2,460	..	3,780	5.1E	24	60
Granodiorite, St. Cloud, Minnesota	U	150	1,010	1,470	3,670	9,250	..	8,220	3.7	26	66
	U	500	5,070	3,230	6,090	9,250	9,270	9,320	19.2	21	66
Halite, artificial (load ∥ *a* axis)	..	24	0	100	130	200	260	270	10.8	**	69
	..	24	1,010	110	150	220	300	580*	30.5	..	69
	..	24	1,010	100	130	210	290	560*	24.3E	..	69
	..	150	1,010	80	100	140	180	260*	23.6	..	69
	..	24	2,020	140	160	230	320	630*	29.3	..	69
	..	24	2,020	110	140	220	290	490*	33.7E	..	69
	..	150	2,020	90	110	140	190	330*	28.2	..	69
	..	150	2,020	100	120	140	170	250*	27.8E	..	69
	..	300	2,020	80	90	90	90	100*	30.8	..	69
	..	300	2,020	90	100	100	100	100*	28.1E	..	69
Halite, Grand Saline, Texas (load ∥ *a* axis)	..	24	1,010	180	190	190	290	610*	30.0	**	66
	..	300	1,010	180	180	170	160	200	38.3	..	66
	..	500	1,010	180	190	180	170	190	28.4	..	66
Labradorite (An₅₇)	A51	400	5,000	3,680	4,670	..	..	5,220	5.3	36	18
	B52	400	5,000	3,630	7,130	9,170	..	9,220	8.0	36	18
	B52	500	5,000	2,290	4,260	4,720	5,060	5,370	14.5	31	18
Limestone, Alabama	U	24	510	740	1,110	2,620	3,200	530	.2	30	66
	U	24	1,020	955	1,290	1,950	2,610	4,150	28.3	30	66
	U	24	2,030	960	1,430	2,550	3,370	3,130	29.9	27	66
	U	24	5,050	2,300	2,910	4,270	4,630	4,650*	27.4	..	66
	U	24						5,390*	16.2	..	66

Rock	Or.	T	(1)	(2)	(3)	(4)	(5)	(6)	%	Angle	Ref
Limestone, "Austin chalk," Texas	U	24	5,050	2,400	3,580	3,990	4,190	4,190*	10.0E	..	66
	U	300	5,050	1,620	1,770	2,290	2,870	3,430*	20.5	..	66
	U	300	5,050	700	1,150	1,700	2,160	2,690	18.2E	20	66
Limestone, Becraft, New York	U	24	0	..	..	..	..	140	.4	15	22
	U	24	520	150	280	530	810	830*	10.8	..	22
	U	24	690	150	320	690	1,110	1,730*	24.5	..	22
Limestone, Beldens, "Danby marble," Vermont	N	24	0	..	..	..	..	980	.4	**	139
	N	24	590	1,960	2,060	2,160	2,160	2,160	14.0	**	139
	N	24	880	2,340	2,850	3,040	3,240	3,430	30.0	..	139
	N	24	2,940	2,850	3,530	4,320	..	5,390*	6.6	..	139
	P	24	0	..	..	..	..	450	.5	..	139
	P	24	390	1,370	1,470	1,570	1,860	1,960	11.2	30	139
	P	24	880	1,770	2,060	..	..	2,650	4.2	**	139
	P	24	2,450	2,260	2,650	3,400	..	4,530*	8.4	**	139
	P	24	3,920	2,450	2,650	3,430	4,320	5,350*	12.4	..	139
Limestone, Beldens, "Rutland white marble," Vermont	N	24	0	..	..	..	..	390	.3	..	139
	N	24	490	1,770	..	..	..	2,060	.7	..	139
	P	24	980	2,060	2,750	..	..	2,060*	1.5	..	139
	P	24	2,940	2,160	2,750	3,530	..	4,270*	7.7	..	139
	P	24	3,920	..	..	..	..	2,940*	2.5	..	139
Limestone, Carrara marble, Italy	U	24	0	1,990	1,860	..	..	1,340	.6	27	164
	U	24	230	2,490	2,600	2,430	..	2,010	4.6	29	164
	U	24	490	2,620	2,770	2,790	..	2,620	7.5	32	164
	U	24	670	2,740	2,980	3,130	..	2,830	8.6	35	164
	U	24	830	3,180	3,560	4,180	..	3,150*	5.1	..	164
	U	24	1,620	2,320	3,900	4,550	..	4,710*	9.2	..	164
	U	24	2,440	3,470	4,020	4,990	..	4,920*	6.0	..	164
	U	24	3,200	2,060	2,220	..	..	2,230	5.0	20	16
	U	24	3,780	2,340	2,980	3,160	..	3,200	2.3E	26	16
	U	24	4,420	2,470	3,200	3,580	..	3,590	8.3E	17	16
	U	24	4,920	2,650	3,370	3,810	..	3,870	5.8E	25	16
	U	24	5,370	2,940	3,650	4,020	..	4,080	8.3E	26	16

TABLE 11-3. Continued

Material	Or	Temperature (°C)	Confining pressure (bars)	Differential stress—bars Strain—per cent 1	2	5	10	Ultimate strength (bars)	Total strain (%)	Fault angle (°)	Ref.
Limestone, "Carthage marble," Missouri (1)	U	24	0	..	..	..	..	730	.3	26	22
	U	24	690	2,410	2,490	2,380	..	2,490	5.0	31	22
Limestone, "Carthage marble," Missouri (2)	U	24	0	..	..	..	..	520	.3	22	22
	U	24	170	1,150	..	..	..	1,180*	1.2	:	22
	U	24	350	1,820	1,870	..	..	1,880	2.2	36	22
	U	24	520	1,910	2,000	1,820	1,590	2,000	21.5	36	22
	U	24	690	2,070	2,160	2,090	1,980	2,160	11.0	36	22
Limestone, "Chico," Texas	U	24	0	..	..	..	..	890	.7	34	22
	U	24	170	..	..	..	..	2,030	.9	29	22
Limestone, "Chico," Texas (50% dol., 30% calc., 20% qtz.)	U	24	0	..	..	..	..	760	.7	29	22
	U	24	520	2,070	2,280	2,250	2,030	2,280	27.0	33	22
	U	24	690	2,070	2,450	2,620	2,520	2,620	19.5	33	22
Limestone, "D-1 formation," Alberta, Canada	U	24	0	..	..	..	..	1,590	.3	25	22
	U	24	350	1,380	2,410	..	..	2,410	2.0	24	22
	U	24	520	3,920	5,100	..	..	5,100	2.0	18	22
	U	24	690	3,870	3,800	3,440	2,960	4,000	17.0	29	22
	U	24	1,030	5,160	5,310	4,340	4,070	5,990	13.0	29	22
Limestone, Devonian, Texas	N	24	0	..	..	..	..	790	.7	27	68
	N	24	1,010	2,280	2,760	2,970	3,160	3,360	>30	**	68
	N	24	2,020	2,750	3,300	4,120	4,750	5,570*	21.4	:	68
Limestone, Fusselman, Texas	N	24	0	370	..	..	..	380	1.1	:	68
	N	24	1,010	2,180	2,570	2,710	2,770	2,860	>30	**	68
	N	24	2,020	2,520	3,290	3,920	4,480	5,020*	>30	:	68
Limestone, Leadville, "Yule Marble," Colorado	N	24	0	..	..	..	..	390	.4	:	68
	N	24	1,010	1,070	1,690	2,740	3,460	3,830	23.0	24	69
	N	24	2,020	1,730	2,370	3,260	4,310	5,650*	26.9	:	69
	N	24	2,790	3,560	3,920	4,610	5,560	6,130	18.8	**	70
	N	24	5,050	2,110	3,190	3,890	4,610	5,390*	19.5	:	58

N	24	10,100	2,400	3,090	3,870	4,660	5,880*	>20	:	57
N	24	2,790	1,160	1,350	1,700	1,960	2,060*	16.1E	:	70
N	24	5,050	1,180	1,640	2,290	2,880	3,680*	20E	:	58
N	24	5,250	1,570	1,910	2,380	2,920	3,790	28.6E	0	63
N	24	10,100	1,470	1,960	2,650	3,340	4,220*	>20E	:	57
N	24	4,070†	790	:	:	:	850	1.0	:	49
N	24	8,090†	1,570	:	:	:	1,620	4.5	:	49
N	150	10,100†	2,210	1,620	3,530	3,970	5,150*	24	:	49
N	150	1,010	1,070	2,940	1,880	2,520	3,580	30.6	22	69
N	150	2,020	980	1,380	2,230	3,260	5,100*	27.6	:	69
N	150	10,100	1,330	1,460	2,500	3,340	3,730*	13	:	58
N	300	10,100	1,030	1,770	1,770	2,260	2,500*	>20E	:	58
N	300	1,010	530	1,330	1,250	1,770	2,650*	31.4	:	69
N	300	2,020	810	780	1,730	2,440	3,390*	28.7	:	69
N[43]	300	5,050	1,230	1,060	2,110	2,750	3,340*	>20	:	58
N	300	5,050	900	1,520	1,420	1,870	2,550*	>20E	:	58
N	400	3,040	620	1,080	1,460	1,670	1,840	40	**	54
N	400	3,040	1,020	1,090	1,880	2,180	2,420	20	:	54
N	400	3,040	760	1,400	1,250	1,510	2,050	30E	**	54
N	500	5,050	840	930	1,130	1,330	1,550*	>20E	:	54
N	600	3,040	650	980	860	1,030	1,900*	163E[44]	:	54
N	800	5,070	150	740	430	580	770*	83E[44]	:	60
N[38]	150	10,100	540	290	1,470	2,110	2,850*	18.8	:	58
N[41]	150	10,100	980	930	1,870	2,600	3,430*	19.5	:	58
N[37]	150	10,100	1,330	1,330	2,360	3,090	4,020*	18.5	:	58
N[38]	300	5,050	840	1,720	1,670	2,360	2,990*	19.0	:	59
N[42]	300	5,050	640	1,080	1,470	2,110	2,600*	17.0	:	59
N[39]	300	5,050	300	880	980	1,330	1,380*	12.0	:	68
P	24	1,010	900	540	1,800	2,110	2,690	26.8	**	68
P	24	2,020	1,440	1,280	2,630	3,310	5,270*	28.6	:	68
P	24	2,790	1,510	1,880	2,990	4,950	5,030*	20.0	:	70
P	24	5,050	1,520	2,120	3,190	:	4,110*	9.9	:	66
P	24	5,050	1,570	2,320	3,010	3,680	4,510*	19.3	:	58
P	24	10,100	1,770	2,190	3,190	3,920	5,300*	>20	20	57
P	24	2,790	1,380	2,500	:	:	2,360	3.0E	:	70
P	24	2,870	2,210	2,450	:	:	2,430	4.0E	:	70

TABLE 11-3. *Continued*

Material	Or	Temperature (°C)	Confining pressure (bars)	Differential stress—bars Strain—per cent				Ultimate strength (bars)	Total strain (%)	Fault angle (°)	Ref.
				1	2	5	10				
Limestone, Continued Leadville, "Yule Marble," Colorado, *Continued*	P	24	4,560	2,850	3,140	3,480	...	3,530	7.5E	:	70
	P	24	4,810	2,800	3,200	3,530	4,000	4,100	12.8E	0	66
	P	24	5,050	3,040	3,610	4,150	4,470	4,530	13.7E	:	58
	P[43]	24	5,070	3,500	4,030	4,510	...	4,600	9.9E	20	60
	P	24	5,070	2,650	3,560	4,250	4,360	4,460	10.0E	20	60
	P	24	6,080	2,940	3,380	3,880	4,170	4,170	13.8E	:	60
	P	24	8,090	3,380	3,730	4,370	4,760	5,050	13E	:	60
	P	24	10,100	3,090	3,730	4,510	5,250	6,180*	>20E	:	57
	P	24	10,100	3,380	3,730	4,510	5,250	>5,880*	15E	:	60
	P	150	2,020	850	1,170	1,700	2,420	4,240*	28.4	:	66
	P	150	5,370	1,300	1,620	2,210	2,920	3,840*	18	:	58
	P	150	10,100	1,330	1,620	2,160	2,360	3,630*	17	:	58
	P	150	5,050	2,020	2,370	3,070	3,730	3,860*	11.8E	:	58
	P	150	10,100	1,620	1,960	2,550	3,090	3,730*	>20E	:	58
	P	300	2,020	780	980	1,480	2,020	2,470*	30.6	:	66
	P	300	5,050	1,230	1,470	1,910	2,450	3,140*	>20	:	59
	P	300	5,050	1,330	1,620	2,110	2,700	3,190*	>20E	:	59
	P	300	5,100	1,120	1,270	1,660	2,220	2,470*	14.3	:	66
	P	400	3,040	590	1,000	1,500	1,810	2,440*	41	:	54
	P[43]	500	5,050	850	1,000	1,160	1,250	1,280*	15.9	:	54
	P[43]	500	5,070	950	1,150	1,320	1,420	2,950*	340E[44]	:	60
	P	500	5,050	1,080	1,320	1,620	1,770	1,860*	>20E	:	54
	P	500	5,070	1,100	1,400	1,760	2,020	2,380*	44E[44]	:	60
	P	550	5,070	820	1,090	1,380	1,590	2,140*	98E[44]	:	60
	P[43]	550	5,070	710	870	990	1,060	1,560*	335E[44]	:	54
	P	600	3,040	770	990	1,070	1,180	1,940*	590E[44]	:	54
	P	600[5]	5,070	590	730	800	850	1,440*	450E[44]	:	60
	P	650	5,070	730	810	900	1,020	2,340*	530E[44]	:	60
	P	700	5,070	710	740	790	900	2,230*	1,400E[44]	:	54

Material											
Limestone, "Marble," Italy	P	800	5,070	450	470	500	500	1,700*	1,000E⁴⁴	:	60
	P⁴³	800	5,070	330	360	380	380	430*	45E	:	60
	P³⁸	150	10,100	590	840	1,420	1,960	2,940*	18.5	:	58
	P³⁸	150	10,100	880	1,230	1,670	2,160	2,260*	12.7E	:	58
	U	300	5,390	1,830	2,090	2,770	3,460	4,370	26.3E	20	66
Limestone, Marianna, Florida	N	24	0	:	:	:	:	430	.5	10	68
	N	24	500	800	1,150	840	:	1,150	5.7	25	68
	N	24	1,000	770	1,190	1,960	2,410	2,520	30.4	27	68
	N³	24	1,000	690	1,090	1,180	1,210	1,240	25.8	32	66
	N	150	1,000	880	1,360	2,080	2,500	2,600	24.6	30	69
	N	300	1,000	1,150	1,730	2,240	2,690	3,230	30.0	25	69
	N³	24	2,000	940	1,450	2,400	3,290	4,310	28.0	**	68
	N¹⁴	24	2,000	700	1,270	1,980	2,520	3,330*	25.6	:	66
	N²⁴	24	2,000	1,160	1,550	1,820	2,250	2,640	25.6	35	66
	N²⁵	24	2,000	1,180	1,550	1,670	2,000	2,140	24.5	35	66
	N	24	2,000†	820	1,200	1,190	1,130	1,240	26.0	34	66
	N¹⁴	24	2,000	230	180	170	200	400	23.7	30	66
	N	150	2,000	820	:	:	:	850	1.5E	15	69
	N	300	2,000	880	1,420	2,490	3,380	3,970	20.9	15	69
	N¹⁴	300	2,000	880	1,360	2,340	3,150	3,830	25.7	22	66
	N	300	2,400	1,100	1,450	1,540	1,860	1,880	19.3	23	66
	N	24	2,400	950	1,500	2,630	3,360	4,640*	25.1	:	66
	N	24	5,000†	360	700	550	430	700	29.4	**	66
Limestone, New Scotland, New York	N	24	0	:	:	:	:	1,280	.5	40	139
	N	24	490	:	:	:	:	3,190	.7	30	139
	N	24	2,940	3,630	:	:	:	4,950*	1.5	:	139
Limestone, Solenhofen, Bavaria	U	24	0	:	:	:	:	2,750	.9	:	139
	U	24	0	3,400	:	:	:	3,470	1.1	:	72
	U	24	300	2,550	3,240	3,320	:	3,530	4.5	25	139
	U	24	770	3,830	4,580	3,920	3,830	4,740	6.8	25	72
	U	24	980	3,240	3,730	4,260	3,970	3,920	21	**	139
	U	24	1,020	4,550	4,700	4,460	3,940	4,750	11.2	30	72
	U⁵	24	1,120	:	4,830	:	:	4,900	10.0	31	72

TABLE 11-3. *Continued*

Material	Or	Temperature (°C)	Confining pressure (bars)	Differential stress—bars Strain—per cent				Ultimate strength (bars)	Total strain (%)	Fault angle (°)	Ref.
				1	2	5	10				
Limestone, *Continued* Solenhofen, Bavaria, *Continued*	U^8	24	1,120	..	..	..	..	4,670	1.9	26	72
	U	24	1,270	4,600	4,920	4,820	4,650	5,070	11.3	30	72
	U^{15}	24	1,330	..	..	4,750	..	4,900	9.0	29	72
	U	24	1,530	4,140	5,060	5,050	5,000	5,070	11.8	**	72
	U^{14}	24	1,530	3,940	5,050	5,060	4,880	5,100	10.8	**	72
	U^{29}	24	1,530	3,720	4,800	4,970	4,850	4,970	10.8	**	72
	U^{17}	24	1,530	4,000	4,850	4,950	4,800	4,960	11.8	**	72
	U^{18}	24	1,530	3,670	4,950	5,000	4,850	5,000	10.3	..	72
	U^{31}	24	1,530	4,000	..	..	..	4,060	1.2	**	72
	U^{20}	24	1,530	4,000	4,650	4,820	4,750	4,820	11.0	**	72
	U^{23}	24	1,530	4,000	..	..	..	4,530	1.8	28	72
	U	24	1,960	3,340	4,120	4,810	4,900	5,980*	32	..	139
	U^{14}	24	2,030	3,860	5,100	5,390	5,450	5,470	10.9	**	72
	U^{27}	24	2,030	..	4,800	4,720	..	4,810	9.7	29	72
	U^{28}	24	2,030	..	3,960	..	..	4,340	5.7	30	72
	U^{26}	24	2,540	4,180	5,060	5,670	5,930	5,930*	10.0	..	72
	U	24	2,940	3,340	3,900	4,900	5,690	5,980*	19	..	139
	U	24	3,040	3,770	5,390	5,890	6,300	6,330*	10.5	..	72
	U^{14}	24	3,040	4,070	5,440	5,980	6,180	6,330*	9.8	..	72
	U^{33}	24	3,040	3,480	..	..	..	3,860	1.1	..	72
	U	24	3,040	4,540	5,300	5,820	6,180	6,210*	9.0	..	66
	U	24	3,920	3,340	4,020	5,100	..	7,940*	22	..	139
	U^{34}	24	4,060	2,110	3,850	..	..	4,020	2.9E	10	72
	U	24	4,060	..	..	..	..	3,800	.8	..	72
	U	24	5,080	4,670	5,440	6,380	7,180	7,350*	10.6	25	72
	U^{35}	24	5,080	2,400	4,390	..	..	4,680	3.4E	..	72
	U	24	5,080	..	..	..	..	3,880	.8	..	72
	U	24	7,100	4,700	5,410	5,220	..	5,840	7.7E	..	72
	U	24	7,610	4,700	5,740	6,300	..	6,300	7.8E	22	72

Specimen										
U	24	2,020†					2,550	.8		49
U	24	4,020†					3,200	1.0		49
U	24	6,080†	3,200	3,920	3,830	1,860	3,920	11.0	**	49
U	24	8,090†	3,630	4,320	4,900	5,490	5,880*	>22		49
U	24	10,100†	3,830	4,660	5,200	6,280	9,410*	>22		49
U	150	510	3,920				4,350	1.5	24	72
U	150	635	4,080	2,720			3,860	2.9	30	72
U	150	760		4,380	4,230		4,470	4.9	30	72
U^{1}	150	810	4,050	4,060	4,120		4,200	3.0	27	72
U^{2}	150	910		4,250	3,940	4,150	4,300	6.9	28	72
U^{5}	150	910	4,020	4,140	4,430		4,160	10.5	**	72
U^{6}	150	910	3,750	3,960	4,100	4,540	3,960	8.2	27	72
U^{10}	150	1,020	3,000	4,450	3,900	4,110	4,550*	10.3		72
U^{11}	150	1,130	3,500	4,000	3,360		4,160	10.3	**	72
U^{12}	150	1,130	3,750	3,960			3,960	8.3	30	72
U^{13}	150	1,130	3,500	3,820	2,940		3,820	7.2	27	72
U^{14}	150	1,130	3,000	3,580			3,870	4.0	28	72
U^{16}	150	1,130		3,580			3,820	5.3	32	72
U^{17}	150	1,130		3,470			3,640	2.7	25	72
U^{4}	150	1,340		3,600	4,060	4,360	3,700	3.5	27	72
U^{5}	150	1,340		3,720	3,800		4,390	10.2	**	72
U^{7}	150	1,530		3,680	4,360	4,420	3,800	7.5	27	72
U^{10}	150	1,530		4,370	4,300	4,490	4,420*	10.1		72
U^{19}	150	1,530		4,130	4,410	4,720	4,490*	10.9		72
U^{21}	150	1,530		4,160	4,070		4,740*	11.2		72
U^{22}	150	1,530		4,130	3,750		4,130	7.6	26	72
U^{24}	150	1,530		3,870	3,740	3,850	3,870	6.1	27	72
U	150	1,530		3,680	3,870	4,230	3,870*	10.6		72
U^{32}	150	1,530		3,620	3,660	3,720	4,240*	10.2		72
U	150	2,540		3,500	5,100	5,640	3,730*	10.5		72
U	150	2,540	4,400	4,730			5,800*	10.8		72
U	150	3,040			5,390	5,890	3,650	.6		72
U	150	4,060	3,580	4,610			6,090*	10.1		72
U	150	5,080	2,720	3,830	5,450		3,830	2.6E		72
U	150	6,600	3,580	4,690	5,600	6,330	6,490*	11.7		72
U	150			4,710			5,700	9.1E	20	72

Table 11-3. *Continued*

Material	Or	Temperature (°C)	Confining pressure (bars)	Differential stress—bars Strain—per cent 1	2	5	10	Ultimate strength (bars)	Total strain (%)	Fault angle (°)	Ref.
Limestone, *Continued* Solenhofen, Bavaria, *Continued*	U	300	300	3,400	3,890	..	..	4,000	2.9	31	72
	U	300	410	3,010	3,880	..	..	3,890	2.4	18	72
	U	300	510	3,430	2,830	..	..	3,840	3.6	26	72
	U	300	760	3,610	4,080	4,270	4,460	4,470*	10.2	..	72
	U^{32}	300	2,540	..	..	..	..	3,500	.8	..	72
	U	300	3,040	3,190	4,120	4,900	..	5,390*	9.8	..	72
	U	300	3,040	3,770	4,240	4,630	4,980	4,980*	10.0	..	66
	U	300	4,060	1,960	3,630	..	..	4,020	2.8E	13	72
	U	300	5,080	2,620	3,970	4,660	5,150	5,210*	10.8	..	72
	U	300	5,080	..	3,920	..	..	4,700	3.3E	16	72
	U^{35}	350	5,080	3,450	..	..	..	3,570	1.2	..	72
	U^{35}	375	5,080	3,400	..	..	..	3,430	1.8	..	72
	U	400	0	..	..	..	..	3,140	.7	..	72
	U	400	100	..	3,810	..	..	3,650	1.0	..	72
	U	400	200	2,700	3,490	..	..	3,810	2.2	27	72
	U	400	310	3,210	3,630	..	..	3,500	2.7	18	72
	U	400	410	2,990	3,600	3,750	..	3,640	3.4	28	72
	U	400	510	3,310	3,880	4,220	4,410	3,820	5.2	19, 27	72
	U	400	3,040	2,060	3,530	..	..	4,430*	10.7	..	72
	U	400	4,060	3,140	3,680	4,070	4,320	4,020	4.2E	9	72
	U	400	5,080	2,240	3,580	4,350	4,630	4,350*	10.2	..	72
	U	400	5,080	..	3,500	3,700	..	4,660*	10.5E	..	72
	U^{35}	400	5,080	1,910	3,500	..	..	3,710*	5.5	..	72
	U	450	0	..	2,750	..	..	3,720	3.0	..	72
	U	450	3,040	2,030	3,580	..	..	2,900	3.3E	..	72
	U	480	0	2,750	3,240	..	..	3,730	4.1	**	72
	U	500	0	2,800	3,180	3,430	..	3,430	5.4	..	72
	U	500	100	2,830	3,070	3,290	..	3,300*	5.9	..	72
	U	500	200	..	..	3,140	..	3,160	5.7	23	72

	U	500	310	2,700	2,970	2,990	..	3,030*	5.7	..	72
	U	500	410	2,450	2,780	2,830	..	2,860	6.6	19	72
	U[30]	500	1,020	..	2,810	3,040	3,240	3,240	10.6	..	72
	U	500	1,020	2,600	2,790	2,960	..	2,960	5.7	..	72
	U	500	2,030	2,360	2,840	3,050	3,200	3,200	11.0	..	72
	U	500	3,040	2,450	2,650	2,900	3,060	3,110*	10.4	..	72
	U	500	3,040	1,770	2,570	2,700	2,780	2,790*	10.6	..	66
	U	500	3,040	1,720	2,420	2,750	..	2,750	5.9E	**	72
	U	600	310	1,770	2,140	2,260	1,960	2,260	12.0	**	72
	U	600	410	450	2,090	2,150	2,100	2,160	10.6	..	72
	U	600	1,520	700	590	..	..	790	3.3E	..	72
	U	600	2,030	1,630	960	1,840	..	1,290	4.2E	..	72
	U	600	3,040	790	1,770	1,540	1,840	1,840*	10.8	..	72
	U	600	3,040	..	1,180	280	1,640	1,640*	10.5E	..	72
	U	700	880	330	180	450	..	330*	8.5E	..	72
	U	800	5,070	530	390	750	..	470*	7.4	..	54
	U	800	5,070	..	620	..	820	1,390*	260E[44]	..	54
Limestone, Tula (silicified), Russia	N	24	1,010	7,470	8,040	..	..	8,040	4.7	20	66
Limestone, Viola, Oklahoma	N	24	5,050	2,500	3,920	4,930	6,030	6,160*	10.3	..	66
Limestone, Wells Station, Australia	N	24	200	2,000	..	..	..	2,160	1.6	..	134
	N	24	340	2,390	..	..	..	2,400	3.9	**	134
	N	24	800	2,910	..	..	..	3,180*	>5	..	134
	N	24	1,000	3,000	..	..	..	3,470*	>5	..	134
Limestone, "white dolomite," source unknown	U	24	0	..	..	..	..	830	.8	28	22
	U	24	690	2,760	..	..	..	3,240	1.3	31	22
	U	24	1,030	3,510	3,070	..	..	3,510	3.0	34	22
Limestone, Wm. Henry Bay, Alaska	U	24	2,940	2,550	2,950	3,830	..	4,860*	7.8	..	139
Limestone, "Wombeyan marble," Australia	N	24	0	..	..	..	..	720	.4	25	134
	N	24	35	920	..	..	..	920	.7	26	134
	N	24	100	1,180	..	..	..	1,030	1.7	28	134
	N	24	140	1,140	1,090	980	980	1,200	1.9	30	134
	N	24	210	..	..	..	..	1,220	>20	31	134

TABLE 11-3. *Continued*

Material	Or	Temperature (°C)	Confining pressure (bars)	Differential stress—bars Strain—per cent				Ultimate strength (bars)	Total strain (%)	Fault angle (°)	Ref.
				1	2	5	10				
Limestone, *Continued* "Wombeyan marble," Australia, *Continued*	N	24	270	1,380	1,300	1,190	1,190	1,380	>20	33	134
	N	24	340	1,380	1,360	1,350	1,370	1,390	>20	**	134
	N	24	450	1,580	1,580	1,600	1,700	1,600	>20	**	134
	N	24	700	1,670	1,780	1,970	2,170	2,450*	>20	..	134
	N	24	1,000	1,880	2,070	2,430	2,850	3,600*	>20	..	134
Limestone, Wolfcamp (3a), Texas	N	24	0	820	..	..	..	820	1.0	..	68
	N	24	1,010	2,430	2,960	3,190	3,090	3,190	19.6	32	68
	N	24	2,020	2,720	3,220	4,410	5,250	5,600	27.4	**	68
Limestone, Wolfcamp (6a), Texas	N	24	0	820	..	..	..	1,110	1.1	..	68
	N	24	500	1,970	2,540	2,750	..	2,730	4.4	**	69
	N	75	500	1,750	2,360	2,370	2,100	2,750	5.1	26	69
	N	150	500	1,640	2,180	..	..	2,390	11.5	24	69
	N	24	1,010	3,450	3,810	3,910	3,880	3,910	26.5	20	69
	N	150	1,010	1,570	2,170	2,870	3,270	3,450	18.3	**	69
	N	300	1,010	1,310	1,960	2,630	3,130	3,830*	27.2	..	69
	N	24	2,020	4,120	4,610	5,160	5,500	5,870*	30.0	..	69
	N	150	2,020	2,970	3,310	3,970	4,720	6,080*	21.6	..	69
	N	300	2,020	2,620	2,950	3,570	4,080	4,610*	27.3	..	69
Magnesite crystal (load ‖ c_v)	:	24	5,000	4,210	5,150	6,050	..	6,640*	7.9	..	76
	:	24	5,000	2,000	..	..	..	2,280	1.5E	25	76
	:	300	5,000	5,800	5,810	..	..	5,840*	2.4	..	76
	:	300	5,000	..	..	..	..	2,720	.9E	25	76
	:	500	5,000	3,930	..	..	..	4,260	1.1	40	76
Migmatite, "paragneiss," New York	N	150	1,010	1,250	2,000	7,220	..	7,250	2.9	25	66
	N	500	5,050	2,500	4,600	8,280	8,650	9,860	16.0	28	66
	P	150	1,010	2,320	6,900	5,950	..	7,580	2.2	29	66
	P	500	5,050	4,160	5,630	6,400	6,670	6,700	11.4	26	66
Monzonite, Colorado	U	150	1,010	1,260	2,010	..	..	6,400	7.5	26	66
	U	500	5,050	3,720	6,340	9,650	8,700	9,650	14.0	32	66

Material	Type	Temp.	Confining pressure						Strain	Angle	Ref.
Peridotite, Dun Mountain, New Zealand	N	24	5,070	19,000	22,000	20,200	...	22,500	8.1	27, 33	60
	N	300	5,070	12,000	14,070	14,600	15,400	15,450	10.4	34	60
	N	500	5,070	5,400	8,700	10,350	10,750	10,800	10.9	32, 37	60
	N	800	5,070	4,200	6,000	8,000	8,400	8,500	13.4	31, 36	60
	N	800	5,070	1,230	1,870	...	...	1,870	3.1E	15, 28	60
Peridotite, Mt. Burnette, Alaska	U	500	5,070	10,550	12,120	12,000	11,650	12,120	10.0	**	60
	U	800	5,070	3,300	4,830	6,200	...	7,810*	9.8	:	60
Peridotite, Vermont	N	150	1,010	1,460	4,510	...	...	5,080	2.4	29	66
	N	500	5,050	2,540	3,970	3,480	3,230	3,970	13.2	28	66
	P	150	1,010	1,460	...	...	...	4,480	1.7	32	66
	P	500	5,050	2,210	3,410	3,650	3,090	3,640	22.6	35	66
Pyrite, Utah	U	24	0	...	...	...	...	1,470	.8	35	139
	U	24	490	...	...	...	...	5,000	.6	32	139
	U	24	2,160	...	...	...	...	7,850	.5	30	139
Pyroxenite, California	U	24	5,070	12,230	16,500	16,660	12,500	17,350	9.8	:	60
	U	300	5,070	6,370	9,630	11,650	9,100	12,530	10.3	**	60
	U	500	5,070	4,400	7,400	8,400	3,400	9,300	25.9	**	60
	U	500	5,070	3,400	4,200	4,000	6,700	4,250	23.6E	:	54
	U	800	5,070	3,300	5,000	6,700	...	6,700	12.1	28	60
Pyroxenite, North Carolina	U	150	1,010	1,600	4,150	...	...	5,310	3.1	37	66
	U	500	5,050	2,940	5,660	6,150	6,400	6,400	14.4	:	66
Quartz[53] (load ∥ c_v)	:	24	0	7,000	14,000	...	...	25,000	4.8	:	60
	:	24	2,580	12,500	24,000	...	...	51,000	4.8	:	60
	:	24	5,070	14,500	28,000	...	...	52,000	4.3	:	60
	:	500	5,070	8,200	16,500	...	...	30,000	4.8	:	60
	:	600	5,070	...	...	...	...	19,000	4	:	60
	:	800	5,070	7,000	12,600	14,000	11,000	20,000	12.4	:	60
Quartz[53] (load ⊥ r)	:	24	5,070	10,000	20,000	...	...	35,000	4.5	:	60
	:	500	5,070	9,000	17,000	...	...	31,000	4.8	:	60
	:	600	5,070	7,000	13,000	12,000	...	25,000	4.0	45	60
	:	800	5,070	5,000	9,500	...	...	25,000	6.8	0	60
	:	800	5,070	4,000	...	...	...	4,000	1.2E	:	60
Quartzite, Eureka, Nevada	U	500	5,070	5,600	11,600	...	...	16,900	3.7	:	54

Table 11-3. *Continued*

Material	Or	Temperature (°C)	Confining pressure (bars)	Differential stress—bars Strain—per cent				Ultimate strength (bars)	Total strain (%)	Fault angle (°)	Ref.
				1	2	5	10				
Quartzite, Sioux, Minnesota	U	24	0	2,160	2,550	:	:	3,590	2.5	:	68
	U	24	1,010	2,310	2,800	9,320	:	10,790	5.2	25	68
	U	24	2,020	6,470	12,940	:	:	12,940*	2.0	:	68
Rhyolite, Tishomingo, Oklahoma	U	150	1,010	1,430	5,150	:	:	8,000	2.6	24	66
	U	500	5,050	4,220	8,440	10,300	9,270	10,470	30.6	34	66
Salt, rock, artificial	:	24	0	290	390	:	:	380*	1.9	:	147
	:	24	100	310	420	:	:	430*	2.4	:	147
	:	24	300	330	480	:	:	480*	2.6	:	147
	:	24	390	360	450	:	:	550*	2.7	:	147
	:	24	540	340		:	:	550*	3.2	:	147
Salt, rock, Blaine, Oklahoma	N	24	130	300	610	760	780	780	18.5	:	66
	N	24	1,020	250	610	540	710	780*	13.9	:	66
	N	105	1,060	330	690	1,200	:	1,200	8.3	**	66
Salt, rock, "Hockley," Texas	N	24	0	50	100	260	:	260	7.7	:	63
	N	24	25	60	130	220	380	440	21.8	:	63
	N	24	100	170	370	540	680	770	28.2	:	63
	N	24	530	310	480	600	740	830	>40	:	63
	N	24	1,180	390	540	750	840	>1,080	>70	:	63
	N	24	2,060	390	540	740	930	1,130	>40	:	63
	N	24	2,850	540	620	840	1,040	>1,180	15.1	:	63
	N	24	500	370	:	:	:	450*	1.4E	:	63
	N	24	1,060	290	380	550	770	920	21.3E	0	63
	N	24	2,010	360	490	620	780	910	20.0E	0	63
	N	24	3,000	380	510	640	790	1,130	31.5E	0	63
	N	24	3,970	420	520	640	790	1,170*	28.7E	:	63
	N	24	5,150	480	540	640	760	760*	10.4	:	63
	N	24	250†	260	350	480	550	580	34.9	:	63
	N	24	930*	180	350	520	570	570	32.8	:	63
Sand, artificial, glass beads (40–105 μ)	:	24	2,130	670	1,140	1,590	1,940	2,060*	13.2	:	66

Material	Ref										
Sand, artificial, glass beads (105–125 μ)	..	24	2,260	540	950	1,590	2,070	2,750*	16.9	..	66
Sand, beach, Galveston, Texas	..	24	2,010	370	640	1,620	2,360	3,190*	14.3	..	66
	..	24	2,060	710	850	1,110	1,210	1,210	14.8E	..	63
Sand, crystal (load ∥ c_v of calcite)	..	150	1,020	1,340	1,810	..	..	2,240	2.9	26	66
		300	2,050	4,000	5,500	6,000	6,050	6,050	22.1	**	66
		300	2,050	1,450	1,500	1,530	1,400	1,530	13.5E	**	66
		300	5,050	3,090	3,390	3,520	..	3,530*	5.1E	..	66
Sand, crystal (load ⊥ c_v of calcite)	..	150	1,010	400	..	..	..	510*	1.7	..	66
		300	2,000	760	1,550	3,490	..	4,270	8.5	38	66
Sand, St. Peter, Illinois, (250–300 μ)		24	490	60	110	280	560	970*	21.6	..	17
		24	490	150	260	470	600	600*	10.3E	..	17
		24	1,010	200	360	720	1,220	2,340*	28.2	..	17
		24	1,010	260	490	600	770	1,000*	17.1E	..	17
		24	1,380	260	460	920	1,590	3,220*	22.3	..	17
		24	2,020	350	690	1,580	2,850	4,860*	19.9	..	17
		24	2,020	440	830	1,200	1,330	1,340*	10.7E	..	54
		24	5,050	1,280	2,450	5,300	9,020	10,250*	11.8	..	17
		300	1,010	180	340	690	..	1,020*	8.3	..	17
		300	1,010	280	450	540	..	570*	7.2E	..	54
	14	500	5,070	1,080	2,260	4,650	8,200	9,700*	12.4	..	60
	3, 43	500	5,070	3,730	4,780	6,180	7,500	9,300*	22.0	..	54
		500	5,070	3,140	5,690	8,250	10,400	10,700	15.6	**	60
	40	600	5,070	1,670	2,450	4,620	..	7,250*	8.7	..	60
		800	5,070	3,900	6,400	10,000	12,500	13,600*	8.2	..	60
Sand, St. Peter, Illinois (105–125 μ)	..	24	1,010	170	310	620	1,080	1,820*	22.0	..	17
	..	24	1,380	160	260	640	1,250	2,600*	21.2	..	17
Sand, St. Peter, Illinois (180–210 μ)	..	24	1,010	150	260	580	1,040	2,290*	24.0	..	17
Sand, St. Peter, Illinois (70% 250–300 μ; 30% 105–125 μ)	..	24	1,010	200	360	690	1,130	1,980*	21.2	..	17
	..	24	1,380	190	340	710	1,570	3,540*	17.5	..	17
Sand, St. Peter, Illinois (bulk)	..	24	1,010	260	430	780	1,330	2,220*	20.6	..	17

TABLE 11-3. *Continued*

Material	Or	Temperature (°C)	Confining pressure (bars)	Differential stress—bars Strain—per cent				Ultimate strength (bars)	Total strain (%)	Fault angle (°)	Ref.
				1	2	5	10				
Sandstone, Alberta, Canada (70% sand, 30% carbonate and silica cement)	N	24	0	430	..	..	..	590	1.3	23	22
	N	24	350	1,460	1,520	1,210	1,050	1,610	20.0	36	22
	N	24	690	1,810	2,170	2,000	1,850	2,190	26.0	41	22
	N	24	350†	1,590	..	..	..	1,590	1.0	38	22
	N	24	690†	1,110	..	..	..	1,120	1.2	48	22
	N[54]	24	350	1,030	1,150	920	870	1,160	29.0	41	22
	N[54]	24	690	1.380	1,520	1,440	1,390	1,520	21.0	**	22
	N[54]	24	0	..	..	..	..	480	.7	21	22
	N[54]	24	350†	..	..	..	..	480	.7	23	22
	N[54]	24	690†	..	..	..	..	480	.7	24	22
Sandstone, Barns, Texas	N	24	0	..	..	..	..	400	.6	10	68
	N	24	510	740	1,300	..	..	1,690	2.8	38	68
	N	24	1,010	830	1,750	2,310	2,390	2,550	29.8	25	69
	N	150	1,010	830	1,750	2,260	2,320	2,470	30.2	33	69
	N	300	1,010	780	1,550	2,190	2,210	2,260	28.5	36	69
	N	24	2,020	1,240	2,450	3,580	4,000	4,180	27.6	30	69
	N	150	2,020	980	1,950	3,050	3,800	4,090	26.1	34	69
	N	300	2,020	980	1,950	2,910	3,380	3,630*	19.6	:	69
	P	24	510	660	1,200	..	..	1,470	3.0	**	68
	P	24	1,010	660	1,420	2,700	2,730	2,730	13.2	30	68
	P	24	2,020	840	1,790	3,370	3,730	4,020	20.8	**	68
Sandstone, Bartlesville, Oklahoma	N	24	0	..	..	..	..	410	.6	10	68
	N	24	1,010	2,210	2,260	2,260	2,260	2,290	21.6	**	68
	N	24	2,020	2,330	2,680	3,460	4,270	4,730	28.7	20	68
Sandstone, Berea, Ohio	N	24	0	390	430	..	..	460	2.2	26	65
	N	24	0†	280	260	230	190	720	19.4	30	65
	N	24	500	940	1,370	1,410	1,530	1,590	12.3	27	65
	N	24	500†	820	350	280	230	820	19.9	35	65
	N	24	1,000	1,220	2,140	2,200	2,240	2,480	32.8	34	65
	N[3]	24	1,000	1,150	1,590	1,580	1,580	1,900	18.0	38	65

Material	Type										
Sandstone, Mutenberg, Germany	N	24	1,000†	680	550	340	330	780	22.0	35	65
	N	24	1,500†	650	400	210	200	750	23.7	35	65
	N	24	2,000	1,660	2,380	3,000	3,520	4,250	30.4	29	65
	N[3]	24	2,000	1,660	2,280	2,800	3,170	3,410	27.5	30	65
	N[24]	24	2,000	1,190	1,660	2,370	2,420	2,480	27.1	33	65
	N[25]	24	2,000	1,120	1,330	1,530	1,520	1,740	25.8	34	65
	N	24	2,000†	420	220	1,080	1,090	1,330	9.1	34	65
	N[14]	24	2,000	720	720	190	190	620	25.4	35	65
	N	300	2,000	940				730	2.5E	25	65
	N[14]	300	2,000	1,320	1,600	2,540	3,300	4,250	26.5	31	66
	N	24	5,000†	420	1,810	1,930	2,090	2,360	25.4	32	66
	N	24	3,100	1,530	360	200	190	630	15.8	32	66
	N	300	3,100	1,000	2,350	3,570	4,950	5,850	20.1	38	66
	N	24	4,120	1,230	1,710	3,160	4,550	5,700*	20.6	:*	66
	N	300		970	2,020	3,590	5,060	6,450	16.3	**	66
	N	300			1,770	4,100	6,380	7,200	14.5	35	66
	U	24	0					680	.6	19	164
	U	24	280	1,720	1,960			2,000	3.1	35	164
	U	24	550	1,910	2,530	2,210		2,530	6.0	37	164
	U	24	1,520	1,910	2,700	3,140		3,240*	7.1		164
	U	24	2,430	1,910	3,430	3,970		4,170*	7.4		164
Sandstone, Oil Creek, Texas	N	24	0					960	.5	10	68
	N	24	1,010	2,650	4,220			6,870	3.3	14	69
	N	150	1,010	2,550				7,360	2.1	20	69
	N	300	1,010	2,550				6,910	2.1	16–30	69
	N	24	2,020	1,130	2,800			10,790	3.8	25	69
	N	150	2,020	1,180	2,940			9,900	2.8	27	69
	N	300	2,020	1,080	2,940			9,120	2.4	32	69
Sandstone, Pico, California	N	24	0†	40	60	130		280*	6.2		66
	N	24	1,000	400	800	1,320	1,930	2,430	30.0	30	66
	N[9]	24	1,250	400	630	890	1,160	1,410	26.8	32	66
	N	24	2,000	400	800	1,970	3,460	4,250	29.0	32	66
	N[14]	24	2,000	400		1,420	2,000		24.5	31	66
	N	300	2,000	820	1,220	2,450	3,950	4,450	24.4	25	66

TABLE 11-3. *Continued*

Material	Or	Temperature (°C)	Confining pressure (bars)	Differential stress—bars Strain—per cent				Ultimate strength (bars)	Total strain (%)	Fault angle (°)	Ref.
				1	2	5	10				
Sandstone, Repetto, California	45	24	490	930	2,210	...	...	2,940	2.4	27	66
	45	24	1,030	950	2,700	...	...	5,590	4.0	28	66
	45	150	1,010	510	1,060	...	...	3,900	3.3	30	66
Sandstone, Rush Springs, Oklahoma	N	24	0	...	...	...	...	1,870	.7	18	22
	N	24	690	4,410	...	...	...	5,590	1.8	21, 30	22
	N	24	1,020	5,240	...	...	...	6,210	1.8	28	22
Sandstone, silty, Texas	N	24	0	1,000	...	...	...	1,030	1.2	17	22
	N	24	690	1,730	2,320	...	...	2,520	3.0	34	22
	N	24	1,020	1,730	2,930	3,010	2,600	3,050	19.2	34	22
Sandstone, Supai, Nevada	N	300	2,020	1,220	1,780	2,040	...	2,040	9.2	29	66
	N	300	5,050	1,620	2,430	4,180	6,900	6,900*	10.0	..	66
Sandstone, Tensleep, Wyoming	N	150	1,010	1,300	3,170	...	...	4,660	3.9	29	66
	N	150	1,010	340	1,060	...	...	1,160	4.3E	10	66
	N	150	2,020	1,610	1,670	...	...	1,690*	2.1E	..	66
Sandstone, "Weeks Island S," Louisiana	N	24	0	100	...	...	...	100	1.0	..	68
	N	24	510	730	1,080	1,380	...	1,380	6.3	..	68
	N	24	1,010	1,020	1,380	1,650	1,690	1,760	16.6	**	68
	N	24	2,020	1,160	1,510	2,060	2,850	3,460	17.5	25	68
Schist, hornblende, New York	46	24	1,000	850	3,000	...	...	6,350	3.5	30	66
	47	24	1,000	1,050	3,500	5,500	...	6,400	6.4	38	66
	45	24	1,000	250	860	...	...	6,230	4.0	..	66
	48	24	1,000	250	800	6,900	...	6,800	7.5	..	66
	49	24	1,000	800	1,630	6,540	...	7,060	5.7	..	66
Schist, mica, New York	47	24	1,000	590	1,030	1,660	1,980	2,550*	24.1	..	66
	46	24	1,000	1,000	1,450	1,950	2,200	2,300*	18.2	..	66
Schist, mica, "Keystone," South Dakota	N	150	1,010	1,300	1,910	2,000	...	2,240	8.2	32	66
	N	500	5,050	2,080	3,980	5,450	5,900	6,100	22.2	38	66
	N	500	5,050	1,100	1,860	2,510	2,670	2,690*	31.4E	..	66

Rock											
Shale, Anahuac, Texas	P	150	1,010	890	1,440	1,760		1,760	7.9	33	66
	P	500	5,050	940	1,880	4,020	4,940	5,310	19.3	30	66
Shale, Crockett, Texas	N[83]	24	390	160	200	210	230	270	23.8	**	66
Shale, "5,900-foot sands," Texas	N	110	700	340	460	480	440	490	30.4	38	66
	N	24	0	..	..	..	..	740	.6	10	68
	N	24	1,010	1,000	1,520	2,280	..	2,450	7.5	**	68
	N	24	2,020	2,060	2,400	2,900	..	2,900	9.0	25	68
Shale, Green River, Colorado (calcareous)	N	24	0	420	580	..	..	640	2.6	5	68
	N	24	260	510	770	890	840	980	15.0	**	68
	N	24	510	670	960	1,350	1,530	1,610	28.6	10	68
	N	24	1,010	940	1,200	1,610	1,930	2,100	30.5	10	68
	N	24	2,060	1,100	1,500	2,130	2,650	2,980	35.2	**	68
	P	24	0	..	..	..	..	<100	..	0	68
	P	24	510	100	180	360	440	440	18.0	0	68
	P	24	1,010	340	490	570	..	580	9.4	22	68
	N	24	2,020	510	1,150	1,820	1,940	2,050	16.6	**	68
Shale, Muddy, Colorado	N	24	0	..	..	..	..	390	.6	10	68
	N	24	0†	680	330	..	..	830	4.2	0–40	66
	N	24	500	590	1,080	380	..	1,370	2.5	..	68
	N	24	500†	690	1,380	2,250	2,230	1,460	5.4	35	66
	N	24	1,000	810	1,560	580	510	2,430	16.1	33	69
	N	24	1,000†	820	1,630	2,000	..	1,810	24.3	36	66
	N	150	1,000	780	1,420	1,440	..	2,010	5.8	23–33	69
	N	300	1,500†	650	1,010	640	580	1,470	6.2	36	69
	N	24	2,000	820	1,630	3,430	3,780	1,920	23.6	35	66
	N	24	2,000†	810	1,570	410	340	3,900	26.8	30	69
	N	24	2,000	950	1,910	3,280	..	2,000	18.2	**	66
	N	150	2,000	810	1,570	1,910	1,770	3,370	10.0	33	69
	N	300		810	1,540	..	..	1,910	12.3	34	69
Shale, Paradox, Utah	N[55]	100	690	1,350	1,830	..	..	1,840	3.3	19	66
	N[55]	100	690	2,050	2,350	..	..	2,500	2.8	25	66
Shale, Vicksburg, Texas	N[55]	100	590	230	400	..	..	680	4.8	**	66
Siltstone, Permian "red beds," Texas	N	24	0	340	..	..	..	480	1.4	20	66
	N	24	500	1,110	1,450	1,470	1,410	1,470	19.5	30	66

TABLE 11-3. *Continued*

Material	Or	Temperature (°C)	Confining pressure (bars)	Differential stress—bars, Strain—per cent				Ultimate strength (bars)	Total strain (%)	Fault angle (°)	Ref.
				1	2	5	10				
Siltstone, *Continued* Permian "red beds," Texas, *Continued*											
	N	150	500	760	1,200	1,370	...	1,420	7.1	32	66
	N	24	1,010	1,210	1,750	2,260	2,170	2,260	25.2	**	66
	N	150	1,010	820	1,200	1,650	1,710	1,720	30.0	**	66
Siltstone, Repetto, California	45	24	0	280	...	...	...	280	1.0	0, 24	66
	45	24	500	640	1,010	1,050	910	1,300	12.6	28	68
	45	24	1,000	640	1,070	1,690	1,710	1,710	27.8	36	69
	45	24	1,000†	550	590	470	430	630	13.2	**	66
	45	24	1,000	750	...	...	...	960*	1.5E	..	66
	45,3	150	1,000	760	1,290	1,670	1,740	1,790	25.4	38	66
	45	150	1,000	450	800	1,330	1,090	1,340	13.2	25, 33	69
	45	300	1,000	450	660	860	...	860	9.4	34	69
	45,36	24	2,000	640	1,140	2,300	2,540	2,550	28.0	39	69
	45,14	24	2,000	960	1,310	1,620	1,760	1,900	25.4	34	66
	45,24	24	2,000	510	890	2,340	2,820	2,840	22.6	36	66
	45,25	24	2,000	1,330	1,570	2,780	2,740	2,780	22.9	35	66
	45	24	2,000	1,340	1,910	2,860	2,960	3,000	23.8	40	66
	45	24	2,000†	100	90	170	330	410	30.0	40	66
	45	150	2,000	640	1,060	1,870	2,120	2,360	31.0	30	66
	45	300	2,000	580	860	1,250	1,390	1,400	32.2	**	69
Slate, Cambridge, Massachusetts	N	24	0	...	...	...	...	3,140	.7	16	139
	N	24	300	5,200	...	...	...	5,200	1.0	16, 31	139
Slate, Mettawee, New York	N	150	1,010	1,900	2,400	...	...	5,040	2.7	29	66
	N	500	5,050	1,150	2,310	5,820	6,320	6,430	21.1	32	66
	P	150	1,010	910	2,630	...	...	5,190	2.9	22	66
	P	500	5,050	1,740	3,430	4,750	5,540	5,820	27.0	30	66
Slate, Mettawee, Vermont	N	24	0	830	...	...	...	980	1.2	10	68
	N	24	1,010	2,140	...	...	...	2,960	1.7	37, 45	69
	N	150	1,010	1,510	1,880	2,330	...	2,400	7.4	37, 45	69

Material	Test	T (°C)	P (bars)					(strength)	ε (%)	Angle	Ref.
Syenite, "Victor," Colorado	N	300	1,010	1,890	2,570			2,750	2.7	38, 45	69
	N	24	2,020	2,700	4,220			4,510	2.4	45	69
	N	150	2,020	1,030	2,190	4,370		4,370	7.8	43	69
	N	300	2,020	810	1,800			4,320	4.0	36, 43	69
Sylvite rock, New Mexico	U	150	1,010	980	3,310			5,320	2.4	25	66
	U	500	5,050	3,180	4,360	4,310	3,620	4,360	27.7	27	66
	N	24	240	270	440	590	660	1,050*	28.3		66
	N	24	550	380	480	460		560	5.6E	**	66
Brass		24	0	1,630		2,190	2,770	4,340*	30.6		69
		24	1,000	2,400	2,010	3,130	3,560	4,560*	25.3		69
		24	1,000	1,910	2,840	2,660	2,920	3,340*	32.0E		69
		150	1,000	1,790	2,250	3,130	3,630	5,030*	22.4		69
		150	1,000	1,470	2,750	2,330	2,510	2,750*	25.0E		69
		300	1,000	1,240	2,080	1,890	2,040	2,260*	26.8		69
		24	2,000	1,470	1,680	2,230	2,360	2,380*	13.0E		69
		24	2,000	2,790	2,050	3,330	3,730	4,220*	20.9		69
		150	2,000	2,220	3,040	3,610	4,170	4,830*	41.8E		69
		150	2,000	1,790	3,020	3,240	3,730	4,810*	22.5		69
		300	2,000	2,220	2,880	3,480	3,790	3,850*	11.2E		69
		300	2,000	1,240	3,050	1,980	2,110	2,110*	26.6		69
		24	5,000	1,600	1,760	2,260	2,440	2,630*	58.8E		69
		24	5,000	2,590	2,920	3,330	3,680	4,530*	25.1		69
		300	5,000	2,300	3,010	3,510	3,960	4,320*	34.2E		69
		300	5,000	2,110	2,330	2,490	2,500	2,510*	26.2		69
		500	5,000	1,870	2,170	2,380	2,490	2,490	31.0E		69
		500	5,000	380	390	430	470	480*	24.8		69
		500	5,000	400	400	410		440*	9.0E		69
Copper		24	0	200	370	780	1,260	2,060*	33.6		69
		24	1,000	300	540	1,120	1,650	2,520*	30.8		69
		24	1,000	590	850	1,200	1,550	1,740*	13.1E		69
		150	1,000	300	540	1,080	1,510	2,200*	27.8		69
		150	1,000	590	820	1,050	1,290	1,450*	16.0E		69
		300	1,000	280	420	650	880	1,320*	28.8		69
		300	1,000	450	660	930	1,130	1,430*	15.6E		69

Handbook of Physical Constants

TABLE 11-3. *Continued*

Material	Or	Temperature (°C)	Confining pressure (bars)	Differential stress—bars Strain—per cent				Ultimate strength (bars)	Total strain (%)	Fault angle (°)	Ref.
				1	2	5	10				
Copper, *Continued*											
	::	500	1,000	310	380	420	470	490*	13.7	::	66
	::	24	2,000	300	540	1,120	1,670	2,590*	27.5	::	69
	::	24	2,000	590	850	1,220	1,610	2,450*	76.8E	::	69
	::	150	2,000	300	540	1,120	1,550	2,150*	29.6	::	69
	::	150	2,000	590	850	1,160	1,340	1,350*	11.6E	::	69
	::	300	2,000	300	470	710	980	1,450*	29.0	::	69
	::	300	2,000	450	670	930	1,180	1,590*	29.2E	::	69
Lead	::	24	5,130	30	30	35	40	50*	23.6E	::	66

1 290 bars pore water pressure
2 360 bars pore water pressure
3 500 bars pore water pressure
4 510 bars pore water pressure
5 620 bars pore water pressure
6 670 bars pore water pressure
7 710 bars pore water pressure
8 730 bars pore water pressure
9 750 bars pore water pressure
10 810 bars pore water pressure
11 850 bars pore water pressure
12 900 bars pore water pressure
13 950 bars pore water pressure
14 1000 bars pore water pressure
15 1040 bars pore water pressure
16 1090 bars pore water pressure
17 1190 bars pore water pressure
18 1280 bars pore water pressure
19 1340 bars pore water pressure
20 1350 bars pore water pressure
21 1390 bars pore water pressure
22 1450 bars pore water pressure
23 1460 bars pore water pressure
24 1500 bars pore water pressure
25 1750 bars pore water pressure
26 1990 bars pore water pressure
27 2000 bars pore water pressure
28 2030 bars pore water pressure
29 1000 bars pore CO_2 pressure
30 1020 bars pore CO_2 pressure
31 1330 bars pore CO_2 pressure
32 2540 bars pore CO_2 pressure
33 3040 bars pore CO_2 pressure
34 4060 bars pore CO_2 pressure
35 5080 bars pore CO_2 pressure
36 1000 bars pore kerosene pressure
37 containing .1 per cent distilled water
38 containing .5 per cent distilled water
39 containing 2.9 per cent distilled water
40 containing 5 per cent distilled water
41 containing .2 per cent carbonated water
42 containing 1.6–10 per cent $MgCl_2$ solution
43 strain rate .1 normal
44 strain at neck
45 load axis approximately 45° to foliation, schistosity, or bedding
46 load axis approximately 30° to schistosity
47 load axis approximately 38° to schistosity
48 load axis approximately 60° to schistosity
49 load axis approximately 75° to schistosity
50 specimen thrown into folds with axes normal to direction of loading
51 load axis 45° to (010), quasinormal to *a* axis
52 load axis perpendicular to orientation A[51]
53 values are approximate; each represents estimate based on several poorly reproducible experiments
54 water saturated before testing
55 preservation of original fluid content attempted

TABLE 11-4. CRUSHING STRENGTHS, COHESIVE STRENGTHS, INTERNAL FRICTION, AND PRINCIPAL STRESS RELATIONSHIPS AT FRACTURE OF ROCKS COMPRESSED UNDER LOW CONFINING PRESSURES

A. From tests by U.S. Bureau Reclamation (after Balmer, Refs. 7–10; Florey and King, Ref. 43; Monfore, Ref. 104; Ore, Ref. 132). All at room temperature on rubber-jacketed 75-per cent water-saturated, 5- or 15- by 10- or 30-cm cylindrical specimens. Average crushing strength for several tests; range (in parentheses) between maximum and minimum values measured. Mohr envelope and principal stress relationship taken as best straight line fit of test data. Numbers following rock name indicate more than one sampling of a given formation. Loaded normal to bedding if present.

Material		Crushing strength (bars)		Cohesive strength (bars)	$\tan \phi$	$\sigma_1 = a + b\sigma_3$ a (bars)	b
Calaveras phyllite, graphitic, California		70		20	1.1	110	6.6
Calaveras phyllite, quartzose		90	(60)	20	1.2	90	7.5
Calaveras phyllite, sericite		100	(35)	20	1.1	105	6.9
Tensleep Sandstone, Wyoming	(1)	610	(520)	120	1.1	610	6.8
	(2)	850	(360)	170	1.1	900	7.0
Idaho Springs biotite	(1)	530		150	.5	500	3.0
schist, Colorado	(2)	840		90	1.9	690	15.7
Idaho Springs biotite	(1)	360		25	1.7	190	13.7
chlorite schist	(2)	820		55	2.3	510	22.5
	(3)	1180		..	..	..	..
Idaho Springs biotite	(1)	80		35	1.3	200	8.6
sillimanite schist	(2)	350		25	2.9	300	34.6
Calaveras sericite schist, California		150		25	1.4	160	9.9
Mauv calcareous shale, Arizona		360	(330)	80	2.1	710	19.7
Mauv quartzose shale		1230	(700)	240	1.0	1130	5.8
Chico siltstone, California		250	(180)	50	1.2	280	7.7
Miocene lithic tuff, Oregon		35	(15)	5	.9	30	4.9
Siltstone, Texas		50		5	1.4	35	9.3
Silty claystone, Texas		15		3	1.0	10	6.0
Calcareous claystone, Texas		20		4	.8	15	4.6
Calcareous subgraywacke, India	(1)	910	(280)	150	1.4	890	9.2
	(2)	660	(410)	110	1.5	700	10.8
Calcereous conglomerate, India		1060	(210)	180	1.4	1100	9.8
Lime silicate hornfels, Thailand		1360	(25)	260	1.1	1340	7.1
Granodiorite, Australia		1270	(1200)	170	1.5	1110	10.7
Salt Lake (?) hypersthene andesite,	(1)	1330	(250)	290	1.0	1380	6.1
Idaho	(2)	1290	(240)	280	1.0	1310	5.7
Miocene basalt, Oregon	(1)	1690	(680)	320	1.2	1700	7.4
	(2)	2190	(1160)	440	1.1	2240	6.6
Quartz diorite, Idaho batholith		870	(100)	140	1.4	850	9.2
Swandyke diorite gneiss, Colorado	(1)	630		110	1.3	660	9.0
	(2)	1040		180	1.4	1110	10.0
Colville Granite, Washington		1490	(840)	230	1.6	1540	11.8
Altered Colville Granite		650	(340)	100	1.6	670	11.9
Precambrian granite, Colorado		720	(530)	140	1.5	920	11.1
Precambrian pegmatite	(1)	420	(300)	70	1.6	500	11.8
granite, Colorado	(2)	580	(10)	80	1.3	460	8.9

TABLE 11-4. *Continued*

Material		Crushing strength (bars)		Cohesive strength (bars)	tan ϕ	$\sigma_1 = a + b\sigma_3$ a (bars)	b
Chico graywacke, California, coarse-grained	(1)	550	(250)	120	1.1	600	6.5
	(2)	300		60	1.2	340	7.4
Chico graywacke, fine-grained		480	(310)	120	1.0	530	5.5
Chico graywacke, medium-grained	(1)	490	(190)	110	1.0	530	5.9
	(2)	510	(260)	120	1.0	530	5.9
Redwall Limestone, Arizona, fine-grained		810	(240)	150	1.6	1060	12.6
Redwall Limestone, medium-grained		1280		360	.7	1410	3.7
Redwall Limestone, porous		1330	(1530)	170	1.1	870	6.8
Redwall Limestone, chalcedonic		1080	(600)	180	1.5	1260	10.5
Redwall Limestone, oölitic		990	(360)	210	1.0	950	5.4
Redwall Limestone, stylolitic		800	(870)	130	1.7	950	13.0
Eniwetok limestone, reef breccia	(1)	340	(290)	..	..	..	..
	(2)	60	(15)	15	.6	45	2.9
Monzonite porphyry, Colville batholith, Washington	(1)	1250	(770)	170	1.7	1200	13.4
	(2)	1730	(650)	200	2.1	1660	17.7
	(3)	1700	(1530)	220	1.5	1410	10.3

B. From tests by Price (Ref. 135). All at room temperature on dry, rubber-jacketed, 2.5-by 5-cm cylindrical specimens. All values represent averages from several tests. Or = orientation of load: *P*—parallel to, *N*—normal to bedding.

Material	Or	Crushing strength (bars)	Cohesive strength (bars)	tan ϕ	$\sigma_1 = a + b\sigma_3$ a (bars)	b
Pennant sandstone, South Wales	N	1460	350	.90	1540	5.0
	P		320	.95	1390	5.4
Snowdown sandstone, Kent, England	N	1520	390	.85	1590	4.4
	P		340	.70	1460	4.0
Snowdown siltstone, Kent, England	N	1020	350	.45	1120	2.5
	P		280	.60	930	3.7
Chislet siltstone, Kent, England	P	900	290	.55	900	3.2

TABLE 11-5. COMPRESSIVE BREAKING STRENGTH
UNDER EXTREME HYDROSTATIC PRESSURES

All tests at room temperature at ordinary strain rates and on unjacketed specimens exposed to pentane unless otherwise noted.

Material	Confining pressure (kb)	Breaking stress (kb)	Remarks	Ref.
Carboloy 905	25	108	Shortened 9 per cent before fracture	28
Diamond	23	126	No flow	28
Pyrex glass	27	46	Lead jacket. Slip on 25-degree plane	29
Quartz*	32	16	No flow.	
	38	23	Cut ‖ c axis.	28
	39	25	Reduced to powder	
Quartz*	0	24	Confining pressure of soft	55
	9	27	metal. Most sheared on	55
	12	33	41-degree plane. Load ‖ c	55
	16	50	axis	55
	19	117		55
	25	147		27
Quartz glass	25	39	. .	28
Sapphire	0	21	c axis $\perp$ length.	
(synth. Al_2O_3)	0	41	c axis ‖ length.	30
	24	52	c axis $\perp$ length. Twinning	
	27	89	c axis ‖ length. Shear 36° to length	
Spinel	25	61	No flow	28
Steel ("Teton")	0	29		
	25	47	Shortened 9 per cent	28
TaC, 97 per cent; VaC, 2 per cent; Mo$_2$C, 1 per cent	23	35	No flow	29
TaC and .3 per cent Ni binder	25	30	No flow	29
Tourmaline	25	87	No flow	28
WC and .3 per cent Co binder	25	47	No flow	29

* Griggs [49], using a confining medium of lead, and Goranson [167] using a true liquid, both measured strengths similar to those of the second group. Later Griggs and others [60] found high values for jacketed specimens in CO_2 (Table 11-3), but Christie and others [34] reported low values like those of the first group for crystals imbedded in bismuth (Table 11-13). The reasons for these inconsistencies are not understood.

TABLE 11-6. BRIDGMAN'S DATA ON TENSILE BREAKING STRENGTH
UNDER EXTREME HYDROSTATIC PRESSURE

All tests at room temperature at ordinary strain rates on jacketed specimens

Material	Jacket	Confining pressure (kb)	Breaking stress (kb)	Remarks	Ref.
Antimony (single crystal)	?	26	2.5	.8 strain before "tensile" fracture	31
Beryllium	Copper	27	7.8	.69 strain	29
	None	18	5.3	.22 strain	
Boric anhydride glass	Copper	28	10.0	2.04 strain before fracture (type unspecified)	31
γ Brass (single crystal)	Copper	26	14.0*	Not broken 1.04 strain	31
Carboloy 999	?	26	53.5	No flow	29
Cast iron	Copper	29	33.0	45° shear after 1.77 strain	30
Halite (single crystal)	Copper	29.2	.5	Not broken .22 strain	29
Pipestone (Catlinite)	Copper	29	12.0	Not broken .19 strain	30
Pyrex glass	Lead	27	15.2	"Tensile" break	30
	Copper	26.2	23.8	"Tensile" break	
Sapphire, synth. (single crystal)	Copper	27	27.0	$C_v \parallel$ length. Not broken	30
	Copper	26	26.0	$C_v \perp$ length. Not broken	
Solenhofen limestone	Copper	27	14.0	Shear 57° to length	30

* Ultimate strength based on original cross section.

TABLE 11-7. STRENGTH OF HOLLOW CYLINDERS OF ROCKS AND MINERALS
UNDER EXTERNAL HYDROSTATIC PRESSURE

A. From room-temperature tests of Bridgman [Ref. 23] on rubber-jacketed specimens with a 5.5 wall ratio. Cylinder axes of single crystals parallel to optic axes

Material	Pressure (kb)	Type of failure
Andesite	8.0	No flow. Hole filled with powder
Barite	3.2	Spalling in hole and flow
Calcite	15.0	Spalling in hole and flow
Glass	12.0	Random fracturing. No spalling
Granite	5.0	Hole filled. Possibly some flow
Microcline	5.0	No flow. Hole filled with powder
Quartz	6.0	Radial cracks 120° apart
	7.5	Some flaking
	11.5	No flow. Hole filled with powder
Quartz (negative crystal)	18.0	No detectable changes
Tourmaline	12.0	No flow. Hole filled with powder

TABLE 11-7. *Continued*

B. From room-temperature tests of Robertson [Ref. **139**] on rubber-jacketed specimens with an .8-cm outside radius unless otherwise noted. *Or* = orientation; *P*—cylinder axis parallel to; *N*—normal to bedding, foliation, or fissility; *U*—unknown

Material	Or	Wall ratio r_0/r_i	Maximum pressure (bars)	Pressure at failure (bars)	Type of failure
Calcite	..	1.65	290	290	Rupture
(axis ⊥ cleavage)	..	2.9	..	2580	Gliding flow
	..	3.2	..	2720	Gliding flow
	..	3.8	..	3450	Gliding flow
Copper ore, Montana	U	1.66	1290	1290	Rupture
(mostly pyrite)	U	1.85	2030	2030	Rupture
	U	1.92	2120	2120	Rupture
	U	3.15	4100	4100	Rupture
Diabase, Holyoke,	N	1.65	2050	2050	Rupture
Mass.	N	2.33	3050	3050	Rupture
	N	3.20	4500	4500	Rupture
Diabase, Vinal Haven,	U	2.40	3360	3360	Rupture
Maine	U	3.18	>4800	>4800	Slight spalling
	U	3.42	4600	4600	Rupture
Feldspar, microcline	..	1.64	1570	1570	Rupture
(axis ‖ c axis)	..	3.18	3880	3880	Rupture
	..	2.34	3100	3100	Rupture
Fluorite	U	1.62	1230	1230	Rupture
	U	2.96	3860	3860	Rupture
	U	3.16	4350	4350	Rupture
Granite, Barre,	N	1.43	1090	1090	Rupture
Vermont	N	1.66	1620	1620	Rupture
	N	1.90	2190	2190	Rupture
	N	3.23	4000	4000	Rupture
Granite, Chelmsford,	N	1.67	1850	1850	Rupture
Mass.	N	2.34	3250	3250	Rupture
	N	3.19	4620	4620	Rupture
Limestone, Becraft,	N	1.66	1000	1000	Rupture
New York	N	1.87	1320	1320	Rupture
	N	2.98	2800	2800	Rupture
Limestone, Beldens,	P	1.60	500	500	Rupture
Vermont,	P	1.90	830	830	Rupture
"Danby marble"	P	2.84	1690	1690	Rupture
Limestone, Beldens,	N	1.64	530	530	Rupture
Vermont, "Rutland	N	1.89	1000	1000	Rupture
white marble"	P	3.03	1320	1320	Rupture
Limestone, Leadville,	P	2.26	1100	1100	Rupture
Colorado,	N	2.32	1400	1400	Rupture
"Yule marble"	P	4.55	2600	2500	Spalling
	N	4.52	2600	2500	Spalling
Limestone,	N	1.63	1210	1210	Rupture
New Scotland,	N	1.92	2000	2000	Rupture
New York	N	2.91	2880	2880	Rupture
	N	3.15	3410	3340	Rupture; some flow
Limestone, "Red	U	1.65	1420	1420	Rupture
marble," Italy	U	1.90	2250	2250	Rupture
	U	3.10	4350	4350	Rupture
Limestone, Solenhofen,	U	1.42	1110	1110	Rupture
Bavaria	U	1.65	1330	1330	Rupture
(r_0 = .8 cm)	U	2.36	2150	2150	Rupture

TABLE 11-7. *Continued*

Material	Or	Wall ratio r_0/r_i	Maximum pressure (bars)	Pressure at failure (bars)	Type of failure
	U	3.27	3100	2700	Rupture; some flow
	U	3.38	4100	2570	Spalling and flow
	U	4.50	3600	3100	Spalling and flow
Limestone, Solenhofen,	U	1.43	1030	1030	Rupture
Bavaria	U	2.51	2320	2320	Rupture
($r_0 = 1.6$ cm)	U	3.33	2940	2940	Some spalling
	U	5.01	3430	3430	Some spalling
Limestone, Solenhofen,	U	1.55	1470	1470	Rupture
Bavaria	U	1.78	1640	1640	Rupture
($r_0 = .24$ cm)	U	2.46	2940	2940	Rupture
	U	3.57	3920	3920	Some spalling
	U	5.57	4400	4400	Some spalling
Quartz	..	1.90	4550	4550	Rupture
(axis $\parallel$ c axis)	..	3.19	8000	8000	Rupture
Quartzite, Cheshire,	U	1.93	3340	3340	Rupture
Vermont	U	1.42	1620	1620	Rupture
	U	3.16	4350	4350	Rupture
Sandstone, Hudson River, New York, "green"	N	3.17	3040	3040	Rupture
Sandstone, Hudson	N	1.35	340	340	Rupture
River, New York,	N	1.90	1080	1080	Rupture
"red"	N	2.66	1030	1030	Rupture
Serpentine, Vermont,	U	1.41	1390	1390	Rupture
"Verde antique"	U	1.62	1760	1760	Rupture
	U	2.32	4020	4020	Rupture
	U	3.18	4400	4400	Small flow
Slate, Cambridge,	N	1.66	1720	1720	Rupture
Massachusetts	N	1.90	1920	1920	Rupture
	N	3.05	4570	4570	Rupture
Soapstone, Virginia	N	1.92	640	640	Rupture
	N	2.39	780	780	Rupture
	N	3.05	630	630	Rupture
	N	4.56	1370	1370	Rupture
	N	5.00	1470	1470	Rupture

C. From high-temperature tests of Robertson [Ref. 139] on copper-jacketed specimens with a .8-cm outside radius

Ratio of radii	Pressure (kb)	Temp (°C)	Duration (hours)	Max decrease in OD (cm)	Rupture pressure at 20° (kb)
		SOLENHOFEN LIMESTONE			
2.50/1	2.5	650	3	.15	2.4
2.55/1	2.4	700	2	.15	2.4
2.40/1	1.5	400	20	<.002	2.3
..	1.7	400	48	.005	..
2.35/1	1.8	400	50	.075	2.3
2.40/1	2.1	400	56	.015	2.3
..	3.8	400	1	Rupture	2.5
2.40/1	1.4	500	20	<.002	2.3
..	2.0	500	12	.040	..
..	5.0	500	7	.074	..
		YULE MARBLE			
2.38/1	1.4	300	2	Rupture	1.3
2.37/1	2.1	400	20	.245	1.3
2.40/1	.6	400	13	.002	1.4

TABLE 11-8. Bursting Strength of Hollow Cylinders of Rocks
Under Internal Hydrostatic Pressure

Specimens unjacketed and filled with penetrating oil or nonpenetrating oil-well drilling mud under pressure. For those subjected also to confining pressure, external pressure provided by the nonpenetrating fluid. Cylinder axes normal to bedding unless otherwise indicated (after Scott and others, Ref. 148)

Material	Wall ratio r_0/r_i	Fluid	Bursting pressure (bars)	Confining pressure (bars)	Axial load (bars)	Tensile strength (bars)	Fracture
Cement	10.6	Mud	50	0	0	13	..
Shale	11.3	Mud	60	0	0	1	..
Sandstone	9.3	Mud	290	0	0	34	..
Sandstone	9.3	Mud	380	0	0	26	..
Sandstone	5.3	Oil	18	0	0	14	..
Sandstone	5.3	Oil	12	0	0	8	..
Sandstone	5.3	Mud	54	0	0	..	Vertical
Sandstone*	5.3	Mud	30	0	0	..	Vertical
Sandstone	5.3	Oil	13	0	0	..	Horizontal
Sandstone*	5.3	Oil	14	0	0	..	Vertical
Sandstone	9.3	Mud	185	0	0	..	Vertical
Sandstone	9.3	Mud	135	0	0	..	Vertical
Sandstone	9.3	Mud	155	0	0	..	Vertical
Sandstone	9.3	Oil	85	0	0	..	Horizontal
Sandstone	9.3	Oil	100	0	0	..	Horizontal
Sandstone	9.3	Oil	100	0	0	..	Horizontal
Sandstone	Infinite†	Mud	330	0	0	..	Vertical
Sandstone	Infinite	Mud	290	0	0	..	Unknown
Sandstone	Infinite	Mud	290	0	0	..	Unknown
Sandstone	Infinite	Mud	260	0	0	..	Unknown
Sandstone	Infinite	Oil	80	0	0	..	Unknown
Sandstone	Infinite	Oil	40	0	0	..	Horizontal
Sandstone	Infinite	Oil	50	0	0	..	Horizontal
Sandstone	Infinite	Oil	45	0	0	..	Unknown
Sandstone	9.3	Oil	210	0	70	..	Unspecified
Sandstone	9.3	Oil	230	0	135	..	Unspecified
Sandstone	9.3	Oil	260	35	135	..	Unspecified
Sandstone	9.3	Oil	290	70	135	..	Unspecified
Sandstone	9.3	Oil	330	105	135	..	Unspecified

* Bedding vertical and parallel to cylinder axis
† Tests with holes drilled into a sandstone outcrop

TABLE 11-9. SHEARING STRENGTH UNDER HIGH CONFINING PRESSURE

Average shearing strength at different average normal pressures of lensoidal powder specimens pressed between a piston and steadily rotating anvil. Double 60-degree rotation in about 10 seconds. (After Bridgman, Refs. **24, 25**)

Mineral or rock name	Shear strength (kb) At normal pressure of (kb)					Remarks
	10	20	30	40	50	
Andalusite	2.4	6.6	10.7	13.0	15.1	Snaps beyond 15, radial fibers
Anorthite	2.2	7.6	11	14	14	
Augite	1.1	2.9	6.2	10	13	Rotates with snapping, radial fibers
Basalt glass (artificial)	2.9	7.5	13	14	17	Rotates with snapping
Bronzite	1.8	3.3	9	13	16	⎫
Diopside	2.4	5.8	9	12	14	⎬ Rotates with snapping,
Garnet	..	..	..	..	17	⎪ radial fibers
Hornblende	1.1	3.0	6.3	10	13	⎭
Mullite (synthetic)	1.8	5.1	8.8	10.3	10.6	Snaps
Obsidian	3.8	8	12	14	15	Rotates with snapping
Pyroxene	1.4	4.4	8	11	15	Rotates with snapping, radial fibers
Pyroxenite	2.7	6.3	9	12	14	Rotates with snapping
Sericite	..	..	..	..	13	Snaps, oriented, B axis ⊥ disc, optic axial plane radial
Sillimanite	2.1	6.0	9.9	11.0	11.6	Snaps beyond 12
Ag	1.0	2.1	3.0	3.8	4.6	
AgCl	.5	.7	.9	1.1	1.3	⎫
$AgNO_3$	1.7	2.1	2.7	3.3	3.8	⎪
Ag_2O	.9	1.7	2.5	3.0	3.4	⎬ Rotates smoothly
Ag_2S	1.5	2.0	2.4	2.5	2.9	⎪
Ag_2SO_4	.5	.6	.6	.5	.5	⎭
Al	1.0	1.6	2.1	2.5	3.0	Rotates quietly
Al_2O_3	2.6	5.4	7.7	9.3	9.2	Rotates with snapping
Al_2S_3	2.2	5.5	8.7	9.6	10.6	Rotates quietly with snapping below 50
As	1.8	4.4	7.0	9.1	10.9	
As_2O_3	.9	4.7	6.8	7.9	8.7	Rotates smoothly
As_2S_3	2.1	3.9	5.1	5.9	6.6	Chatters below 8; smooth beyond
Au	.7	1.6	3.1	3.8	4.4	
Ba	.5	.7	.9	1.1	1.2	⎫
$BaCl_2$	1.1	2.4	2.9	3.4	3.7	⎬ Rotates smoothly
$BaCO_3$	2.1	4.5	5.8	6.6	7.3	⎭
$Ba(NO_3)_2$	1.3	2.4	2.8	3.1	3.6	Chatters to 26
BaO	.6	2.4	3.2	3.8	4.4	Rotates smoothly
BaS	1.6	4.5	6.1	6.6	6.9	Snaps to 27
$BaSO_4$	2.2	5.7	7.6	8.6	9.3	Snaps 18 to 24
Bi	.4	.7	.6	1.0	1.7	
Bi_2O_3	1.3	3.1	2.6	2.5	2.7	Dissociates to Bi with snapping below 24
Bi_2S_3	1.4	2.1	2.8	2.8	7.6	Free Bi(?)
C (Graphite)	2.8	4.6	6.8	8.8	9.7	Increasingly violent snapping beyond 10
Ca	.7	1.0	1.3	1.5	1.7	⎫
$CaCO_3$	2.7	5.0	6.3	7.4	8.4	⎬ Rotates smoothly
$CaCO_3$ (Solenhofen limestone)	1.0	3.4	5.7	6.8	7.2	⎭

TABLE 11-9. *Continued*

Mineral or rock name	Shear strength (kb) At normal pressure of (kb)					Remarks
	10	20	30	40	50	
CaO	2.3	6.0	9.0	11.1	13.1	Rotates smoothly with occasional snapping beyond 15
$CaSO_4$	1.5	4.1	6.6	7.8	8.4	Chatters and snaps
$CaSO_4 \cdot 2H_2O$	1.0	1.6	2.7	4.2	5.0	Rotates smoothly
$CaSO_4 \cdot 2H_2O$ (Gypsum)	..	..	..	..	5.0	Rotates smoothly, changed xl. form
Cd	.6	1.0	1.3	1.6	1.9	
CdS	1.8	3.5	4.6	5.5	6.3	
Cu	1.0	2.3	3.7	4.5	4.8	
$CuCO_3 Cu(OH)_2$ (Malachite)	..	..	..	..	10.9	
$2CuCO_3 \cdot Cu(OH)_2$ (Azurite)	..	..	..	..	8.3	Rotates smoothly
Cu_2O	2.2	6.1	8.0	9.2	10.1	
CuS	1.3	3.0	3.9	4.4	4.8	
Cu_2S (Cubic)	1.5	2.8	3.2	3.5	3.9	
Cu_2S (Chalcocite)	1.6	2.7	3.4	3.7	3.6	Rotates smoothly, transforms to cubic Cu_2S
Cu_5Sn	1.5	3.3	4.4	4.9	5.1	Rotates smoothly, slight chatter beyond 25
CuZn	.9	1.7	2.3	2.5	2.7	
Cu_5Zn_8	.4	.9	1.6	2.2	2.7	Rotates smoothly
Fe	1.1	5.1	7.9	9.8	..	
Fe_2O_3	2.3	6.8	10.7	13.7	16.4	Rotates with snapping
$Fe_2O_3 \cdot H_2O$ (Lepidocrocite)	1.3	3.7	6.5	8.7	11.2	Rotates smoothly
$2Fe_2O_3 \cdot 3H_2O$ (Limonite)	..	..	..	..	8.7	Rotates with snapping
FeS	2.0	5.9	9.0	10.8	11.7	Snaps beyond 37
FeS_2 (Pyrite)	2.3	6.2	9.5	11.3	12.3	Chatters and snaps, below 34
FeS_2 (Marcasite)	1.7	5.1	8.2	10.6	12.2	Snaps beyond 10
HgO (red)	1.2	3.0	4.5	5.7	6.7	
HgO (yellow)	1.3	3.1	4.8	6.2	7.1	
HgO (black; free Hg)	.8	2.5	4.1	4.8	5.4	
HgS altered	1.8	3.8	4.7	5.1	5.7	
KCl	.6	1.2	2.2	2.6	3.1	Rotates smoothly
K_2CO_3	1.0	2.2	2.8	3.2	3.6	
$K_2Cr_2O_7$	1.1	2.1	2.6	3.2	3.8	
K_2CrO_4	1.2	3.0	4.5	5.1	5.5	
$KMnO_4$	1.1	1.7	4.0	6.0	7.4	
K_2SO_4	1.3	3.1	5.1	6.3	7.2	Polymorphic trans. at 21
Mg	.6	.7	.7	.8	.9	
$MgCO_3$	2.0	4.5	6.8	8.0	8.8	Rotates quietly
MgO	1.4	4.6	7.0	8.9	10.7	Rotates quietly, infrequent snapping
Mo	.6	2.4	5.1	8.0	11.9	
Na	.2	1.0	2.2	3.5	5.1	
NaCl (Halite)	.9	1.8	2.2	2.4	2.9	Rotates quietly
Na_2CO_3	1.4	3.8	3.9	4.6	5.1	
$NaNO_3$	1.3	2.4	2.8	3.2	3.4	
Na_2SO_4	1.4	3.6	5.3	6.2	6.9	
Na_2WO_4	1.2	3.3	4.6	5.5	6.5	
Ni	1.0	2.7	5.1	7.4	8.5	Rotates smoothly
NiS	.9	1.7	2.7	3.8	4.7	
Pb	.2	.3	.4	.5	.7	

TABLE 11-9. *Continued*

Mineral or rock name	Shear strength (kb) At normal pressure of (kb)					Remarks
	10	20	30	40	50	
$Pb(AsO_2)_2$	1.7	3.1	3.9	4.7	5.1	Violent snapping
$PbCO_3$	.8	1.8	1.9	2.0	2.1 ⎫	
PbO	.6	1.3	1.7	2.0	2.4 ⎭	Rotates smoothly
Pb_3O_4	2.1	5.8	6.9	7.5	7.9	Snaps to 25
PbO_2	1.5	5.7	9.7	..	..	Violent snapping and detonation
PbS	.5	.9	1.3	1.4	1.6 ⎫	
$PbSO_4$	.8	1.5	1.8	2.1	2.4 ⎬	Rotates smoothly
S (crystalline)	1.8	3.2	4.6	5.9	7.0 ⎭	
Sb	1.5	3.1	4.0	4.3	4.3	
Sb_2O_3	2.1	4.5	6.5	7.7	8.6	Snaps to 15
Sb_2O_5	1.2	2.9	4.8	6.7	8.4 ⎫	
Sb_2S_3	1.6	3.5	4.4	5.1	5.7 ⎪	
Sb_2S_5	1.4	2.8	3.9	4.8	5.3 ⎬	Rotates smoothly
$Sb_2(SO_4)_3$	2.0	3.4	4.4	5.2	5.7 ⎭	
Si	1.0	2.4	4.6	6.8	8.6	
SiO_2 (Quartz)	..	..	..	..	14.2	Rotates with snapping, optic axis tangential
SiO_2 (Crystobalite)	..	..	..	..	14.7	Rotates smoothly, some snaps, inverts to an unknown form of SiO_2
SiO_2 (Opal)	3.5	7.0	9.8	12	18	Rotates with much snapping, partly inverts to quartz
Sn	.3	.4	.6	.7	.8	
SnO	2.2	5.2	8.0	10.3	12.5	Snaps above 36
SnO_2	1.6	5.0	8.1	10.3	12.3	Rotates smoothly, alters to SnO
SnS	.8	1.7	2.2	2.5	2.7	Rotates smoothly
SnS_2	2.0	4.1	5.2	5.9	6.5	Snaps to 26
$SnSb$	2.0	3.1	3.2	3.3	3.5	
Sr	.6	.8	1.1	1.4	2.2	Rotates smoothly
SrS	1.6	4.9	7.2	7.9	8.4	Snaps below 34
U	.7	2.7	5.0	7.2	8.6 ⎫	
UO_2Cl_2	.9	2.1	2.9	3.5	.. ⎪	
Zn	.8	.9	1.2	1.5	1.8 ⎬	Rotates smoothly
$ZnCO_3$	1.8	3.8	5.4	6.7	8.6 ⎭	
ZnS	1.3	3.0	4.9	7.1	7.9	Snaps beyond 15
ZnS (Sphalerite)	1.6	3.1	5.1	6.2	8.5	Rotates with snapping
ZnS (Wurtzite)	1.6	2.7	3.4	3.8	4.3 ⎫	Rotates smoothly
$ZnSO_4$	1.9	3.9	5.3	5.9	6.6 ⎭	

TABLE 11-10. STRENGTH OF CALCITE AND MARBLE
IN TORSION UNDER CONFINING PRESSURE

All tests on jacketed, about 3 by 5 (Böker) or 1- by 2-cm, cylindrical specimens twisted at about .1 radian per minute at room temperature unless otherwise noted. "Ultimate strength" in terms of maximum torque achieved (M) and maximum shearing stress (τ_m) at surface where $\tau_m = 2M/\pi r^3$. Total axial pressure is sum of hydrostatic confining pressure and superposed differential stress. Or = orientation of cylinder axis; P—parallel to; N—normal to foliation; U—unknown; crystallographic planes for single crystals.

Or	Confining pressure (kb)	Axial pressure (kb)	"Ultimate Strength" Torque, M (dyne-cm × 10⁸)	Stress, τ_m (kb)	Fracture type	Total twist (rad/cm)
			CARRARA MARBLE (after Böker, ref. **16**)			
U	0	0	9.3	.18	Tensile	<.01
U	.30	.30	35.6	.67	Tensile	.03
U	.47	.47	39.8	.75	Tensile	.01
U	1.02	1.02	76.7	1.44	None	.02
U	1.28	1.28	69.0	1.30	Tensile	.03
U	1.64	1.64	9.55	1.81	None	.02
U	1.94	1.94	9.80	1.85	None	.01
U	2.38	2.38	10.20	1.92	None	.02
U	.57	2.34	7.30	1.38	Tensile, shear	.07
U	.65	2.72	8.48	1.60	Tensile, shear	.12
U	.88	2.74	11.50	2.17	Shear	.13
			YULE MARBLE (after Handin and others, ref. **71**)			
P	1.0	1.0	2.30	1.41	Tensile	.55
P*	1.0	.5	1.85	1.07	Tensile	.22
P	2.0	2.0	2.60	2.29	Tensile	1.41
P†	2.0	2.0	2.35	2.07	Tensile	1.40
P**	2.0	2.0	2.24	1.83	None	.91
P	2.0	2.5	2.49	1.48	Shear	.29
P	2.0	3.0	2.20	1.32	Shear	.50
P	2.7	2.7	5.70	3.39	Tensile	.96
P	2.7	3.7	7.95	4.68	None	1.61
N	1.0	1.0	1.22	.72	Uncertain	.46
N	2.0	2.0	3.40	2.16	Tensile	.68
			CALCITE CRYSTALS (after Handin and others, ref. **66, 71**)			
⊥ c	1.0	1.0	1.37	.85	Uncertain	.54
	2.7	2.7	4.10	2.54	None	.29
⊥ r	1.0	1.0	1.35	.84	None	.14
	2.7	2.7	2.00	1.24	None	.55
⊥ e	1.0	1.0	1.22	.76	Uncertain	.59
	2.7	2.7	2.70	1.67	Shear	.82
⊥ a	1.0	1.0	1.30	.81	None	.42
	2.7	2.7	3.04	1.86	None	.28

* Extension test
† 150° C
** 300° C

TABLE 11-11. EFFECT OF ANISOTROPY ON THE BREAKING
STRENGTH OF MARTINSBURG SLATE UNDER
TRIAXIAL COMPRESSION

All tests at room temperature on rubber-jacketed 2.5- by 6-cm cylindrical specimens at ordinary strain rates. β = inclination of slaty cleavage relative to axis of specimen (σ_1). θ = observed angle of fracture relative to σ_1 (after Donath, Ref. 36).

Confining pressure, σ_3 (bars)	Cleavage angle, β (degrees)	Breaking strength, $\sigma_1 - \sigma_3$ (kb)	Fracture angle, θ (degrees)
	0	1.26	0
	15	.47	15
	30	.18	30
35	45	.40	45
	60	.72	46
	75	1.23	47–51
	90	1.91	29
	0	1.62	0
	15	.76	15
	30	.33	30
105	45	.60	45
	60	.91	41–44
	75	1.46	50
	90	2.27	30
	0	2.35	6–8
	15	.95	15
	30	.50	30
350	45	.73	29–45
	60	1.16	41–60
	75	1.80	43–61
	90	2.97	30–32

TABLE 11-12. FRACTURE OF QUARTZ CRYSTALS UNDER HIGH CONFINING PRESSURE

All tests at room temperature on copper-jacketed cylindrical specimens compressed in medium of bismuth at 27 kb confining pressure. Four cozonal load orientations: normal to positive and negative unit rhombohedrons r ($10\bar{1}1$) and z ($\bar{1}011$), base c (0001), and prism m ($10\bar{1}0$). (After Christie and others, Ref. 34.)

Load	Predominant fracture Parallel to	Predominant fracture Angle to load axis	Subsidiary fractures Parallel to	Subsidiary fractures Angles to load axis	Breaking strength (kb)
$\perp c$	z	38°	r, z	38, 38	47
$\perp r$	c	38°	z	43	43
$\perp z$	c	38°	r, m	43, 38	42
$\perp m$	r	23°	r, z	52, 52	43

TABLE 11-13. COMPRESSIVE BREAKING STRENGTHS OF QUARTZ CRYSTALS
AND QUARTZITE UNDER CONFINING PRESSURES OF ALKALINE SOLUTIONS

Temperature ($^\circ$ C)	Confining pressure (kb)	Time (hours)	Solution	Breaking strength (kb)	Ref.
			QUARTZITE		
25	0	<1	Air	2.10	41
150	.83	<1	$10\% \text{ Na}_2 \text{CO}_3$	.40	41
315	1.03	1	$1\% \text{ Na}_2 \text{CO}_3$	.93	41
315	1.03	3	$1\% \text{ Na}_2 \text{CO}_3$	.33	41
			QUARTZ		
400	~.30	~1	$10\% \text{ Na}_2 \text{CO}_3$	~4.0	55

TABLE 11-14. REPRESENTATIVE DATA ON TRANSIENT FLOW

All compression tests at room temperature. Specimens under confining pressure were jacketed unless otherwise noted. Slope of the linear strain (ε) — log time (t), creep curve given as 2.3 $\dot{\varepsilon}t$ (compiled by Robertson, Ref. **140**).

Material	Confining pressure (kb)	Differential pressure (kb)	Total time (10^3 seconds)	2.3 $\dot{\varepsilon}t \times 10^4$	Ref.
Calcite, $\parallel c_v$	2.2	3.4	.3	37	140
Calcite, $\parallel a$	3.0	2.3	.6	5	140
Gypsum	0	.1	520	.7	51
	0	.4	1250	2.1	51
Halite	0	.06	1040	12	51
Limestone,	2.5	1.8	5.2	7.5	140
Danby Marble	2.5	4.1	.9	18.0	140
	4.0	2.1	.3	9.0	140
	4.0	3.3	.3	27.0	140
Limestone,	3.1	2.7	1.0	22.0	140
Rutland Marble	4.0	2.5	1.9	17.5	140
Limestone,	0	1.4	$>3 \times 10^5$	.5	51
Solenhofen,	.3	3.4	1.0	4.0	140
Bavaria	.6	2.6	10.0	7.0	140
	1.1	3.7	1.0	18.0	140
	2.0	3.0	3.9	2.5	140
	2.1	5.9	1.0	28.0	140
	3.1	4.2	.3	14.0	140
	3.1	3.4	7.2	9.0	140
	4.1	4.3	1.0	20.0	140
	4.0	3.2	.3	11.0	140
	4.1	7.9	1.0	29.0	140
	10.0*	3.3	3.6	8.0	49
	10.0*	4.3	3.6	20	49
	10.0*	5.4	8.4	100	49
	10.0*	6.6	7.2	250	49
Limestone, Urgonian	.5	1.8	1.2	210	45
Marl	.5	.4	1.2	32	45
Shale, Conchas	0	.01	4320	216	51

* Unjacketed, exposed to kerosene

TABLE 11-15. CREEP DATA ON WATER-SATURATED GYPSUM

Specimens under constant load at room temperature and 0 or 1 kb confining pressure (*after* Griggs, Ref. 52).

Compressive stress (bars)	Steady strain rate (10^{-6}/day)	Strain before fracture (per cent)	Duration to fracture (days)	Equivalent viscosity (poises $\times 10^{16}$)
CONFINING PRESSURE $= 0$				
300	2000	.9	2.5	.4
250	440	1.4	13.5	1.6
200	219	2.3	48	2.6
180	100	3.0	133	5.1
160	77	3.6	285	6.0
150	67	>1.1	>110	6.4
125	25	3.8	308	14.4
100	7	>.7	>520	41.0 (?)
CONFINING PRESSURE $= 1$ kb				
300	13,600	.5	.2	.1
250	2650	~1.5	2.7	.3
200	390	..	>7.0	1.5

TABLE 11-16. STRESS-STRAIN RELATIONSHIPS OF ROCKS FROM TRIAXIAL COMPRESSION TESTS AT DIFFERENT CONSTANT RATES OF STRAIN

A. Tests on dry, copper-jacketed, 1- by 2-cm cylindrical specimens of Yule marble at 5 kb confining pressure and in extension. *Or* = orientation of load; *P*—parallel to; *N*—normal to foliation (optic-axis fabric maximum approximately normal to foliation plane).* Stress-strain curve still rising at termination of test (always prior to rupture). Load fluctuation due to stick-slip of piston. [1]Extrapolated through 10 per cent strain. (*After* Heard, **74, 168**.)

Or	Tempera-ture (° C)	Strain rate (sec^{-1})	Differential stress—bars strain—per cent				Ultimate strength (bars)	Total strain (per cent)	Load fluc-tuation (bars)
			1	2	5	10			
N	25	4.0×10^{-1}	1620	2270	3070	3720[1]	3720*	8.0	0
N	25	4.0×10^{-2}	1550	2190	2980	3590	3680*	11.1	0
N	25	4.0×10^{-3}	1550	2160	2920	3600	3630*	10.6	0
N	25	3.3×10^{-4}	1550	2070	2840	3520	3670*	11.5	0
N	25	3.3×10^{-5}	1440	1990	2810	3500	3590*	10.7	0
N	25	3.3×10^{-6}	1440	1940	2690	3390	3520*	11.2	0
N	25	3.3×10^{-7}	1370	1850	2610	3290	3400*	11.2	0
N	300	4.0×10^{-1}	1000	1280	1850	2400	2430*	10.3	0
N	300	4.0×10^{-2}	1000	1260	1780	2330	2460*	11.4	0
N	300	4.0×10^{-3}	1000	1260	1760	2300	2490*	12.2	0
N	300	3.3×10^{-4}	1000	1250	1730	2260	2490*	12.6	0
N	300	3.3×10^{-5}	1000	1230	1710	2200[1]	2200*	8.0	0
N	300	3.3×10^{-6}	970	1220	1660	2090	2100*	10.1	0
N	300	3.3×10^{-7}	970	1220	1610	1980	1980*	10.1	0
N	300	3.3×10^{-8}	920	1180	1550	1820	1860*	11.2	0
N	400	4.0×10^{-1}	970	1180	1630	2110	2310*	12.6	0
N	400	4.0×10^{-2}	950	1200	1610	2050	2170*	11.8	0
N	400	4.0×10^{-3}	950	1150	1570	1990	2110*	12.0	0
N	400	3.3×10^{-4}	950	1160	1520	1890	2060*	13.2	0
N	400	3.3×10^{-5}	940	1130	1480	1760	1820*	11.7	0
N	400	3.3×10^{-6}	900	1080	1340	1550	1560*	10.4	0
N	400	3.3×10^{-7}	840	980	1170	1280	1290*	10.3	20

TABLE 11-16. *Continued*

	Tempera-ture	Strain rate	Differential stress—bars strain—per cent				Ultimate strength	Total strain	Load fluc-tuation
Or	(°C)	(sec⁻¹)	1	2	5	10	(bars)	(per cent)	(bars)
N	400	3.3×10^{-8}	750	860	970	1080	1080	10.2	20–30
N	500	4.0×10^{-1}	800	1020	1420	1830	1900*	10.9	0
N	500	4.0×10^{-2}	800	1000	1340	1670	1740*	11.1	0
N	500	4.0×10^{-3}	800	970	1270	1530	1600*	11.4	0
N	500	3.3×10^{-4}	780	950	1220	1410	1440*	11.4	0
N	500	3.3×10^{-5}	780	900	1050	1150	1170*	10.8	0
N	500	3.3×10^{-6}	610	680	770	870	880*	10.5	50–70
N	500	3.3×10^{-7}	530	570	670	730	730	10.6	100
N	500	3.3×10^{-8}	330	380	440	470	470	10.7	100–150
P	300	3.3×10^{-4}	1450	1900	2570	3160	3160*	10.0	0
P	300	3.3×10^{-5}	1450	1860	2510	3000	3010*	10.1	0
P	300	3.3×10^{-6}	1450	1860	2480	2880¹	2880*	9.3	0
P	300	3.3×10^{-7}	1300	1750	2260	2590	2600*	10.6	0
P	300	3.3×10^{-8}	1300	1730	2160	2340	2350*	10.4	0–50
P	400	3.3×10^{-4}	1300	1770	2310	2640	2670*	11.1	0
P	400	3.3×10^{-5}	1300	1680	2110	2320	2330	10.9	0
P	400	3.3×10^{-6}	1230	1560	1830	1940	1940	10.8	0
P	400	3.3×10^{-7}	1170	1390	1550	1580	1580	10.9	20
P	400	3.3×10^{-8}	970	1110	1160	1230¹	1230	9.5	10–30
P	500	4.0×10^{-1}	1100	1460	2030	2410	2470*	11.3	0
P	500	4.0×10^{-2}	1100	1440	1950	2260	2330*	12.0	0
P	500	4.0×10^{-3}	1100	1430	1860	2070	2100*	11.5	0
P	500	3.3×10^{-4}	1060	1340	1650	1760	1770*	11.0	0
P	500	3.3×10^{-5}	1060	1270	1430	1480	1490	12.0	0
P	500	3.3×10^{-6}	970	1050	1110	1120	1120	10.7	50
P	500	3.3×10^{-7}	690	730	800	830	830	11.0	80
P	500	3.3×10^{-8}	480	520	560	560¹	560	9.5	150

B. Tests on rubber-jacketed 1- or 2- by 2- or 4-cm cylindrical specimens of sandstone, limestone, and diorite in compression at atmospheric pore pressure. Load normal to bedding of sandstone, otherwise arbitrary. Fault angle measured between load axis and fault surface. (*After* Serdengecti and Boozer, Ref. 152.)

Tempera-ture (° C)	Confining pressure (bars)	Strain rate (sec⁻¹)	Differential stress—bars strain—per cent				Ultimate strength (bars)	Total strain (per cent)	Fault angle (deg)
			1	2	5	10			
			BEREA SANDSTONE (OHIO)						
25	0	2.2×10^{-1}	..	..	..	..	790	.5	28
25	0	1.2×10^{-4}	..	..	..	..	660	.5	29
93	0	1.9×10^{-1}	..	..	..	..	800	.5	35
93	0	1.6×10^{-4}	..	..	..	..	560	.6	25
150	0	1.9×10^{-1}	..	..	..	..	780	.7	35
150	0	1.6×10^{-4}	..	..	..	..	540	.5	35
25	350	4.1×10^{-4}	2020	..	..	..	2230	1.5	27
25	690	1.0×10^{-1}	2530	..	..	..	2920	1.6	..
25	690	1.0×10^{-2}	2480	..	..	..	2710	1.5	32
25	690	2.5×10^{-4}	2530	..	..	..	2530	1.3	38
25	690	6.4×10^{-5}	2510	2220	..	..	2540	3.1	..
93	690	1.2×10^{-1}	2480	..	..	..	2920	1.4	40
93	690	9.7×10^{-4}	2070	2040	..	..	2300	3.7	**
150	690	1.3×10^{-1}	2540	..	..	..	2840	1.4	45
150	690	8.7×10^{-5}	2450	..	..	..	2550	4.0	**

TABLE 11-16. *Continued*

Tempera-ture (° C)	Confining pressure (bars)	Strain rate (sec⁻¹)	Differential stress—bars strain—per cent 1	2	5	10	Ultimate strength (bars)	Total strain (per cent)	Fault angle (deg)
25	1380	1.1×10^{-1}	2880	..	..	..	3630	1.8	40
25	1380	3.2×10^{-2}	3020	3420	..	..	3630	2.6	**
25	1380	2.6×10^{-3}	2980	3160	..	..	3420	2.2	**
25	1380	2.4×10^{-4}	2870	3180	..	..	3280	2.0	**
25	1380	7.0×10^{-5}	2760	3000	..	..	3010	3.6	**
93	1380	1.7×10^{-1}	2760	3250	..	..	3250	3.5	**
93	1380	7.6×10^{-5}	2540	2860	..	..	2870*	3.6	..
150	1380	1.2×10^{-1}	2760	3310	3310	..	3350	8.0	**
150	1380	8.7×10^{-5}	2760	3040	..	..	3090*	3.6	..

SOLENHOFEN LIMESTONE (BAVARIA)

Tempera-ture (° C)	Confining pressure (bars)	Strain rate (sec⁻¹)	1	2	5	10	Ultimate strength (bars)	Total strain (per cent)	Fault angle (deg)
25	0	1.5×10^{-1}	..	..	..	..	3120	.9	..
25	0	9.4×10^{-5}	..	..	..	..	2720	.8	..
93	0	1.3×10^{-1}	..	..	..	..	2840	.7	..
93	0	8.5×10^{-5}	..	..	..	..	2310	.6	..
150	0	1.3×10^{-1}	..	..	..	..	2850	.7	..
150	0	7.2×10^{-5}	..	..	..	..	2600	.5	..
25	350	1.5×10^{-1}	3720	..	..	..	3840	1.1	28
25	350	8.6×10^{-5}	3700	..	..	..	3710	1.2	25
93	350	2.1×10^{-1}	3680	..	..	..	3700	1.2	..
93	350	8.4×10^{-5}	3660	..	..	..	3680	1.2	18
150	350	2.0×10^{-1}	3620	..	..	..	3620	1.1	..
150	350	9.0×10^{-5}	3600	..	..	..	3600	1.0	20
25	690	6.0×10^{-1}	3970	4140	3660	2780	4210	11.0	35
25	690	3.4×10^{-4}	3910	3830	3450	..	3930	7.0	26
93	690	8.5×10^{-1}	3970	4050	3430	3180	4080	11.6	**
93	690	2.5×10^{-4}	3690	3750	3070	..	3780	5.1	28
150	690	7.8×10^{-1}	3820	3630	3350	3240	3910	15.0	**
150	690	3.6×10^{-4}	3500	3740	3690	2770	3780	10.0	39
25	1040	5.2×10^{-1}	4310	4490	4460	..	4540	5.0	**
25	1040	2.6×10^{-4}	3810	4230	4120	..	4270*	6.0	..
93	1040	5.3×10^{-1}	4140	4280	4200	..	4320	5.0	**
93	1040	3.4×10^{-4}	3720	4070	4150	..	4150	5.0	**
150	1040	5.5×10^{-1}	4080	4210	4210	..	4210	5.0	..
150	1040	2.8×10^{-4}	3660	3850	4100	..	4100	5.0	..
25	1380	4.7×10^{-1}	3860	4840	4550	3620	4900	12.0	35
25	1380	1.9×10^{-4}	3940	4590	4550	4550	4590	10.0	**
93	1380	4.8×10^{-1}	3830	4590	4350	3800	4590	12.0	**
93	1380	2.2×10^{-4}	3700	4280	4350	4350	4350	10.0	..
150	1380	4.8×10^{-1}	3760	4390	4240	3660	4380	12.0	**
150	1380	2.6×10^{-4}	3450	4000	4140	4140	4140	10.0	..

PALA DIORITE (CALIFORNIA)

Tempera-ture (° C)	Confining pressure (bars)	Strain rate (sec⁻¹)	1	2	5	10	Ultimate strength (bars)	Total strain (per cent)	Fault angle (deg)
25	0	2.0×10^{-1}	..	..	..	..	2760	.6	..
25	0	8.5×10^{-2}	..	..	..	..	2920	.6	..
25	0	2.0×10^{-3}	..	..	..	..	2420	.4	..
25	0	4.8×10^{-5}	..	..	..	..	2140	.3	35
25	690	1.0×10^{-1}	6750	..	..	..	7800	1.6	35
25	690	1.6×10^{-3}	6390	..	..	..	6870	1.3	35
25	690	3.8×10^{-5}	5840	..	..	..	6490	1.4	35
25	1380	4.1×10^{-1}	7620	..	..	..	10100	1.9	35
25	1380	9.2×10^{-5}	7510	..	..	..	9450	1.9	35

* Test terminated before fracture; stress-strain curve still rising.
** Stress-strain curve peaked, but cohesion maintained.

TABLE 11-17. EQUIVALENT VISCOSITY OF PSEUDOVISCOUS FLOW

Equivalent viscosity (η) determined at steady strain rate ($\dot{\varepsilon}$), constant stress difference ($\Delta\sigma$), temperature, and confining pressure as $\eta = \Delta\sigma/3\dot{\varepsilon}$. All specimens jacketed except as noted. C = compression; E = extension.

Material	Temp. (°C)	Confining pressure (kb)	Stress difference, $\Delta\sigma$ (10^9 dynes/cm²)	Strain rate, $\dot{\varepsilon}$ (sec⁻¹)	Total time (10^3 sec)	Equivalent viscosity, η (poises)	Ref.
Gypsum	25	0	.42 C	7×10^{-12}	3460	$>2 \times 10^{19}$	51
Halite	25	0	.06 C	7×10^{-10}	3630	3×10^{17}	51
($\parallel a$ axis)	25	.14	.07 C	3×10^{-7}	120	4×10^{14}	88
	25	.14	.25 C	3×10^{-6}	60	8×10^{13}	88
Limestone,	400	1.5	1.10 C	4×10^{-8}	270	9×10^{15}	66
Yule Marble	300	5.0	≈2.6 C	1×10^{-6}	50	$\approx1 \times 10^{15}$	59
($\perp$ foliation)	300	5.0	≈3.0 C	1×10^{-6}	75	$\approx7 \times 10^{14}$	59
	300	5.0	≈3.2 C	3×10^{-6}	20	$\approx3 \times 10^{14}$	59
	400	5.0	1.08 E	3×10^{-8}	3000	1.1×10^{16}	74
	500	5.0	.73 E	3×10^{-7}	300	7.3×10^{14}	74
	500	5.0	.47 E	3×10^{-8}	3000	4.7×10^{14}	74
Limestone,	400	5.0	2.33 E	3×10^{-5}	3	2.3×10^{13}	74
Yule Marble	400	5.0	1.94 E	3×10^{-6}	30	1.9×10^{14}	74
($\parallel$ foliation)	400	5.0	1.58 E	3×10^{-7}	300	1.6×10^{15}	74
	400	5.0	1.23 E	3×10^{-8}	3000	1.2×10^{16}	74
	500	5.0	1.49 E	3×10^{-5}	3	1.5×10^{13}	74
	500	5.0	1.12 E	3×10^{-6}	30	1.1×10^{14}	74
	500	5.0	.83 E	3×10^{-7}	300	8.3×10^{14}	74
	500	5.0	.56 E	3×10^{-8}	3000	5.6×10^{15}	74
Limestone,	25	0	1.4 C	$<2 \times 10^{-14}$	$>3 \times 10^5$	$>2 \times 10^{22}$	51
Solenhofen,	25	10*	4.3 C	5×10^{-7}	3	3×10^{15}	49
Bavaria	25	10*	5.4 C	2×10^{-6}	10	9×10^{14}	49
	25	10*	6.6 C	1×10^{-5}	69	2×10^{14}	49
Rock salt,	25	0	.05 C	5×10^{-9}	250	3.5×10^{16}	153
natural	400	0	.05 C	1×10^{-7}	250	1.3×10^{15}	153
Rock salt,	25	0	.07 C	6×10^{-9}	290	4×10^{15}	91
artificial	105	0	.07 C	8×10^{-8}	350	3×10^{14}	91
	29	1.0	.07 C	5×10^{-9}	650	4×10^{15}	91
	29	1.0	.14 C	4×10^{-8}	1340	1×10^{15}	91
	105	1.0	.04 C	2×10^{-9}	1480	6×10^{15}	91
	105	1.0	.07 C	3×10^{-8}	290	9×10^{14}	91
	198	1.0	.07 C	1×10^{-7}	340	2×10^{14}	91

* Unjacketed; exposed to kerosene

SECTION 12

VISCOSITY

by Sydney P. Clark, Jr.

Contents

Illustrations

Handbook of Physical Constants—*Revised Edition*
THE GEOLOGICAL SOCIETY OF AMERICA MEMOIR 97, 1966

According to Newton's law of fluid friction, viscosity is defined as the ratio of the shearing stress to the rate of shear. If the stress is measured in dynes/cm^2 and the rate of shear in sec^{-1}, the viscosity is given in dynes sec/cm^2, or equivalently in gm/cm sec. This unit is called the poise and is used in the tables in this section. The unit of kinematic viscosity is the stokes; it is the viscosity in poises divided by the density in gm/cm^3.

Real liquids may be categorized as "Newtonian" or "viscous," and "non-Newtonian". The former show viscosities independent of rate of shear over wide ranges of shear rate. Silicates are believed to fall in this category, although verification of true viscous behavior in glasses becomes difficult as the viscosity becomes high. Non-Newtonian behavior is observed in colloidal suspensions, solutions of high polymers, greases, asphalt, etc. No single value of viscosity is sufficient to describe the flow of such materials. For many liquids, viscous flow is a simple activated process, and the viscosity, η, is well represented as a function of temperature by the expression $\eta = \eta_0 \exp(E_\eta/RT)$. Such a law is fairly well obeyed by SiO_2 and by some binary silicate liquids. It is not obeyed by water, B_2O_3, many complex silicates, or binary barium silicates. The viscosities of some binary calcium silicates and some more complex silicate liquids can be represented by a sum of terms, each of the form given in the above expression, but with different pre-exponential constants and with different activation energies. This may be due to temperature-dependent changes in the structures of the liquids.

The pre-exponential constant, η_0, corresponds mathematically to the limiting viscosity at very high temperatures. As such it is found by extrapolation and can be accurately determined only if data are available over a wide range of temperatures. The same remark applies to a lesser extent to the activation energy, E_η. Even careful recent studies of viscosity have yielded accuracies which are little better than 5 per cent. Because of the rapid variation of viscosity with temperature, E can nevertheless be accurately determined. Considerable uncertainty in η_0 is contributed by such experimental error, however, and it also causes difficulty in comparing the results of different observers.

Viscosities have been determined in the field by observing the rate of movement of lava streams. The results are subject to uncertainty because the size and shape of the channel is only approximately known. Direct comparison with laboratory results is further complicated by the possible presence of dissolved gases and crystals in the flowing lavas.

Russian and Japanese investigators have made a large number of measurements of the viscosities of melts of natural rocks; these have been collected with references [25]. The effect of pressure on the viscosity of large numbers of organic liquids and mercury is given, with references, by Bridgman [4].

REFERENCES FOR SECTION 12

1. Arndt, Z. Elektrotech. 13, 578, 1907
2. Bockris and Lowe, Proc. Roy. Soc. (London) A 226, 423, 1954
3. Bockris, Mackenzie, and Kitchener, Trans. Faraday Soc. 51, 1734, 1955
4. Bridgman, The physics of high pressure, G. Bell, London, 1952
5. Dane and Birch, Jour. Appl. Phys. 9, 669, 1938
6. English, Jour. Soc. Glass Technol. 8, 205, 1924; 9, 83, 1925
7. Hardy and Cottington, Jour. Research Natl. Bur. Standards 42, 573, 1949
8. Kani, Proc. Imp. Acad. (Tokyo) 10, 29 and 79, 1934
9. —— Proc. Imp. Acad. (Tokyo) 11, 334, 1935
10. Kani and Kozu, Proc. Imp. Acad. (Tokyo) 11, 383, 1935

11. Lillie, Jour. Am. Ceram. Soc. **22**, 367, 1939
12. Machin and Yee, Jour. Am. Ceram. Soc. **31**, 200, 1948; **37**, 177, 1954
13. Machin, Yee, and Hanna, Jour. Am. Ceram. Soc. **35**, 322, 1952
14. Mackenzie, Trans. Faraday Soc. **52**, 1564, 1956
15. Minakami, Bull. Earthquake Research Inst., Tokyo Univ. **29**, 491, 1951
16. Nichols, Jour. Geol. **47**, 290, 1939
17. Parks and Spaght, Physics **6**, 67, 1935
18. Shartsis, Capps, and Spinner, Jour. Am. Ceram. Soc. **36**, 319, 1953
19. Shartsis, Spinner, and Capps, Jour. Am. Ceram. Soc. **35**, 155, 1952
20. Solomin, Jour. Phys. Chem. (USSR) **14**, 235, 1940
21. Swindells, Coe, and Godfrey, Jour. Research Nat. Bur. Standards, **48**, 1, 1952
22. Timroth-Vucalovitch, Thermodynamic properties of water and water vapor, Moscow, 1951. Translation by General Electric Co., Schenectady 1954. Quoted in Am. Inst. Physics Handbook, McGraw-Hill Book Co., New York, 2-209, 1957
23. J. Verhoogen, communication to R. A. Daly
24. Volarovich and Fridman, Acta Phys. USSR **6**, 393, 1937
25. Volarovich and Korcemkin, Comptes Rendus Acad. Sci. USSR **17**, 417, 1937
26. Volarovich and Leontieva, Trans. Soc. Glass Technol. **20**, 139, 1936
27. Volarovich and Tolstoi, Trans. Soc. Glass Technol. **20**, 54, 1936

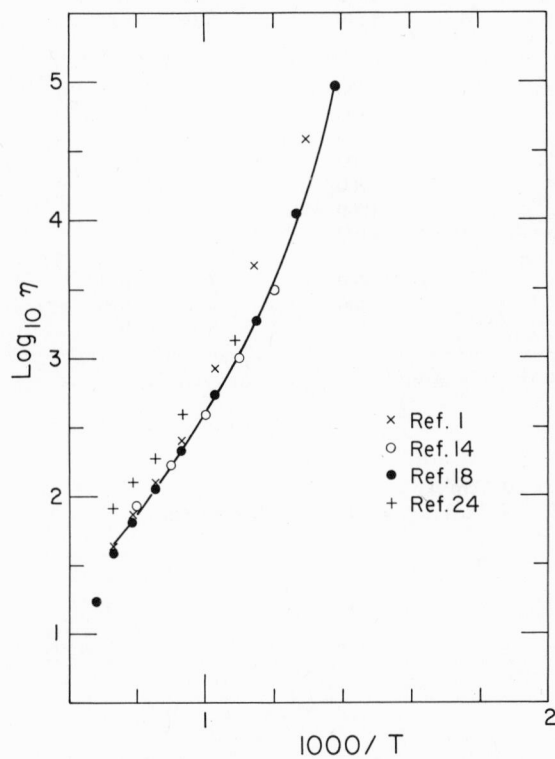

Figure 12-1. Viscosity of B_2O_3 glass as a function of temperature according to several workers

TABLE 12-1. VISCOSITY OF SiO_2 AND B_2O_3
(*See also* Fig. 12-1)

Liquid	Temperature, °C	Viscosity, poises	Ref.
SiO_2	1924	1.47×10^5	3
$E_\eta = 134.1 \pm 8.7$ kcal/mol	2060	2.40×10^4	
$\log_{10} \eta_0 = 8.2 \pm 0.9$			
	1720	2.94×10^6	20
$E_\eta = 156.3$ kcal/mol	1800	5.74×10^5	
$\log_{10} \eta_0 = 10.7$	1880	1.47×10^5	
	1940	5.60×10^4	
	2000	2.825×10^4	
	1100	4.7×10^{13}	26
$E_\eta = 107$ kcal/mol	1220	7.4×10^{12}	
$\log_{10} \eta_0 = -3.5$	1300	1.05×10^{12}	
	1400	4.62×10^{10}	
	1440	1.08×10^{10}	
B_2O_3			
(*See also* Fig. 12-1)	500	16,000	14, 18
	600	1800	
	700	510	
	800	210	
	900	120	
	1000	76	
	1100	43	
	260	6.1×10^{11}	17
	300	4.4×10^9	
	400	1.6×10^6	

Effect of pressure on viscosity of B_2O_3 [5]:
If

$$\eta = \eta_0 \exp(\alpha P),$$

then

at 359° C $\alpha = 15 \times 10^{-4}$ cm²/kg
at 516° C $\alpha = 4.6 \times 10^{-4}$ cm²/kg, for $0 < P < 2000$ kg/cm²

TABLE 12-2.   VISCOSITY IN BINARY ALKALI SILICATE SYSTEMS

Composition weight per cent	η_0 poise	E_η kcal/mol	Viscosity, poises 1100° C	1400° C	1700° C	Ref.
11.0 Li$_2$O 89.0 SiO$_2$	6.2×10^{-4}	42	..	191	27.5	3
17.6 Li$_2$O 82.4 SiO$_2$	1.0×10^{-3}	34	(265)	28.2	..	3
21.1 Li$_2$O 78.9 SiO$_2$	8.9×10^{-4}	32	(107)	13.5	..	3
28.9 Li$_2$O 71.1 SiO$_2$	1.3×10^{-3}	26	(16.9)	3.09	..	3
37.9 Li$_2$O 62.1 SiO$_2$	2.4×10^{-3}	18	..	.53	..	3
17.8 Li$_2$O 72.2 SiO$_2$	3.9×10^{-4}	37	300	27	..	19
20.0 Li$_2$O 80.0 SiO$_2$	5.1×10^{-4}	35	190	19	..	19
25.9 Li$_2$O 74.1 SiO$_2$	5.0×10^{-4}	31	44	5.6	..	19
10.3 Na$_2$O 89.7 SiO$_2$	4.7×10^{-5}	58	..	..	123	3
20.5 Na$_2$O 79.5 SiO$_2$	3.3×10^{-4}	42	..	100	..	3
30.7 Na$_2$O 69.3 SiO$_2$	4.6×10^{-4}	38	513	41.7	..	3
35.8 Na$_2$O 64.2 SiO$_2$	3.4×10^{-4}	37	263	22.9	..	3
21.9 Na$_2$O 78.1 SiO$_2$	2.2×10^{-4}	44	1900	130	..	11
31.7 Na$_2$O 68.3 SiO$_2$	2.4×10^{-4}	40	500	42	..	11
39.7 Na$_2$O 60.3 SiO$_2$	1.8×10^{-4}	38	180	16	..	11
20.0 Na$_2$O 80.0 SiO$_2$	2.8×10^{-4}	44	2900	160	..	19
30.8 Na$_2$O 69.2 SiO$_2$	2.2×10^{-4}	40	530	40	..	19
36.9 Na$_2$O 63.1 SiO$_2$	4.9×10^{-4}	36	260	26	..	19
3.9 K$_2$O 96.1 SiO$_2$	1.2×10^{-4}	65	..	..	1780	3
15.9 K$_2$O 84.1 SiO$_2$	3.5×10^{-4}	50	..	1180	(120)	3
24.2 K$_2$O 75.8 SiO$_2$	3.5×10^{-4}	46	7080	355	..	3
35.2 K$_2$O 64.8 SiO$_2$	1.5×10^{-4}	45	2190	115	..	3
44.0 K$_2$O 56.0 SiO$_2$	6.0×10^{-5}	46	1260	60.3	..	3
23.9 K$_2$O 76.1 SiO$_2$	2.6×10^{-4}	47	7900	380	..	19
29.9 K$_2$O 70.1 SiO$_2$	3.8×10^{-4}	44	3800	210	..	19
38.7 K$_2$O 61.3 SiO$_2$	3.0×10^{-5}	49	2000	87	..	19
43.6 K$_2$O 56.4 SiO$_2$	2.6×10^{-5}	48	1150	50	..	19

TABLE 12-3. VISCOSITY IN BINARY ALKALINE EARTH SILICATE SYSTEMS

Composition weight per cent	η_0 poises	E_η kcal/mol	Viscosity, poises 1500° C	1700° C	1800° C	Ref.
35.5 MgO 64.5 SiO_2	1.0×10^{-4}	41	(11)	3.42	2.09	3
40.1 MgO 59.9 SiO_2	1.2×10^{-4}	38	(5.6)	1.79	1.18	3
29.0 CaO 71.0 SiO_2	..	..	..	13.6	8.5	2
37.2 CaO 62.8 SiO_2	3.1×10^{-5}	46	14.1	3.92	2.5	2
47.0 CaO 53.0 SiO_2	2.6×10^{-4}	34	(4.05)	1.50	.99	2
56.0 CaO 44.0 SiO_2	..	..	(2)	.74	.54	2
30.3 SrO 69.7 SiO_2	..	..	..	80.4	43.1	3
54.0 SrO 46.0 SiO_2	1.8×10^{-4}	40	(15.5)	4.79	2.95	3
63.6 SrO 36.4 SiO_2	3.4×10^{-4}	34	(5.4)	1.95	1.30	3
46.1 BaO 53.9 SiO_2	..	..	110	21.4	12.5	3
56.3 BaO 43.7 SiO_2	..	..	26.3	7.20	4.50	3
71.7 BaO 28.3 SiO_2	..	..	..	1.86	1.50	3

TABLE 12-4. VISCOSITY IN THE SYSTEM CaO-MgO-Al_2O_3-SiO_2 [12, 13]

| Composition, weight per cent | | | | Viscosity, poises | | |
SiO_2	Al_2O_3	MgO	CaO	1300° C	1400° C	1500° C
35	15	15	35	..	5.3	2.6
35	20	10	35	..	8.2	4.1
35	25	10	30	39.8	13.0	5.6
50	10	15	25	33.8	13.1	6.71
50	15	15	20	69.4	24.3	10.9
50	20	20	10	112	33.9	14.3
50	25	10	15	396	93.0	34.1
50	25	20	5	202	54.9	21.0
60	0	15	25	..	18.2	8.72
65	10	10	15	1,010	269	97.2
65	15	10	10	2,920	720	224
65	15	15	5	2,450	557	181
65	20	5	10	11,900	2,410	671
65	20	15	0	4,070	956	263
35	35	0	30	248	54.7	19.0
40	25	0	35	128	34.9	14.3
50	20	0	30	247	70.9	30.2
60	20	0	20	2,530	663	204
70	15	0	15	22,200	4,690	1,320

TABLE 12-5. VISCOSITY OF MISCELLANEOUS GLASSES [6]

Composition, weight per cent		Temperature ° C	Viscosity, poises
SiO_2	78.28	843	3.50×10^6
Na_2O	11.76	892	7.83×10^5
MgO	9.30	1010	5.21×10^4
CaO		1100	1.09×10^4
Al_2O_3	.91	1195	3.06×10^3
Fe_2O_3		1425	2.43×10^2
SiO_2	72.05	500	8.33×10^{12}
Na_2O	20.62	600	7.44×10^9
Al_2O_3	6.85	674	1.56×10^8
CaO		730	8.15×10^6
Fe_2O_3	.20	909	3.68×10^4
		1180	8.96×10^2
		1388	1.86×10^2
SiO_2	71.56	550	1.43×10^{12}
Na_2O	15.28	700	2.08×10^8
Al_2O_3	12.69	797	5.56×10^6
CaO		1000	2.78×10^4
Fe_2O_3	.31	1190	4.55×10^3
		1390	6.27×10^2
SiO_2	74.96	750	3.56×10^7
CaO	9.36	800	2.91×10^6
MgO	.28	890	9.35×10^4
Na_2O	14.88	995	1.03×10^4
Al_2O_3	.42	1100	1.66×10^3
Fe_2O_3	.16	1200	6.50×10^2
		1305	3.18×10^2
		1400	1.63×10^2
SiO_2	76.68	742	3.56×10^7
CaO	.14	796	4.60×10^6
MgO	6.87	902	1.59×10^5
Na_2O	15.78	998	2.11×10^4
Al_2O_3	.42	1100	4.23×10^3
Fe_2O_3	.36	1198	1.24×10^3
		1304	4.48×10^2
		1400	1.80×10^2
SiO_2	73.98	770	1.94×10^7
CaO	7.10	858	1.08×10^6
Al_2O_3	7.10	995	3.15×10^4
Na_2O	11.66	1085	7.31×10^3
Fe_2O_3	.10	1198	1.97×10^3
		1308	8.63×10^2
		1400	5.52×10^2

TABLE 12-6. VISCOSITY IN THE SYSTEM ORTHOCLASE-ALBITE [9]

Or, per cent	100	80	60	40	20	0
Ab, per cent	0	20	40	60	80	100
1300° C	..	..	..	..	..	1.1×10^4
1350	..	..	2×10^6	1.5×10^6	10^6	4.3×10^5
1400	10^7	1.7×10^6	7.6×10^5	6.4×10^5	4.5×10^5	1.8×10^5
1450	4×10^6	7×10^5	3.2×10^5	2.5×10^5	1.8×10^5	..

TABLE 12-7. VISCOSITY IN THE SYSTEM DIOPSIDE-ALBITE-ANORTHITE [10]

Di, per cent	100	80	60	40	20	0
Ab, per cent	0	20	40	60	80	100
1200° C	..	..	..	9700	1.2×10^5	..
1300	..	..	280	1600	2×10^4	1.1×10^6
1400	80	86	110	440	4300	1.8×10^5

Di, per cent	20	40	60	80
An, per cent	80	60	40	20
1300° C	..	5900	150	..
1400	..	100	91	83
1500	110	..	..	..

Ab, per cent	80	60	40	20	0
An, per cent	20	40	60	80	100
1300° C	3.2×10^5	(4.7×10^4)	..	..	..
1400	4.3×10^4	7800	(2500)	..	..
1500	..	..	460	190	..
1555	..	..	..	(130)	110

Di, per cent	60	40	40	20	20	20
Ab, per cent	20	40	20	60	40	20
An, per cent	20	20	40	20	40	60
1200° C	..	4500	..	6.8×10^4	..	..
1300	170	830	470	7500	3700	..
1400	97	230	130	1500	620	360

TABLE 12-8. VISCOSITY OF MELTED ROCK

Rock type	Temperature ° C	Viscosity, poises	Ref.
Tachylite (1924 Mauna Iki flow, Kilauea)	1,074	4,950	23
	1,147	800	
	1,248	150	
	1,314	76	
Olivine basalt, Gembudô, Japan	1,150	37,900	8
	1,200	3,180	
	1,300	296	
	1,400	137	
Olivine basalt, Kônoura, Japan	1,200	732	8
	1,300	173	
	1,400	120	
Andesitic basalt, Motomura, Japan	1,150	80,000	8
	1,200	31,200	
	1,300	260	
	1,400	140	
Nepheline basalt, Nagahama, Japan	1,200	190	8
	1,300	97	
	1,400	80	
Lava, Mt. Vesuvius	1,100	28,300	27
	1,200	2,760	
	1,300	730	
	1,400	256	
Obsidian			
Oki		10^6	
Niijima	1,400	4.4×10^6	
Arita		4.4×10^6	
Erevan		1.7×10^5	25
Hornblende granite	1,400	2×10^6	
Hornblende-mica andesite	1,400	1.6×10^4	
Andesites	1,400	150 to 1,500	
Diabases	1,400	15 to 400	

TABLE 12-9. VISCOSITY COMPUTED FROM FIELD MEASUREMENTS

Locality and Date	Temperature, ° C	Viscosity, poises	Ref.
Alika flow, Hawaii, 1919	..	4.3×10^4	16
Kau flow, Hawaii, 1887	..	4.77×10^4	16
Mihara, Japan, 1951 flow	1038	2.3×10^5	15
	1083	7.1×10^4	
	1108	1.8×10^4	
	1125	5.6×10^3	

Handbook of Physical Constants

TABLE 12-10. VISCOSITY OF WATER AND STEAM

The primary standard of viscosity is pure water at 20° C [21]. The values in parentheses were interpolated or extrapolated from the data of [7]. The temperature coefficients so obtained are not in complete agreement with those found in the high-pressure study [4]

T	Viscosity, poises P, kg/cm²			
° C	1.5	1000	4000	8000
0	(.01786)	.01645	.01984	freezes
10.3	(.01296)	.01327	.01504	.02057
20	.010019	..	..	..
	±.000003	..	..	..
30	(.00797)	.00918	.01175	.01648
40	.006530	..	..	..
60	.006665	..	..	..
75	(.00378)	.00427	.00539	.00795
80	.003548	..	..	..
100	.002820	..	..	..
120	.002320	..	..	..

VISCOSITY OF WATER AND STEAM AT HIGH TEMPERATURES [22]

T	Viscosity, poises P, kg/cm²				
° C	1	20	100	200	300
100	.0001208	.002825	.002874	.002943	.003041
200	.0001605	.001383	.001403	.001432	.001462
300	.0002000	.0002011	.000922	.000942	.000971
400	.0002390	.0002407	.0002493	.0002680	.000451
500	.0002773	.0002796	.0002904	.0003082	.0003343
600	.0003147	.0003177	.0003314	.0003517	.0003772
700	.0003511	.0003547	.0003710	.0003943	.0004220

SECTION 13

MELTING AND TRANSFORMATION POINTS IN OXIDE AND SILICATE SYSTEMS AT LOW PRESSURE

by F. C. Kracek and Sydney P. Clark, Jr.

Contents

Handbook of Physical Constants—*Revised Edition*

The Geological Society of America Memoir 97, 1966

The material in this section has been condensed from a more extensive summary which Dr. Kracek completed shortly before his death in 1960. Most of the data which have been omitted dealt with elements which are of little geologic interest, although in a few cases systems were discarded because it was believed that the results were of insufficient reliability or because conditions such as partial pressure of oxygen were unspecified. Certain binary systems, for example Al_2O_3–MgO, have not been included as such because all available information is given in the figure showing liquidus relations in a ternary system, in this case Al_2O_3–MgO–SiO_2. Hydrous minerals, carbonates, and sulfide minerals are covered elsewhere in this Handbook, as are investigations above atmospheric pressure.

Systems are arranged in the following groups in the following order: systems involving a single metal ion; binary systems not involving SiO_2; binary silicate systems; ternary systems; and quaternary and quinary systems. The arrangement is alphabetical within each group.

Temperatures are given without the degree mark, and any number not otherwise identified denotes the temperature in degrees Centigrade. The temperature scale used is not generally specified, although workers at the Geophysical Laboratory use the Day-Sosman scale of 1912, and recent work elsewhere (mostly at the National Bureau of Standards and Pennsylvania State University) has been based on the International Temperature Scale of 1948. The difference between the two scales is negligible below 1100° C and is only 3° at 1550° C. The melting point of platinum is 1755° C on the Day-Sosman scale and 1769° C on the International scale of 1948.

The following example, drawn from the tables, will serve to indicate the way in which systems are described.

$CaOTiO_2$: $CaTiO_3$, *Perovskite*, m. 1970; eut. with TiO_2, 18 per cent CaO, 1460; tr. 1260.

This means that in the system CaO–TiO_2 there is a 1:1 compound, with mineral name perovskite, which has a transition at 1260° C and which melts at 1970° C. It is a constituent of a eutectic with TiO_2. The temperature of the eutectic is 1460° C and its composition is 18 per cent CaO, 82 per cent TiO_2. *All compositions are given in weight per cent.*

The following abbreviations are used in the tables.

atm.	atmosphere
eut.	eutectic
liqd.	liquid
m.	melting point (congruent)
m.i.	incongruent melting point
s.s.	solid solution
tr.	transition point

REFERENCES FOR SECTION 13

1. Agamawi and White, Trans. Brit. Ceram. Soc. **51**, 293, 1951
2. Allen and Snow, Jour. Am. Ceram. Soc. **38**, 264, 1955
3. Andersen, Am. Jour. Sci. (4) **39**, 407, 1915
4. Aramaki and Roy, Nature **184**, 631, 1959
5. Atlas, Jour. Geol. **60**, 124, 1952
6. Berezhnoi, Ogneupory **15**, 350, 1950
7. Bowen, Am. Jour. Sci. **38**, 207, 1914
8. —— Am. Jour. Sci. (5) **33**, 1, 1937
9. Bowen and Andersen, Am. Jour. Sci. (4) **37**, 487, 1914

10. Bowen and Greig, Jour. Am. Ceram. Soc. **7**, 238, 1924
11. Bowen and Schairer, Am. Jour. Sci. (5) **24**, 177, 1932
12. —— Am. Jour. Sci. (5) **29**, 151, 1935
13. Bowen, Schairer, and Posnjak, Am. Jour. Sci. (5) **26**, 193, 1933
14. Bowen, Schairer, and Willems, Am. Jour. Sci. (5) **20**, 405, 1930
15. Bredig, Jour. Am. Ceram. Soc. **33**, 188, 1950
16. Budnikov, Tresvyatskii, and Kushakovskii, Doklady Akad. Nauk, S.S.S.R. **93**, 281, 1953
17. Bunting, Jour. Research Nat. Bur. Standards **5**, 325, 1930
18. —— Jour. Research Nat. Bur. Standards **11**, 719, 1933
19. Coughanour, Roth, and de Prosse, Jour. Research N. B. S. **52**, 37, 1954
20. Curtis and Sowman, Jour. Am. Ceram. Soc. **36**, 190, 1953
21. Darken and Gurry, Jour. Am. Chem. Soc. **67**, 1398, 1945
22. —— Jour. Am. Chem. Soc. **68**, 798, 1946
23. —— Physical chemistry of metals, McGraw-Hill Book Co., New York, 535 p.
24. DeVries, Roy, and Osborn, The Penn. State College, School of Mineral Industries; Eighth Quarterly Progress Report, April 1 to June 30, Appendix 1, p. 40
25. —— Jour. Phys. Chem. **58**, 1069, 1954a
26. —— Trans. Brit. Ceram. Soc. **53**, 525, 1954b
27. —— Jour. Am. Ceram. Soc. **38**, 158, 1955
28. Fenner, Am. Jour. Sci. (4) **36**, 331, 1913
29. Ferguson and Merwin, Am. Jour. Sci. (4) **48**, 165, 1919
30. Foster, Jour. Am. Ceram. Soc. **33**, 73, 1950
31. Foster and Royal, Jour. Am. Ceram. Soc. **32**, 26–34, 1949
32. Franco and Schairer, Jour. Geol. **59**, 259, 1951
33. Glasser, Am. Jour. Sci. **256**, 398, 1958a
34. Goldsmith, Jour. Geol. **56**, 80, 1948
35. Greig, Am. Jour. Sci. (5) **11**, 1, 1926
36. —— Am. Jour. Sci. **13**, 1, 1927a
37. —— Am. Jour. Sci. **14**, 475, 1927b
38. Greig, Posnjak, Merwin, and Sosman, Am. Jour. Sci. **30**, 239, 1935
39. Grieve and White, Jour. Roy. Tech. Coll., (Glasgow) **4**, 660, 1940
40. Hahn and Muan, Am. Jour. Sci. **258**, 66, 1960
41. Hay, White, and McIntosh, Jour. West. Scot. Iron Steel Inst. **42**, 99, 1934–4
42. Hill and Roy, Jour. Am. Ceram. Soc. **41**, 532, 1958
43. van Hook, and Keith, Am. Mineral. **43**, 69, 1958
44. Iwase and Fukusima, Science Repts. Tohoku Imp. Univ., (1), Honda vol., 454, 1936
45. Iwase and Nishioka, Science Repts. Tohoku Imp. Univ., (1) **25**, 504, 1936–1937
46. Kanolt, Bull. Nat. Bur. Stds. **10**, 295, 1914
47. Keith and Schairer, Jour. Geol. **60**, 181, 1952
48. Lang, Fillmore, and Maxwell, Jour. Research Nat. Bur. Standards **48**, 298, 1952
49. MacChesney and Muan, Am. Mineralogist **46**, 572, 1961
50. McIntosh, Rait, and Hay, Jour. Roy. Tech. Coll. (Glasgow) **4**, 72, 1937
51. Maddocks, Iron Steel Inst., (London), Carnegie Schol. Mem. **24**, 51, 1935
52. Muan, Am. Ceram. Soc., Bull. **37**, 81, 1958
53. —— Am. Jour. Sci. **256**, 171, 1958
54. —— Am. Jour. Sci. **257**, 297, 1959
55. Osborn, Jour. Am. Ceram. Soc. **26**, 321, 1943
56. Osborn and Tait, Am. Jour. Sci., Bowen vol., 413, 1952
57. Rankin and Merwin, Am. Jour. Sci. (4) **45**, 301, 1918
58. Rankin and Wright, Am. Jour. Sci. (4) **39**, 1, 1915
59. Ricker and Osborn, Jour. Am. Ceram. Soc. **37**, 133, 1954
60. Roberts and Merwin, Am. Jour. Sci., (5) **21**, 145, 1931
61. Roberts and Smyth, Jour. Am. Chem. Soc. **43**, 1061, 1921
62. Roedder, Am. Mineralogist **36**, 282, 1951
63. Roth, Jour. Research Nat. Bur. Standards **61**, 437, 1958
64. Russell, Gitzen, Newsome, Ricker, Stowe, Stumpf, Wall, and Wallace, Alumina properties, Tech. Paper No. 10, Aluminum Co. of America, 1956
65. Schairer, Jour. Am. Ceram. Soc. **25**, 241, 1942
66. —— Jour. Geol. **58**, 512, 1950
67. —— Jour. Am. Ceram. Soc. **37**, 501, 1954
68. —— Am. Jour. Sci. **35A**, 289, 1938
69. Schairer and Bowen, Am. Jour. Sci. **240**, 725, 1942
70. —— Bull. Soc. Géol. de Finlande **20**, 67, 1947
71. —— Am. Jour. Sci. **253**, 681, 1955
72. —— Am. Jour. Sci. **254**, 129, 1956
73. Schairer and Yagi, Am. Jour. Sci., Bowen vol., 471, 1952
74. Schroder, Zeit. Krist. **66**, 493; **67**, 485, 1928
75. Smyth and Roberts, Jour. Am. Chem. Soc. **42**, 2582, 1920
76. Snow, Jour. Am. Ceram. Soc. **26**, 11, 1943

77. Toropov and Galakhov, Doklady Akad. Nauk, S.S.S.R. **78**, 299, 1951
78. —— Izvest. Akad. Nauk, S.S.S.R., Otdel. Khim. Nauk, **(1958)**, 8
79. Tromel, Obst, Konopicky, Bauer and Patzak, Ber. deutsch. keram. Ges. **34**, 397, 1957
80. White, Jour. Iron Steel Inst., (London) **148**, 579 and 695, 1943

Al_2O_3: (a) *High-temperature phases*:

    Alpha alumina, Corundum: trigonal m. 2650 [46]

    Beta aluminas: hexagonal isomorphous compounds from alkali or alkaline earth melts, formed in the ratio 1:11 for Na_2O, K_2O, MgO to Al_2O_3, and 1:6 for CaO, SrO, BaO to Al_2O_3

    Zeta Alumina: $LiAl_5O_8$, cubic from Li_2O containing melts

    (b) *Transition aluminas:* produced in calcination of Al compounds or in oxidation of Al metal. Varieties *rho, chi,* and *kappa* result on dehydration of alpha trihydrate; *eta* and *theta* from beta trihydrate, *gamma* and *delta* from alpha monohydrate, but all have been made by suitable dehydration and rehydration treatment of a single sample of fine grained alpha trihydrate. All varieties convert to alpha at or below ca. 1100. Delta may result from combustion of Al metal. Eta is obtained in oxidation of Al metal at its melting point. Kappa was obtained in thermal decomposition of hydrated aluminum chloride [64]

CaO: m. 2570 [46]

CuO: *Tenorite*, m. > 1240 (75 atm. O_2) dissociates 1104 (1 atm.) to Cu_2O and O_2; eut. of CuO and Cu_2O 1080 (0.51 atm. O_2) 86 per cent Cu, 14 per cent O_2; Cp anomalies −40, −60; these depend on thermal history [75]

Cu_2O: *Cuprite*, m. 1235 [61]

FeO: *Wüstite*, s.s., Fe-deficient; Wüstite (23.16 per cent) eut. with gamma Fe, liqd. (22.91 per cent), 1371; O-rich (25.60 per cent O) m.i. to Fe_3O_4 and liqd. (25.31 per cent O), 1424; liqd. oxide forms 2 liqds. (0.16 and 22.60 per cent O) in equilibrium with delta Fe, 1528; Wüstite (23.26 per cent O) decomposes to alpha Fe and Fe_3O_4 560 [22, 23]

Fe_3O_4: *Magnetite*, m. 1597, 27.64 per cent O; O-rich s.s. in equilibrium with Hematite, eut. ca. 1550 (53); O-rich oxidizes in air below 1388; magnetic tr. natural 580, artificial 510–680; Cp anomaly −159, magnetic anomaly −160 [22, 23]

Fe_2O_3: *Hematite*, m. pt. unknown, dissociates in air 1388, 1 atm. O_2, 1457, to magnetite and O_2; tr. 1030 [38, 22]

    Alpha Hematite: isomorphous with Corundum

    Gamma Hematite: isomorphous with magnetite; it is produced on oxidation of Magnetite, also on dehydration of gamma FeOOH (Lepidocrocite). *See* Figure 13-1

MgO: *Periclase*, m. 2800 [46]

MnO: *Manganosite*, m. 1850 [33]

Mn_3O_4: *Hausmannite*, stable in air below 1200; oxidizes in air to Mn_2O_3 877; m. 1567; tr. tetragonal to cubic, 1160 [43]

Mn_2O_3: *Braunite*, dissociates in air 877, 1 atm. O_2, 968, to Mn_3O_4 plus O_2 [40]

SiO_2: *Quartz*, m. (metastably) ca. 1470; tr. low trigonal–high hexagonal 573 ± 3; tr. Quartz–Tridymite 867 ± 3

    Tridymite, m. (metastably) ca. 1670; impure prepared by heating Quartz in presence of a water-soluble flux, e.g., Na_2WO_4; tr. rhombic

    –low, hexagonal 117 (heating); tr. low, hexagonal–high hexagonal 163 (heating) [28]

    Tridymite, pure, from hydrothermal experiments, identified by X-ray diffraction in two polytypic varieties: tridymite–M (metastable), tr. M I–M II, 113; tr. M II–M III 152; tridymite–S (stable), tr. S I–S II, 64; S II–S III, 113; S III–S IV, 138. Tridymite–S heated dry in Pt persists to 1470 ± 20; above this it converts to

Cristobalite; tridymite–M changes to a mixture of tridymite–S and cristobalite above 1320 $\pm$ 20 [42]

   Cristobalite, m. 1713 $\pm$ 10 (Day-Sosman scale), 1723 $\pm$ 10 (Int. Temp. scale 1948); tr. rhombic–cubic, very pure well crystallized, 267 $\pm$ 2; prepared at about 1100 from SiO_2 gel or silicic acid, tr. as low as 220 [28, 36]

TiO_2: *Rutile*, m. 1825 [18]

   Anatase, artificial by dehydration of TiO_2 gel ca. 900; tr. to Rutile in presence of flux >400, without flux 915; α–β anatase tr. 642

   Brookite, tr. in presence of flux to rutile below 900 [18, 74]

Al_2O_3–BeO: $BeO \cdot Al_2O_3$, *Chrysoberyl*, eut. with BeO, 1825; m. 1870; eut. with (1:3), 1850

   $BeO \cdot 3Al_2O_3$, m. 1910; eut. with Al_2O_3 1890 [48, 31]

Al_2O_3–FeO: $3FeO \cdot Al_2O_3$, decomposes below liquidus to (1:1) and FeO, 1230

   $FeO \cdot Al_2O_3$, *Hercynite*, m.i. to Al_2O_3 and liqd.; 12 per cent Al_2O_3, 1440; eut. with FeO, 7 per cent Al_2O_3, 1350 [50]

CaO–TiO_2: $CaTiO_3$, *Perovskite*, m. 1970; eut. with TiO_2, 18 per cent CaO, 1460; tr. 1260

   $Ca_3Ti_2O_7$, m.i. 1750 to (1:1) and liqd. 60 per cent CaO; eut. with CaO, 63 per cent CaO, 1695 [25, 19, 6, 63]

Fe_2O_3–MgO: $Fe_2O_3 \cdot MgO$, *Magnesioferrite*, m. 1750 in air with loss of O_2 [60]

FeO–TiO_2: Fe_2TiO_4, *Ulvospinel*, m. 1395, eut. with FeO, 10 per cent TiO_2, 1312

   $FeTiO_3$, *Ilmenite*, m. 1400, eut. with Fe_2TiO_4, 47 per cent TiO_2, 1363

   $FeTi_2O_5$, *Pseudobrookite*, m. 1494, eut. with $FeTiO_3$, 58 per cent TiO_2, 1390; eut. with TiO_2, 80 per cent TiO_2, 1430 [49]

MnO–TiO_2: $MnTiO_3$, *Pyrophanite*, m.i. to (2:1) and liqd., 60 per cent TiO_2, 1360

   Mn_2TiO_4, m. 1450, eut. with MnO, 34 per cent TiO_2, 1330 [39]

Al_2O_3–SiO_2: $3Al_2O_3 \cdot 2SiO_2$, *Mullite*, m. 1850 (Int. Temp. Scale 1948); eut. with Cristobalite, 5.5 per cent Al_2O_3, 1595. Mullite has a composition range 71.8 to 74.3 per cent Al_2O_3 (60 to 62.8 mole per cent Al_2O_3); eut. with corundum, 78 per cent Al_2O_3, 1840 [4, 65]

   Original study indicated: mullite m.i. to corundum and liqd. 55 per cent Al_2O_3, 1810 [7]

   Toporov and Galakhov [77] reported congruent melting, 1875, for mullite. *See also* [78, 16, 79] for mullite range of homogeneity *See* Figure 13-2

   $Al_2O_3 \cdot SiO_2$, *Sillimanite, Andalusite, Kyanite*, all decompose to mullite and SiO_2, kyanite between 1000 and 1325, andalusite between 1325 and 1410, sillimanite between 1345 and 1550 [35]

FeO–SiO_2: Fe_2SiO_4, *Fayalite*, m. 1205. *See* Figure 13-3

Fe_2O_3–SiO_2: no compounds; liquidus temperatures are not determined. Cristobalite and two immiscible liqds. of very wide range. Eut. probably near 100 per cent SiO_2 [14, 22, 37, 52]

MgO–SiO_2: *See* Figure 13-4

MnO–SiO_2: Mn_2SiO_4, *Tephroite*, m. 1345; eut. with MnO, 25.5 per cent SiO_2, 1317; eut. with *Rhodonite*, 38.3 per cent SiO_2, 1251

   $MnSiO_3$, *Rhodonite*, m.i. to Tridymite plus liqd., 44.5 per cent SiO_2, 1291

   Cristobalite plus 2 liqds., 55–99 per cent SiO_2, 1705 [33]

TiO_2–SiO_2: no compounds; eut. of SiO_2 and *Rutile*, 10.5 per cent TiO_2, 1550

   Rutile and 2 immiscible liqds., 19–93 per cent TiO_2, 1780 [26]

ZnO–SiO_2: Zn_2SiO_4, *Willemite*, m. 1512; eut. with ZnO, 22.5 per cent SiO_2, 1507; eut. with Tridymite, 50.9 per cent SiO_2, 1432

   Cristobalite and 2 immiscible liqds., 65–98 per cent SiO_2, 1695 [17]

$ZrO-SiO_2$: $ZrSiO_4$, *Zircon*, decomposes to oxides, 1540
  eut. with SiO_2, ZrO_2 and liqd. 1970 [20]
$Al_2O_3-CaO-SiO_2$: *See* Figure 13-5
$Al_2O_3-FeO-SiO_2$: *See* Figure 13-6
$Al_2O_3-K_2O-SiO_2$: *See* Figure 13-7
$Al_2O_3-MgO-SiO_2$: *See* Figure 13-8
$Al_2O_3-MnO-SiO_2$: $2MnO\cdot2Al_2O_3\cdot5SiO_2$, *Manganese Cordierite*, m.i. to mullite and
  liqd. ca. 1168
    $3MnO\cdot Al_2O_3\cdot3SiO_2$, *Spessartite*, m. > 1200 [76]
$Al_2O_3-Na_2O-SiO_2$: *See* Figure 13-9
$Al_2O_3-TiO_2-SiO_2$: no ternary compounds; fields of mullite and corundum, $TiAl_2O_5$,
  rutile and cristobalite; ternary eut. of cristobalite, rutile and $TiAl_2O_5$, ca. 1480 [1]
$CaO-FeO-SiO_2$: *See* Figure 13-10
$CaO-MgO-SiO_2$: $CaO\cdot MgO\cdot2SiO_2$, *Diopside*, m. 1391; forms discontinuous s.s. with
  $MgO\cdot SiO_2$
    $2CaO\cdot MgO\cdot2SiO_2$, *Akermanite*, m. 1454
    $CaO\cdot MgO\cdot SiO_2$, *Monticellite*, m.i. to MgO plus liqd., 1503
    $3CaO\cdot MgO\cdot2SiO_2$, *Merwinite*, m.i. to Ca_2SiO_4 plus liqd., 1575 [29, 36, 59, 7, 68,
  55, 15, 5]. *See also* Figure 13-11
$CaO-TiO_2-SiO_2$: $CaTiSiO_5$, *Titanite (Sphene)*, m. 1382; eut. with $CaTiO_3$, *Perovskite*,
  1375; eut. with Tridymite, 1373; eut. with $CaSiO_3$, 1353; eut. with TiO_2, *Rutile*, 1375
    Liqd. immiscibility region extends from $CaO-SiO_2$ to $CaO-TiO_2$ boundary,
  partly overlying fields of cristobalite and rutile [24, 27, 6, 44, 25]
$FeO-MgO-SiO_2$: *See* Figure 13-12
$FeO-MnO-SiO_2$: no ternary compounds, no ternary eut., low temperatures on
  liquidus lie at $FeO-SiO_2$ binary
    $FeO-MnO$: two series s.s. with tr. 1430
    Two-liqd. region near SiO_2 corner [41, 51, 80]
$Fe_2O_3-Na_2O-SiO_2$: $Na_2O\cdot Fe_2O_3\cdot4SiO_2$, *Acmite*, m.i. to Fe_2O_3 and liqd., 990 eut. with
  $Na_2Si_2O_5$, 810; eut. with (5:1:8), 817
    $5Na_2O\cdot Fe_2O_3\cdot8SiO_2$, m. 838; eut. with Na_2SiO_3, 837, eut. with Fe_2O_3, 816
    $6Na_2O\cdot4Fe_2O_3\cdot5SiO_2$, m. above 1091
    $2Na_2O\cdot Fe_2O_3\cdot SiO_2$, m. above 1145
    Liqd. immiscibility along $Fe_2O_3-SiO_2$ border [14]
$MnO-Mn_2O_3-SiO_2$: in air atmosphere
    Mn_3O_4 (cubic) + Tephroite + liqd., 33 per cent SiO_2, 1230
    Mn_2SiO_4 Tephroite + $MnSiO_3$ s.s. + liqd., 34 per cent SiO_2, 1206
    Mn_3O_4 (cubic) + Mn_2O_3 s.s. + $MnSiO_3$ s.s. 1168
    $MnSiO_3$ s.s. + Tridymite + liqd., 42 per cent SiO_2, 1272
    Mn_2O_3 s.s. + $MnSiO_3$ s.s. + Tridymite, 1048
    Cristobalite + 2 liqds., 55 to 99 per cent SiO_2, 1700 [54]
$Al_2O_3-CaO-FeO-SiO_2$: *See* Figure 13-13
$Al_2O_3-CaO-K_2O-SiO_2$: *See* Figure 13-14
$Al_2O_3-CaO-K_2O-MgO-SiO_2$: *See* Figure 13-15
$Al_2O_3-CaO-K_2O-Na_2O-SiO_2$: *See* Figure 13-16
$Al_2O_3-CaO-MgO-SiO_2$: *See* Figures 13-17 and 13-18
$Al_2O_3-FeO-Na_2O-SiO_2$: *See* Figure 13-19
$Al_2O_3-FeO-K_2O-SiO_2$: *See* Figure 13-20
$Al_2O_3-K_2O-MgO-SiO_2$: *See* Figure 13-21
$Al_2O_3-K_2O-Na_2O-SiO_2$: *See* Figure 13-22

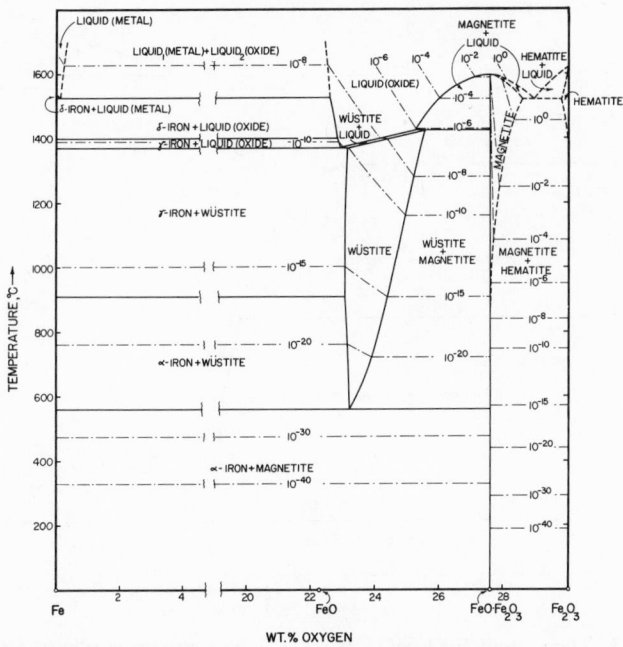

Figure 13-1. The system Fe–O; from [53], mainly after [21, 22]. Solid lines are boundary curves separating phase areas labelled in the diagram; dash-dot curves are oxygen isobars in atmosphere. Dashed curves in the upper part of the figure are inferred boundary curves for which experimental data are lacking; those in the extreme upper right corner are estimated for pressures of oxygen greater than 1 atmosphere

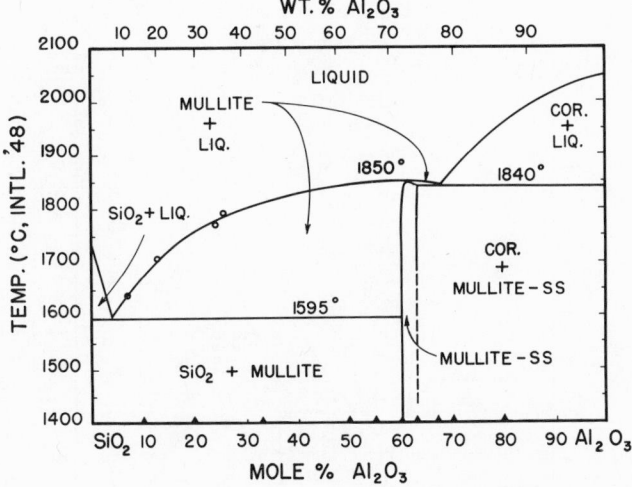

Figure 13-2. The system Al_2O_3–SiO_2; from [4], showing congruent melting of Mullite

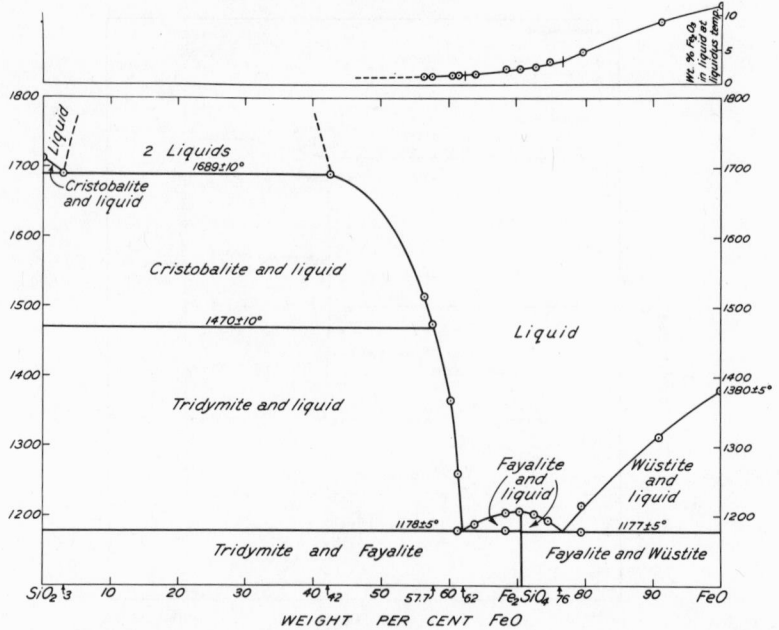

Figure 13-3. The system FeO–SiO$_2$, from [11]. The system is binary only when small contents of Fe$_2$O$_3$ in the liquids are disregarded

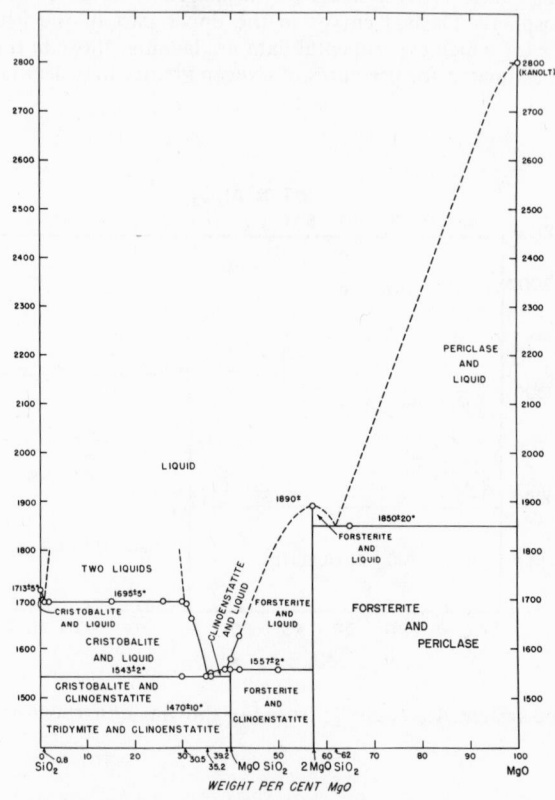

Figure 13-4. The system MgO–SiO$_2$; composite diagram based on [9, 36]

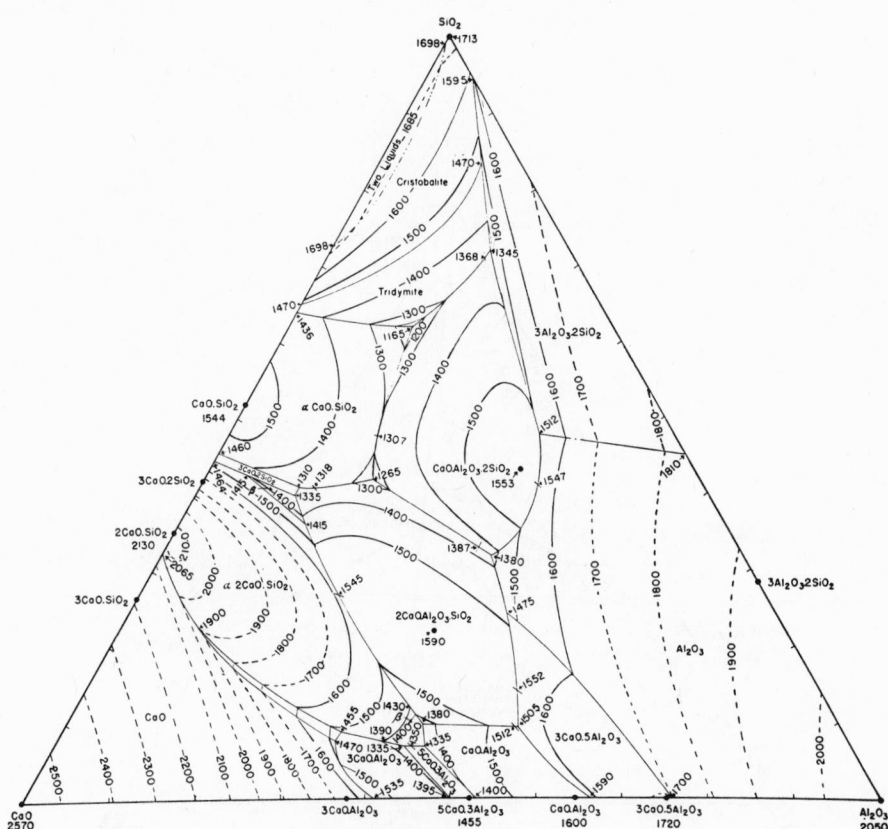

Figure 13-5. The system Al₂O₃–CaO–SiO₂; composite diagram based on [58] and [36]. Goldsmith [34] suggested the compound designated 3CaO·5Al₂O₃ is most probably CaO·2Al₂O₃

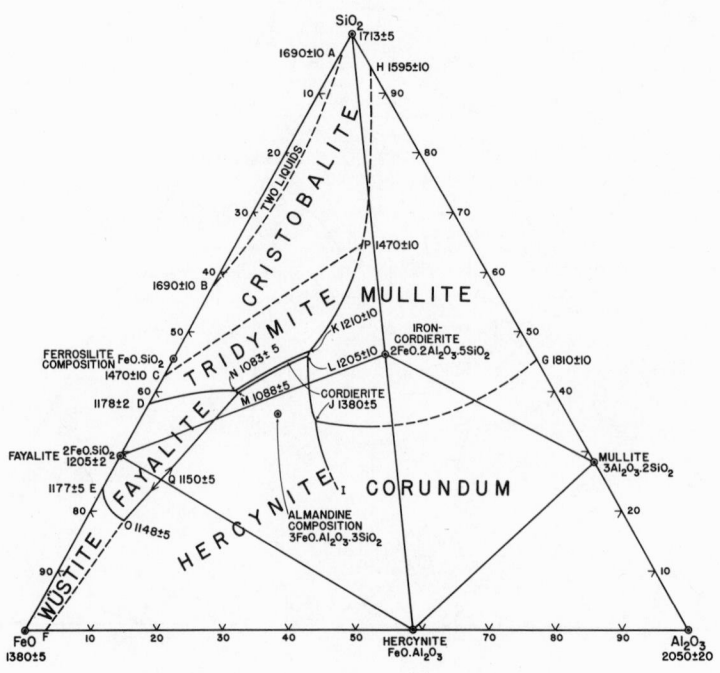

Figure 13-6. The system Al_2O_3–FeO–SiO_2; from [73]. The system is ternary only when small content of Fe_2O_3 in the liquids is disregarded

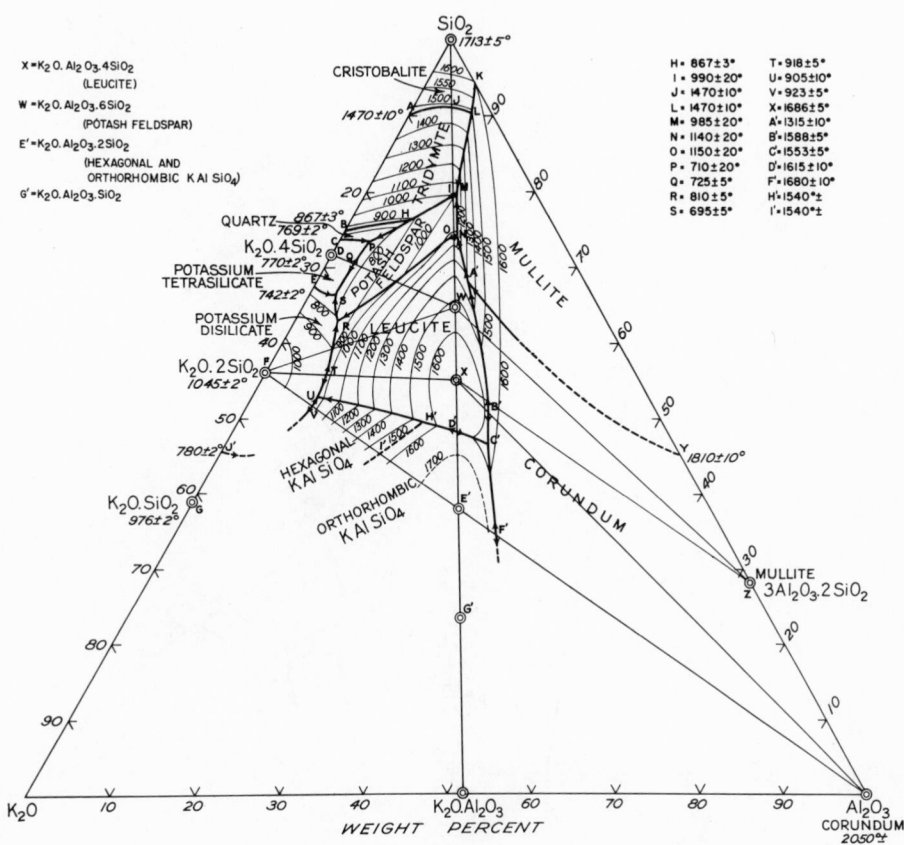

Figure 13-7. The system Al_2O_3–K_2O–SiO_2; from [71]

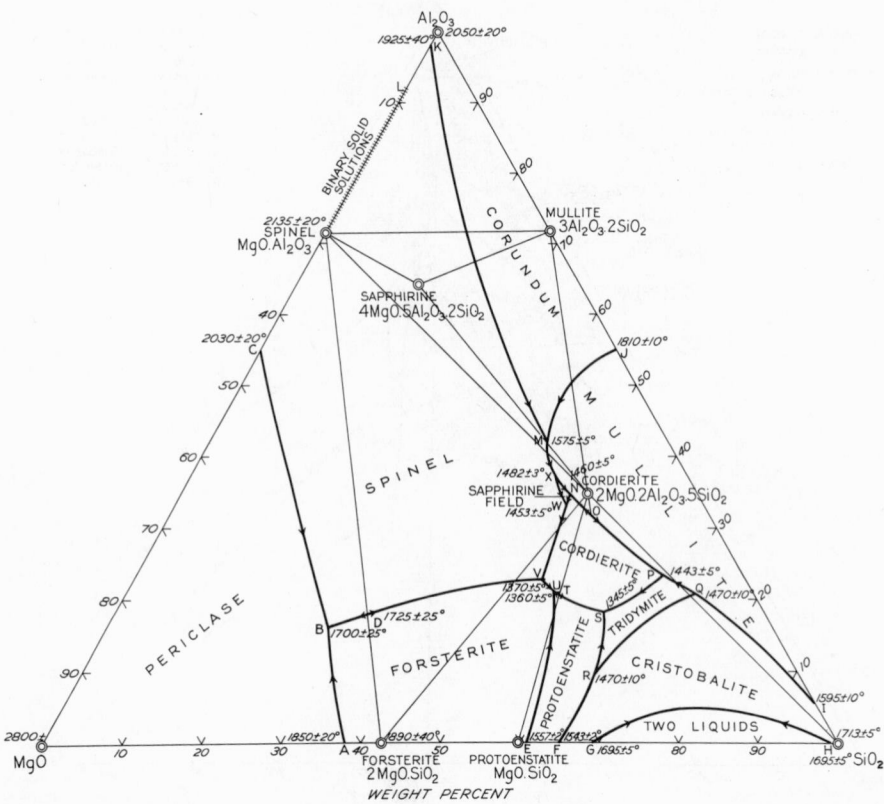

Figure 13-8. The system Al_2O_3–MgO–SiO_2. Composite diagram based on [**57, 10, 36, 65, 30, 47**]

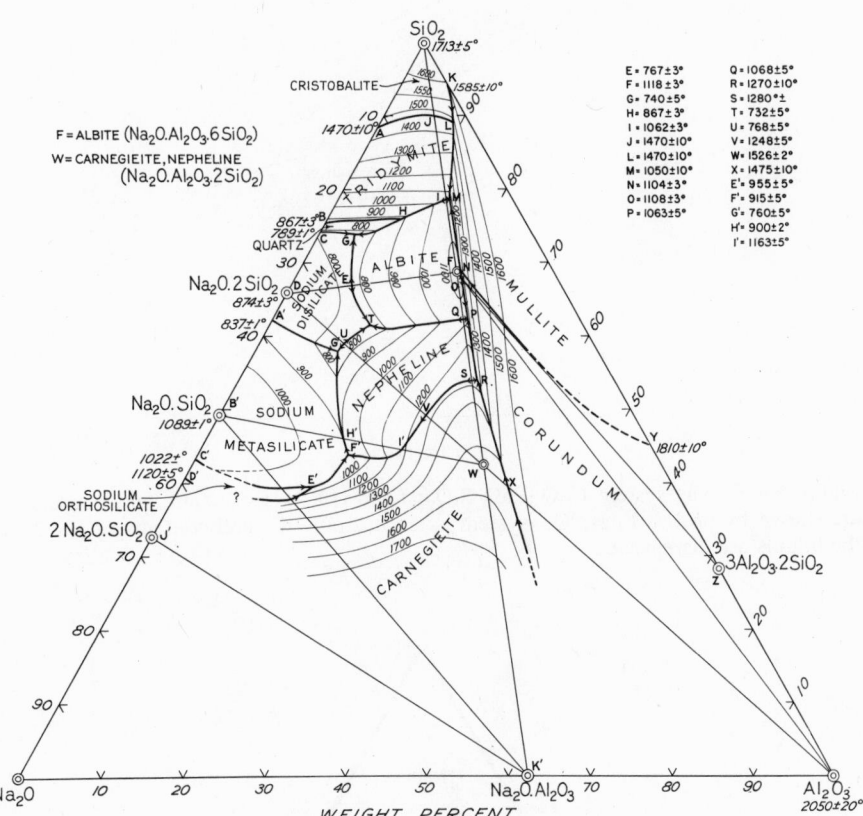

Figure 13-9. The system Al_2O_3–Na_2O–SiO_2; from [72]

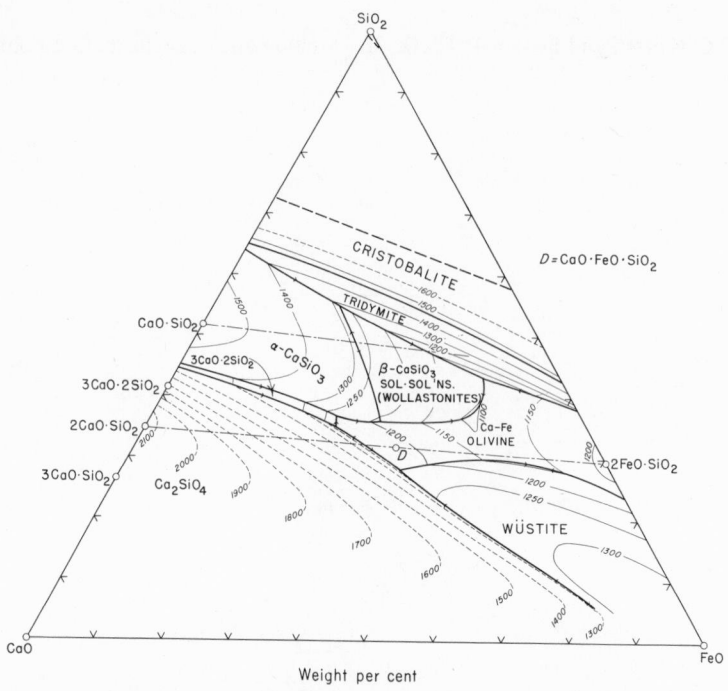

Figure 13-10. The system CaO–FeO–SiO$_2$; from [13, 2]. Estimated field boundaries are shown by broken lines. The system is ternary only if small contents of Fe$_2$O$_3$ in the liquids are disregarded

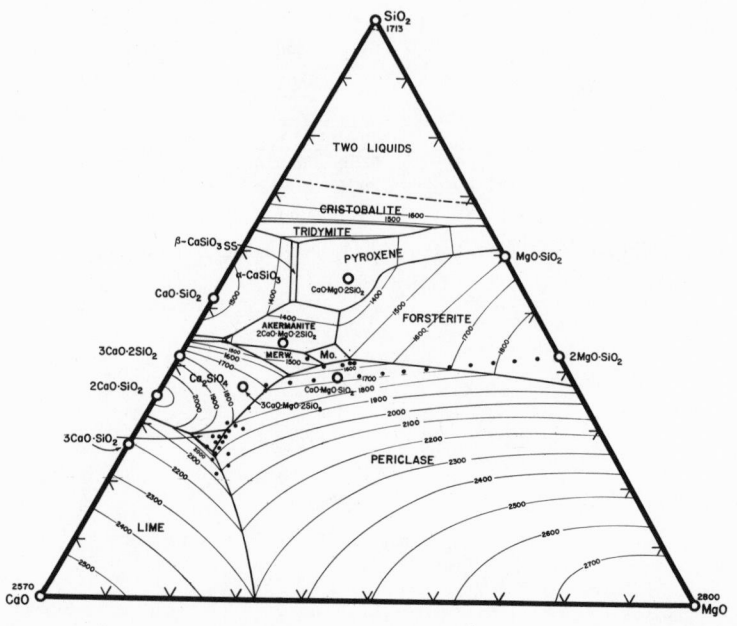

Figure 13-11. The system CaO–MgO–SiO$_2$, from [59]. Composite diagram after [29, 36, 7, 69, 53, 15]

314

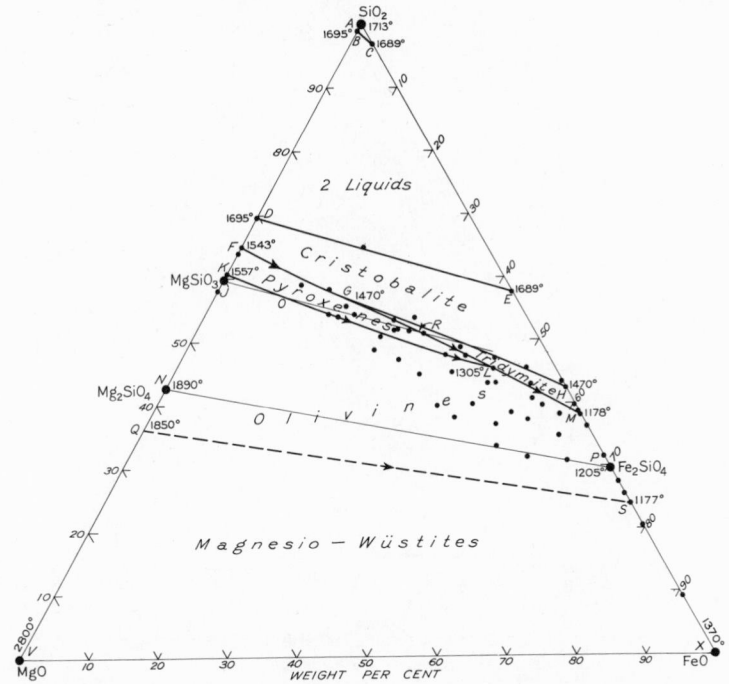

Figure 13-12. The system FeO–MgO–SiO$_2$; from **[12]**. The system is ternary only if small content of Fe$_2$O$_3$ in the liquids is disregarded

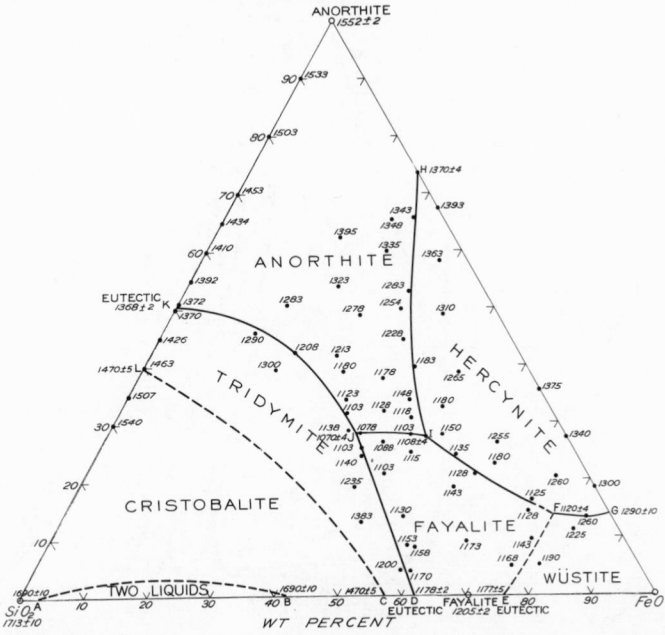

Figure 13-13. The system Al$_2$O$_3$–CaO–FeO–SiO$_2$; the join plane SiO$_2$–FeO–CaAl$_2$Si$_2$O$_8$, *Anorthite*; after **[65]**. The join is not ternary because of the intrusion of FeAl$_2$O$_4$, Hercynite

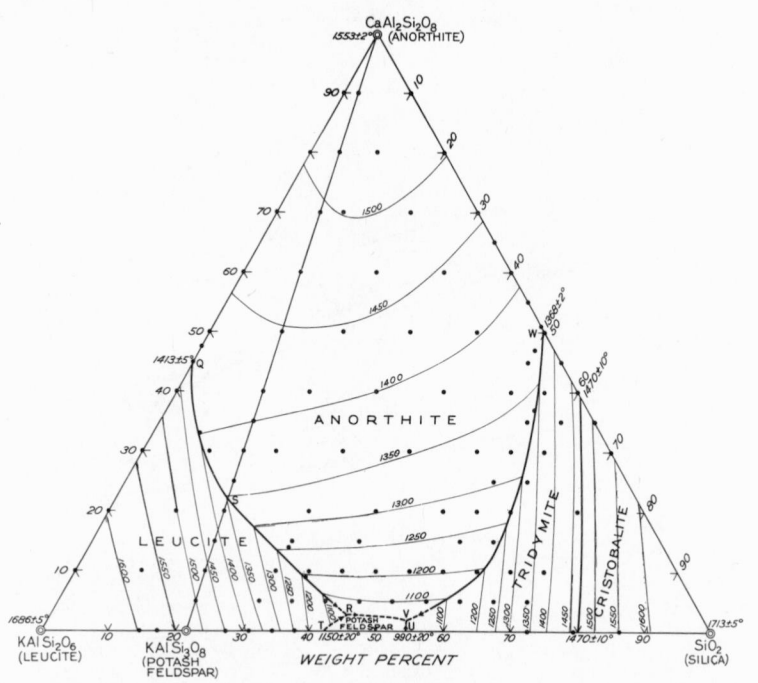

Figure 13-14. The system Al_2O_3–CaO–K_2O–SiO_2; the ternary section $KAlSi_2O_6$, *Leucite*–SiO_2–$CaAl_2Si_2O_8$, *Anorthite*; from [71]

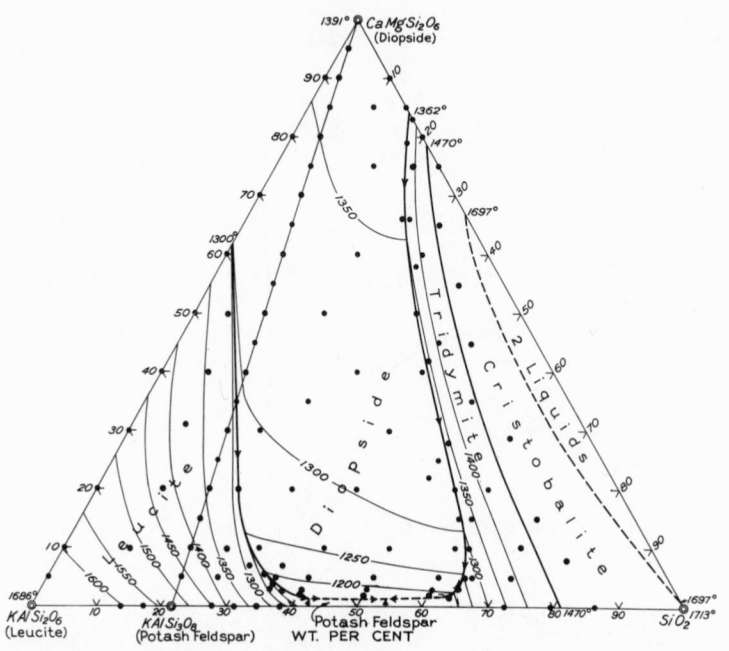

Figure 13-15. The system Al_2O_3–CaO–K_2O–MgO–SiO_2; the ternary section $KAlSi_2O_6$, *Leucite*–SiO_2–$CaMgSi_2O_6$, *Diopside*; from [68]

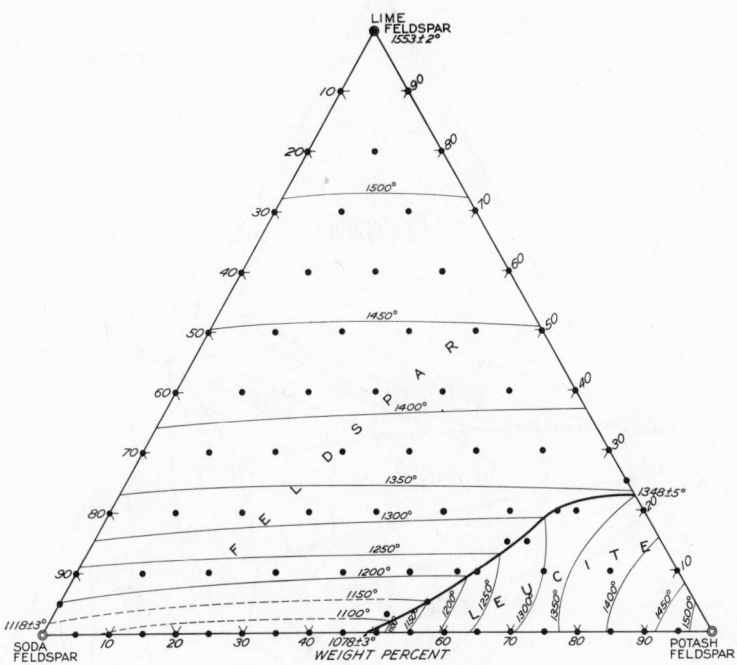

Figure 13-16. The system Al_2O_3–CaO–K_2O–Na_2O–SiO_2; the ternary section $NaAlSi_3O_8$, Na_2O *Feldspar*–$KAlSi_3O_8$, K_2O *Feldspar*–$CaAl_2Si_2O_8$, CaO *Feldspar*; from [32]

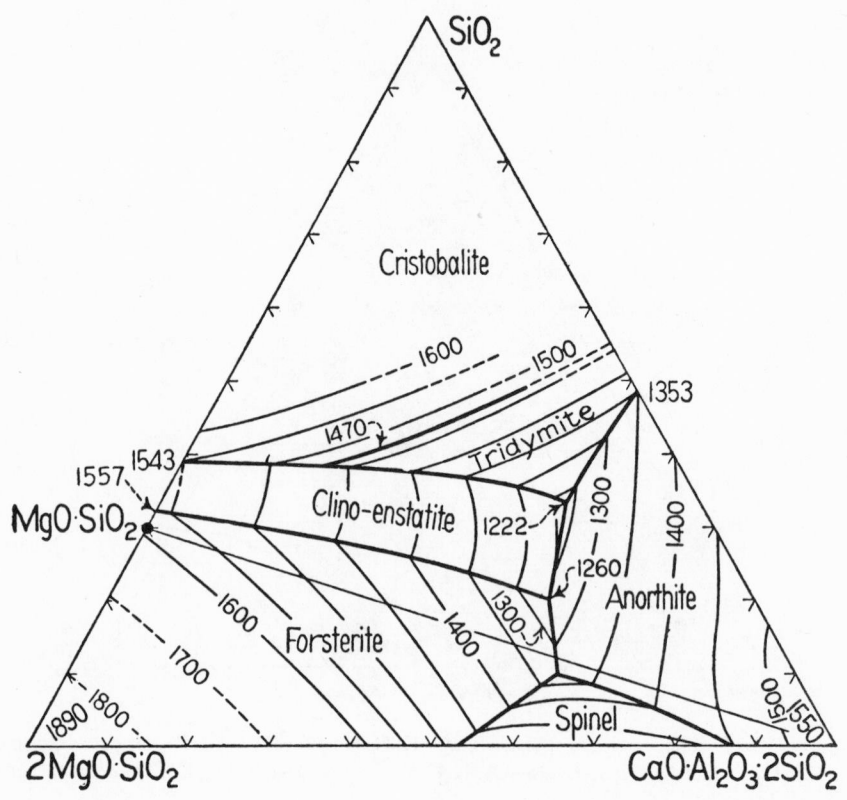

Figure 13-17. The system Al_2O_3–CaO–MgO–SiO_2, the join plane Mg_2SiO_4, *Forsterite*–$CaAl_2Si_2O_8$, *Anorthite*–SiO_2; after [3]. The join fails to be ternary because of the incursion of $MgAl_2O_4$, Spinel

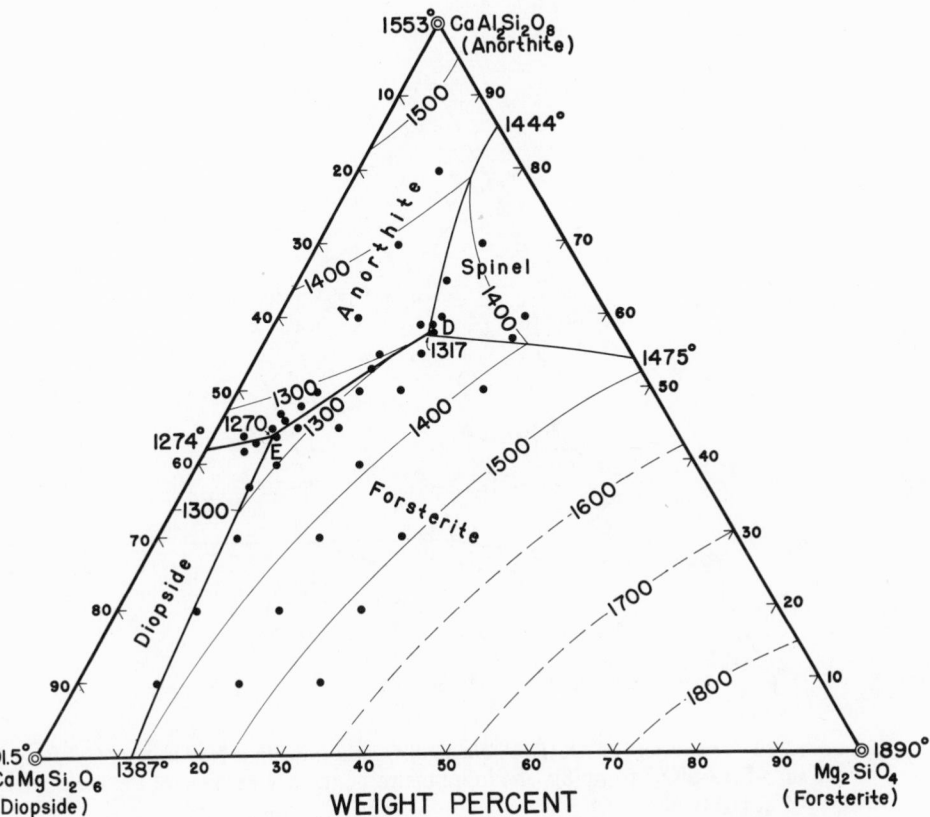

Figure 13-18. The system Al_2O_3–CaO–MgO–SiO_2; the join plane $CaMgSi_2O_6$, *Diopside*–Mg_2SiO_4, *Forsterite*–$CaAl_2Si_2O_8$, *Anorthite*; from [56]. The join fails to be ternary because of the incursion of $MgAl_2O_4$, Spinel

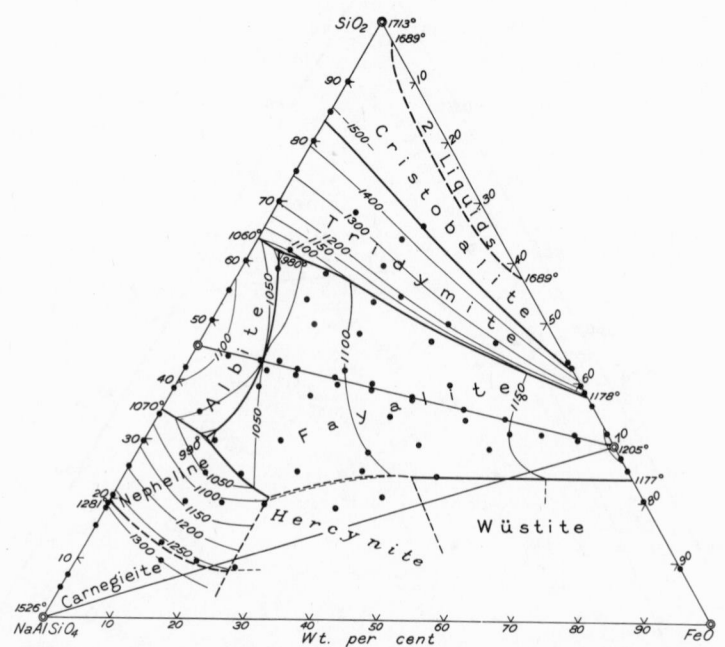

Figure 13-19. The system Al_2O_3–FeO–Na_2O–SiO_2; the join plane $NaAlSiO_4$, *Nepheline*, *Carnegieite*–FeO–SiO_2; from [8]. The join fails to be ternary because of the incursion of $FeAl_2O_4$, Hercynite

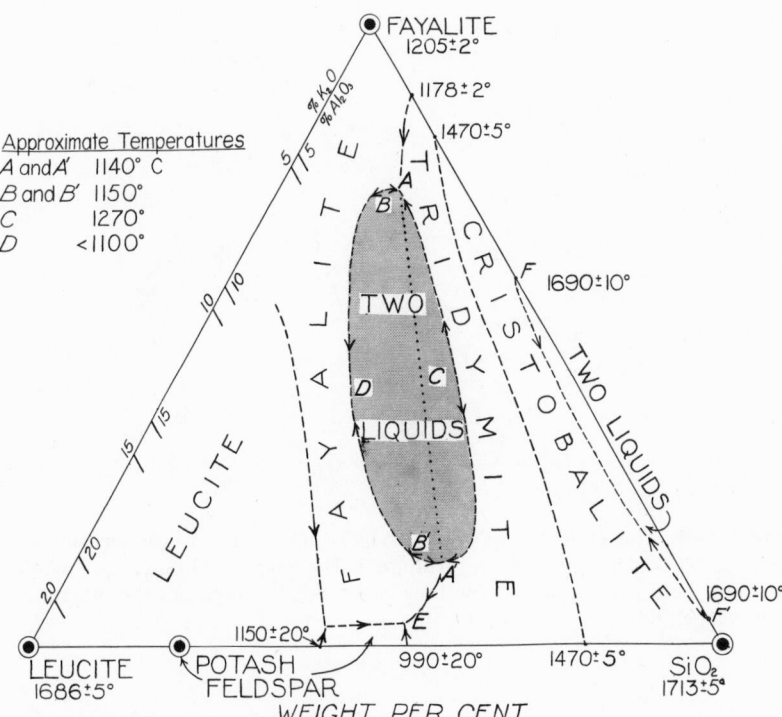

Figure 13-20. The system Al_2O_3–FeO–K_2O–SiO_2; the join plane $KAlSi_2O_6$. *Leucite*–SiO_2–Fe_2SiO_4, *Fayalite*; from [62]. The section is ternary only when small contents of Fe_2O_3 in the liquids are disregarded

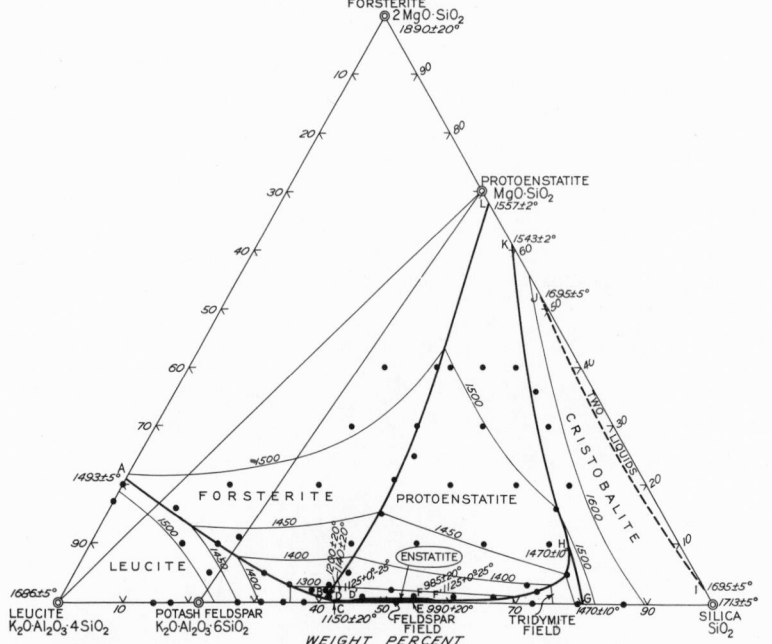

Figure 13-21. The system Al_2O_3–K_2O–MgO–SiO_2; the ternary section $KAlSi_2O_6$, *Leucite*-SiO_2-Mg_2SiO_4, *Forsterite*; from [67]. The fields of $MgSiO_3$, and of $KAlSi_3O_8$, Potassium Feldspar are so narrow they could not be shown in the diagram without some exaggeration

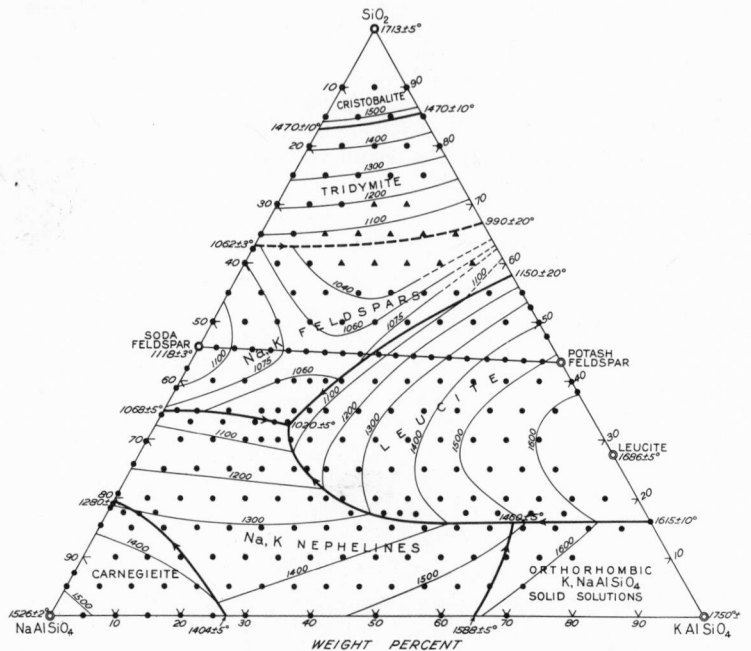

Figure 13-22. The system Al_2O_3–K_2O–Na_2O–SiO_2; the ternary section $NaAlSiO_4$, *Nepheline, Carnegieite*-$KAlSiO_4$, *Kalsilite, Kaliophilite*-SiO_2; from [66]

SECTION 14

PHASE RELATIONS IN SULFIDE-TYPE SYSTEMS

by G. KULLERUD

CONTENTS

BINARY SYSTEMS

Ag-S: Monotectic point at 906 $\pm$ 1° C, 1.8 per cent S; two-liquid region from this point to 11.85 per cent S. Ag_2S, the only compound, melts congruently at 838° C. Eutectic with Ag at 804 $\pm$ 2° C and 12.3 per cent S. A second two-liquid region exists above 740 $\pm$ 2° C from 14.35 to >99 per cent S. Eutectic with S at 119.3 $\pm$ .2° C. Ag_2S has three polymorphs: below 176.3 $\pm$ .5° C (with Ag) and below 177.8 $\pm$ .7° C (with S), it is monoclinic (acanthite). Above this temperature, but below 586 $\pm$ 3° C (with Ag) and below 622 $\pm$ 3° C (with S) it is cubic (argentite). The high-temperature polymorph has unknown structure [26].

Ag-Sb: Maximum solid solution of Sb in Ag is 8.0 per cent at 702.5° C, where a ζ phase with 9.8 per cent Sb melts incongruently to Ag_2Sb solid solution and liquid with 18.6 per cent Sb. The ζ phase is hexagonal and varies in composition from 9.8 to 18 per cent Sb. The ε phase (dyscrasite) with 20 per cent Sb melts incongruently at 558° C to ζ and liquid with 27.3 per cent Sb. It forms solid solutions with 20 to 29 per cent Sb; there are two polymorphs, both of which are orthorhombic. The inversion is at 440° C with ζ and at 449° C with Sb. Eutectic between ε and Sb is at 485° C and 44 per cent Sb [18].

Ag-Se: Monotectic point at about 9 per cent Se and 890° C. Liquid immiscibility from this composition to about 25.5 per cent Se. Eutectic at 840° C and about 26 per cent Se. The only compound, Ag_2Se (naumannite), melts congruently at 897° C, and inverts at 128 $\pm$ 5° C from a high-temperature cubic to a monoclinic or orthorhombic form. A second liquid immiscibility region exists between Ag_2Se and Se above 616° C. It extends from 37 to >95.5 per cent Se. Ag_2Se-Se eutectic is at 217° C and near Se composition [18].

Ag-Te: Eutectic at 870° C and 9.3 per cent Te; two liquids above 881 $\pm$ 3° C from 10.4 to 34.7 per cent Te. Ag_2Te, which melts congruently at 959° C, occurs in three polymorphs. With excess Te the transitions are at 689 $\pm$ 5° C and 105 $\pm$ 25° C, and with excess Ag at 802 $\pm$ 2° C and 145 $\pm$ 2° C. Hessite corresponds to the low-temperature polymorph. Ag_5Te_3, α and β empressite, melts incongruently with a peritectic at 460 $\pm$ 5° C to form Ag_2Te and a liquid with about 50 per cent Te. It has a α-β transition at 419 $\pm$ 5° C in Te-rich, and 417 $\pm$ 2° C in Ag-rich, preparations; a broad transition appears in the 250–310° C range in Ag-rich preparations. The structures of the polymorphs are unknown. Eutectic at 353 $\pm$ .5° C and 70.6 per cent Te [27]. The Ag-Te mineral stuetzite has unknown composition.

As-Co: Eutectic at 918° C and 31 per cent As; at this temperature 7 per cent As occurs in solid solution in Co [18]. Five compounds occur in this system: Co_2As, $CoAs$, $CoAs_2$, $CoAs_3$, and Co_3As_2, which is stable above 940° C. Co_2As inverts at 400–500° C and melts at 958° C. Co_3As_2 melts at ~1100° C. CoAs is orthorhombic below 952 $\pm$ 8° C and hexagonal above; it melts at about 1180° C. $CoAs_2$ (safflorite) appears orthorhombic but is possibly monoclinic; its melting relationships are unknown. $CoAs_3$ (skutterudite) is cubic; its melting relations are unknown [19, 47].

As-Cu: Compounds are $Cu_{5-x}As_2$ (x ranges from 0 to .1), which may be tetragonal [21]; Cu_3As (β domeykite), which is trigonal, and forms a solid solution containing from 28.2–30.40 per cent As at 560° C; and a hexagonal ε-type compound of Cu_8As composition (algodonite or γ domeykite) stable below about 340° C. Under pressures in excess of about 200 bars a cubic compound of probable $Cu_{15}As_4$ (α domeykite) composition becomes stable below about 225° C. A tentative phase diagram showing the phase relations under sufficient pressure to stabilize $Cu_{15}As_4$ is given in Figure 14-1.

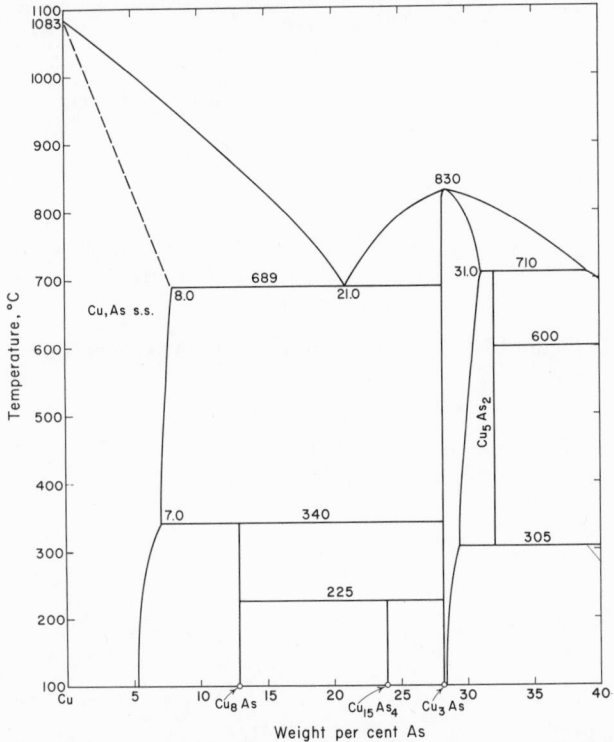

Figure 14-1. Tentative phase diagram of the Cu-As system drawn from data by Hansen and Anderko [18] and Heyding and Despault [21]

As-Fe: Compounds in the system are Fe_2As, which is tetragonal; FeAs, which is orthorhombic; $FeAs_2$ (loellingite), which is orthorhombic; and a questionable ε phase (*See* Figure 14-2) of unknown symmetry. $FeAs_2$ melts congruently at 1016 ± 8° C; the $FeAs_2$-As eutectic is at 800 ± 10° C and about 5 per cent Fe [18, 19, 11].

As-Ni: Compounds in the system are $Ni_{5-x}As_2$ (x ranges from 0 to .38, 33.8–35.6 per cent As), which is hexagonal; $Ni_{11}As_8$ (maucherite), which is tetragonal; $Ni_{1\pm x}As$ (niccolite) ($1 \pm x$ ranges from 1.028 to .963 at 800° C), which is hexagonal; and $NiAs_2$, which has two orthorhombic polymorphs, rammelsbergite and pararammelsbergite [18, 55]. The phase relations of the system are shown in Figure 14-3.

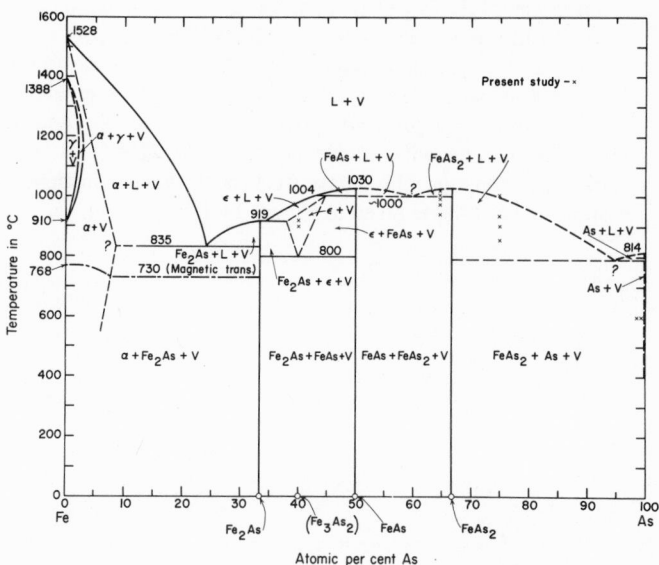

Figure 14-2. Phase relations in the Fe-As system **[11]**

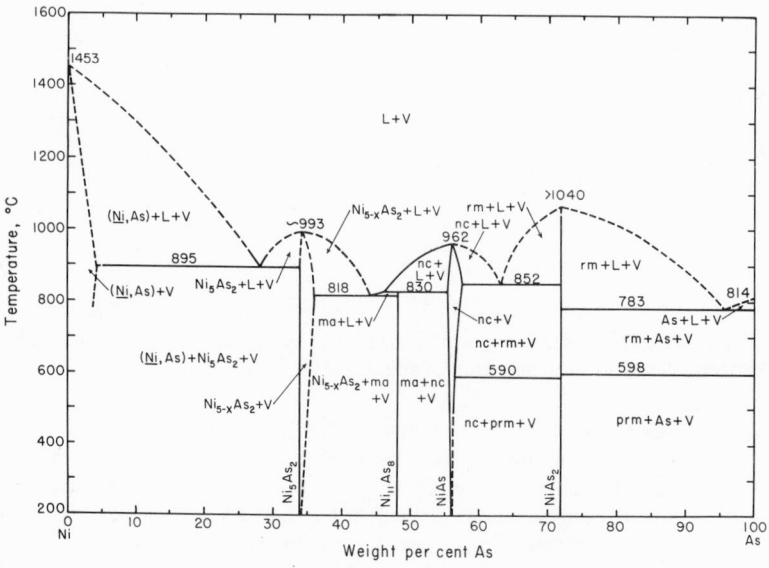

Figure 14-3. *T-X* diagram of the "condensed" system Ni-As (*after* Yund, **55**). Dashed lines represent work predating Yund's **[55]** or relationships which were not accurately determined

As-Pt: Eutectic 13 per cent As, 597° C. Compounds are $PtAs_2$ (sperrylite),
          which is cubic, and possibly Pt_2As_3.

As-S: AsS (realgar) is monoclinic and melts congruently at 310° C; As_2S_3
          (orpiment) is also monoclinic and melts congruently at 321° C [18, 11].
          (*See* Figure 14-4.)

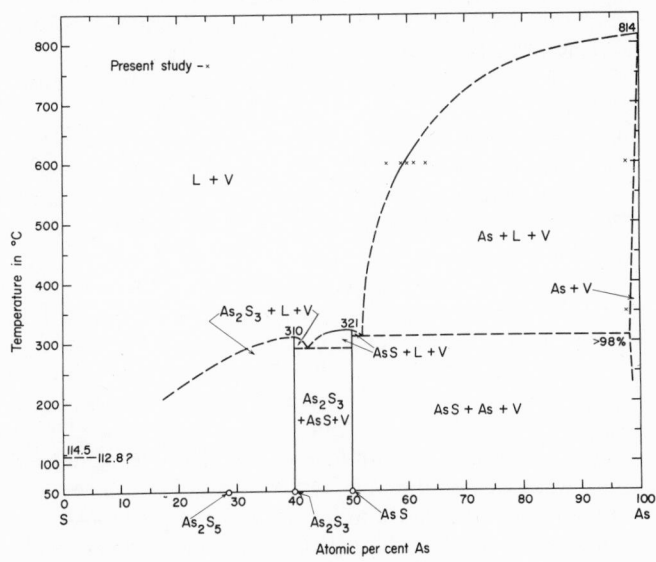

Figure 14-4. Phase relations in the system As-S [11]

Au-Bi: Eutectic 82 per cent Bi, 241° C. Au_2Bi (maldonite), which is cubic, is the
          only compound; it melts incongruently at 373° C to Au + liquid with
          about 65 per cent Bi [18].

Au-Sb: Eutectic 25 per cent Sb, 360° C, at which temperature .40 per cent Sb
          occurs in Au solid solution. The only compound is $AuSb_2$ (aurostibite),
          which has pyrite structure and which melts at 400° C.

Au-Te: Eutectic between Au and $AuTe_2$ at ~42 per cent Te, 447° C. $AuTe_2$ is
          the only compound; it melts at 464° C. Eutectic between $AuTe_2$ and
          Te at 82.5 per cent Te, 416° C. $AuTe_2$ exists in a low-temperature
          orthorhombic form and a high-temperature monoclinic form with an
          inversion about 180° C. Mineral equivalents are krennerite (ortho-
          rhombic) and calaverite (monoclinic) [18].

Bi-S: Bi_2S_3 (bismuthinite) is the only compound. It is orthorhombic and melts
          congruently at 760 ± 5° C. A wide two-liquid region exists above
          715° C in the Bi_2S_3-S part of the system containing more than 22.1 per
          cent S (and extends to more than 98 per cent S) [18, 11].

Bi-Se: The compounds are Bi_2S_3 (guanjuatite), BiSe, and possibly Bi_3Se_4.
          Bi_2Se_3 is rhombohedral; it melts congruently at 706° C. BiSe is cubic;
          it melts incongruently at 605° C. Eutectic exists between Bi and BiSe at
          268° C and almost pure Bi. Liquid immiscibility exists between Bi_2Se_3
          and Se from about 50 to beyond 95 per cent Se [18].

Bi-Te: Bi_2Te_3 (tetradymite) is the only compound. It forms solid solutions on both sides of Bi_2Te_3 composition, from about 40 to 53 per cent Te at 400° C. Eutectic between Bi and Bi_2Te_3 at 266° C and 1.5 per cent Te, and between Bi_2Te_3 and Te at 413° C and 85 per cent Te [18]. The existence of three additional phases is indicated. $Bi_{14}Te_6$ (hedleyite) is orthorhombic; it forms peritectically at 312° C. A Bi_2Te phase (solid solution from 22.5 to 26 per cent Te) forms peritectically at 420° C, and a solid solution series of composition from 34 to 42.5 per cent Te is formed by peritectic reaction at 540° C [1].

Ca-S: CaS (oldhamite) with the NaCl structure is the only known compound [18].

Cd-S: CdS is the only known compound. It occurs in two crystallographic modifications: a low-temperature hexagonal form (greenockite) and a high-temperature cubic form (hawleyite). Inversion takes place at 700–800° C. CdS sublimes; it melts at about 1750° C under $\sim$100 bars pressure.

Co-S: Eutectic at 877° C and 26.6 per cent S. $Co_{4\pm x}S_3$ [48] is unquenchable and of unknown structure; it is stable between 780 and 930° C, where it melts incongruently. Co_9S_8 is cubic, and breaks down at 835° C; $Co_{1-x}S$ [48] is stable between 460° C and its melting point, 1182° C; it is hexagonal and always Co-deficient. Co_3O_4 (linneite) is cubic and breaks down at $660 \pm 3°$ C [35]. CoS_2 (cathierite) is cubic [25]; incongruent melting indicated at about 950° C [48]. The alleged mineral jaipurite, with CoS composition, is rather questionable since $Co_{1-x}S$ solid solution does not extend to the stoichiometric ratio [48].

Co-Se: Two-liquid region above 1448° C from 4.5 to 37.5 per cent Se. Eutectic between Co and CoSe at 900° C, 47.5 per cent Se. CoSe has hexagonal (NiAs-type) structure, melts congruently at 1055° C. $CoSe_2$ is also reported as a compound with pyrite structure [18]. Minerals in the system are bornhardite, which has Co_3Se_4 composition and cubic linneite-type structure; trogtalite, which has $CoSe_2$ composition and cubic pyrite-type structure; and hastite, which has $CoSe_2$ composition and orthorhombic marcasite-type structure [46].

Cu-S: Eutectic 1067° C, 0.77 per cent S. Two liquids above 1105° between 1.5 and 19.8 per cent S. Cu_2S (chalcocite) does not at any temperature form measurable solid solution on Cu side of stoichiometric composition but at elevated temperatures forms complete solid solution with Cu_9S_5 (digenite). Highest melting point of the solid solution is at 1129° C and a composition of 20.23 per cent S [23]. Cu_2S occurs in three crystallographic modifications: below 100.3° C it is orthorhombic, between this temperature and 440° C it is hexagonal, and above 440° C it is cubic. Cu_9S_5 is cubic above 70° C; below that temperature it is rhombohedral. CuS is hexagonal; it melts incongruently at 507° C [29]. A fourth compound, $Cu_{1.96}S$ (djurleite) [44], is of low symmetry below 100° C and tetragonal at higher temperature [15]. Recent D.T.A. work [35] indicates that the inversion is at $86 \pm 2°$ C and that $Cu_{1.96}S$ breaks down at $154 \pm 2°$ C.

Cu-Se: Shows similarity to Cu-S system. Eutectic 1063°, 2.2 per cent Se, with two liquids above 1107° between 5 and 37 per cent Se. Cu_2Se (berzelianite), which melts congruently at about 1112° C, is cubic at elevated temperatures and has a deformed cubic structure below 110° C; Cu_3Se_2 (umangite), which is orthorhombic, is only stable below 170° C. CuSe (klockmannite), which is hexagonal, melts incongruently at about 700° C. A fourth compound, $Cu_{1.96}$ Se, which is tetragonal, is indicated to exist below 103° C [18].

Fe-S: In addition to compounds Fe_{1-x} S (troilite, pyrrhotite) and FeS_2 shown in Figure 14-5, a third compound, Fe_3S_4 (smythite), is probably stable

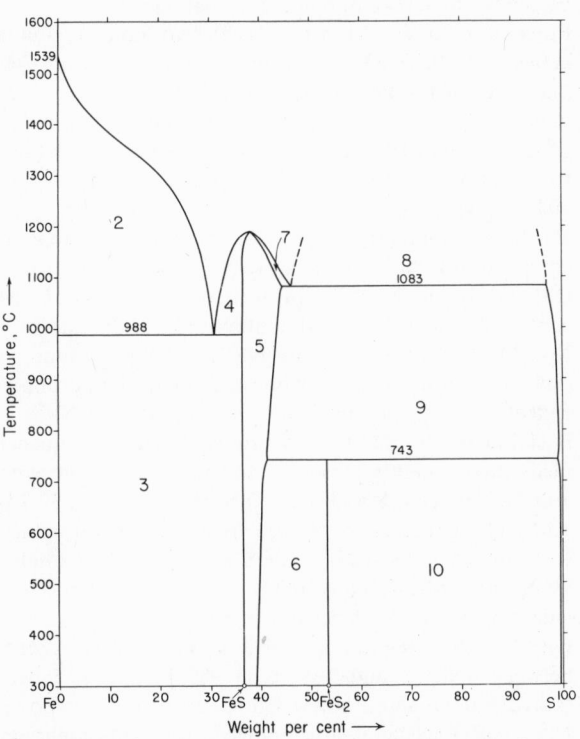

Figure 14-5. The Fe-S system (Hansen and Anderko; Kullerud and Yoder; Kullerud; Arnold) [18, 36, 32, and 3]

at low temperature ($< 70°$ C). FeS_2, which has a "low-temperature" orthorhombic (marcasite) form, and a high-temperature cubic form (pyrite), melts incongruently at 743° C. A wide field of liquid immiscibility exists above 1083° C [18, 36, 32, 3].

Fe-Se: Eutectic 940° C, 5.5 at. per cent Se. A two-liquid region exists between Fe and FeSe above 960° C and between 6.5 and 46.0 at. per cent S. A second two-liquid region exists above 790° C between 71.5 and >98 at. per cent Se. Three compounds are known in the system: $Fe_{1-x}Se$, Fe_3Se_4, and $FeSe_2$. $Fe_{1-x}Se$ occurs in three polymorphs: stoichiometric FeSe is tetragonal below 353° C, hexagonal between 335° and 870° C, and has a different but as yet unknown structure from 870° to its melting point. The melting relationships of $Fe_{1-x}Se$ mix-crystals are very similar to those of $Fe_{1-x}S$. The maximum melting point is at 1065° C and 52.5 at. per cent Se. Fe_3Se_4 is monoclinic at low temperature but becomes hexagonal below 600° C. It apparently melts incongruently at 725° C. $FeSe_2$ (ferroselite) is orthorhombic and melts incongruently at 588° C [52].

Hg-S: Phase relations are unknown in this system, which only contains the compound HgS. A (red) hexagonal (cinnabar) polymorph is stable below 344° C; above this temperature a cubic form (metacinnabar) becomes stable [14]. Sublimates, 1 bar 446° C.

Mn-S: Eutectic 1230° C, .14 per cent S; two-liquid region above 1580° C between 0.3 and 33.2 per cent S. Compounds are MnS and MnS_2 (hauerite). MnS melts congruently at 1610° C; it exists in three polymorphs: green cubic (alabandite), red cubic, and red hexagonal [18]. MnS_2 is cubic (Pa3 type); it decomposes on heating to MnS + S. Invariant point (MnS + MnS + L + V) is situated at or slightly below 404° C [34].

Mo-S: The known compounds are MoS_2 and Mo_2S_3 (or approximately Mo_2S_3 composition). MoS_2 exists in two polymorphs, hexagonal (molybdenite) [13] and rhombohedral [6]; it melts at about 1350° C. Mo_2S_3 is monoclinic [22] and is only stable above 610° C (invariant point at which Mo, Mo_2S_3, and V are stable [45]); its melting point is unknown. The "mineral" jordisite is probably equivalent to amorphous MoS_2.

Ni-S: Eutectic 635° C, 21.5 per cent S. Rhombohedral Ni_3S_2 (heazlewoodite) is stable below 556° C. It is stoichiometric. Unquenchable $Ni_{3\pm x}S_2$ melts incongruently at 806° C and forms eutectoid with Ni at 533° C and 24.2 per cent S and with Ni_7S_6 at 524° C and 30.7 per cent S. The Ni_7S_6 phase occurs in two polymorphs, with inversion at 400°C. It decomposes to $Ni_{3-x}S_2 + \alpha NiS$ at 573° C. NiS (millerite) inverts to αNiS with NiAs structure at 379° C. This inversion is lowered to 282° C when maximum Ni deficiency in $\alpha Ni_{1-x}S$ exists. Maximum melting in the $\alpha Ni_{1-x}S$ series occurs at 992° C and 38.2 per cent S. The eutectic between $\alpha Ni_{1-x}S$ and NiS_2 is at 985° C and 40.5 per cent S. Ni_3S_4 (polydymite) is stable below 356° C, where it decomposes to $\alpha Ni_{1-x}S + NiS_2$. NiS_2 (vaesite) is stoichiometric and melts congruently at 1007° C. A two-liquid region exists between NiS_2 and S above 991° C from 54.5 to >97.6 per cent S [38] (*See* Figure 14-6).

Pb-S: The only compound, PbS (galena), is cubic; it melts congruently at 1127° C [18, 7].

Pb-Se: PbSe (clausthalite) is the only compound. It is cubic and melts congruently at 1076° C [18]. One two-liquid region exists above 860° C from 3 to 9 per cent Se, and another above 681° C from 55 to 97 per cent Se [18].

Pb-Te: Eutectic 326.7° C and .025 per cent Te. PbTe (altaite) is the only compound; it is cubic and melts congruently at 924° C [41]. A second eutectic exists between PbTe and Te at 405° C and 78.5 per cent Te [18].

Pt-S: Two compounds are known: PtS (cooperite), which is tetragonal, and PtS_2, which is hexagonal [18].

S-Sb: Two-liquid region exists above 615° C from 1.5 to 25 per cent S. Eutectic between Sb and Sb_2S_3 is at 520° C and 26 per cent S. Sb_2S_3

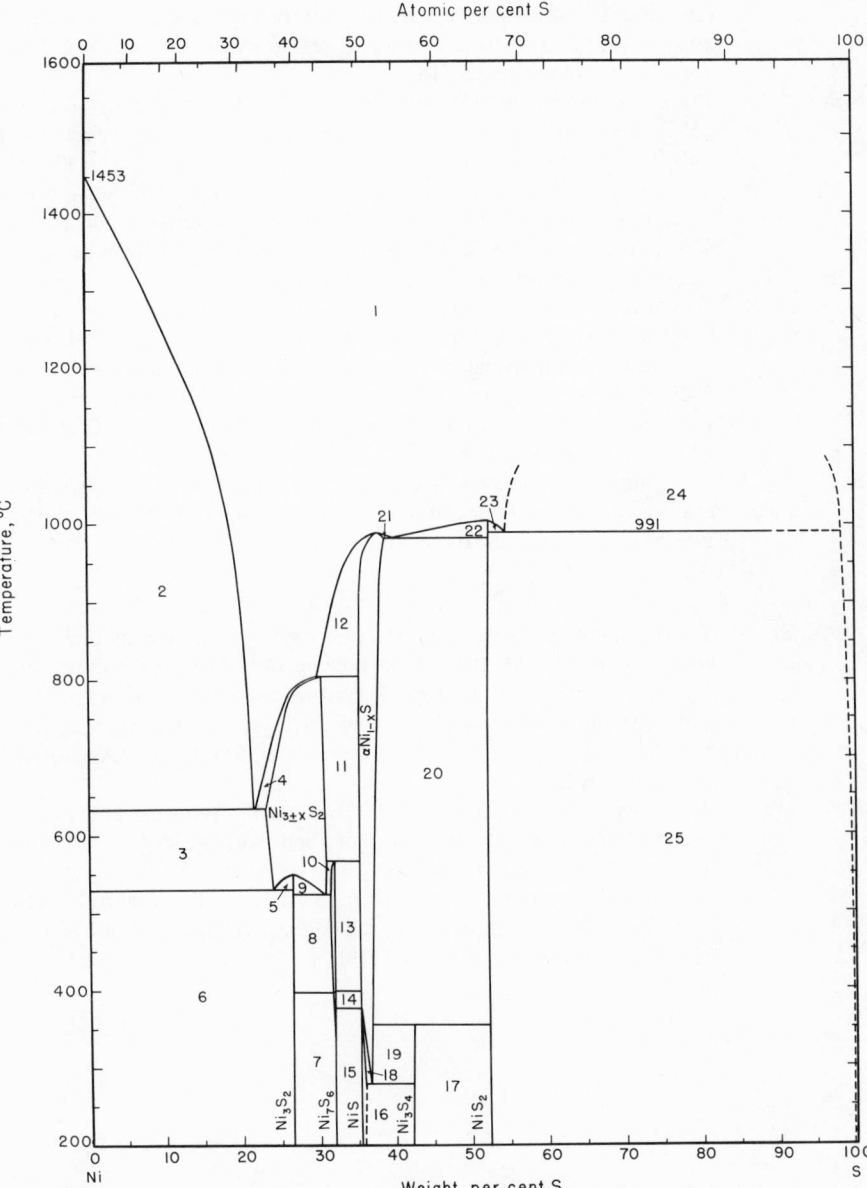

Figure 14-6. The "condensed" diagram of the system Ni-S above 200° C. Vapor is present in all assemblages, and the pressure of the system is not constant. Phases present in addition to vapor in the numbered fields are as follows: 1, L; 2, L + Ni s.s.; 3, Ni s.s. + $Ni_{3+x}S_2$; 4, L + $Ni_{3\pm x}S_2$; 5, Ni_3S_2 + $Ni_{3+x}S_2$; 6, Ni s.s. + Ni_3S_2; 7, Ni_3S_2 + βNi_7S_6; 8, Ni_3S_2 + αNi_7S_6; 9, Ni_3S_2 + $Ni_{3-x}S_2$; 10, $Ni_{3-x}S_2$ + Ni_7S_6; 11, $Ni_{3-x}S_2$ + αNiS; 12, L + $\alpha Ni_{1-x}S$; 13, αNi_7S_6 + αNiS; 14, βNi_7S_6 + αNiS; 15, βNi_7S_6 + βNiS; 16, $\beta Ni_{1-x}S$ + Ni_3S_4; 17, Ni_3S_4 + NiS_2; 18, α + $\beta Ni_{1-x}S$; 19, $\alpha Ni_{1-x}S$ + Ni_3S_4; 20, $\alpha Ni_{1-x}S$ + NiS_2; 21, $\alpha Ni_{1-x}S$ + L; 22, L + NiS_2; 23, NiS_2 + L; 24, two liquids; 25, NiS_2 + L [38]

(stibnite) is the only compound. It is orthorhombic and melts congruently at 546° C. A second two-liquid region exists above 530° C from about 31 to 97 per cent S [18].

S-Sn: Eutectic very near Sn composition at 232° C; two-liquid region above 858° C between 2.23 and 19.8 per cent S. Four compounds are reported: SnS (herzenbergite) is orthorhombic and melts congruently at 881° C; Sn_3S_4 and Sn_2S_3 are stable somewhere below 700° C; and SnS_2, which is hexagonal, is stable below 870° C. Eutectic between SnS and SnS_2 at 470° C and about 24.8 per cent S. A second two-liquid field exists above 860° C from about 39 to 71 per cent S [2].

S-Zn: ZnS is only known compound. It is trimorphic. A cubic modification (sphalerite) is stable below about 600° C. A rhombohedral form, which is almost indistinguishable from cubic ZnS, is stable between 600 and 1020° C [8]. A hexagonal form (wurtzite) with several polytypes [17] is stable above 1020° C. ZnS sublimates considerably at 1170° C and has no distinct melting point.

Se-Zn: Only one compound ZnSe is known in this system. It exists in two polymorphs: cubic low-temperature (stilleite) and hexagonal high-temperature analogous to ZnS. Its melting temperature lies above 1100° C.

TERNARY SYSTEMS

Ag-As-S: Ternary compounds are Ag_3AsS_3 and $AgAsS_2$. Ag_3AsS_3 is dimorphic with hexagonal and monoclinic polymorphs (proustite and xanthoconite). It melts at 490° C. $AgAsS_2$ exists in two monoclinic polymorphs (smithite and arsenomiargyrite) and melts at 420° C. Ag_3AsS_3-Ag_2S eutectic is at 470° C; Ag_3AsS_2 eutectic is at 400° C. The Ag_2S-As_2S_3 join is binary [58].

Ag-Au-Te: A ternary eutectic occurs at 330° C where the solid phases $Ag_{5-x}Te_3$ and $AgAuTe_4$ coexist with a liquid of about $Au_4Ag_{35}Te_{61}$ composition. The ternary compounds $AuAgTe_4$ (sylvanite) and $AuAg_3Te_2$ (petzite) both melt incongruently, the former to $AuTe_2$ + liquid and the latter to an AuAg alloy + liquid. Subsolidus phase relations in the system at 300° C are shown in Figure 14-7 [39].

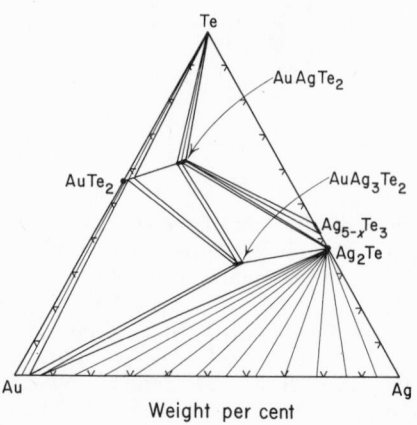

Figure 14-7. Phase relations in the ternary system Ag-Au-Te at 300° C [39]

Ag-Cu-S: At elevated temperatures a two-liquid region extends across from the Ag-Ag₂S to the Cu-Cu₂S boundaries. The Ag_2S-Cu_2S join is binary. Minimum at 675° C and 33 at. per cent Cu_2S. Extensive mix-crystal formation. The compound $(Ag, Cu)_2S$ (stromeyerite) is stable at low temperatures (<250° C) [50, 16].

Ag-Fe-S: The Ag_2S-FeS join is binary with eutectic at 610° C and 11 per cent FeS. The compound $AgFeS_2$ is tetragonal with chalcopyrite-type structure. The mineral sternbergite is the mineral equivalent of a compound of $AgFe_2S_3$ composition [58].

Ag-Pb-S: The Ag_2S-PbS join is binary with eutectic at 630° C and 23 per cent PbS [58].

Ag-S-Sb: The Ag_2S-Sb_2S_3 join is binary [24]. The compounds on the join are: Ag_3SbS_3, which occurs in hexagonal and monoclinic polymorphs (pyrargyrite and pyrostilpnite), which melt at 485° C; and $AbSbS_2$ (miargyrite), which melts at 510° C. Ag_3SbS_3 forms eutectics with Ag_2S at 465° C and with $AgSbS_2$ at 455° C. $AgSbS_2$ forms a eutectic with Sb_2S_3 at 450° C [58].

Ag-S-Zn: The Ag_2S-ZnS join is binary. Eutectic at 810° C and 4 per cent ZnS [58].

As-Co-Fe: The As-rich part is given in Figure 14-8, which shows considerable solid solution of Fe in $CoAs_3$ and nearly complete solid solution between $FeAs_2$ and $CoAs_2$ at 800° C [47].

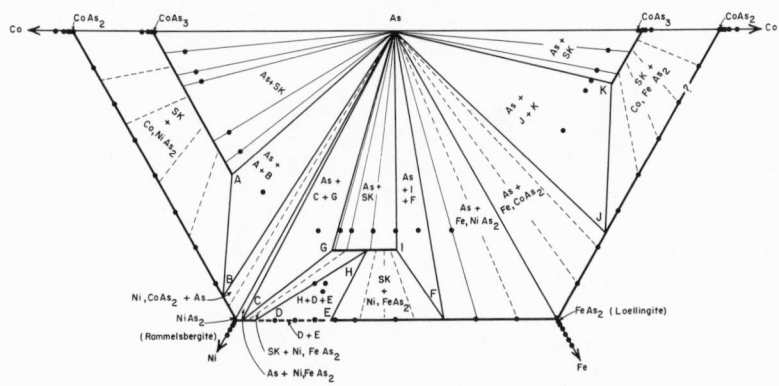

Figure 14-8. Relationships between the solid phases in the systems $CoAs_2$-$NiAs_2$-As, $NiAs_2$-$FeAs_2$-As, and $FeAs_2$-$CoAs_2$-As at 800° C and in the presence of a vapor phase. A, 65 per cent $NiAs_3$ 35 per cent $CoAs_3$; B, 92 per cent $NiAs_2$ 8 per cent $CoAs_2$; C, 98 per cent $NiAs_2$ 2 per cent $FeAs_2$; D, 94 per cent $NiAs_2$ 6 per cent $FeAs_2$; E, 70 per cent $NiAs_2$ 30 per cent $FeAs_2$; F, 35 per cent $NiAs_2$ 65 per cent $FeAs_2$; G, 76 per cent $NiAs_3$ 24 per cent $FeAs_3$; H, 61.5 per cent $NiAs_3$ 38.5 per cent $FeAs_3$; I, 49.5 per cent $NiAs_3$ 50.5 per cent $FeAs_3$; J, 70 per cent $FeAs_2$ 30 per cent $CoAs_2$; K, 24 per cent $FeAs_3$ 76 per cent $CoAs_3$; all values to ±1 per cent; Sk, skutterudite, $(Co, Ni, Fe)As_{3-x}$ [47]

As-Co-Ni: The As-rich part is given in Figure 14-8, which shows extensive solid solution of Ni in $CoAs_3$ and in $CoAs_2$ [47].

As-Fe-Ni: The As-rich part is given in Figure 14-8, which shows the existence of a ternary $(Fe, Ni)As_3$ phase, extensive solid solution of Ni in $FeAs_2$, and much less solid solution of Fe in $NiAs_2$ [47]. More recently an additional ternary phase $(Fe, Ni)_2As$ (oregonite) has been synthesized at 800° C [9].

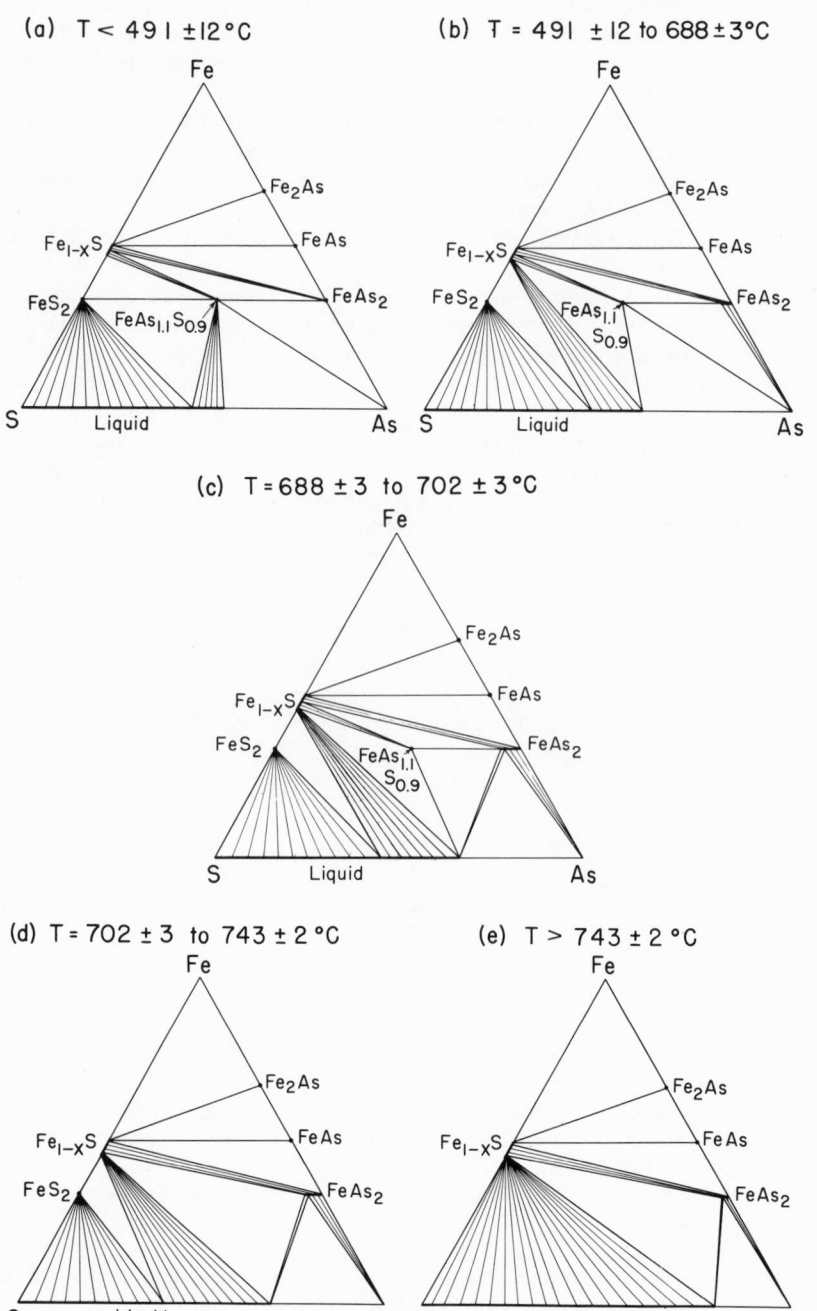

Figure 14-9. Phase diagrams of the Fe-As-S system depicting the assemblages stable with vapor at various temperatures [10]

As-Fe-S: The only ternary compound (arsenopyrite) has, above 600° C, the
           approximate composition $FeAs_{1.1}S_{.9}$, but it approaches FeAsS at
           lower temperatures. The equilibrium phase relations in the system are
           shown in Figure 14-9. The pyrite-arsenopyrite mineral pair is stable
           below 491° C in the presence of vapor. The arsenopyrite-arsenic tie line
           is broken at 688° C, and arsenopyrite melts at 702° C [10].

As-Ni-S: The only ternary compound (gersdorffite) has composition $Ni(As, S)_2$
           where the As/S ratio varies considerably but the $Ni/(As + S)$ ratio
           remains constant. The phase relations in the system at 600° C are shown
           in Figure 14-10. Complete solid solution exists between $Ni_{1\pm x}As$ and
           $\alpha Ni_{1-x}S$, but the crest of the solvus appears slightly below 600° C and
           at about 50 per cent. The extent of solid solution on both sides decreases
           very rapidly with temperature [56].

Bi-S-Te: The Bi_2S_3-Bi_2Te_3 join is binary. The compound $Bi_4S_3Te_3$ (tetradymite)
           melts at 615° C. Eutectics are situated at 614° C and near $Bi_4S_3Te_3$
           composition, and at 570° C and 97 mole per cent Bi_2Te_3 [58].

Co-Fe-S: The solubility of Co_4S_3 in FeS ranges from 42.4 per cent at the eutectic

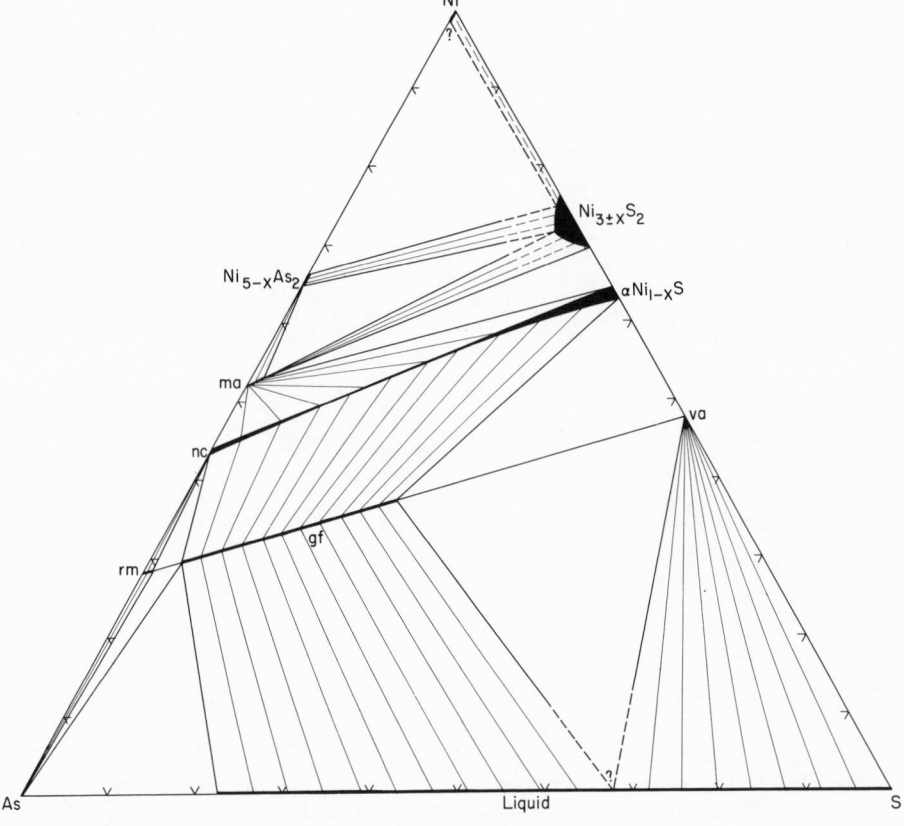

Weight per cent

Figure 14-10. Phase relations in the **Ni-As-S** system at 600° C. The vapor pressure
varies with the assemblage [56]

temperature of about 900° C to 21.5 per cent at room temperature. The reported solubility of FeS in Co_4S_3 is 20 per cent at all temperatures [43].

Cu-Fe-S: Ternary phases are Cu_5FeS_6 (idaite), Cu_5FeS_4 (bornite), $CuFeS_{2-x}$ (chalcopyrite), and $CuFe_2S_3$ (cubanite). The phase relations in the system at 700° C are given in Figure 14-11 [57], where complete solid solution is seen to exist between digenite, chalcocite, and bornite. At lower temperatures solvi separate these three compounds. The crest of the Cu_9S_5-Cu_5FeS_4 solvus lies at about 330° C [31]. The phase relations in the system at variable temperatures but under constant sulfur vapor pressure of 455 mm are shown in Figure 14-12 [40]. *See also* [49, 51].

Cu-Ni-S: There are no ternary phases and solid solution between the binary compounds is very limited, as shown in Figure 14-13, which gives the phase relations at 600° C [42].

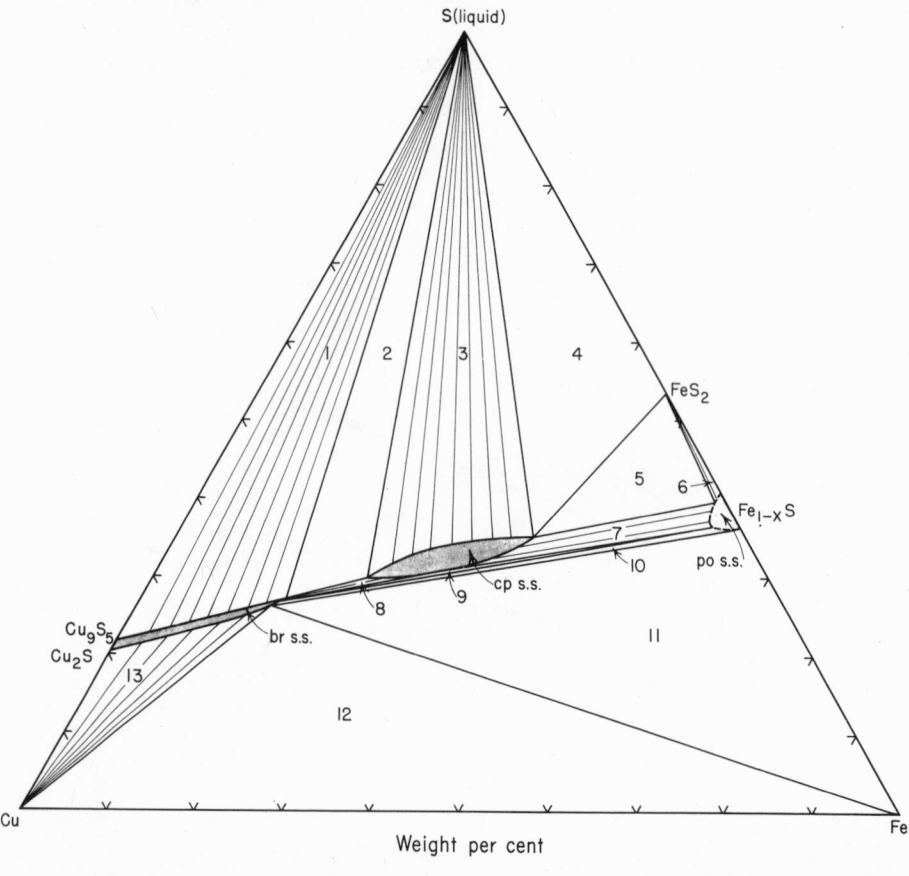

Figure 14-11. The system Cu-Fe-S at 700° C. Bornite, chalcopyrite, and pyrrhotite s.s. (br s.s.; cp s.s.; and po s.s.) are shown as stippled areas. The numbered areas are: 1, br s.s.-L-V; 2, br s.s.-cp s.s.-L-V; 3, cp s.s.-L-V; 4, cp s.s.-py-L-V; 6, py-cp s.s.-po s.s.-V; 6, py-po s.s.-V; 7, cp s.s.-po s.s.-V; 8, br s.s.-cp s.s.-V; 9, br s.s.-cp s.s.-po s.s.-V; 10, br s.s.-po s.s.-V; 11, br s.s.-po s.s.-Fe-V; 12, br s.s.-Fe-Cu-V; 13, br s.s.-Cu-V (L, liquid; V, vapor; py, pyrite) [57]

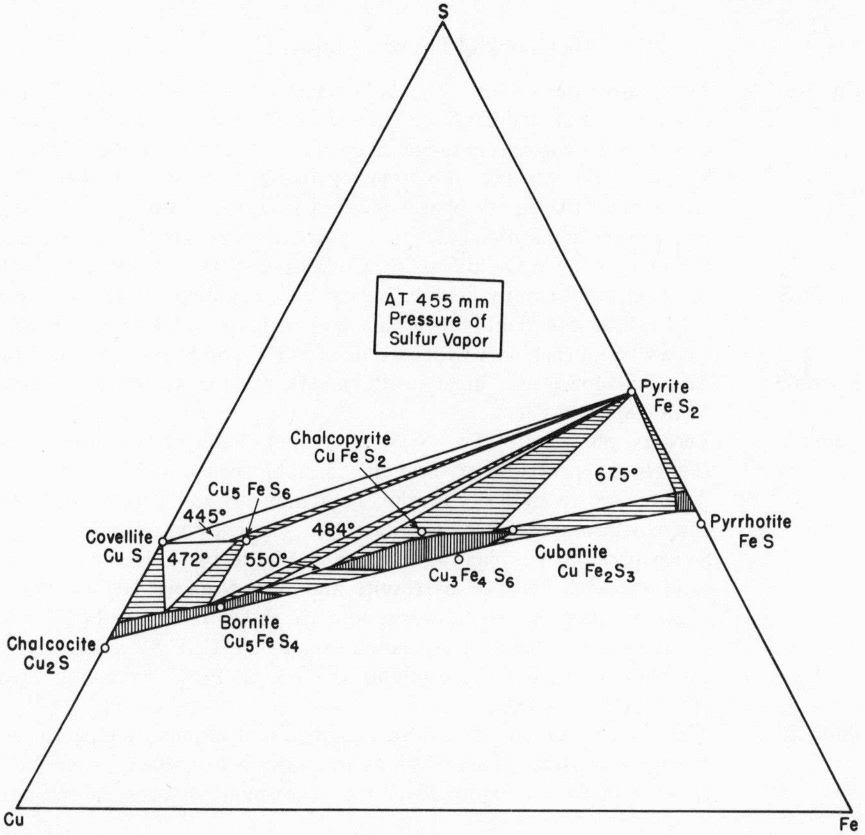

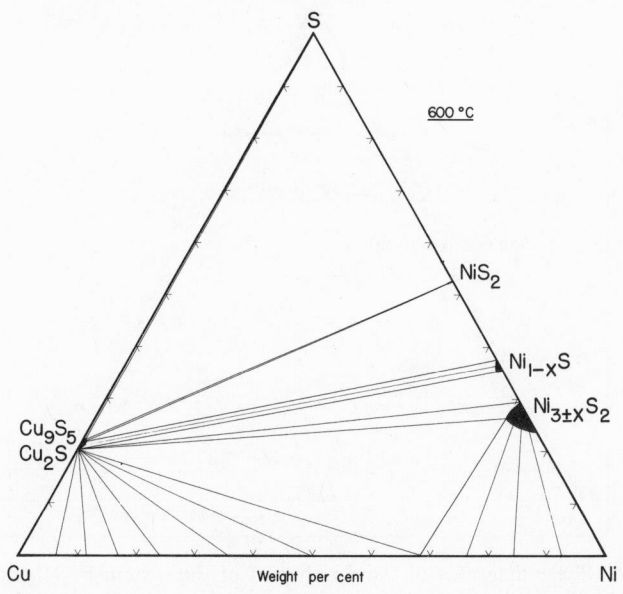

Figure 14-12. Phase relations in the system Cu-Fe-S at 455 mm pressure of sulfur vapor [40]

Figure 14-13. Isothermal section of the Cu-Ni-S system at 600° C [42]

337

Cu-O-S: There are three ternary phases: $CuSO_4$ (chalcocyanite), $Cu_2(SO_4)O$
               (dolerophanite), and Cu_2SO_4. The $Cu-Cu_2O-Cu_2S$ assemblage is stable
               over a wide temperature range. Even at as low a temperature as 250° C
               a liquid field transects the system prohibiting tie lines between the
               ternary and the binary phases (CuO, Cu_2O, Cu_2S, Cu_9S_5, and CuS).
               The univariant assemblages in the condensed system are $Cu-Cu_2O-Cu_2S$,
               $CuO-Cu_2O-L$, Cu_2O-Cu_2S s.s.-L, Cu_2S s.s.-CuS-L, and $CuS-L-S_L$ [37].

Cu-Pb-S: A liquid immiscibility field extends at elevated temperatures from the
               $Cu-Cu_2S$ boundary into the ternary system almost to the Pb corner. The
               Cu_2S-PbS join is binary with eutectic at 540° C and 51 per cent PbS [58].

Fe-Mn-S: The FeS-MnS join is binary with eutectic at 1165° C and 6 per cent
               MnS [58].

Fe-Ni-S: Ternary phases are (Fe, Ni)S_2 (bravoite), $FeNi_2S_4$ (violarite), and
               (Fe, Ni)$_9S_8$ (pentlandite). Bravoite is stable below 137° C, where it
               decomposes to pyrite + vaesite. Pentlandite is stable below 610° C,
               where it decomposes to pyrrhotite + $Ni_{3\pm x}S_2$. The phase relations in the
               S-rich part of the system are shown in Figure 14-14. Complete solid
               solution exists between pyrrhotite and $Ni_{1-x}S$ above 600° C. Phase
               relations along the pyrite-vaesite join are shown in Figure 14-15. The
               pyrite-vaesite mineral pair is stable below 729° C. FeS_2 is extensively
               soluble in NiS_2 but the solubility of NiS_2 in FeS_2 is rather limited
               [12, 33]. *See also* [53].

Fe-O-S: There are no ternary phases in this system at elevated temperatures.
               In Figure 14-16 the phase relations are shown below 560° C, where FeO
               is not a phase. In Figure 14-17 the phase relations between 560 and

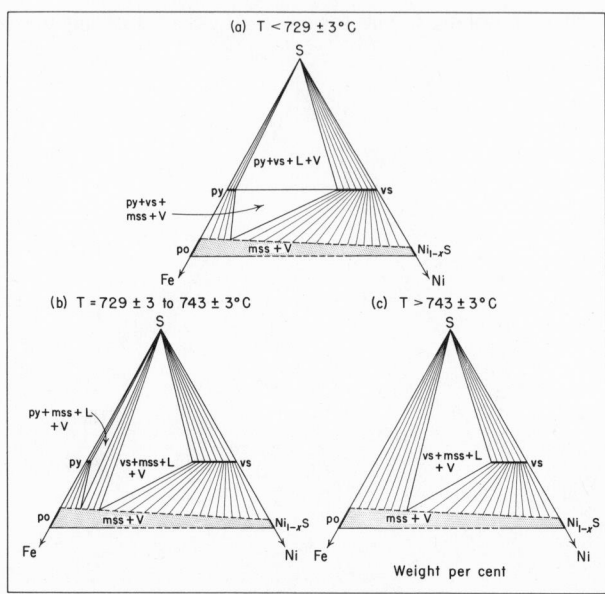

Figure 14-14. Phase diagrams of the S-rich part of the system Fe-Ni-S depicting the
assemblages stable within the specified temperature ranges; po, pyrrhotite; py, pyrite;
vs, vaesite; L, liquid; and V, vapor [12]

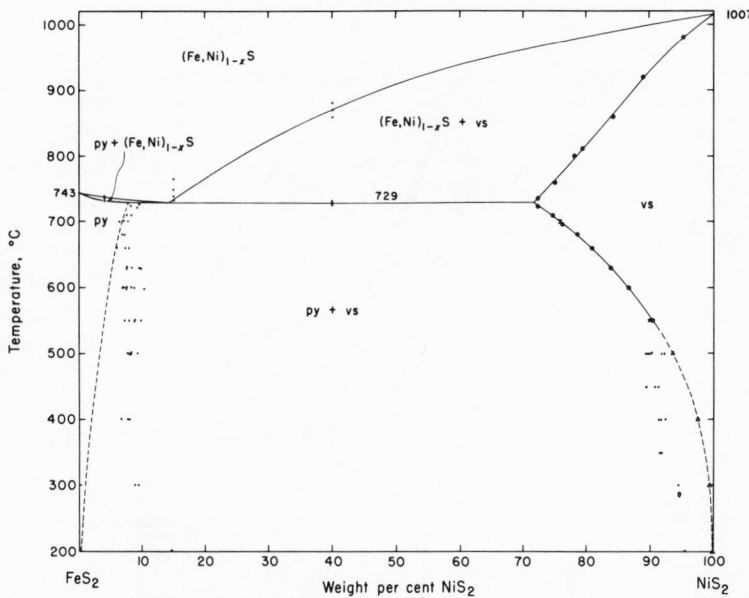

Figure 14-15. Phase relations between pyrite and vaesite as determined in the presence of a sulfur-rich liquid and vapor [12]

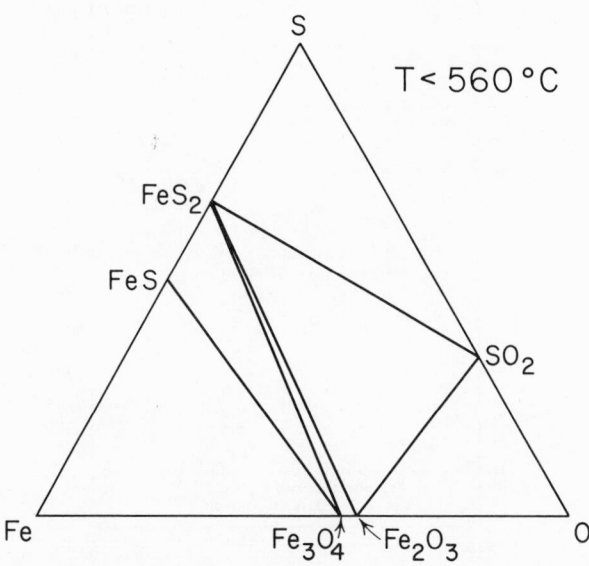

Figure 14-16. Phase relations in the Fe-S-O system below 560° C [30]

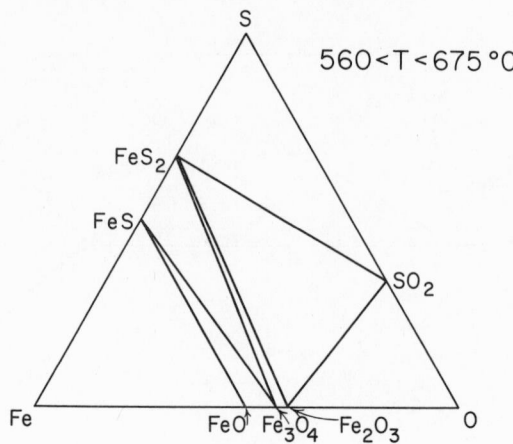

Figure 14-17. Phase relations in the Fe-S-O system between 560° C and 675° C [30]

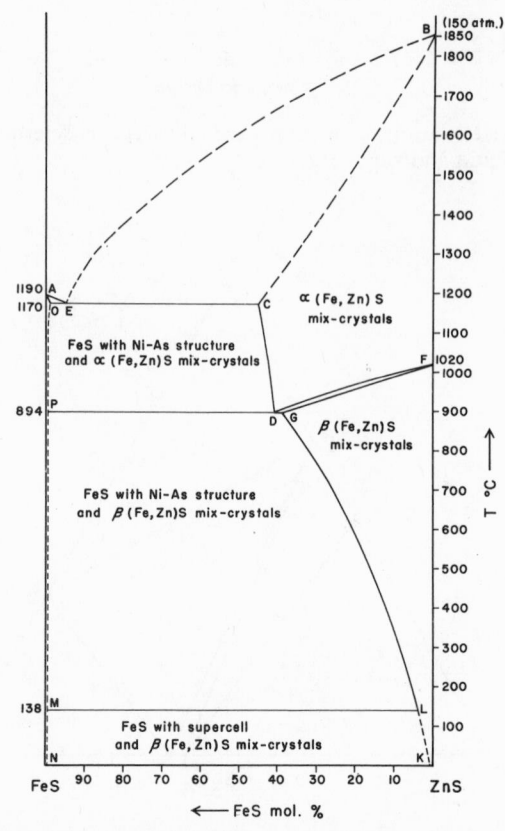

Figure 14-18. The FeS-ZnS equilibrium diagram. All phases are in equilibrium with vapor [28]

675° C are given. At about 675° C the tie line Fe_3O_4-FeS_2 is replaced by one connecting Fe_2O_3 and FeS. At about 700° C the Fe_2O_3-FeS_2 tie line is broken and FeS + SO_2 (gas) coexist. Pyrite disappears as a phase at 743° C [30, 5]. Along the FeS-FeO join eutectic conditions exist at 940° C and about 40 per cent FeS [54].

Fe-P-S: Only the Fe-Fe_2P-FeS portion has been investigated. It contains no ternary compounds. Ternary eutectic is situated at 953° C. A liquid immiscibility region extends from the Fe_2P-FeS join toward Fe. At 1240° C this field boundary lies at 4 per cent P and 4.5 per cent S [58].

Fe-Pb-S: Only the Fe_{1-x}S-PbS join has been studied. Eutectic (?) conditions exist at 863° C and 70 per cent PbS [58].

Fe-S-Zn: There are no ternary phases. The phase relations along the join FeS-ZnS are shown in Figure 14-18. Considerable amounts of FeS go into solid solution in ZnS, but very little ZnS is soluble in FeS. Eutectic conditions exist at 1170° C and 5 per cent ZnS. The rhombohedral-hexagonal inversion in ZnS is lowered from 1020° C for pure ZnS to 894° C when 36.5 per cent FeS occurs in solid solution [28].

Pb-S-Sn: The PbS-SnS join is binary with eutectic at 820° C and 9 per cent SnS [58].

Pb-S-Zn: The PbS-ZnS join is binary with eutectic at 1045° C and 6 per cent ZnS [58].

QUATERNARY SYSTEMS

As-Co-Fe-Ni: The phase relations at 800° C in the As-rich part of the bounding ternary systems are shown in Figure 14-8. The extent of Co, Ni, and Fe substitution in skutterudite at 800° C is shown in Figure 14-19A; and

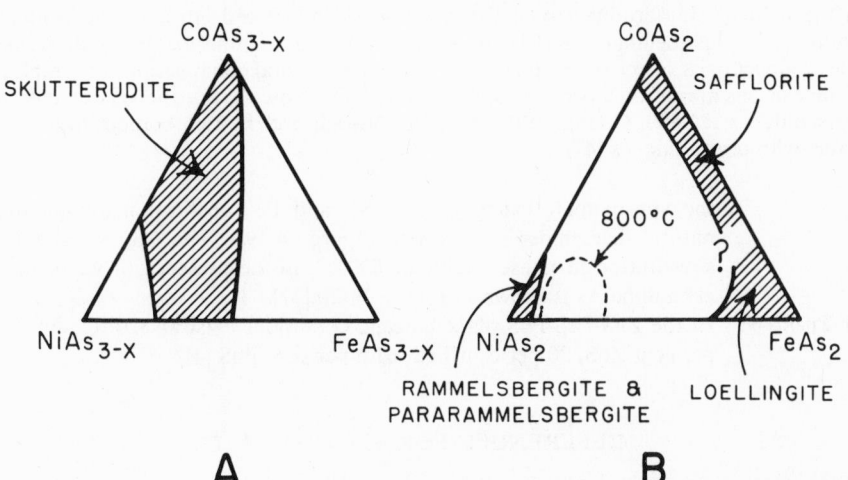

Figure 14-19. The extent of Co, Ni, and Fe substitution in synthetic skutterudite (A) and the natural diarsenides (B) at 800° C. The compositions $NiAs_{3-x}$ and $FeAs_{3-x}$ are neither compounds nor minerals [47]. B, the natural s.s. are shown by shading. At 800° C the s.s. cover all the triangle except for the area within the dashed lines [47]

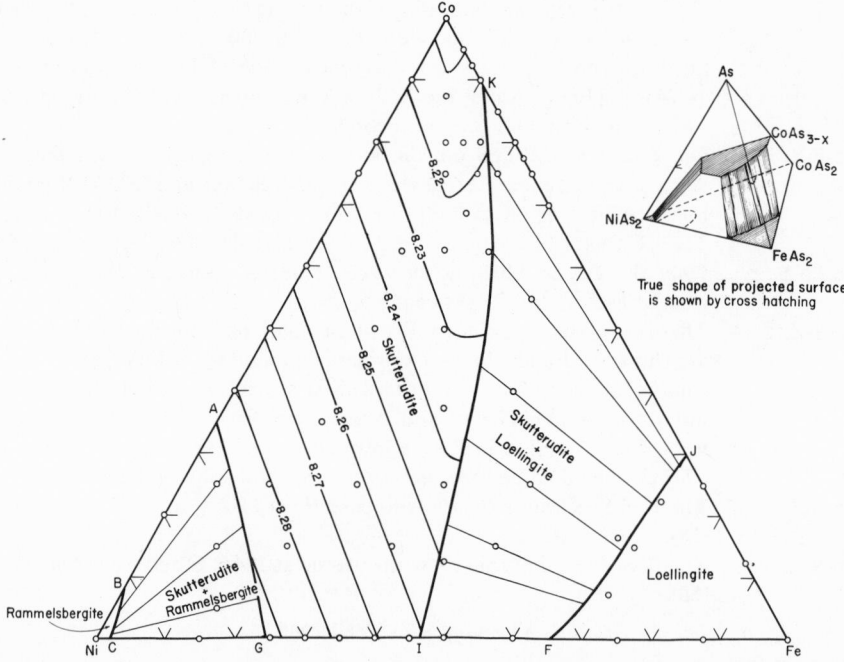

Figure 14-20. Co, Ni, and Fe substitution in phases stable at 800° C in the presence of vapor (about 25 atm. vapor pressure) and crystalline As. The diagram can be viewed as a projection from the As corner of the tetrahedron (*See* insert) onto the $CoAs_2$-$NiAs_2$-$FeAs_2$ base. The fields of loellingite, FJFe, and rammelsbergite, BCNi, lie on the base, and the other three fields are projected onto the base. The numbered contours in the field of skutterudite, AGIKCo, are lines of equal cell edge. In the field of skutterudite plus loellingite, KIFJ, and skutterudite plus rammelsbergite, ABCG, tie lines connect pairs of coexisting phases. Circles indicate total compositions of samples. Compositions are in mole per cent of Ca + Ni + Fe. Note that of the very extensive diarsenide s.s. at 800° C (Fig. 19B), only the Ni-rich and Fe-rich compositions are stable with crystalline As [47]

the approximate extent of Co, Ni, and Fe substitution among the natural diarsenides is shown in Figure 14-19B. The Co, Ni, and Fe substitution in phases stable at 800° C, in the presence of vapor and crystalline As is shown in Figure 14-20 [47].

Fe-Zn-Pb-S: In the ZnS-FeS-PbS plane eutectic conditions exist at 820° C and 8.5 per cent ZnS, 30 per cent FeS, 61.5 per cent PbS [4].

REFERENCES FOR SECTION 14

1. Abrikosov and Bankina, Zhur. Neorg. Khim. **3**, 659, 1958 (Chem. Abs. **52**, 19377, 1958)
2. Albers and Schol, Philips Res. Rept. **16**, 329, 1961; and Albers, Haas, Vink, and Wasscher, Jour. Appl. Phys., Suppl. **32**, No. 10, 2220, 1961
3. Arnold, Econ. Geol. **57**, 72, 1962
4. Avetisyan and Gnatyshenko, Izvest. Akad. Nauk, Kazakh. S.S.R., Ser. Gorn. Dela Stroimaterialov i Met., No. 6, 11, 1960 (Chem. Abs. 54, 16155, 1960)
5. Barnes and Kullerud, Econ. Geol. **56**, 648, 1961

6. Bell and Herfert, Jour. Am. Chem. Soc. **79**, 3351, 1957
7. Bloem and Kroger, Z. physik. Chem., (Frankfurt), N.F. 7, 1, 1956. (C.A. 50, 8310, 1956)
8. Buck and Strock, Am. Min. **40**, 192, 1955
9. Buseck, Carnegie Inst. Wash. Year Book 61, 152, 1962
10. Clark, Econ. Geol. **55**, 1345, 1631, 1960
11. Clark, L. A., unpub. Ph.D. Thesis, McGill University, 1959
12. Clark, L. A., and Kullerud, G., in press
13. Dickinson and Pauling, Jour. Am. Chem. Soc. **45**, 1465, 1923
14. Dickson and Tunell, Am. Min. **44**, 471, 1959
15. Djurle, Acta Chem. Scand. **12**, 1415, 1958
16. —— Acta Chem. Scand. **12**, 1427, 1958 (Chem. Abs. 54, 2067, 1960)
17. Frondel and Palache, Am. Min. **35**, 29, 1950
18. Hansen and Anderko, Constitution of binary alloys, McGraw-Hill Book Co., Inc., 1305 p., 1958
19. Heyding and Calvert, Can. Jour. Chem. **35**, 449, 1957
20. —— Can. Jour. Chem. **35**, 1205, 1957
21. Heyding and Despault, Can. Jour. Chem. **38**, 2477, 1960
22. Jellinek, Nature **192**, 1065, 1961
23. Jensen, Avhand, Norske Videnskaps-Akad., Oslo. I. Mat. Naturv. Klasse, 6, 1947
24. Jensen, Norske Vidensk. -Akad. Oslo, Mat. -Naturv. Kl., 2, 1947
25. Kerr, Am. Min. **30**, 483, 1945
26. Kracek, Trans. Am. Geophys. Union **27**, 364, 1946
27. Kracek and Ksanda, Geol. Soc. America Bull. **69**, 1762, 1958
28. Kullerud, Norsk Geol. Tidsskrift **32**, 61, 1953
29. —— Carnegie Inst. Wash. Year Book 56, 195, 1957
30. —— Carnegie Inst. Wash. Year Book 56, 198, 1957
31. —— Carnegie Inst. Wash. Year Book 59, 114, 1960
32. —— Carnegie Inst. Wash. Year Book 60, 174, 1961
33. —— Carnegie Inst. Wash. Year Book 61, 1962
34. —— G., unpub. D.T.A. experiments, 1960
35. —— G., unpub. research, 1962
36. Kullerud and Yoder, Econ. Geol. **54**, 533, 1959
37. Kullerud and Yund, Carnegie Inst. Wash. Year Book 60, 182, 1961
38. —— Jour. Petrology 3, No. 1, 126, 1962
39. Markham, Econ. Geol. **55**, 1148, 1460, 1960
40. Merwin and Lombard, Econ. Geol. **32**, 203, 1937
41. Miller, Komarek, and Cadoff, Trans. Am. Inst. Mech. Eng. **215**, 882, 1959 (Chem. Abs. 54, 5228, 1960)
42. Moh and Kullerud, Carnegie Inst. Wash. Year Book 61, 1962
43. Moleva, Kusakin, Vetrenko, and Diev, Zhur. Neorg. Khim. 3, 904, 1958 (Chem. Abs. 52, 16852, 1958)
44. Morimoto, Min. Jour. (Japan), 3, 338, 1962
45. Morimoto and Kullerud, Carnegie Inst. Wash. Year Book 61, 143, 1962
46. Ramdohr and Schmitt, Neues Jahrb. Mineral. Geol., Monatsh. 133, 1955
47. Roseboom, Carnegie Inst. Wash. Year Book 56, 201, 1957, and Am. Min. **47**, 310, 1962
48. Rosenqvist, Jour. Iron Steel Inst. **176**, 37, 1954
49. Schlegel and Schüller, Bergakad. Freiberg, Forsch. Beih., Reihe B, Hüttenw. 2, 32 pp., 1952 (Chem. Abs. 48, 4377, 1954)
50. Suhr, Econ. Geol. **50**, 347, 1955
51. Tavasci and Schromek, Univ. Studi Trieste, Fac. ing. Ist. Chim. Appl., 7, 1, 1959 (Chem. Abs. 54, 11678, 1960)
52. Tröften and Kullerud, Carnegie Inst. Wash. Year Book 60, 176, 1961
53. Vanyukov, Vanyukov, and Tarashchuk, Sbornik Nauch. Trudov Moskov, Inst. Tsetnykh Metal. i. Zolata i Vsesoyna. Nauch Inzhener. Tekh. Obshchestvo Tsvetnoi Met. **26**, 108, 1957 (Chem. Abs. 53, 15929, 1959)
54. Yazawa and Kameda, Technol. Repts. Tohoku Univ. **18**, 40, 1954 (Chem. Abs. 48, 8154, 1954)
55. Yund, Econ. Geol. **56**, 1273, 1961
56. —— Carnegie Inst. Wash. Year Book 58, 148, 1959
57. Yund and Kullerud, Carnegie Inst. Wash. Year Book 59, 111, 1960
58. Kracek, F. C., Experimental data, which only partly have been listed in the 1942 edition of "Handbook of Physical Constants"

The literature on effects of high pressure has expanded enormously in recent years, making possible a complete revision of the section in the old edition. Attention has been confined to materials of geologic interest.

Most of the data in this section are in the form of lines of univariant equilibria projected into the pressure-temperature plane. Pressure effects on multivariant equilibria have been much less studied; a few cases are given in diagrams. Work on two important groups of minerals, the clays and zeolites, has been largely omitted. Many members of these groups are stable only at low temperatures, and difficulty in reaching chemical equilibrium is extreme. As a consequence conflicting results are to be found in the literature, and a certain amount of erroneous data must have been published.

In compiling the tables a critical selection of data has been attempted. Several reactions which have been studied have been omitted because it was not felt that the results were sufficiently reliable. In some cases results from one laboratory have been included in preference to those from another; results from two conflicting studies have both been included when no suitable basis for choosing between them could be found. Virtually all the data given here have been obtained from direct studies of phase equilibria at high pressures and temperatures. Thermodynamic calculations have been accepted when experimentally verified (diamond-graphite equilibrium) and in the case of the spinel-olivine transition in forsterite, which is still beyond the reach of direct experimentation.

Most of the data entered in the tables have been read from graphs to the nearest 5° C. Few curves have actually been determined to this accuracy, but it has been maintained for the sake of smoothness.

Pressure Units and Pressure Scales. Units of bars and kilobars (10^6 or 10^9 dynes/cm² respectively) are used exclusively. This is in keeping with the recommendations resulting from several recent conferences on high pressure. Conversions to other commonly used high-pressure units are as follows: 1 bar = 1.0197 kg/cm² = .9869 atmospheres = 14.504 lb/in².

The pressure scale above the I-II transition in bismuth (25.4 kb at room temperature) has recently been revised. Fixed points on the new scale, which is used here, are the I-II transition in barium at 59 kb and a transition in bismuth at 90 kb. Both pressures refer to room temperature. For further particulars *see* the article by Kennedy and LaMori in *Progress in very high pressure research*, edited by Bundy, Hibbard, and Strong (John Wiley & Sons, New York, 1961), and the paper by Balchan and Drickamer in Review of Scientific Instruments, **32,** 308, 1961.

SECTION 15

HIGH-PRESSURE PHASE EQUILIBRIA

by Sydney P. Clark, Jr.

Contents

Illustrations

Handbook of Physical Constants—*Revised Edition*
THE GEOLOGICAL SOCIETY OF AMERICA MEMOIR 97, 1966

The literature on effects of high pressure has expanded enormously in recent years, making possible a complete revision of the section in the old edition. Attention has been confined to materials of geologic interest.

Most of the data in this section are in the form of lines of univariant equilibria projected into the pressure-temperature plane. Pressure effects on multivariant equilibria have been much less studied; a few cases are given in diagrams. Work on two important groups of minerals, the clays and zeolites, has been largely omitted. Many members of these groups are stable only at low temperatures, and difficulty in reaching chemical equilibrium is extreme. As a consequence conflicting results are to be found in the literature, and a certain amount of erroneous data must have been published.

In compiling the tables a critical selection of data has been attempted. Several reactions which have been studied have been omitted because it was not felt that the results were sufficiently reliable. In some cases results from one laboratory have been included in preference to those from another; results from two conflicting studies have both been included when no suitable basis for choosing between them could be found. Virtually all the data given here have been obtained from direct studies of phase equilibria at high pressures and temperatures. Thermodynamic calculations have been accepted when experimentally verified (diamond-graphite equilibrium) and in the case of the spinel-olivine transition in forsterite, which is still beyond the reach of direct experimentation.

Most of the data entered in the tables have been read from graphs to the nearest $5°$ C. Few curves have actually been determined to this accuracy, but it has been maintained for the sake of smoothness.

Pressure Units and Pressure Scales. Units of bars and kilobars (10^6 or 10^9 dynes/cm^2 respectively) are used exclusively. This is in keeping with the recommendations resulting from several recent conferences on high pressure. Conversions to other commonly used high-pressure units are as follows: 1 bar $= 1.0197$ kg/cm$^2 = .9869$ atmospheres $= 14.504$ lb/in^2.

The pressure scale above the I-II transition in bismuth (25.4 kb at room temperature) has recently been revised. Fixed points on the new scale, which is used here, are the I-II transition in barium at 59 kb and a transition in bismuth at 90 kb. Both pressures refer to room temperature. For further particulars *see* the article by Kennedy and LaMori in *Progress in very high pressure research*, edited by Bundy, Hibbard, and Strong (John Wiley & Sons, New York, 1961), and the paper by Balchan and Drickamer in Review of Scientific Instruments, **32**, 308, 1961.

TABLE 15-1. SOLID-SOLID TRANSITIONS

Most solid-solid univariant lines are linear to within experimental error. This is true even in cases such as the breakdown of pyrope, where the phases on one side of the reaction vary in composition. Hence the reactions may be expressed by the equation

$$P = P_0 + aT,$$

where P is pressure, T temperature, and P_0 and a are constants. Terms P_0 and a are given in Table 15-1, along with the co-ordinates of the curves at the upper and lower ends of the range over which experimental data were obtained. In the first column of the table the high-pressure assemblage is written first.

Reaction	Range of data T °C	P (kb)	P_0 (kb)	a (kb/°C)	Ref.
Coesite-quartz	700	27.3	19.5	.0112	3
$SiO_2 = SiO_2$	1750	39.1			
(See also Figure 15-9)					
Aragonite-calcite	0	3.4	3.4	.0166	7
$CaCO_3 = CaCO_3$	575	12.9$_5$			
Kyanite-sillimanite	1000	17.3	4.1	.0132	8
$Al_2SiO_5 = Al_2SiO_5$	1500	23.9			
Almandine-fayalite +	882	4	−31.3	.0400	16
Fe-cordierite + hercynite	1032	10			
$5Fe_3Al_2SiO_3O_{12} = 5Fe_2SiO_4$					
$+ 2Fe_2Al_4Si_5O_{18} + FeAl_2O_4$					
Pyrope-Al-enstatite	1100	17.2	6.2	.0100	4
+ sapphirine + sillimanite	1500	21.2			
Jadeite + quartz-albite	600	18	6	.02	2
$NaAlSi_2O_6 + SiO_2 = NaAlSi_3O_8$	1000	26			
Jadeite-albite + nepheline	700	13.7	1	.0181	14
$2NaAlSi_2O_6 = NaAlSi_3O_8 +$					
$NaAlSiO_4$					
Wollastonite + monticellite-	720	2			11
akermanite	735	4			
$CaSiO_3 + CaMgSiO_4 =$					
$Ca_2MgSi_2O_7$					

Three nonlinear phase boundaries are given in the following table. The diamond-graphite curve has been located experimentally by the researchers at the General Electric Co. [6] at pressures between 50 and 90 kb. The results are in good agreement with thermodynamic calculations [1]. The phase boundary is linear above 40 kb, but curves at lower pressures. The γ-α transition in iron has been followed experimentally to 80 kb [9]; the results also agree with thermodynamic data [12]. The α-β quartz transition has been determined experimentally to 10 kb [15].

DIAMOND-GRAPHITE, γ-α IRON AND α-β QUARTZ EQUILIBRIA

Reaction	Pressure (kb)	Temperature (°C)	Ref.
Diamond-graphite	16	25	6
(above 40 kb the equilibrium	20	190	
curve is linear with slope	30		
.0273 kilobars/° C)	50	1290	
	100	3110	
γ iron–α iron	0	910	9
	10	870	
	20	760	
	30		
	50	650	
	80		

Handbook of Physical Constants

Table 15-1. *Continued*

Reaction	Pressure (kb)	Temperature (°C)	Ref.
α quartz–β quartz	0	572	15
	2	626	
	4	679	
	6	728	
	8	773	
	10	815	

It has been predicted that olivine inverts to a spinel structure at high pressure, and this phase change has been used to explain the transition zone in the outer mantle. The inversion between the olivine structure and the spinel structure in Mg_2GeO_4 has been studied over a considerable range of pressure [10], and it has also been found in Fe_2SiO_4 [4, 13]. The pressures at which an analogous inversion might be expected to take place in Mg_2SiO_4 have been predicted by extrapolations of thermodynamic data [10, 13]. The results given in the table are uncertain by more than the apparent agreement between the two sets of data indicates.

OLIVINE-SPINEL INVERSIONS

Substance	Temperature (°C)	Pressure (kb)	Ref.
Mg_2GeO_4	810	0	10
	942	55	
Mg_2SiO_4	542	100	10
	1500	174	
	660	90	13
	1500	175	
Fe_2SiO_4	600	38	13
	1500	60	4

REFERENCES FOR TABLE 15-1

1. Berman and Simon, Zeits. Elektrochem. **59**, 333, 1955
2. Birch and Lecomte, Am. Jour. Sci. **208**, 209, 1960
3. Boyd and England, Jour. Geophys. Research **65**, 749, 1960
4. —— Ann. Rept. Director Geophysical Lad., 83, 1959
5. —— Ann. Rept. Director Geophysical Lab., 48, 1960
6. Bundy, Bovenkerk, Strong, and Wentorf, Jour. Chem. Phys. **35**, 383, 1961
7. Clark, Am. Min. **42**, 564, 1957; Jamieson, Jour. Chem. Phys. **21**, 1385, 1953
8. —— Am. Jour. Sci. **259**, 641, 1961
9. Claussen, Rev. Sci. Instr. **31**, 878, 1960
10. Dachille and Roy, Am. Jour. Sci. **258**, 225, 1960
11. Harker and Tuttle, Am. Jour. Sci. **254**, 468, 1956
12. Kaufman, discussion of paper by Strong *in* Bundy, Hibbard, and Strong, *Progress in very high pressure research*, John Wiley & Sons, New York, 1961
13. Ringwood, Geochim. Cosmochim. Acta **15**, 18, 1958
14. Robertson, Birch, and MacDonald, Am. Jour. Sci. **255**, 115, 1951
15. Yoder, Trans. Am. Geophys. Union **31**, 827, 1950
16. —— Geol. Soc. America Special Paper **62**, 505, 1955

Tables 15-2 and 15-3 list the pressures and temperatures of univariant reactions in which either H_2O or CO_2 is released as a nearly pure phase. The pressure of the volatile constituent invariably equals the total pressure on the system and hence the results usually represent the upper limits of stability of the hydrous phases and carbonates.

If the evolved H_2O or CO_2 behaves as an ideal gas with volume large compared with the change in volume of the solid phases, and if the heat of reaction is constant, then the logarithm of the equilibrium pressure is a linear function of the reciprocal of the absolute temperature. In this case the slope of the equilibrium curve is positive and increases rapidly with increasing temperature and pressure. Qualitatively this is the shape shown by the curves in these sections, but nevertheless the logarithm of the equilibrium pressure will only accidentally be a linear function of the reciprocal temperature because none of the assumptions leading to such a relationship is likely to be valid over the entire range of conditions given here.

The phase relations of certain amphiboles at high temperatures are complicated by the intersection of the dehydration curve and the solidus. The phase diagrams are shown following Table 15-2. The breakdown temperature of the iron-bearing amphiboles, and also of iron biotites and chlorites, depends on the fugacity of oxygen as well as on the water pressure. Different breakdown curves and breakdown assemblages are given in Table 15-2 and the figures for different oxygen buffers.

TABLE 15-2.   REACTIONS INVOLVING DEHYDRATION

Reaction	Pressure (kb)	Temperatures (°C)				
		.5	1.0	2.0	5.0	Ref.
Brucite — Periclase + H_2O $Mg(OH) = MgO + H_2O$		570	610	660	..	1
Gibbsite — boehmite + H_2O* $Al(OH)_3 = AlOOH + H_2O$		100	110	135	140	10, 7
Diaspore — corundum + H_2O $2AlOOH = Al_2O_3 + H_2O$		355	365	375	430	10, 7
Goethite — hematite + H_2O $2FeOOH = Fe_2O_3 + H_2O$		150	170	..	..	14, 12
Gypsum — anhydrite + H_2O $CaSO_4 \cdot 2H_2O = CaSO_4 + 2H_2O$		..	55	70	110	11
Brucite + serpentine — forsterite + H_2O $Mg(OH)_2 + Mg_3Si_2O_5(OH)_4$ $= 2Mg_2SiO_4 + 3H_2O$		420	430	440	..	2
Serpentine — forsterite + talc $5Mg_3Si_2O_5(OH)_4 = 6Mg_2SiO_4$ $+ Mg_3Si_4O_{10}(OH)_2 + 9H_2O$		500	500	505	..	2
Talc + forsterite — enstatite + H_2O $Mg_3Si_4O_{10}(OH)_2 + Mg_2SiO_4 = 5Mg \cdot SiO_3 + H_2O$		635	660	680	..	2
talc — enstatite + quartz + H_2O $Mg_3Si_4O_{10}(OH)_2 = 3MgSiO_3 + SiO_2 + H_2O$		765	795	830	..	2
Pyrophyllite — mullite + quartz + H_2O $3Al_2Si_4O_{10}(OH)_2 = Al_6Si_2O_{13} + 10SiO_2 + 3H_2O$		510	550	615	..	11
Hemimorphite — willemite + H_2O $Zn_4Si_2O_7(OH)_2 \cdot H_2O = 2Zn_2SiO_4 + 2H_2O$		235	245	255	..	13
Analcite — albite + Nepheline + H_2O $2NaAlSi_2O_6 \cdot 2H_2O = NaAlSi_3O_8$ $+ NaAlSiO_4 + 4H_2O$		490	525	570	..	9
Paragonite — albite + corundum + H_2O $NaAl_2AlSi_3O_{10}(OH)_2 = NaAlSi_3O_8$ $+ Al_2O_3 + H_2O$		595	625	655	..	20
Muscovite — sanidine + corundum + H_2O $KAl_2AlSi_3O_{10}(OH)_2 = KAlSi_3O_8 + Al_2O_3 + H_2O$		635	665	715	..	19
Muscovite + quartz — sanidine + mullite + H_2O $3KAl_2AlSi_3O_{10}(OH)_2 + 2SiO_2$ $= 3KAlSi_3O_8 + Al_6Si_2O_{13} + 3H_2O$		635	665	..	750	15

TABLE 15-2. *Continued*

Reaction	Pressure (kb)	.5	1.0	2.0	5.0	Ref.
Brucite + aluminous serpentine − forsterite + spinel + H_2O $2Mg(OH)_2 + Mg_5Al_2Si_3O_{10}(OH)_8$ $= 3Mg_2SiO_4 + MgAl_2O_4 + 6H_2O$		480	485	490	..	17
Talc + clinochlore − forsterite + cordierite + H_2O $6Mg_3Si_4O_{10}(OH)_2 + 10Mg_5Al_2Si_3O_{10}(OH)_8 =$ $29Mg_2SiO_4 + 5Mg_2Al_4Si_5O_{18} + 46H_2O$		630	655	675	..	17
Clinochlore − forsterite + cordierite + spinel + H_2O $5Mg_5Al_2Si_3O_{10}(OH)_8 = 10Mg_2SiO_4$ $+ Mg_2Al_4Si_5O_{18} + 3MgAl_2O_4 + 20H_2O$		660	675	705	..	17
Pyrophyllite + amesite − cordierite + H_2O $2Al_2Si_4O_{10}(OH)_2 + Mg_4Al_4Si_2O_{10}(OH)_8$ $= 2Mg_2Al_4Si_5O_{18} + 6H_2O$		..	..	475	525	21
Daphnite − mullite + magnetite + hematite + quartz + H_2O		..	..	565	..	16
Daphnite − fayalite + iron-cordierite + hercynite + H_2O		..	570	600	..	16
Tremolite − enstatite + diopside + quartz + H_2O $Ca_2Mg_5Si_8O_{22}(OH)_2 = 3MgSiO_3$ $+ 2CaMgSi_2O_6 + SiO_2 + H_2O$		795	835	870	..	3
Phlogopite − forsterite + leucite + kalsilite + H_2O $2KMg_3AlSi_3O_{10}(OH)_2 = 3Mg_2SiO_4$ $+ KAlSi_2O_6 + KAlSiO_4 + 2H_2O$		1010	1045	1080	1110	18
Annite + oxygen − sanidine + magnetite + hematite + H_2O $3KFe_3AlSi_3O_{10}(OH)_2 + 2O_2 = 3KAlSi_3O_8$ $+ Fe_3O_4 + 3Fe_2O_3 + 3H_2O$		..	400	425	..	8
Annite − kalsilite + leucite + fayalite + iron + oxygen + H_2O $3KFe_3AlSi_3O_{10}(OH)_2 = KAlSiO_4 + 2KAlSi_2O_6$ $+ 4Fe_2SiO_4 + Fe + \frac{1}{2}O_2 + 3H_2O$		720	760	785	..	8
Annite + oxygen − kalsilite + leucite + fayalite + magnetite + H_2O $9KFe_3AlSi_3O_{10}(OH)_2 + \frac{1}{2}O_2 + 3KAlSiO_4$ $+ 6KAlSi_2O_6 + 12Fe_2SiO_4 + Fe_3O_4 + 9H_2O$		745	785	825	..	8
Annite + quartz + oxygen − sanidine + fayalite + magnetite + H_2O $3KFe_3AlSi_3O_{10}(OH)_2 + 3SiO_2 + \frac{1}{2}O_2$ $= 3KAlSi_3O_8 + 3Fe_3SiO_4 + Fe_3O_4 + 3H_2O$		..	685	705	..	8

* Boehmite is a metastable phase according to [10]. Diaspore is stable.

REFERENCES FOR TABLE 15-2

1. Barnes and Ernst, Am. Jour. Sci. **261**, 129, 1963
2. Bowen and Tuttle, Geol. Soc. America Bull. **60**, 439, 1949
3. Boyd *in* Abelson, Researches in geochemistry, John Wiley & Sons, New York, 1959
4. Ernst, Geochim. Cosmochim. Acta **19**, 10, 1960
5. —— Am. Jour. Sci. **259**, 735, 1961
6. —— Jour. Geol. **70**, 689, 1962
7. Ervin and Osborn, Jour. Geol. **59**, 381, 1951
8. Eugster and Wones, Jour. Petrol. **3**, 82, 1962
9. Greenwood, Jour. Geophys. Research **66**, 3923, 1961
10. Kennedy, Am. Jour. Sci. **257**, 563, 1959

11. —— in Lansberg advances in geophysics, VII, Academic Press, New York, 1961
12. Posnjak and Merwin, Jour. Am. Chem. Soc. **44**, 1965, 1922
13. Roy and Mumpton, Econ. Geol. **51**, 432, 1956
14. Schmalz, Jour. Geophys. Research **64**, 575, 1959
15. Segnit and Kennedy, Am. Jour. Sci. **259**, 280, 1961
16. Turnock, Ann. Rept. Director, Geophysical Lab., 98, 1960
17. Yoder, Am. Jour. Sci. **250A**, 569, 1952
18. Yoder and Eugster, Geochim. Cosmochim. Acta **6**, 157, 1954
19. —— Geochim. Cosmochim. Acta **8**, 225, 1955
20. —— Ann. Rept. Director Geophysical Lab., 111, 1954
21. Yoder and Schreyer, Ann. Rept. Director, Geophysical Lab., 100, 1959
22. Wyllie and Tuttle, Jour. Petrol. **1**, 1, 1960

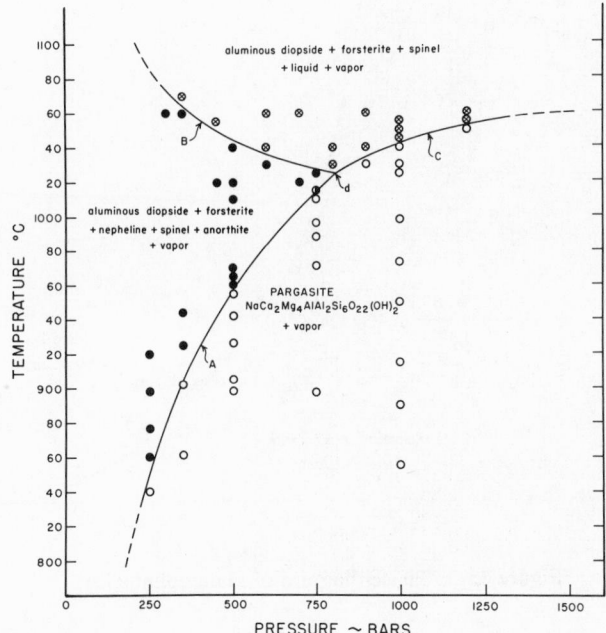

Figure 15-1. Phase diagram of pargasite, with water pressure equal to total pressure [3]

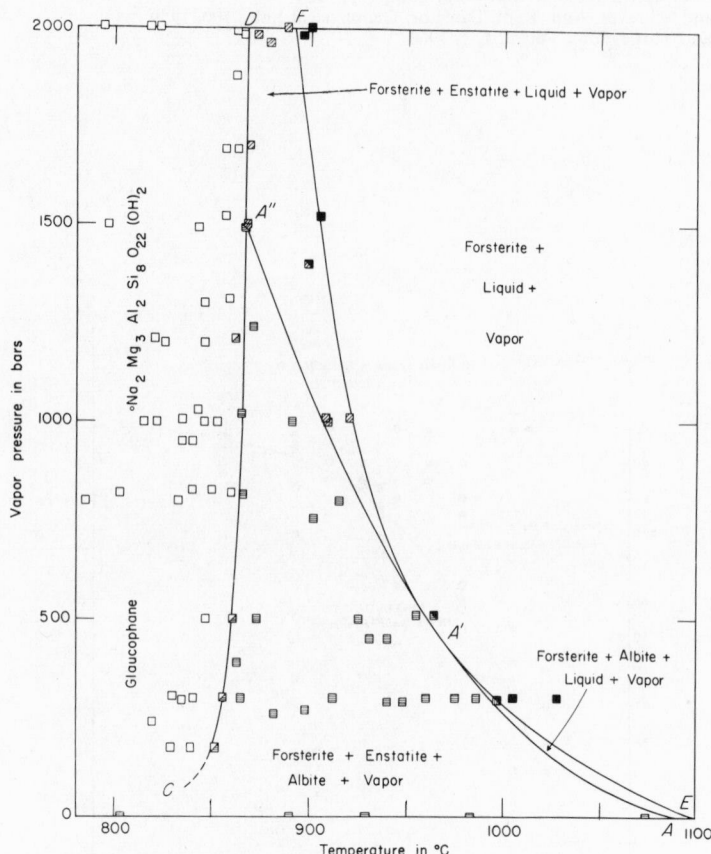

Figure 15-2. Phase diagram of glaucophane [5]

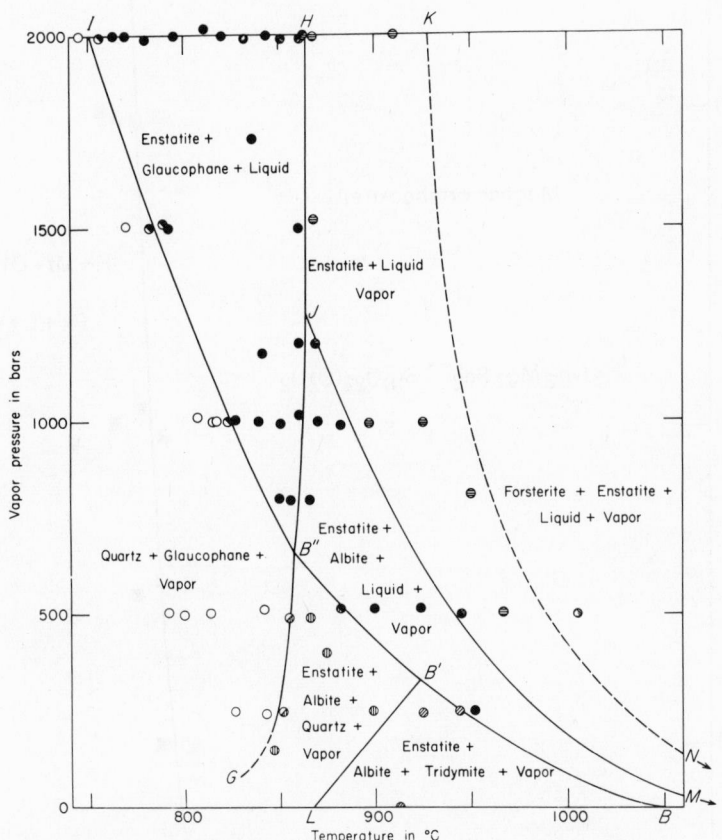

Figure 15-3. Phase diagram of glaucophane + 2SiO$_2$ [5]

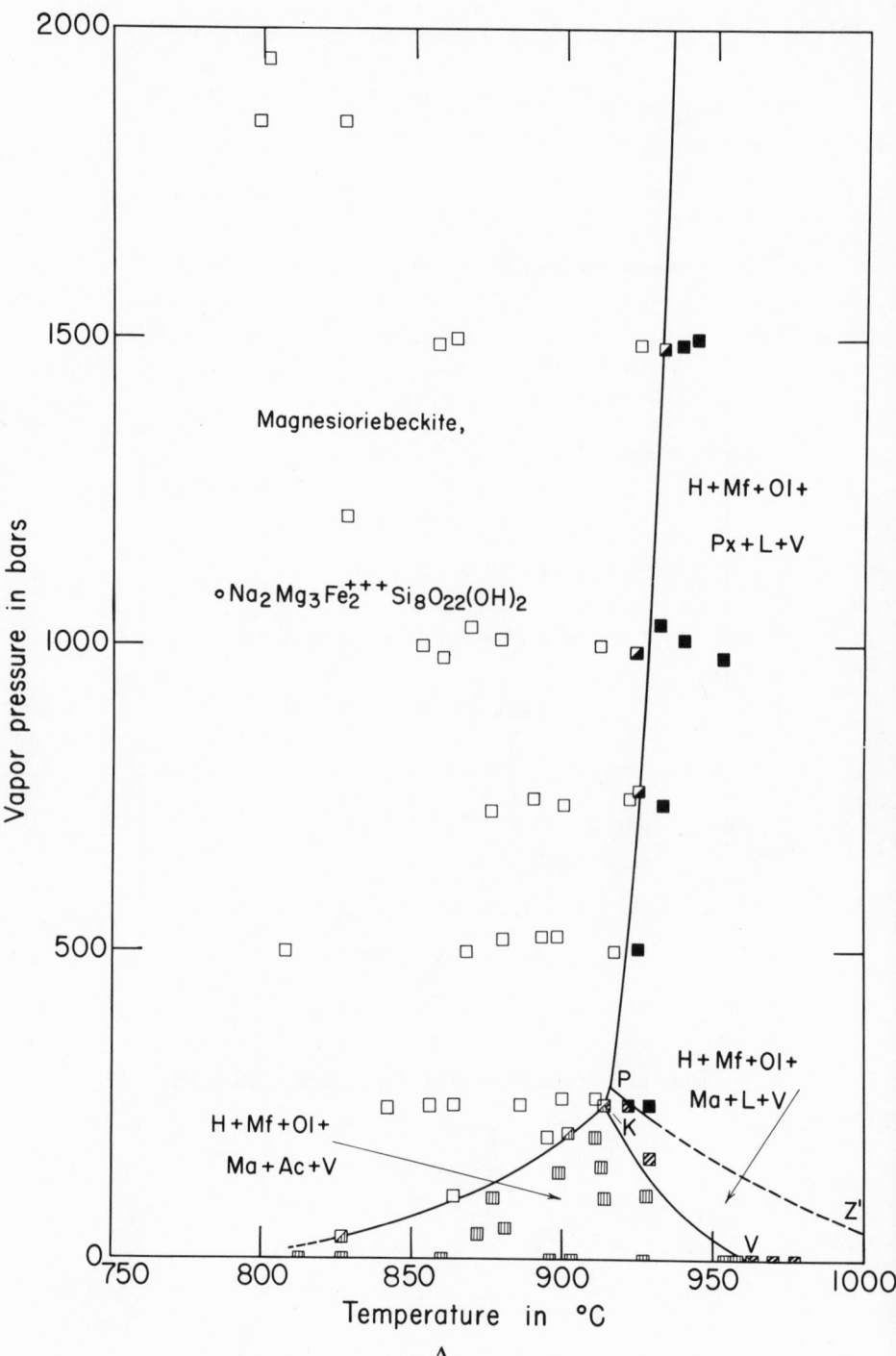

Figure 15-4. Phase diagrams of magnesioriebeckite. In Figure 15-4A, the fugacity of oxygen is controlled by the hematite-magnetite buffer; in Figure 15-4B it is controlled by magnetite-wüstite. Abbreviations used are Mf, Magnesioferrite; H, hematite; Ol, olivine; Px, pyroxene; L, liquid; V, vapor; Ma, $Na_2O \cdot 5(Fe, Mg)O \cdot 12SiO_2$; Ac, acmite; Mw, magnesiowüstite; N, $Na_2O \cdot 2(Fe, Mg)O \cdot 6SiO_2$ [4]

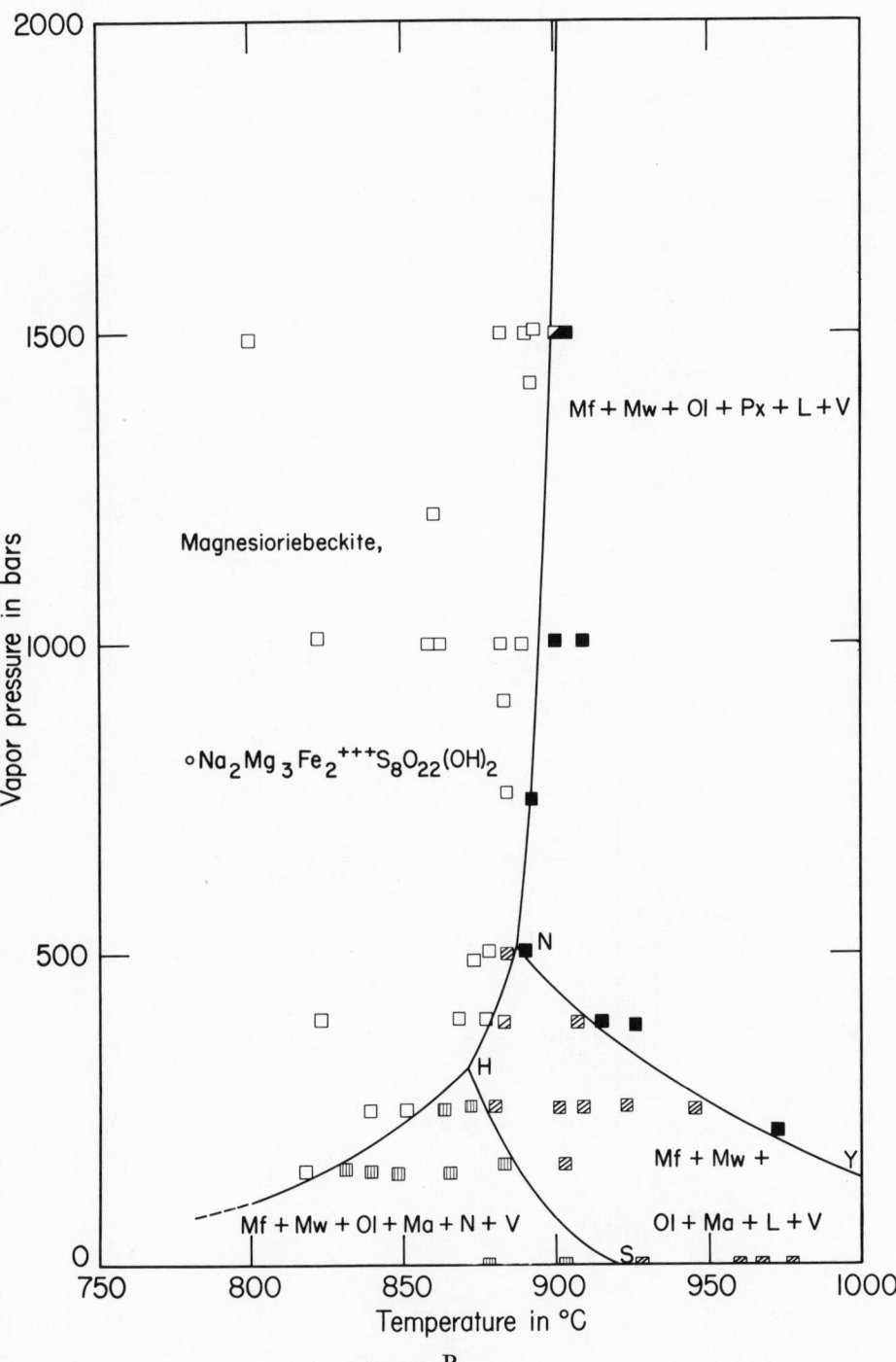

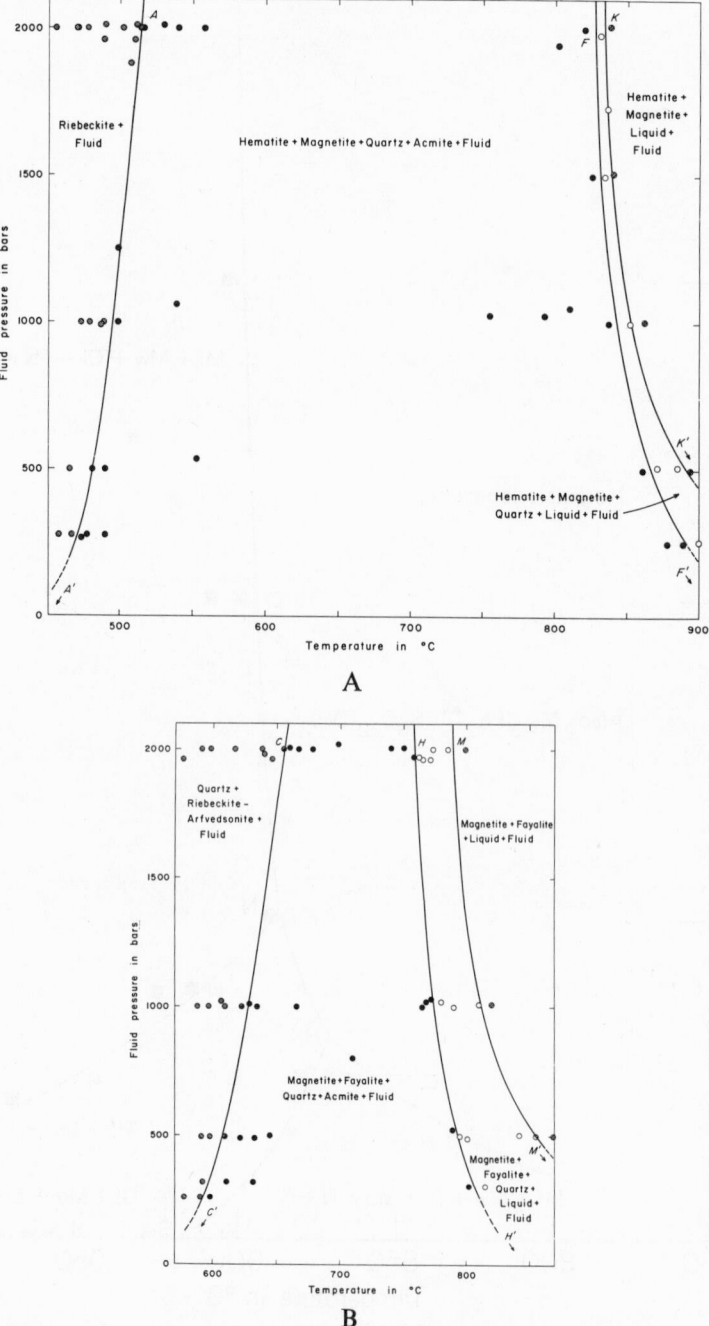

Figure 15-5. Phase diagrams of riebeckite ($Na_2O \cdot 5FeO_x \cdot 8SiO_2$ with x ranging from about 1.1 to 1.2). In Figure 15-5A, the fugacity of oxygen is controlled by the hematite-magnetite buffer; in Figure 15-5B it is controlled by magnetite + quartz-fayalite; in Figure 15-5C it is controlled by wüstite-iron [6]

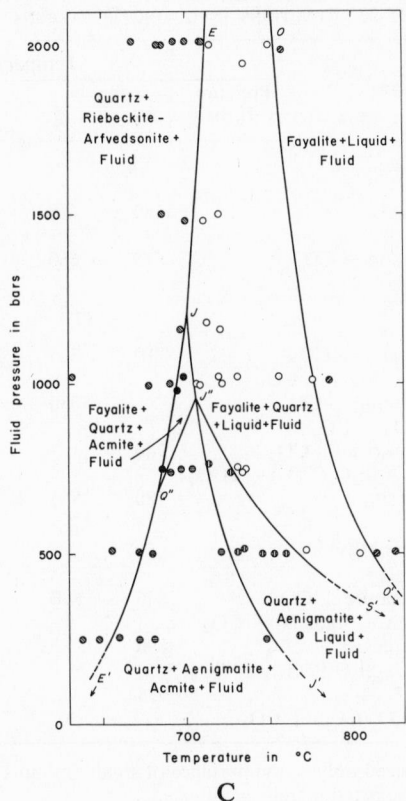

C

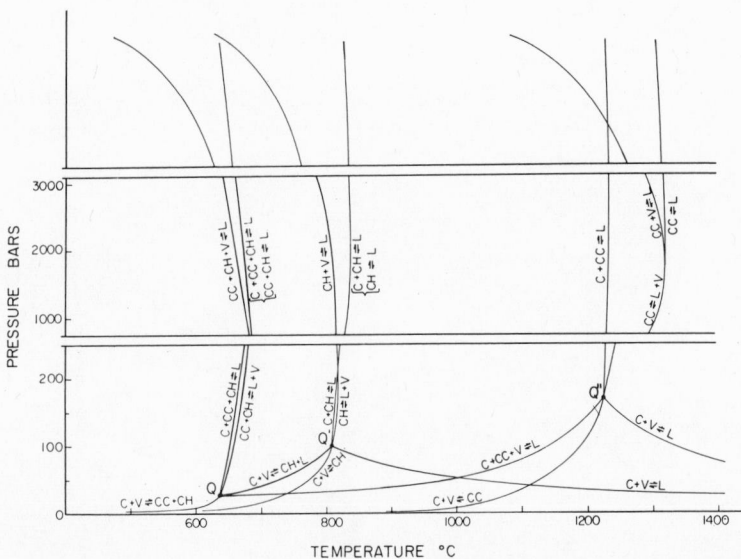

Figure 15-6. Univariant curves in the system CaO-CO$_2$-H$_2$O. Abbreviations are CC, calcite; CH, Ca(OH)$_2$; C, CaO; L, liquid; V, vapor [22]

Handbook of Physical Constants

TABLE 15-3. REACTIONS INVOLVING DECARBONATION

Reaction	Pressure (kb)	Temperatures (°C)				Ref.
		.25	.5	1.0	2.0	
Calcite − lime + CO_2	See Figure 15-7					
$CaCO_3 = CaO + CO_2$						
Magnesite − periclase + CO_2		650	710	775	850	4
$MgCO_3 = MgO + CO_2$						
Rhodochrosite − manganosite + CO_2		615	660	710	775	1
$MnCO_3 = MnO + CO_2$						
Smithsonite − zincite + CO_2		..	285	340	410	3
$ZnCO_3 = ZnO + CO_2$						
Dolomite − calcite + periclase + CO_2		710	765	825	900	4
$CaMg(CO_3)_2 = CaCO_3 + MgO + CO_2$						
Calcite + quartz − wollastonite + CO_2		..	630	680	745	5
$CaCiO_3 + SiO_2 = CaSiO_3 + CO_2$						
Wollastonite + calcite − spurrite + CO_2		960	..	..	..	8
$2CaSiO_3 + 3CaCO_3 = Ca_5Si_2O_8(CO_3) + 2CO_2$						
Calcite + diopside + forsterite − monticellite + CO_2		780	865	965	..	6
$2CaCO_3 + CaMgSi_2O_6 + Mg_2SiO_4 = 3CaMgSiO_4 + 2CO_2$						
Calcite + diopside − akermanite + CO_2		845	890	965	..	6
$CaCO_3 + CaMgSi_2O_6 = Ca_2MgSi_2O_7 + CO_2$						
Calcite + wollastonite − Tilleyite + CO_2*		890	..	..	..	2
$3CaCO_3 + 2CaSiO_3 = Ca_5Si_2O_7(CO_3)_2 + CO_2$						
Tilleyite − spurrite + CO_2*		935	..	..	..	2
$Ca_5Si_2O_7(CO_3)_2 = Ca_5Si_2O_8(CO_3) + CO_2$						

* Tilleyite could be synthesized only in the presence of small amounts of Al_2O_3 and fluorine, although the latter may have acted merely as a flux.

REFERENCES FOR TABLE 15-3

1. Goldsmith and Graf, Geochim. Cosmochim. Acta **11**, 310, 1957
2. Harker, Am. Jour. Sci. **257**, 656, 1959
3. Harker and Hutta, Econ. Geol. **51**, 375, 1956
4. Harker and Tuttle, Am. Jour. Sci. **253**, 209, 1955
5. —— Am. Jour. Sci. **254**, 239, 1956
6. —— final rept. on ONR contract Nonr 656, Task 6, Project No. Nr081-204
7. Smyth and Adams, Jour. Am. Chem. Soc. **45**, 1167, 1923
8. Tuttle and Harker, Am. Jour. Sci. **255**, 226, 1957

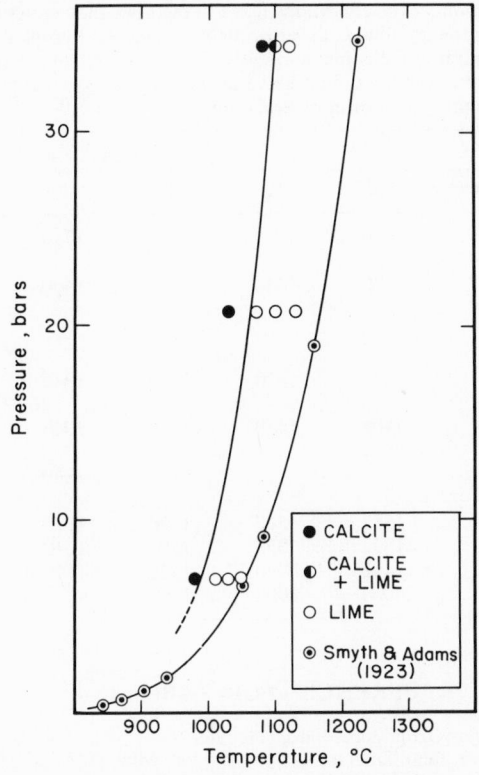

Figure 15-7. The reaction $CaCO_3 = CaO + CO_2$. The results of quenching experiments [4] are compared with those of Smyth and Adams [7]

TABLE 15-4. EFFECT OF PRESSURE ON MELTING POINTS

This table lists the effect of inert pressure on melting points. That is, the medium which transmits the pressure is such that it neither reacts with the solid nor dissolves in the liquid phase. Under these conditions it is found that the melting curve is decidedly nonlinear if it is followed through a sufficiently large range of pressure. The curve may be represented by the Simon equation, $P/P_o = (T/T_o)^c - 1$. Here P_o and c are adjustable constants, and T_o is the melting temperature at atmospheric pressure.

The use of Simon's equation to extrapolate the melting curves of silicates is extremely hazardous. All the melting temperatures given in this table refer to congruent melting, and it is only in this circumstance that the Simon equation may be expected to be valid. But a silicate which melts congruently under the conditions listed in the table may either melt incongruently or even not be stable on the liquidus at lower or higher pressures. Pyrope does not melt stably at low pressures, and enstatite melts incongruently. The feldspars behave in a similar fashion at high pressures. These examples should serve as warnings of the dangers involved in the extrapolation of the melting curve of a mineral composed of more than one oxide.

Substance	Temperatures (° C)						
	Pressure (kb)	0	10	20	30	50	Ref.
Diopside, $CaMgSi_2O_6$		1390	1520	1630	1710	1870	3
Albite, $NaAlSi_3O_8$		1120	1240	1320	1400	..	3
Pyrope, $Mg_3Al_2Si_3O_{12}$		..	..	..	..	1840	2
Enstatite, $MgSiO_3$		..	1670	1760	1840	1970	4
Forsterite, Mg_2SiO_4		1900	1950	1990	2040	2140	6
Jadeite, $NaAlSi_2O_6$		..	..	..	1360	1600	1
Iron, Fe		1532	1560	1590	1615	1670	7
Iron, Fe		1532	1555	1580	1610	1660	8
Nickel, Ni		1452	1490	1525	1560	1625	8
Halite, NaCl		800	1000	1160	..	..	5

REFERENCES FOR TABLE 15-4

1. Bell, Ann. Rept. Director Geophysical Lab., 171, 1964
2. Boyd and England, Ann. Rept. Director Geophysical Lab., 109, 1962
3. —— Jour. Geophys. Res. 68, 311, 1963
4. Boyd, England, and Davis, Jour. Geophys. Res. 69, 2101, 1964
5. Clark, Jour. Chem. Phys. 31, 1526, 1958
6. Davis and England, Jour. Geophys. Res. 69, 1113, 1964
7. Sterrett, Klement, and Kennedy, Jour. Geophys. Res. 70, 1979, 1965
8. Strong in Bundy, Hibbard, and Strong, Progress in very high pressure research, John Wiley & Sons, New York, 1961

TABLE 15-5. EFFECT OF WATER PRESSURE ON MELTING POINTS

At high pressures, water vapor is dissolved in silicate melts and produces a decrease in melting temperature with increasing pressure. In the simplest case a single solid phase melts completely to a liquid in the presence of a vapor phase, and hence the melting curve is uni-variant. In more complicated cases a mineral may melt to a liquid plus crystalline phases. Such cases are noted in the table; where no solid phases are mentioned, only liquid and vapor are present above the melting curve. Some binary and ternary relationships are shown in Figures 15-9 to 15-15. Experimental conditions are invariably such that the vapor pressure of water equals the total pressure on the system and a vapor phase is present.

Some of the curves given in Table 15-5 are complicated by polymorphism of the solids at high temperatures and low pressures. This is shown in Figures 15-8 and 15-9 for silica and sanidine. Nepheline inverts to carnegieite at 1250° C, and the latter is the stable solid phase along the melting curve below about 400 bars. This particular polymorphic inversion has virtually no effect on the shape of the melting curve.

Composition of solid	Water pressure (kb)	Temperatures (° C)					Ref.
		0	1	2	5	10	
Albite, $NaAlSi_3O_8$		1120	905	845	745	..	4, 6, 12
Nepheline, $NaAlSiO_4$		1525*	1135	1025	830	675	6
Sanidine, $KAlSi_3O_8$ (See Fig. 15-7)		..	..	..	875	..	4, 12
Quartz, SiO_2 (See Fig. 15-8)		..	..	1130	1065	(1035)	5, 6, 7
		..	..	1130	1090	(1085)	1
Anorthite, $CaAl_2Si_2O_8$		1550	1405	1340	1230	1115	6
Diopside, $CaMgSi_2O_6$		1390	1330	1315	1290	..	6
Cordierite, $Mg_2Al_4Si_5O_{18}$ (melts to various crystalline phases + liquid, depending on pressure).		1465	1330	1250	1100	960	10
Muscovite composition, $KAl_2AlSi_3O_{10}(OH)_2$, Sanidine + corundum − Leucite + corundum + liquid.		1140	935	935	915	..	9

* Carnegieite stable solid phase

REFERENCES FOR TABLE 15-5

1. Kennedy, Wasserburg, Heard, and Newton, Am. Jour. Sci. **260**, 501, 1962
2. W. S. MacKenzie, unpub.
3. Schairer, Jour. Geol. **58**, 512, 1950
4. Tuttle and Bowen, Geol. Soc. America Memoir 74, 1958
5. Tuttle and England, Geol. Soc. America Bull. **66**, 149, 1955
6. H. S. Yoder, unpub.
7. D. B. Stewart, unpub.
8. Yoder and Chinner, Ann. Rept. Director Geophysical Lab., 78, 1960
9. Yoder and Eugster, Geochim. Cosmochim. Acta **8**, 225, 1955
10. Yoder and Schreyer, Ann. Rept. Director Geophysical Lab., 100, 1959
11. Yoder, Stewart, and Smith, Ann. Rept. Director Geophysical Lab., 206, 1957
12. H. S. Yoder, D. B. Stewart, and J. R. Smith, unpub.
13. Yoder and Tilley, Ann. Rept. Director Geophysical Lab., 169, 1956

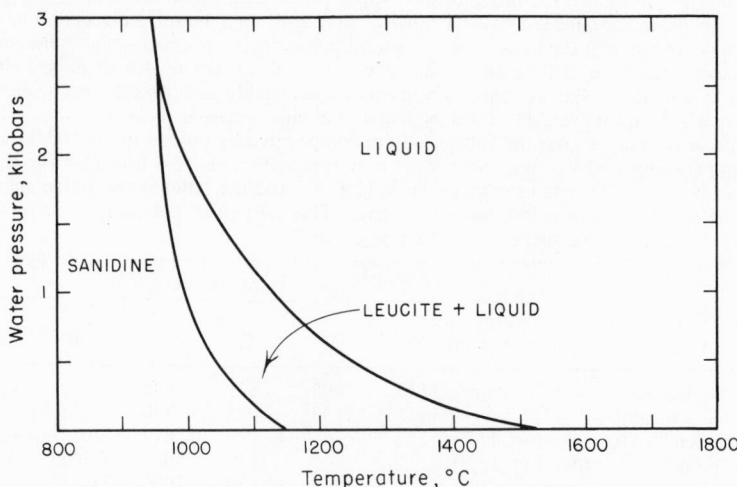

Figure 15-8. Phase relations of $KAlSi_3O_8$ under water pressure [4]

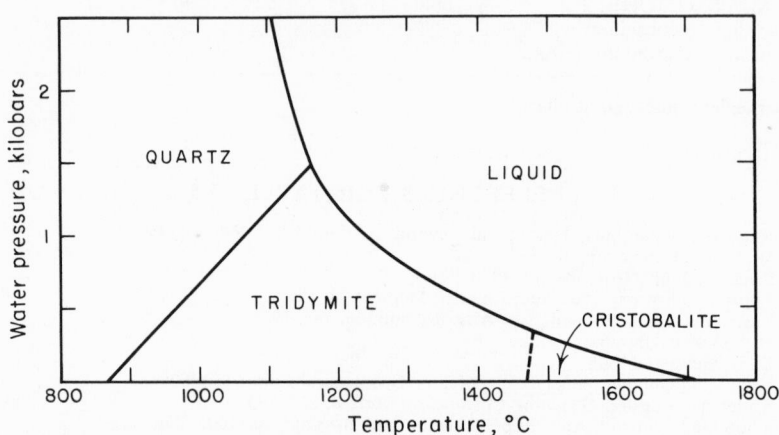

Figure 15-9. Phase relations of silica under water pressure. Water acts as an inert substance toward the solid-solid equilibria [1]

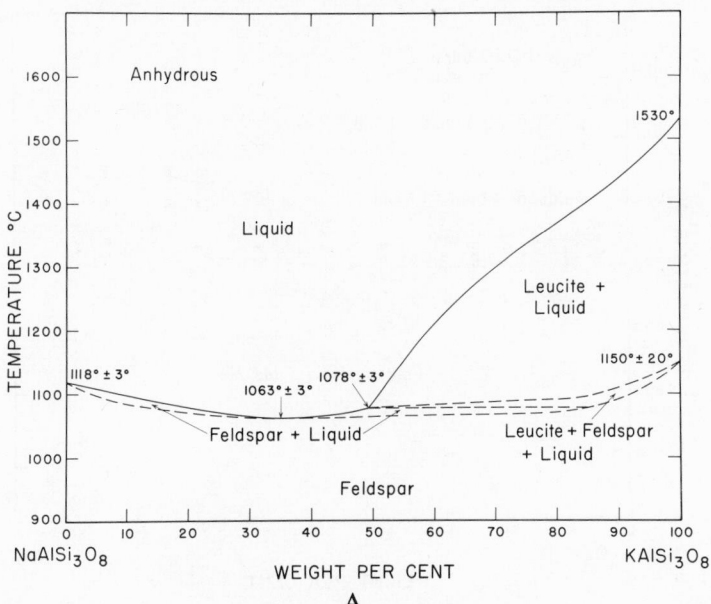

Figure 15-10. Melting relationships of the alkali feldspars under water pressure. Anhydrous relationships are shown in Figure 15-10A [3], relationships at 2000 kg/cm² (1961 bars) water pressure in Figure 15-10B (replotted from data of Tuttle and Bowen [4], and relationships at 5000 bars water pressure in Figure 15-10C [11])

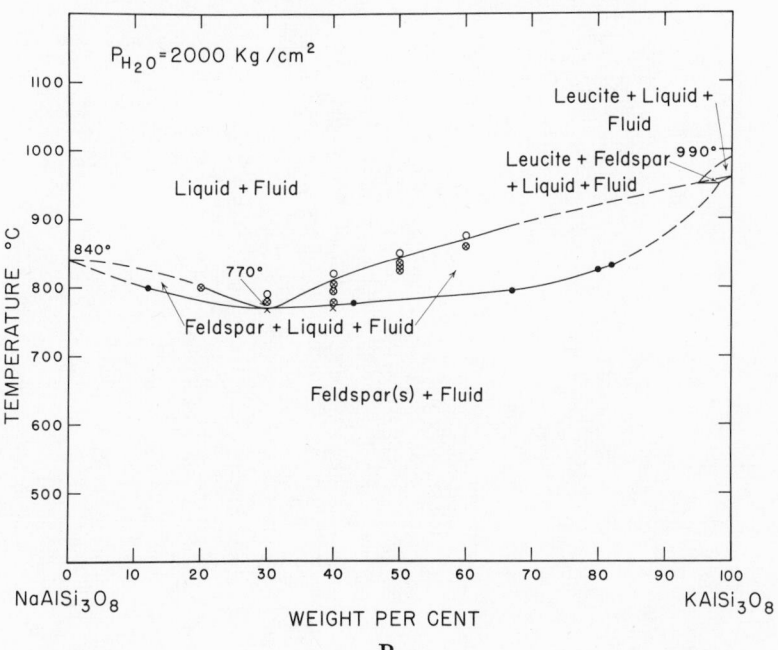

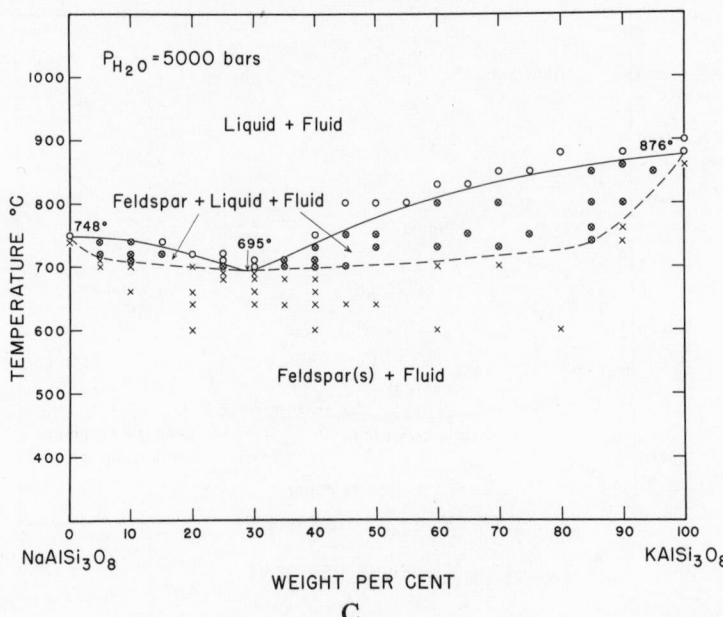

C

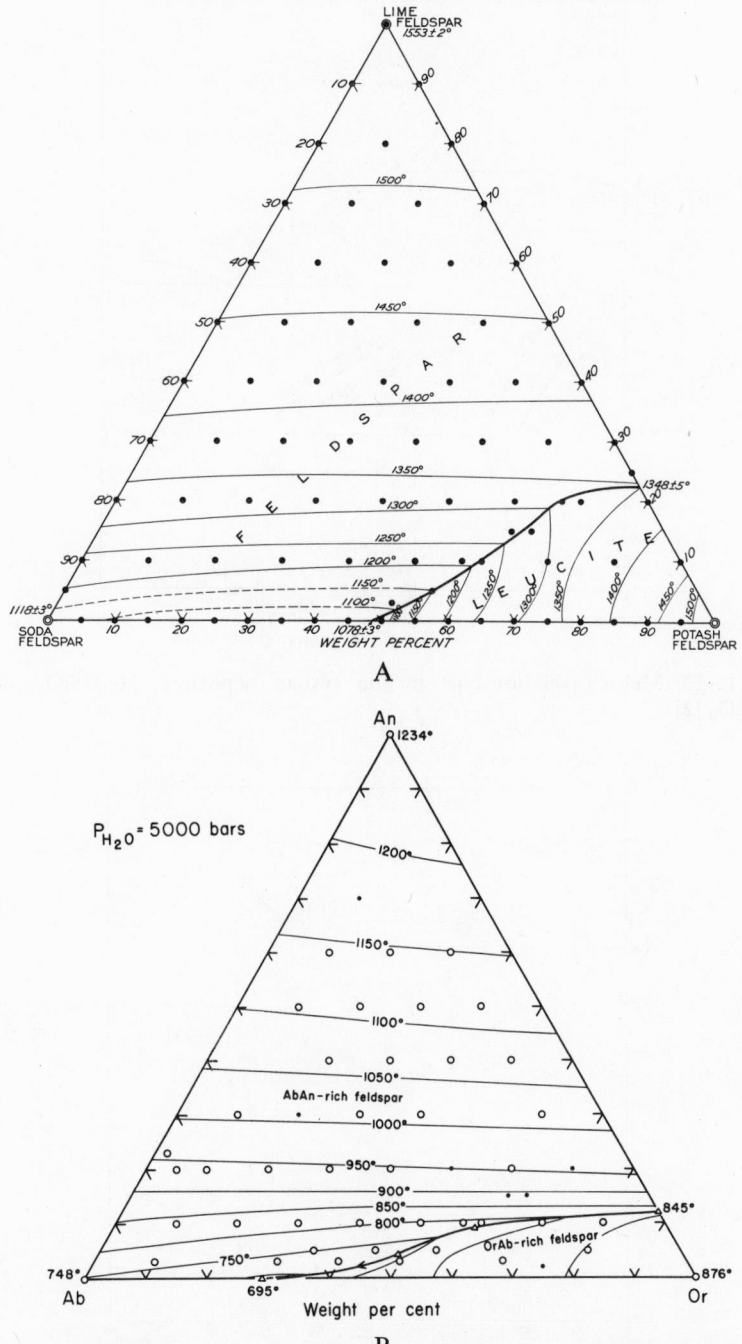

Figure 15-11. Liquidus temperatures in the system CaO feldspar-Na$_2$O feldspar-K$_2$O feldspar under anhydrous conditions (Figure 15-11A [3]) and under 5000 bars water pressure (Figure 15-11B) [11]

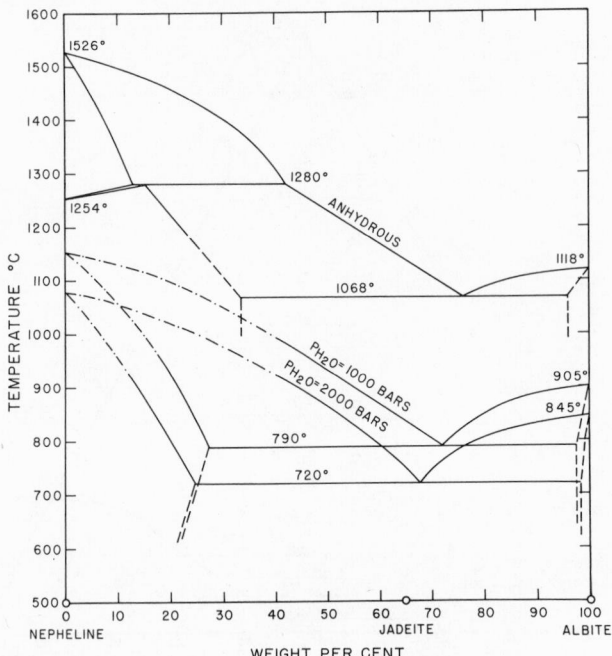

Figure 15-12. Melting relationships in the system nepheline, $NaAlSiO_4$, albite, $NaAlSi_3O_8$ [2]

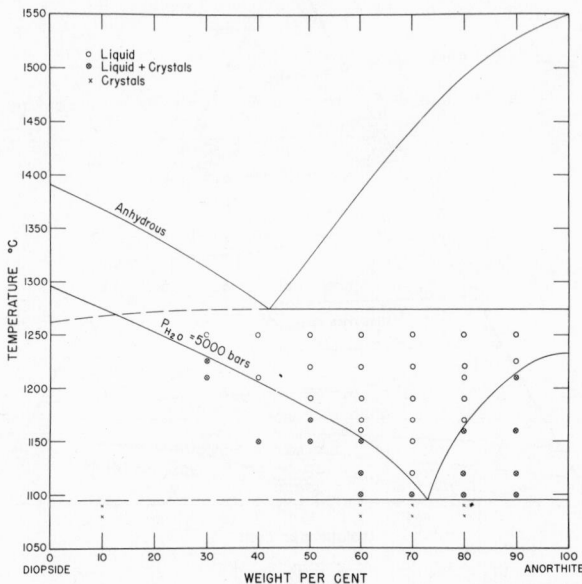

Figure 15-13. Melting relationships in the system diopside, $CaMgSi_2O_6$, -anorthite, $CaAl_2Si_2O_8$ [6]

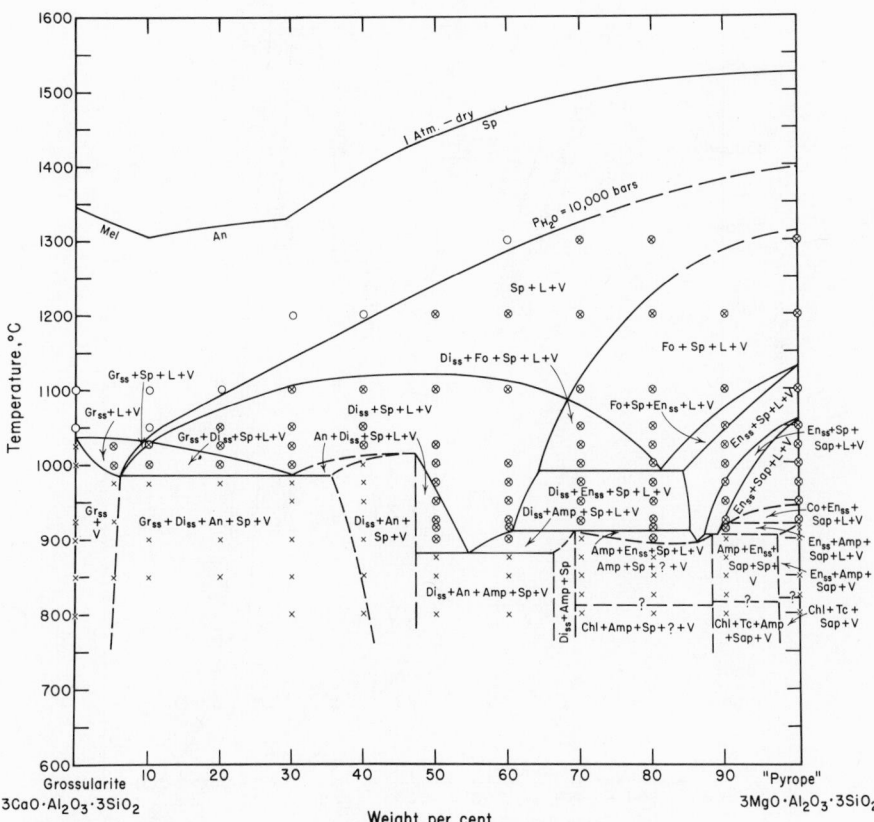

Figure 15-14. Melting relationships along the join "pyrope", $Mg_3Al_2Si_3O_{12}$,-"grossularite", $Ca_3Al_2Si_3O_{12}$ [7]. Abbreviations used are Amp, amphibole; An, anorthite; Chl, chlorite; Co, cordierite; Di, diopside; En, enstatite; Fo, forsterite; Gr, grossularite; Mel, melilite; L, liquid; Sap, sapphirine; Sp, spinel; Tc, talc; V, vapor.

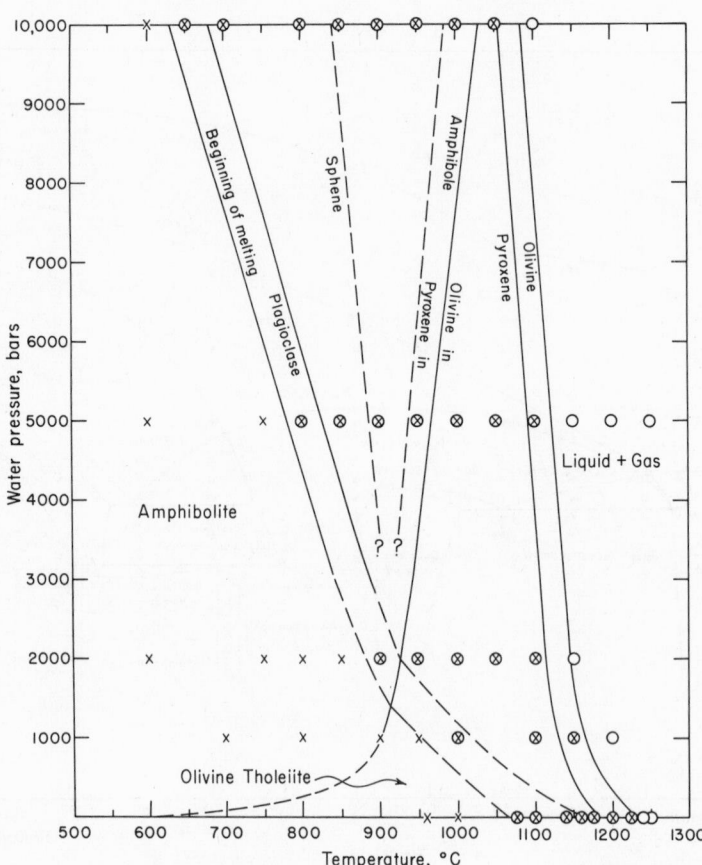

Figure 15-15. Melting relationships of an olivine tholeiite (basalt) from the 1921 eruption of Kilauea [13]

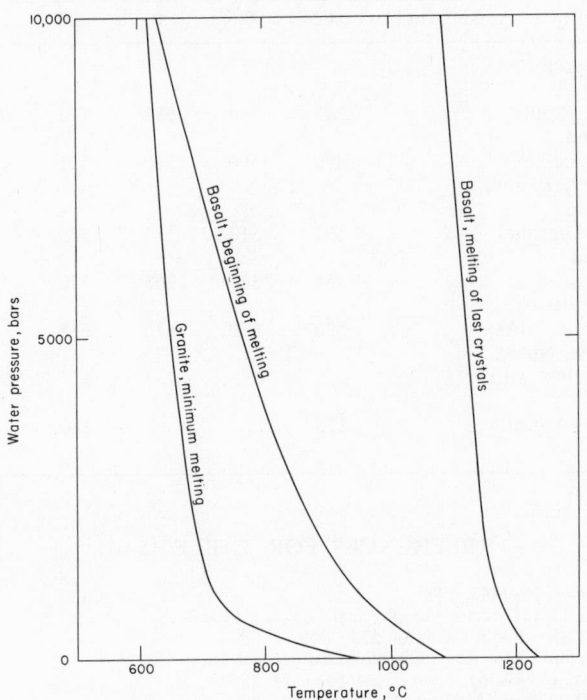

Figure 15-16. Minimum melting curve of granite [4] compared with the melting interval of basalt from the 1921 eruption of Kilauea [13]

Table 15-6. Effect of Pressure on Reactions Involving Sulfides and Arsenides

The phase boundaries given in this section are linear to within experimental error, although many of the more complicated equilibria involve melting to a sulfur-rich, and in some cases arsenic-rich liquid. Also, the effect of pressure on these transitions is smaller than the effect usually found in the silicates.

In the first column of the table, the high-pressure assemblage is written first.

Reaction	Temperatures ($^\circ$C)						
	Pressure (in kb)	0.02	0.5	1.0	2.0	5.0	Ref.
Sulfur, phase diagram (*See* Fig. 15-16)							
Pyrite, FeS_2, –pyrrhotite, $Fe_{1-x}S$, + liquid		745	750	755	770	810	3
Arsenopyrite, FeAsS, + Pyrite, FeS_2, –Pyrrhotite, $Fe_{1-x}S$, + liquid		490	500	510	525	..	1
Covellite, CuS, –Digenite, Cu_9S_5, + liquid		505	510	515	525	..	2
Polydymite, Ni_3S_4– $\alpha Ni_{1-x}S$ + vaesite, NiS_2		355	360	365	370	..	4
Pararammelsbergite, $NiAs_2$– Rammelsbergite, $NiAs_2$, both in equilibrium with $Ni_{1-x}As$		590	600	610	635	..	7
Acanthite, Ag_2S, –Argentite, Ag_2S		175	..	..	180	..	5

REFERENCES FOR TABLE 15-6

1. Clark, Econ. Geol. **55**, 1345, 1960
2. Kullerud, Ann. Rept. Director Geophysical Lab., 196, 1957
3. Kullerud and Yoder, Econ. Geol. **54**, 533, 1959
4. Kullerud and Yund, Ann. Rept. Director Geophysical Lab., 176, 1961
5. Roy, Majumdar, and Hulbe, Econ. Geol. **54**, 1278, 1959
6. Tuller, *Sulfur Data Book*, McGraw-Hill Book Co., New York, 1954
7. Yund, Econ. Geol. **56**, 1273, 1961

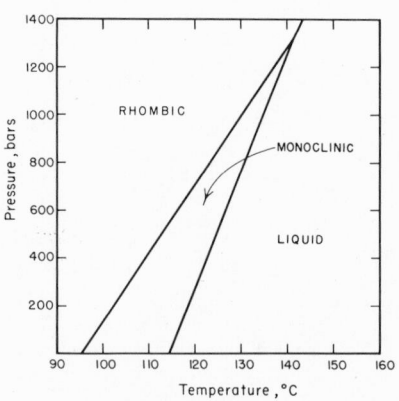

Figure 15-17. The phase diagram of sulfur [6]

SECTION 16

PRESSURE-VOLUME-TEMPERATURE AND PHASE RELATIONS OF WATER AND CARBON DIOXIDE*

by George C. Kennedy and William T. Holser

Contents

Illustrations

* Publication # 479, Institute of Geophysics and Planetary Physics, University of California, Los Angeles

Handbook of Physical Constants—*Revised Edition*
The Geological Society of America Memoir 97, 1966

The relationships between the various forms of solid H_2O and solid-liquid H_2O equilibria are well understood owing to the extensive work of P. W. Bridgman [1, 2, 4, 5, 6]. These relationships are shown in Figure 16-1. Bridgman's [3] curve for solid-liquid equilibrium in CO_2 is also shown in this figure. The specific volumes of water in cm^3/gm as a function of pressure and temperature are given in Table 16-1. The sources of these data are as follows:

1 bar,	0°–100° C	Tilton and Taylor [22]
		Owen, White, and Smith [19]
10–1400 bars,	0°–100° C	Bridgman [2] as recomputed
		by Goranson [9]
1600–10,000 bars,	90°–100° C	Bridgman [4, 5]
Vapor region,	120°–180° C	Juza [11] as tabulated by
		Faxen
Liquid region to 350 bars,	100°–360° C	Smith and Keyes [21]
400–2500 bars,	120°–180° C	Interpolated
Vapor–100 bars,	200°–1000° C	Kennedy [14]
150–1400 bars,	380°–800° C	Holser and Kennedy [10]
		Kirillin, Rumyantsev, and
		Zubaryev [17]
		Keyes, Smith, and Gerry [16]
1600–2500 bars,	380°–600° C	Kennedy [12] corrected and
		smoothed
1600–2500 bars,	600°–800° C	Extrapolated on isometrics
150–2500 bars,	850°–1000° C	Extrapolated on isometrics
5000–250,000 bars,	120°–1000° C	Rice and Walsh [20]
5000–50,000 bars,	80°–180° C	Bridgman [7]

Table 16-2, the specific volumes of water at saturation, are taken from Osborne, Stimson, and Ginnings [18], Tilton and Taylor [22], and Owen, White, and Smith [19]. Table 16-3, the density, pressure, and temperature for CO_2 are taken from Kennedy [13].

REFERENCES FOR SECTION 16

1. Bridgman, Proc. Am. Acad. **47**, 441, 1911
2. —— Proc. Am. Acad. **48**, 309, 1912
3. —— Phys. Rev. **3**, 158, 1914
4. —— Proc. Am. Acad. **66**, 219, 1931
5. —— Jour. Chem. Phys. **3**, 597, 1935
6. —— Jour. Chem. Phys. **5**, 964, 1937
7. —— Proc. Am. Acad. **74**, 399, 1942
8. Faxen, Thermodynamic tables *in* the Metric system for water and steam, Nordisk Rotogravyrs, Stockholm, 1953
9. Goranson, Geol. Soc. America Special Paper 36, 208, 1942
10. Holser and Kennedy, Am. Jour. Sci. **256**, 744, 1958; Am. Jour. Sci. **257**, 71, 1959
11. Juza, Engineering **146**, 1, 1938
12. Kennedy, Am. Jour. Sci. **248**, 540, 1950
13. —— Am. Jour. Sci. **252**, 225, 1954
14. —— Am. Jour. Sci. **255**, 724, 1957
15. Kennedy, Knight, and Holser, Am. Jour. Sci. **256**, 590, 1958
16. Keyes, Smith, and Gerry, Proc. Am. Acad. **70**, 319, 1936
17. Kirillin, Rumyantsev, and Zubaryev, 5th Internat. Steam Conference, Papers submitted by the U.S.S.R. **29**, 1956
18. Osborne, Stimson, and Ginnings, U.S. Nat. Bur. Stds. Jour. Res. **23**, 261, 1939
19. Owen, White, and Smith, Jour. Am. Chem. Soc. **78**, 356, 1956
20. Rice and Walsh, Jour. Chem. Phys. **26**, 824, 1957
21. Smith and Keyes, Proc. Am. Acad. **69**, 285, 1934
22. Tilton and Taylor, U.S. Nat. Bur. Stds. Jour. Res. **18**, 205, 1937

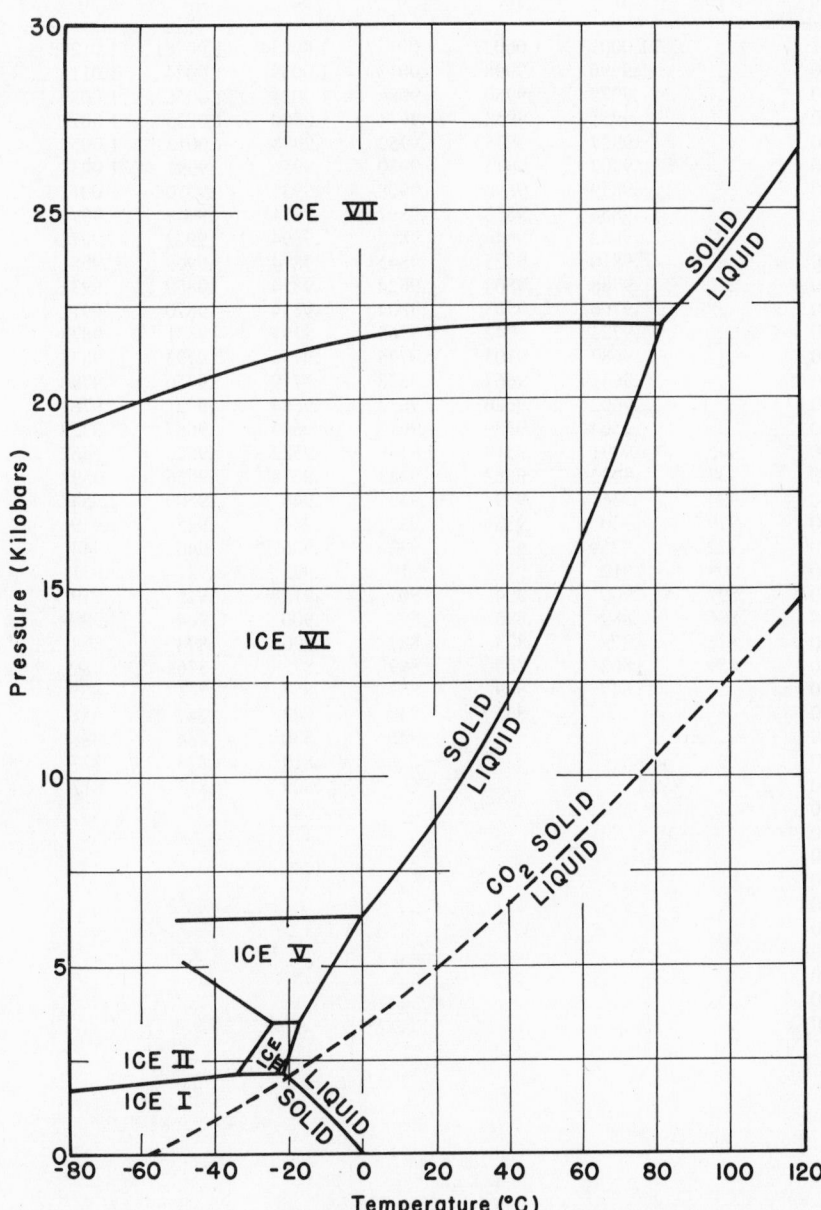

Figure 16-1. Phase diagram of water and the melting curve of carbon dioxide

Handbook of Physical Constants

TABLE 16-1. SPECIFIC VOLUME OF WATER IN CM³/GM

P, bars	Temperature, °C						
	−10	0	10	20	30	40	50
1	..	1.00013	1.00027	1.00177	1.00434	1.00781	1.01208
10	..	.9996	.9998	1.0013	1.0039	1.0074	1.0116
50	..	.9975	.9980	.9986	1.0021	1.0056	1.0099
100	..	.9951	.9958	.9974	1.0000	1.0035	1.0077
150	..	.9927	.9935	.9952	.9978	1.0013	1.0055
200	..	.9903	.9913	.9930	.9956	.9991	1.0033
250	..	.9879	.9890	.9908	.9935	.9970	1.0012
300	..	.9856	.9868	.9887	.9914	.9949	.9991
350	..	.9833	.9846	.9866	.9894	.9929	.9971
400	..	.9810	.9825	.9845	.9874	.9909	.9951
450	..	.9788	.9804	.9824	.9854	.9889	.9931
500	..	.9766	.9783	.9804	.9834	.9870	.9911
600	..	.9723	.9742	9765	9795	9831	9873
700	..	9682	9703	.9726	.9756	.9793	.9835
800	..	.9641	.9664	.9688	.9719	.9756	.9798
900	..	.9602	.9626	.9652	.9684	.9721	.9763
1,000	..	.9564	.9589	.9616	.9649	.9687	.9729
1,200	.945	.9491	.9519	.9548	.9582	.9620	.9662
1,400	.939	.9422	.9452	.9483	.9518	.9556	.9598
1,600	.934	.936	.939	.942	.946	.950	.954
1,800	.929	.930	.933	.937	.941	.945	.949
2,000	.922	.925	.928	.932	.936	.940	.944
2,500	.909	.912	.915	.919	.923	.927	.931
3,000	.897	.900	.904	.907	.911	.915	.919
3,500	.886	.889	.893	.897	.900	.904	.908
4,000	.876	.879	.883	.887	.890	.894	.898
5,000	.859	.862	.865	.869	.872	.876	.880
6,000	..	.847	.849	.853	.857	.861	.865
7,000	..	..	.835	.839	.843	.847	.851
8,000	..	..	..	.826	.830	.834	.838
9,000	..	..	..	..	.819	.823	.827
10,000	..	..	..	..	.809	.813	.817
15,000	..	..	..	..	..	..	..
20,000	..	..	..	..	..	..	..
25,000	..	..	..	..	..	..	..
30,000	..	..	..	..	..	..	..
40,000	..	..	..	..	..	..	..
50,000	..	..	..	..	..	..	..
100,000	..	..	..	..	..	..	..
150,000	..	..	..	..	..	..	..
200,000	..	..	..	..	..	..	..
250,000	..	..	..	..	..	..	..

P, bars	Temperature, ° C						
	60	70	80	90	100	120	140
1	1.01706	1.02271	1.02900	1.0359	1.0434	1794.	1890.
10	1.0166	1.0223	1.0285	1.0354	1.0429	1.0598	1.0794
50	1.0148	1.0204	1.0266	1.0434	1.0408	1.0577	1.0769
100	1.0126	1.0181	1.0243	1.0310	1.0384	1.0550	1.0739
150	1.0104	1.0159	1.0220	1.0287	1.0359	1.0523	1.0709
200	1.0082	1.0137	1.0198	1.0264	1.0336	1.0497	1.0680
250	1.0061	1.0115	1.0176	1.0241	1.0313	1.0471	1.0652
300	1.0040	1.0094	1.0154	1.0219	1.0290	1.0445	1.0625
350	1.0019	1.0073	1.0132	1.0197	1.0267	1.0421	1.0598
400	.9999	1.0052	1.0111	1.0175	1.0245	1.0397	1.0570
450	.9979	1.0132	1.0090	1.0154	1.0223	1.0373	1.0543
500	.9959	1.0012	1.0070	1.0133	1.0201	1.0349	1.0516
600	.9920	.9973	1.0030	1.0092	1.0158	1.030	1.046
700	.9882	.9934	.9990	1.0051	1.0117	1.025	1.041
800	.9845	.9896	.9952	1.0012	1.0076	1.021	1.037
900	.9809	.9860	.9915	.9974	1.0037	1.017	1.032
1,000	.9774	.9824	.9878	.9937	.9999	1.013	1.028
1,200	.9707	.9756	.9809	.9866	.9927	1.005	1.019
1,400	.9643	.9691	.9742	.9798	.9858	.998	1.011
1,600	.958	.963	.968	.974	.979	.991	1.004
1,800	.953	.958	.963	.968	.973	.985	.997
2,000	.948	.953	.958	.963	.968	.979	.991
2,500	.935	.940	.945	.950	.955	.965	.975
3,000	.924	.928	.933	.938	.943	..	..
3,500	.913	.917	.921	.926	.931	..	..
4,000	.902	.906	.911	.916	.921	..	..
5,000	.884	.888	.893	.897	.902	.911	.919
6,000	.869	.873	.877	.881	.885	..	..
7,000	.855	.859	.862	.866	.870	..	..
8,000	.842	.846	.849	.853	.857	..	..
9,000	.831	.835	.838	.842	.846	..	..
10,000	.821	.825	.829	.833	.837	.845	.852
15,000	.780	.784	.787	.791	.794	.800	.805
20,000	..	..	.757	.760	.762	.766	.770
25,000	..	..	..	..	..	.739	.742
30,000	..	..	..	..	..	..	..
40,000	..	..	..	..	..	..	..
50,000	..	..	..	..	..	..	..
100,000	..	..	..	..	..	..	..
150,000	..	..	..	..	..	..	..
200,000	..	..	..	..	..	..	..
250,000	..	..	..	..	..	..	..

TABLE 16-1. *Continued*

P, bars	Temperature, ° C						
	160	180	200	220	240	260	280
1	1984.	2079.	2171.	2264.7	2358.6	2452.1	2552.9
10	1.1018	194.4	206.8	216.3	227.1	237.6	247.9
50	1.0990	1.1242	1.1531	1.1868	1.2265	1.2747	42.30
100	1.0955	1.1202	1.1483	1.1810	1.2189	1.2647	1.3217
150	1.0922	1.1163	1.1437	1.1753	1.2118	1.2553	1.3086
200	1.0889	1.1125	1.1392	1.1698	1.2050	1.2466	1.2968
250	1.0857	1.1088	1.1349	1.1645	1.1986	1.2384	1.2860
300	1.0826	1.1052	1.1307	1.1596	1.1926	1.2308	1.2762
350	1.0796	1.1018	1.1267	1.1548	1.1868	1.2236	1.2670
400	1.0765	1.0983	1.1227	1.1501	1.1812	1.2168	1.2582
450	1.0735	1.0949	1.1187	1.1455	1.1758	1.2100	1.2498
500	1.0704	1.0914	1.1147	1.1410	1.1705	1.2036	1.2418
600	1.064	1.085	1.1072	1.1325	1.1604	1.1916	1.2273
700	1.059	1.079	1.1003	1.1245	1.1509	1.1806	1.2142
800	1.054	1.073	1.0936	1.1169	1.1421	1.1704	1.2021
900	1.049	1.067	1.0872	1.1096	1.1339	1.1609	1.1911
1,000	1.044	1.061	1.0811	1.1027	1.1261	1.1520	1.1807
1,200	1.035	1.051	1.0696	1.0900	1.1117	1.1357	1.1620
1,400	1.026	1.041	1.0591	1.0783	1.0988	1.1211	1.1454
1,600	1.018	1.033	1.050	1.068	1.087	1.108	1.131
1,800	1.010	1.025	1.040	1.058	1.076	1.096	1.117
2,000	1.003	1.017	1.032	1.048	1.065	1.084	1.105
2,500	.985	.997	1.010	1.024	1.040	1.056	1.075
3,000	..	..	..	..	..	..	..
3,500	..	..	..	..	..	..	..
4,000	..	..	..	..	..	..	..
5,000	.927	.936	.944	..	..	..	..
6,000	..	..	..	..	..	..	..
7,000	..	..	..	..	..	..	..
8,000	..	..	..	..	..	..	..
9,000	..	..	..	..	..	..	..
10,000	.859	.866	.872	..	..	..	..
15,000	.810	.815	.821	..	..	..	..
20,000	.774	.778	.783	..	..	..	..
25,000	.746	.750	.754	..	..	..	..
30,000	.724	.728	.732	..	..	..	..
40,000	..	..	.700	..	..	..	..
50,000	..	..	..	..	..	..	..
100,000	..	..	..	..	..	..	..
150,000	..	..	..	..	..	..	..
200,000	..	..	..	..	..	..	..
250,000	..	..	..	..	..	..	..

TABLE 16-1. *Continued*

P, bars	Temperature, ° C						
	300	320	340	360	380	400	420
1	2638.6	2731.6	2824.4	2922.1	3009.9	3102.6	3195.3
10	257.9	267.9	277.6	287.5	296.9	306.6	316.2
50	45.34	48.13	50.71	53.18	55.55	57.88	60.11
100	1.3970	19.27	21.52	23.32	24.94	26.42	27.80
150	1.3771	1.4725	1.6300	12.58	14.25	15.69	16.90
200	1.3599	1.4431	1.5694	1.8235	8.267	9.965	11.20
250	1.3448	1.4207	1.5265	1.6965	2.254	6.015	7.553
300	1.3313	1.4008	1.4930	1.6272	1.883	2.799	4.900
350	1.3191	1.3832	1.4653	1.5792	1.767	2.127	3.062
400	1.3077	1.3676	1.4420	1.5448	1.695	1.916	2.363
450	1.2970	1.3534	1.4222	1.5145	1.643	1.812	2.091
500	1.2869	1.3404	1.4046	1.4869	1.596	1.732	1.944
600	1.2688	1.3171	1.3735	1.4433	1.532	1.634	1.772
700	1.2528	1.2971	1.3477	1.4089	1.484	1.571	1.677
800	1.2384	1.2795	1.3257	1.3803	1.446	1.516	1.606
900	1.2253	1.2636	1.3061	1.3558	1.414	1.477	1.552
1,000	1.2131	1.2491	1.2885	1.3342	1.387	1.442	1.506
1,200	1.1913	1.2234	1.2581	1.2978	1.342	1.389	1.440
1,400	1.1724	1.2016	1.2326	1.2677	1.306	1.348	1.391
1,600	1.1559	1.183	1.211	1.242	1.277	1.315	1.353
1,800	1.142	1.166	1.192	1.221	1.252	1.287	1.321
2,000	1.127	1.151	1.174	1.203	1.229	1.260	1.293
2,500	1.095	1.116	1.137	1.161	1.183	1.209	1.236
3,000	..	..	..	..	..	..	..
3,500	..	..	..	..	..	..	..
4,000	..	..	..	..	..	..	..
5,000	.995	..	..	..	..	1.065	..
6,000	..	..	..	..	..	..	..
7,000	..	..	..	..	..	..	..
8,000	..	..	..	..	..	..	..
9,000	..	..	..	..	..	..	..
10,000	.907	..	..	..	..	.937	..
15,000	.846	..	..	..	..	.873	..
20,000	.806	..	..	..	..	.826	..
25,000	.774	..	..	..	..	.794	..
30,000	.751	..	..	..	..	.770	..
40,000	.713	..	..	..	..	.731	..
50,000	.681*	..	..	..	..	.698	..
100,000	.575*	..	..	..	..	.587	..
150,000	.514*	..	..	..	..	.523*	..
200,000	.478*	..	..	..	..	.483*	..
250,000	.454*	..	..	..	..	.459*	..

TABLE 16-1. *Continued*

P, bars	Temperature, ° C						
	440	460	480	500	550	600	650
1	3288.0	3380.6	3473.3	3565.7	3797.	4028.	4261.
10	325.8	335.3	345.0	354.3	377.8	401.2	424.3
50	62.24	64.39	66.46	68.58	73.66	78.58	83.55
100	29.13	30.40	31.63	32.81	35.56	38.28	40.99
150	17.99	18.99	19.92	20.81	22.89	24.84	26.75
200	12.25	13.18	14.01	14.78	16.53	18.15	19.70
250	8.673	9.611	10.44	11.17	12.73	14.12	15.43
300	6.224	7.207	8.012	8.709	10.17	11.43	12.60
350	4.396	5.417	6.259	6.954	8.340	9.507	10.56
400	3.209	4.114	4.943	5.640	6.978	8.077	9.057
450	2.594	3.260	4.001	4.645	5.929	6.971	7.888
500	2.276	2.724	3.294	3.901	5.112	6.095	6.960
600	1.963	2.225	2.570	2.959	3.949	4.823	5.593
700	1.812	1.986	2.207	2.468	3.219	3.975	4.657
800	1.712	1.844	2.004	2.190	2.757	3.390	3.978
900	1.641	1.744	1.867	2.012	2.453	2.969	3.480
1,000	1.582	1.672	1.774	1.892	2.246	2.670	3.111
1,200	1.498	1.562	1.636	1.720	1.973	2.281	2.618
1,400	1.438	1.490	1.549	1.616	1.806	2.037	2.303
1,600	1.393	1.437	1.486	1.538	1.688	1.869	2.085
1,800	1.357	1.395	1.436	1.481	1.607	1.753	1.927
2,000	1.326	1.361	1.397	1.435	1.540	1.666	1.814
2,500	1.265	1.296	1.325	1.356	1.436	1.525	1.626
3,000	..	..	..	..	..	..	..
3,500	..	..	..	..	..	..	..
4,000	..	..	..	..	..	..	..
5,000	..	..	..	1.139	..	..	..
6,000	..	..	..	..	..	..	..
7,000	..	..	..	..	..	..	..
8,000	..	..	..	..	..	..	..
9,000	..	..	..	..	..	..	..
10,000	..	..	..	.978	..	..	..
15,000	..	..	..	.900	..	..	..
20,000	..	..	..	.848	..	..	..
25,000	..	..	..	.814	..	..	..
30,000	..	..	..	.789	..	..	..
40,000	..	..	..	.749	..	..	..
50,000	..	..	..	.715	..	..	..
100,000	..	..	..	.599	..	..	..
150,000	..	..	..	.531*	..	..	..
200,000	..	..	..	.489*	..	..	..
250,000	..	..	..	.463*	..	..	..

| P, bars | Temperature, ° C | | | | | | |
	700	750	800	850	900	950	1000
1	4491.	4721.	4951.	5183.	5413.	5644.	5875.
10	447.6	470.8	494.0	517.6	540.6	563.9	587.3
50	88.39	93.21	98.06	102.89	107.64	112.39	115.1
100	43.56	46.06	48.54	51.01	53.47	55.91	58.39
150	28.59	30.35	32.06	33.77	35.45	37.14	38.85
200	21.14	22.49	23.83	25.15	26.46	27.77	29.08
250	16.64	17.78	18.89	19.99	21.08	22.16	23.24
300	13.66	14.65	15.61	16.56	17.50	18.43	19.35
350	11.53	12.43	13.28	14.12	14.95	15.76	16.57
400	9.948	10.76	11.53	12.29	13.04	13.77	14.50
450	8.717	9.465	10.18	10.87	11.56	12.23	12.88
500	7.735	8.440	9.104	9.750	10.38	10.99	11.59
600	6.279	6.909	7.498	8.070	8.621	9.157	9.675
700	5.269	5.840	6.371	6.884	7.377	7.849	8.307
800	4.524	5.053	5.542	6.006	6.451	6.874	7.285
900	3.968	4.450	4.906	5.329	5.735	6.119	6.495
1,000	3.547	3.988	4.406	4.792	5.163	5.518	5.863
1,200	2.966	3.328	3.682	4.009	4.320	4.624	4.927
1,400	2.590	2.885	3.182	3.458	3.730	3.997	4.264
1,600	2.322	2.571	2.823	3.065	3.301	3.536	3.772
1,800	2.124	2.338	2.555	2.768	2.976	3.186	3.400
2,000	1.980	2.161	2.348	2.536	2.722	2.909	3.097
2,500	1.735	1.857	1.993	2.138	2.287	2.434	2.576
3,000	..	..	..	..	..	..	..
3,500	..	..	..	..	..	..	..
4,000	..	..	..	..	..	..	..
5,000	..	1.350	..	..	..	..	1.616
6,000	..	..	..	..	..	..	..
7,000	..	..	..	..	..	..	..
8,000	..	..	..	..	..	..	..
9,000	..	1.078	..	..	..	..	1.189
10,000	..	.969	..	..	..	..	1.040
15,000	..	.903	..	..	..	..	.959
20,000	..	.864	..	..	..	..	.914
25,000	..	.838	..	..	..	..	.886
30,000	..	.794	..	..	..	..	.839
40,000	..	.757	..	..	..	..	.799
50,000	..	.628	..	..	..	..	.658
100,000	..	.552	..	..	..	..	.573
150,000	..	.504	..	..	..	..	.519
200,000	..	.473*	..	..	..	..	.484
250,000	..	..	..	..	..	..	..

* Probably supercooled with respect to ice.

TABLE 16-2. WATER AT SATURATION

Temperature (°C)	Pressure (bars)	Volume, cm³/gm Liquid	Volume, cm³/gm Vapor
0*	.0061076	1.00013	206,290.
5	.0087191	1.00001	147,150.
10	.012271	1.00027	106,420.
20	.023368	1.00177	57,836.
30	.042418	1.00434	32,929.
40	.073750	1.00781	19,546.
50	.12335	1.01208	12,045.
60	.19919	1.01706	7,677.6
70	.3116	1.02271	5,045.3
80	.4736	1.02900	3,408.3
90	.7011	1.0359	2,360.9
100	1.0133	1.0434	1,673.0
120	1.9854	1.0603	8,917.1
140	3.6136	1.0798	508.66
160	6.180	1.1021	306.85
180	10.027	1.1275	193.85
200	15.550	1.1565	127.19
220	23.202	1.1900	86.062
240	33.480	1.2291	59.674
260	46.941	1.2755	42.149
280	64.19	1.3321	30.133
300	85.92	1.4036	21.643
320	112.89	1.4992	15.451
340	146.08	1.639	10.779
360	186.74	1.894	6.943
374.15	221.29	3.1	3.1

* Supercooled liquid.

TABLE 16-3. DENSITY

Temperature, °C	25	50	75	100	150	200	250	300	350	Pressure, 400
0	.0601	.947	.954	.969	.997	1.0170	1.0350	1.0530	1.0670	1.0792
10	.0561	.864	.891	.914	.950	.9770	1.0000	1.0190	1.0350	1.0502
20	.0527	.1423	.810	.855	.901	.9335	.9600	.9832	1.0030	1.0200
30	.0499	.1251	.655	.782	.850	.8887	.9190	.9460	.9685	.9882
40	.0476	.1135	.2305	.638	.785	.8415	.8771	.9077	.9339	.9559
50	.0456	.1052	.1932	.3901	.705	.7855	.8347	.8687	.8990	.9233
60	.0437	.0984	.1726	.2868	.604	.7240	.7889	.8292	.8634	.8905
70	.0421	.0930	.1584	.2478	.504	.6605	.7379	.7882	.8270	.8575
80	.0406	.0883	.1469	.2215	.430	.5935	.6872	.7466	.7898	.8243
90	.0391	.0845	.1381	.2019	.373	.5325	.6359	.7040	.7522	.7909
100	.0378	.0810	.1305	.1877	.333	.4815	.5880	.6630	.7160	.7571
150	.0325	.0674	.1054	.1461	.2337	.3267	.4151	.4925	.5549	.6079
200	.0288	.0586	.0898	.1220	.1900	.2591	.3271	.3907	.4491	.5006
250	.0257	.0518	.0788	.1065	.1629	.2192	.2743	.3274	.3773	.4237
300	.0233	.0468	.0707	.0951	.1434	.1923	.2388	.2850	.3279	.3691
350	.0213	.0427	.0643	.0857	.1292	.1725	.2137	.2540	.2928	.3284
400	.0197	.0393	.0591	.0788	.1178	.1565	.1942	.2308	.2650	.2979
450	.0183	.0365	.0547	.0726	.1086	.1441	.1786	.2117	.2431	.2738
500	.0171	.0340	.0509	.0677	.1009	.1339	.1658	.1962	.2253	.2536
550	.0160	.0319	.0477	.0635	.0945	.1250	.1546	.1833	.2104	.2370
600	.0151	.0301	.0449	.0597	.0887	.1174	.1450	.1722	.1979	.2227
650	.0143	.0284	.0424	.0563	.0837	.1107	.1368	.1626	.1872	.2102
700	.0135	.0269	.0402	.0534	.0794	.1048	.1296	.1538	.1767	.1992
750	.0128	.0256	.0382	.0508	.0754	.0995	.1233	.1460	.1682	.1895
800	.0122	.0244	.0364	.0484	.0718	.0948	.1173	.1391	.1603	.1806
850	.0117	.0233	.0348	.0462	.0686	.0906	.1123	.1328	.1532	.1729
900	.0112	.0223	.0333	.0442	.0657	.0868	.1073	.1272	.1468	.1657
950	.0107	.0213	.0319	.0422	.0630	.0832	.1026	.1222	.1404	.1589
1000	.0103	.0205	.0307	.0407	.0604	.0797	.0986	.1174	.1350	.1527

OF CO_2 IN GM/CM³

bars 450	500	600	700	800	900	1000	1100	1200	1300	1400
1.0900	1.1024	1.1227	1.1405	1.1569	1.1698	1.1841	1.1990	1.2101	1.2211	1.2305
1.0635	1.0759	1.0974	1.1167	1.1340	1.1485	1.1636	1.1788	1.1908	1.2022	1.2127
1.0351	1.0482	1.0719	1.0928	1.1112	1.1272	1.1431	1.1586	1.1716	1.1835	1.1949
1.0054	1.0200	1.0462	1.0689	1.0885	1.1060	1.1226	1.1386	1.1525	1.1650	1.1772
.9755	.9916	1.0204	1.0450	1.0659	1.0848	1.1022	1.1187	1.1335	1.1466	1.1595
.9451	.9630	.9945	1.0211	1.0434	1.0637	1.0819	1.0990	1.1146	1.1284	1.1419
.9139	.9340	.9686	.9973	1.0210	1.0427	1.0617	1.0795	1.0958	1.1104	1.1244
.8821	.9050	.9427	.9735	.9988	1.0218	1.0417	1.0603	1.0772	1.0926	1.1071
.8516	.8763	.9168	.9498	.9769	1.0010	1.0219	1.0413	1.0589	1.0750	1.0900
.8212	.8478	.8911	.9262	.9552	.9804	1.0023	1.0225	1.0409	1.0576	1.0731
.7911	.8195	.8655	.9038	.9337	.9600	.9830	1.0041	1.0231	1.0405	1.0565
.6501	.6889	.7469	.7928	.8309	.8628	.8912	.9171	.9386	.9590	.9781
.5443	.5833	.6485	.6998	.7423	.7789	.8111	.8391	.8634	.8860	.9072
.4672	.5064	.5709	.6244	.6687	.7065	.7411	.7707	.7971	.8217	.8441
.4072	.4444	.5088	.5626	.6076	.6457	.6805	.7115	.7390	.7651	.7890
.3637	.3967	.4583	.5117	.5563	.5945	.6291	.6607	.6884	.7155	.7400
.3293	.3601	.4172	.4684	.5130	.5514	.5859	.6173	.6450	.6722	.6969
.3019	.3311	.3840	.4325	.4758	.5147	.5487	.5798	.6081	.6350	.6591
.2802	.3068	.3565	.4020	.4438	.4824	.5165	.5470	.5757	.6021	.6264
.2614	.2866	.3335	.3768	.4167	.4539	.4877	.5182	.5467	.5728	.5975
.2457	.2693	.3139	.3553	.3932	.4289	.4620	.4929	.5208	.5467	.5715
.2321	.2546	.2969	.3366	.3729	.4066	.4392	.4699	.4978	.5232	.5477
.2205	.2420	.2819	.3201	.3553	.3876	.4192	.4489	.4770	.5019	.5262
.2101	.2303	.2685	.3052	.3393	.3711	.4015	.4301	.4578	.4826	.5066
.2009	.2197	.2567	.2916	.3249	.3560	.3856	.4134	.4403	.4651	.4888
.1924	.2105	.2461	.2796	.3118	.3422	.3710	.3981	.4245	.4491	.4724
.1841	.2020	.2365	.2689	.2999	.3296	.3579	.3841	.4102	.4345	.4573
.1764	.1941	.2276	.2592	.2893	.3180	.3458	.3717	.3971	.4208	.4434
.1697	.1868	.2194	.2503	.2796	.3079	.3346	.3603	.3850	.4078	.4305

SECTION 17

BINARY MIXTURES OF VOLATILE COMPONENTS

by H. J. Greenwood and H. L. Barnes

Contents

Handbook of Physical Constants—*Revised Edition*

The Geological Society of America Memoir 97, 1966

The data for binary mixtures of volatiles are rather scanty, at least for systems of geological interest, and are of widely differing accuracies. The data are therefore presented in a number of tables with appropriate comments on each so that the uncertainties in the entries may be evaluated. Most of the data have been taken from published work, but not all the data from each source are reported here. In regions of overlap no attempt has been made to arrive at an average value, but instead the data considered to be the better of two sets have been quoted and the other set discarded. Many of the data in the literature are given in non-integral values of composition, pressure, and temperature, and where possible these have been plotted on large-scale graph paper and interpolated to integral values. Where this interpolation is considered to be of the same accuracy as the original data the entries are made with an appropriate number of significant figures, and where the interpolation was over too large a distance or between sets of data due to different authors, or where it was simply extrapolated, the entries are enclosed in parentheses.

The data on this type of system fall naturally into two groups: those on the two-phase regions and those on the one-phase regions. Only the supercritical one-phase regions are considered here, and the two-phase regions presented are all of the liquid-vapor type. In the two-phase region the system is described by giving the temperature in ° C, the pressure in bars, and the compositions of the coexisting phases in terms of the mole fractions of the components, where the mole fraction of component 1 is represented by

$$x_1 = \frac{n_1}{\Sigma_i n_i},$$
(1)

where the n_i's are the numbers of moles of each species in the mixture. Where the information is available, the densities of the phases are also quoted, in grams per cubic centimeter.

In the one-phase regions the data are given as the compressibility factor, Z, where

$$Z = \frac{PV}{RT}.$$
(2)

The term Z is entered in the body of the table at integral values of the temperature, pressure, and mole fraction.

In the absence of data on one-phase binary gas mixtures some idea of the behavior may be obtained by the use of some simple assumptions. The gross behavior and the activities of the two components of a binary mixture of nonpolar molecular species may be estimated with rather good accuracy by an extension of the theory of corresponding states which has been developed by Pitzer and his coworkers. They show [11] that for such molecules the equation of state of the pure end members can be written as

$$Z = f(P_r, T_r, \omega),$$
(3)

where T_r is the reduced temperature, P_r the reduced pressure, and ω a quantity called the acentric factor. The acentric factor accounts for the nonspherical nature of the molecules and is found from

$$\omega = -\log \frac{P_s}{P_c} - 1.000,$$
(4)

where P_s is the vapor pressure at $T_r = .700$ and P_c is the critical pressure. In mixtures, the equation of state is of the form

$$Z = f(P_r, T_r, x, \omega),$$
(5)

where the reduced pressure and temperature are found from pseudocritical constants and the ω from assuming it to be linear with the mole fraction. For complete details and the necessary tables *see* [11].

The volumetric behavior of mixtures involving polar molecules can be calculated from intermolecular force-field theory [7, 9] in the high-temperature, low-pressure range, but at densities much more than about 10 moles per liter empirical data on the pure end members are required before the behavior of the mixtures can be inferred. If such data are available, one may get a good idea of the behavior of the mixtures by assuming that the components mix ideally; i.e.

$$\bar{V}^m = \sum_i x_i \bar{V}_i^0; \tag{6}$$

where $\bar{V}_i^0$ is the molar volume of pure i at the P and T of the mixture. It follows from this that the fugacities of the components in the mixtures are given by

$$f_i^m = x_i f_i^0. \tag{7}$$

The assumption of ideal mixing appears to agree with the data on carbon dioxide and water [5] to within a few per cent, but Table 17-13 indicates that the agreement in the system water-argon [6] is not good above 500 bars particularly at low concentrations of water. It is clear that the assumption of ideality may lead to serious error in some cases, and it should be made with caution.

Since the preparation of these tables, two papers [17, 18] on the system H_2O-CO_2 have appeared which extend and modify to some extent Tables 17-1 and 17-2. Table 17-20 is taken directly from 17.

REFERENCES FOR SECTION 17

1. Barnes, Carnegie Inst. Wash. Year Book **58**, 163, 1959
2. Bierlein, Ph.D. Dissertation, Ohio State Univ., Univ. Microfilms **24**, 101, 1951
3. Bierlein and Kay, Ind. Eng. Chem. **45**, 618, 1953
4. Ellis, Am. Jour. Sci. **257**, 217, 1959
5. Franck and Tödheide, Zeits. für Phys. Chem. **22**, 232, 1959
6. Greenwood, Jour. Geophys. Research **66**, 3923, 1961
7. Hirschfelder, Curtis, and Bird, Molecular theory of gases and liquids, John Wiley & Sons, New York, 1954
8. Khitarov and Malinen, Geochemistry, p. 246, 1956
9. Liley, P. E., Thermodynamic properties of steam, carbon dioxide, and steam-carbon dioxide mixtures, Report to the British Admiralty DEMR/EN/32/16/1/56, 1956
10. Malinen, Geochemistry, p. 292, 1959
11. Pitzer and Brewer, Thermodynamics, McGraw-Hill Book Co., Inc., New York, 1961
12. Selleck, Carmichael, and Sage, Ind. Eng. Chem., 44, 2219, 1952
13. Wiebe and Gaddy, Jour. Am. Chem. Soc. **61**, 315, 1939
14. —— Jour. Am. Chem. Soc. **62**, 815, 1940
15. —— Jour. Am. Chem. Soc. **63**, 475, 1941
16. Wright and Maass, Can. Jour. Res. **6**, 94, 1932
17. Takenouchi and Kennedy, Am. Jour. Sci. **262**, 1055, 1964
18. Tödheide and Franck, Zeits. Für Phys. Chem. **37**, 387, 1963

Handbook of Physical Constants

TABLE 17-1. H_2O—CO_2 Two-Phase Region [4, 10, 13, 14, 15] *See* Table 17-20

Compositions of coexisting phases at each pressure and temperature are given as paired values: x_{H_2O} in CO_2-rich phase ($\times 10^3$) and x_{CO_2} in H_2O-rich phase ($\times 10^3$). Data from three sources are presented: [13, 14, 15] up to 100° C, 700 bars; [10] 200°–330° C, 500 bars; [4] 200° C at 25 bars and 250° C at 50 bars. The data of [13, 14, 15] are the most precise, as may be inferred from the number of significant figures in the table. The data of [10] are more widely spaced than those of [13, 14, 15] and were not obtained with equivalent precision, but they do form a smooth continuation of the former. Data from [4] consist of isolated values of the compositions of coexisting phases at irregular intervals of pressure and temperature and are difficult to include in a table with integral values of P and T. They fit in smoothly with the other data.

P (bars)	12°C	25°C	50°C	75°C	100°C	150°C	200°C	250°C	300°C	330°C
25	..	1.64	6.20	10.61	(77)	(200)	675			
	25.5	15.2	7.40	5.25	4.29	..		1.52		
50	..	1.29	3.83	9.57	(52)	(140)	410	807		
	27.8	21.4	13.3	9.80	8.11	(7)		5.50	2.4	
75	..	2.30	3.49	8.85	(37)	(112)	282	615		
	28.4	24.4	17.8	13.38	11.34	(10)		9.10	6.1	
100	..	3.31	4.48	8.29	(27)	(93)	211	535	890	
	28.8	24.9	19.79	16.21	13.90	(13)		12.3	10.7	3.8
125	..	3.46	5.38	8.51	(25)	(78)	173	480	783	
	29.4	25.4	21.07	18.07	16.2	(16)		15.8	14.9	9.8
150	..	3.59	6.05	9.46	(25)	(72)	162	435	718	930
	29.9	25.8	21.74	19.30	17.80	(18)		18.9	19.2	15.8	8.6
200	..	3.76	6.75	11.20	(22)	(64)	155	358	625	830
	30.9	26.7	22.85	20.91	20.02	(22)		24.7	27.8	27.8	25.6
250	..	3.90	7.03	12.00	(22)	(62)	157	328	563	745
	31.4	27.6	23.75	22.15	21.8	(24.6)		29.3	36.8	41.3	43.8
300	..	3.96	7.25	12.50	(22)	(63)	158	318	538	715
	31.7	28.4	24.55	23.11	23.11	(27)		33.1	44.0	55.0	62.8
350	..	4.01	7.43	12.87	(23)	(65)	162	315	538	725
	32.1	29.2	25.30	23.75	24.22	(28.2)		36.4	50.6	69.4	(85)
400	..	4.01	7.56	13.16	(23)	(70)	164	316	550	(755)
	(32.3)	30.1	26.05	24.52	25.30	(30)		39.0	55.7	82.0	(115)
500	..	3.98	7.76	13.57	(26)	(80)	172	323	598	
		(31.6)	27.32	26.0	27.0	(32.6)		44.4	66.7	(145)	
600			7.88	13.89	(30)	(90)	183	(340)	(725)*	
			28.60	27.6	28.5	..		(46)	(73)	(275)*	
700			8.01	14.00	(35)	(102)	(202)	..		
			29.87	29.19	29.88	..		(48)	(81)		

* On critical curve $x_{CO_2}^V = x_{CO_2}^L$

TABLE 17-2. H_2O—CO_2 Critical Curve [10] *See* Table 17-20

P	220	365	440	600	(825)
T	374	350	330	300	(275)
x_{CO_2}	.00	.13	.18	.27	(.32)

TABLES 17-3, 17-4, 17-5, 17-6, 17-7, AND 17-8

H_2O—CO_2 SUPERCRITICAL REGION, $Z = \dfrac{PV}{RT}$

Data from [5] and [8] overlap in the composition range $x_{H_2O} = .8$ and .7, and in this region the data of [5] have been given preference. The rejected data [8] indicate an unreasonably large volume change on mixing, while [5] indicates that it is small. The data of [5] yield nearly straight lines of Z vs. x (P, T, const.) which extrapolate smoothly toward the end members, while those of [8] become strongly curved where x_{CO_2} exceeds .2. At lower concentrations of CO_2, [8] coincides with a smooth extrapolation toward pure H_2O. The entries in Tables 17-3 and 17-4 should be rounded off to two significant figures, and those in Tables 17-5, 17-6, 17-7, and 17-8 to three figures or 1 per cent.

TABLE 17-3. H_2O—CO_2 [8]; $X_{H_2O} = .05$

$$Z = \frac{PV}{RT}$$

P (bars)	T (° C)			
	350	400	450	500
250	(.225)	.500	.683	.803
300	.220	.419	.620	.750
350	.220	.369	.564	.700
400	.22	.339	.520	.658
450	..	.325	.488	.616
500	..	.333	.465	.594
550	..	.352	.458	.582

TABLE 17-4. H_2O—CO_2 [8]; $X_{H_2O} = .1$

$$Z = \frac{PV}{RT}$$

P (bars)	T (° C)			
	350	400	450	500
250	(.320)	.551	.720	(.822)
300	..	.483	.656	.775
350	.267	.430	.604	.731
400	.270	.400	.558	.683
450	.290	.385	.528	.653
500	.310	.387	.506	.623
550	..	.403	.507	.620

Handbook of Physical Constants

TABLE 17-5. H_2O—CO_2 [5]; $X_{H_2O} = .2$

$$Z = \frac{PV}{RT}$$

P (bars)	T (° C)							
	400	450	500	550	600	650	700	750
300								
400	.941	.993	1.02					
500	.982	1.01	1.03	1.04	1.04	1.04		
600	1.02	1.03	1.05	1.07	1.07	1.06	1.06	1.06
700	1.06	1.07	1.08	1.09	1.10	1.10	1.09	1.08
800	1.10	1.10	1.12	1.13	1.14	1.13	1.12	1.11
900	1.14	1.15	1.16	1.16	1.16	1.16	1.15	1.14
1000	1.19	1.19	1.20	1.20	1.20	1.20	1.18	1.17
1200	1.29	1.29	1.29	1.28	1.27	1.26	1.25	1.24
1400	1.40	1.39	1.38	1.36	1.34	1.33	1.32	1.31
1600	1.51	1.49	1.48	1.45	1.42	1.40	1.39	1.37
1800	1.61	1.59	1.57	1.54	1.50	1.48	1.46	1.44
2000	..	1.66	1.67	1.63	1.58	1.55	1.52	1.50

TABLE 17-6. H_2O—CO_2 [5]; $X_{H_2O} = .4$

$$Z = \frac{PV}{RT}$$

P (bars)	T (° C)							
	400	450	500	550	600	650	700	750
300								
400	.866	.899	.929	.958				
500	.851	.899	.915	.955	.964	.980	.989	.980
600	.868	.903	.934	.967	.984	.990	.995	1.00
700	.890	.920	.960	.988	1.01	1.01	1.01	1.00
800	.922	.954	.980	1.01	1.03	1.03	1.03	1.03
900	.972	.995	1.01	1.03	1.05	1.05	1.05	1.05
1000	1.02	1.04	1.05	1.06	1.08	1.08	1.08	1.08
1200	1.13	1.13	1.14	1.13	1.14	1.14	1.14	1.12
1400	1.22	1.22	1.22	1.22	1.21	1.20	1.19	1.18
1600	..	1.30	1.32	1.30	1.28	1.27	1.26	1.23
1800	..	..	1.41	1.38	1.35	1.33	1.32	1.29
2000	..	..	..	1.46	1.41	1.40	1.37	1.34

TABLE 17-7. H_2O—CO_2 [5]; $X_{H_2O} = .6$

$$Z = \frac{PV}{RT}$$

P (bars)	400	450	500	T (°C) 550	600	650	700	750
300	.755							
400	.694	.778	.841	.879				
500	.679	.753	.815	.864	.878	.908	.923	.933
600	.692	.762	.815	.855	.875	.898	.916	.935
700	.725	.784	.822	.856	.881	.912	.921	.935
800	.758	.816	.844	.866	.896	.923	.937	.950
900	.794	.850	.878	.892	.915	.942	.951	.967
1000	..	.885	.915	.925	.944	.969	.973	.984
1200	..	..	.988	.999	1.01	1.01	1.02	1.02
1400	..	..	..	1.08	1.07	1.07	1.07	1.07
1600	..	..	..	1.16	1.13	1.13	1.12	1.11
1800	..	..	..	..	..	1.19	1.18	1.16
2000	..	..	..	..	..	..	1.23	1.20

TABLE 17-8. H_2O—CO_2 [5]; $X_{H_2O} = .8$

$$Z = \frac{PV}{RT}$$

P (bars)	400	450	500	T (°C) 550	600	650	700	750
300	.596	.723						
400	.511	.630	.728	.801	.854			
500	.483	.594	.692	.765	.815	.852	.883	.911
600	..	.597	.667	.737	.795	.840	.872	.899
700	..	.619	.677	.733	.791	.837	.870	.890
800	..	.641	.703	.742	.799	.837	.867	.892
900	..	..	.733	.764	.803	.838	.872	.897
1000	..	..	..	.794	.825	.849	.880	.905
1200	..	..	..	..	.873	.878	.904	.913
1400	..	..	..	..	..	.919	.953	.946
1600	..	..	..	..	..	..	.996	.993
1800	..	..	..	..	..	..	..	..
2000	..	..	..	..	..	..	..	..

TABLES 17-9, 17-10, AND 17-11

H_2O—CO_2

The entries in the following three tables have been calculated [9] from virial equations having the form $PV = A + BP$. These were derived theoretically [9] using the Lennard-Jones form of the intermolecular potential for CO_2, with $\theta = 203.5°$ K, $\beta = 75.2$ cm³ mol⁻¹, and the Stockmayer form of the potential for H_2O with $\theta = 382.0°$ K, $\beta = 23.42$ cm³ mol⁻¹, and a reduced dipole moment of 1.2. Interactions between the two species were assumed to be of the form suggested by Hirschfelder, Curtis, and Bird [7]. The entries in these tables fit the data on pure CO_2 to better than .1 per cent over most of the pressure range quoted, and the data on pure H_2O to the same precision at the lower pressures. The fit with pure H_2O at the high-pressure, low-temperature limit of the tables is about 2.0 per cent since the equations being used here are at pressures somewhat beyond their strictly applicable range. The equations fit data [9] on the mixtures as well as they do the end members. The figures enclosed in parentheses have been interpolated across an error in the original tabulation [9].

Handbook of Physical Constants

TABLE 17-9. H_2O—CO_2 [9]; $P = 50$ bars

$$Z = \frac{PV}{RT}$$

$T\,(^\circ C)$	1.000	.9071	.7500	X_{H_2O} .5000	.2500	.1000	.000
350	.913	.924	.941	.964	· .982	.990	.994
400	.934	.942	.956	.974	.988	.995	.999
450	.949	.955	.966	.981	.993	.999	1.002
500	.958	.964	.973	.986	.996	1.002	1.005
550	.968	.972	.979	.990	.999	1.004	1.007
600	(.973)	(.977)	(.984)	.993	1.001	1.006	1.008
650	(.978)	(.981)	(.987)	.996	1.003	1.007	1.010
700	.982	.985	.990	.997	1.004	1.008	1.011
750	.986	.988	.993	.999	1.005	1.009	1.011

TABLE 17-10. H_2O—CO_2 [9]; $P = 100$ bars

$$Z = \frac{PV}{RT}$$

$T\,(^\circ C)$	1.000	.9071	.7500	X_{H_2O} .5000	.2500	.1000	.000
350	.825	.848	.882	.928	.963	.979	.988
400	.867	.884	.911	.947	.976	(.988)	(.997)
450	.897	.911	.932	.961	.986	.997	1.004
500	.917	.928	.946	.971	.992	1.003	1.009
550	.935	.944	.959	.980	.998	1.008	1.014
600	(.948)	(.955)	(.967)	(.985)	1.002	1.011	1.017
650	(.957)	(.964)	(.974)	(.990)	1.006	1.014	1.019
700	.965	.971	.980	.995	1.008	1.016	1.021
750	.971	.976	.985	.999	1.011	1.018	1.023

TABLE 17-11. H_2O—CO_2 [9]; $P = 200$ bars

$$Z = \frac{PV}{RT}$$

$T\,(^\circ C)$	1.000	.9071	.7500	X_{H_2O} .5000	.2500	.1000	.000
400	.735	.769	.822	.895	.952	.982	.986
450	.794	.821	.864	.923	.971	.995	1.009
500	.833	.856	.892	.943	.985	1.006	1.019
550	.870	.888	.917	.960	.996	1.015	1.027
600	(.893)	(.908)	(.935)	(.972)	(1.005)	1.022	1.033
650	(.912)	(.926)	(.948)	(.981)	(1.012)	1.028	1.039
700	.929	.941	.960	.990	1.017	1.032	1.043
750	.942	.952	.970	.996	1.022	1.036	1.046

TABLE 17-12. H_2O—Argon [6]; $Z = \dfrac{PV}{RT}$, 500° C

Round off to three figures or 1 per cent

Pressure (bars)	Mole fraction of water in mixture, X_{H_2O}					
	1.0	.8	.6	.4	.2	.0
400	.640	.864	1.00	1.07	1.13	1.15
600	.501	.812	1.00	1.10	1.19	1.20
800	.492	.790	1.01	1.15	1.23	1.27
1000	.531	.802	1.03	1.21	1.29	1.34
1200	.582	.830	1.06	1.24	1.34	1.41
1400	.633	.861	1.10	1.29	1.41	1.48
1600	.688	.899	1.14	1.33	1.46	1.55
1800	.746	.943	1.19	1.39	1.53	1.62
2000	.808	.994	1.24	1.45	1.59	1.70

TABLE 17-13. H_2O—Argon [6]; ACTIVITY OF WATER IN WATER-ARGON MIXTURES AT 500° C

Given as the ratio of the fugacity of water in the mixture to the fugacity of pure water at the temperature and pressure of the mixture. If the mixing were ideal, all the entries in the table would be the same as the corresponding mole fractions. (Standard state is water at the pressure and temperature of the mixture.)

$$\eta_{H_2O} = \frac{f^m_{H_2O}}{f^o_{H_2O}}$$

Pressure (bars)	Mole fraction of water, X_{H_2O}								
	.9	.8	.7	.6	.5	.4	.3	.2	.1
200	.895	.785	.669	.581	.494	.407	.320	.215	.122
400	.919	.842	.747	.667	.582	.481	.379	.270	.154
600	.927	.871	.809	.742	.666	.567	.455	.331	.194
800	.941	.892	.846	.789	.728	.637	.529	.397	.240
1000	.947	.903	.863	.819	.771	.692	.588	.460	.288
1200	.948	.907	.865	.827	.791	.724	.634	.517	.338
1400	.951	.909	.868	.835	.803	.741	.669	.564	.382
1600	.949	.908	.868	.835	.804	.754	.693	.602	.581
1800	.947	.904	.861	.836	.806	.762	.714	.594	.412
2000	.948	.906	.871	.838	.807	.772	.730	.667	.480

TABLE 17-14. H₂S—H₂O [16]; COMPOSITION OF AQUEOUS LIQUID WHICH IS IN EQUILIBRIUM WITH VAPOR (UNSTATED COMPOSITION) UP TO 60° C AND 5 BARS

Pressure (bars)	X_{H_2S} ($\times 10^3$)	Pressure (bars)	X_{H_2S} ($\times 10^3$)	Pressure (bars)	X_{H_2S} ($\times 10^3$)
20° C		25° C		30° C	
.484	.952	.524	.897	.564	.850
.965	1.935	1.04	1.822	1.11	1.725
1.42	2.869	1.53	2.702	1.63	2.551
1.98	3.935	2.11	3.691	2.23	3.484
2.42	4.844	2.58	4.577	2.74	4.321
3.27	6.533	3.50	6.174	3.71	5.842
40° C		50° C		60° C	
.649	.773	.749	.705	.869	.664
1.25	1.556	1.39	1.437	1.55	1.336
1.83	2.283	2.03	2.073	2.24	1.911
2.47	3.118	2.71	2.837	2.95	2.632
3.04	3.888	3.34	3.521	3.64	3.246
4.13	5.277	4.54	4.805	4.94	4.423

TABLE 17-15. H$_2$S—H$_2$O [1, 2]; COMPOSITIONS OF COEXISTING AQUEOUS LIQUID AND H$_2$S-RICH VAPOR AT SEVERAL TEMPERATURES AT PRESSURES ABOVE 5 BARS

Compositions given as paired values of mole fraction of H$_2$O in vapor phase ($\times 10^3$) and mole fraction of H$_2$S in liquid phase ($\times 10^3$)

Pressure (bars)	37.8° C	71.1° C	104.4° C	137.8° C	171.1° C
6.89	10.6 8.2	50.7 5.0			
10.3	7.5 12.3	35.7 7.6			
13.8	6.0 16.5	27.4 10.2	95.4 7.7	262.5 5.7	601.9 2.9
17.2	5.1 20.7	22.9 12.8			
20.7	4.6 25.0	19.9 15.4			
27.6	.. ..	16.3 20.6	52.3 15.6	141.1 12.7	317.2 9.4
41.4	.. ..	13.5 31.0	40.3 23.0	101.6 19.1	222.8 15.5
55.2	.. ..	.. ..	35.3 30.1	84.5 25.0	177.6 21.4
69.0	.. ..	.. ..	33.6 37.1	75.2 30.8	153.4 27.3
86.2	.. ..	.. ..	33.5 46.3	69.3 38.2	135.4 35.1
103.4	.. ..	.. ..	34.9 57.7	67.0 46.3	125.8 43.5
120.7	.. ..	.. ..	37.0 69.0	67.3 55.0	121.2 52.0
137.9	.. ..	.. ..	39.8 (82.3)	69.7 64.7	120.3 61.0
155.1	.. ..	.. ..	43.2 (97.3)	73.7 (75.0)	122.1 (70.5)
172.4	.. ..	.. ..	46.9 (114.5)	78.7 (86.0)	126.0 (80.5)
189.6	.. ..	.. ..	50.9 (134.6)	84.1 (97.8)	131.9 (91.0)
206.8	.. ..	.. ..	54.9 (158.6)	89.6 (110.6)	139.4 (102.4)
241.3	.. ..	.. ..	62.9 ..	101.4 ..	156.4 ..
275.8	.. ..	.. ..	71.2 ..	113.0 ..	175.2 ..
310.3	.. ..	.. ..	79.7 ..	125.0 ..	193.9 ..
344.7	.. ..	.. ..	88.5 ..	137.0 ..	213.6 ..

TABLE 17-16. H_2S—H_2O [12]; THE DENSITY OF THE AQUEOUS LIQUID, IN GM CM^{-3}
WHICH IS IN EQUILIBRIUM WITH VAPOR, AT VARIOUS VALUES OF THE TEMPERATURE,
COMPOSITION IN X_{H_2S}, AND PRESSURE

The pressure in bars is given in italics immediately below each value of the density.

| | | | $T\,°C$ | | |
X_{H_2S}	37.8	71.1	104.4	137.8	171.1
.02267	.994	.968	.941	.909	.859
	18.8	*30.5*	*40.7*	*49.6*	*58.0*
.04351	.991*	.968*	.939	.901	.857
	26.9	*52.4*	*81.2*	*97.8*	*103.4*
.05723	.980*	.954*	.929	.896	.857
	26.9	*52.4*	*103.4*	*123.8*	*130.0*

* Under these conditions, a third phase, hydrogen sulfide-rich liquid is in equilibrium
with aqueous liquid and gas.

TABLE 17-17. H_2S—H_2O, THREE-PHASE REGION [12]

Composition of coexisting aqueous liquid, sulfide liquid, and
vapor phases

| | | Mole fraction H_2S ($\times 100$) | | |
$T(°C)$	P (bars)	Aqueous liquid	Sulfide liquid	Gas
29.5*	22.4	(3.23)	(99.7)	(99.71)
38.9	27.6	3.35	(99.1)	99.58
58.5	41.4	3.69	97.27	99.16
74.1	55.2	4.02	95.54	98.54
87.0	69.0	4.35	94.02	97.58
98.7	86.2	4.79	93.25	95.52
100.2†	90.0	4.88	94.23	94.23

* Quadruple point where the solid ($H_2S\cdot6H_2O$) is in equilibrium
with aqueous liquid, an immiscible hydrogen sulfide-rich liquid and
gas
† Critical point where H_2S liquid and gas become identical in
density and composition

TABLE 17-18. H$_2$S—CO$_2$ [2, 3]; Compositions in X_{CO_2} and Densities in Gm Cm^{-3} of the Coexisting Liquids and Vapors

For each composition and pressure there are two possible states of the system, liquid or vapor, each with its appropriate temperature at that pressure. The density of the liquid (ρ_L) and of the vapor (ρ_V) are given for each composition and pressure, along with their temperature, in the body of the table.

Pressure (bars)	$X_{CO_2} = .0000$			$X_{CO_2} = .0630$				$X_{CO_2} = .1614$			
	°C	ρ_L	ρ_V	°C	ρ_L	°C	ρ_V	°C	ρ_L	°C	ρ_V
15.20	13.28	.813	.0261	1.66	.853	11.67	.0267	…	…	7.72	.0277
20.27	24.50	.785	.0348	13.63	.824	22.79	.0356	3.36	.868	18.62	.0369
25.33	33.64	.759	.0431	23.52	.798	32.00	.0449	13.04	.840	27.65	.0465
30.40	41.55	.736	.0506	32.02	.773	39.85	.0546	21.44	.815	35.44	.0565
35.47	48.58	.714	.0589	39.58	.749	46.92	.0646	28.90	.793	42.12	.0673
40.53	54.99	.696	.0683	46.30	.729	53.17	.0753	35.65	.771	47.97	.0786
45.60	60.83	.676	.0791	52.46	.708	58.89	.0868	41.79	.750	53.25	.0908
50.67	66.28	.655	.0909	58.14	.687	64.16	.0991	47.42	.727	58.20	.104
55.73	71.39	.636	.103	63.45	.666	69.04	.112	52.64	.704	62.87	.118
60.80	76.20	.615	.118	68.43	.643	73.60	.127	57.59	.681	67.21	.133
65.86	80.76	.593	.133	73.11	.617	77.81	.142	62.34	.656	71.20	.150
70.93	85.13	.569	.151	77.52	.591	81.72	.160	66.90	.627	74.85	.169
76.00	89.29	.542	.171	81.70	.564	85.39	.181	71.30	.594	78.12	.192
81.06	93.29	.508	.197	85.75	.532	88.83	.207	75.58	.558	81.15	.219
86.13	97.25	.461	.240	89.83	.487	92.03	.255	79.82	.514	83.76	.264

TABLE 17-18. *Continued*

Pressure (bars)	$X_{CO_2} = .2608$				$X_{CO_2} = .3759$				$X_{CO_2} = .4728$			
	°C	ρ_L	°C	ρ_V	°C	ρ_L	°C	ρ_V	°C	ρ_L	°C	ρ_V
15.20			3.56	.0289								
20.27	6.26	.869	13.94	.0385			8.16	.0407			3.30	.0425
25.33	14.36	.845	22.51	.0487	1.10	.892	16.47	.0512	5.52	.885	11.70	.0534
30.40	21.54	.822	29.96	.0592	8.76	.869	23.57	.0624	12.11	.862	18.42	.0652
35.47	28.07	.799	36.42	.0702	15.61	.846	29.84	.0741	18.05	.836	24.31	.0774
40.53	34.08	.775	42.16	.0820	21.81	.820	35.35	.0865	23.49	.810	29.58	.0904
45.60	39.62	.751	47.35	.0943	27.53	.794	40.33	.100	28.53	.782	34.40	.104
50.67	44.76	.728	52.13	.108	32.84	.768	44.88	.114	33.27	.752	38.86	.119
55.73	49.60	.701	56.56	.122	37.80	.743	49.01	.130	37.78	.719	43.04	.135
60.80	54.23	.674	60.64	.138	42.46	.716	52.78	.147	42.11	.686	46.93	.153
65.86	58.67	.644	64.35	.157	46.89	.687	56.25	.167	46.29	.656	50.45	.175
70.93	62.96	.613	66.59	.179	51.14	.656	59.45	.189	50.34	.614	53.06	.202
76.00	67.18	.577	68.52	.204	55.25	.617	62.18	.216	54.37	.542	55.27	.236
81.06	71.84	.520	70.60	.235	59.37	.569	64.78	.250			57.36	.298
86.13			75.80	.293								

Pressure (bars)	$X_{CO_2} = .6659$				$X_{CO_2} = .8292$				$X_{CO_2} = .9009$				$X_{CO_2} = 1.0000$		
	°C	ρ_L	°C	ρ_V	°C	ρ_L	°C	ρ_V	°C	ρ_L	°C	ρ_V	°C	ρ_L	ρ_V
25.33	.38	.913	.12	.0599											
30.40	6.50	.887	6.69	.0728											
35.47	12.10	.859	12.52	.0868	3.08	.904	4.90	.0951	1.92	.912	2.70	.0982	.65	.921	.100
40.53	17.24	.831	17.77	.102	8.40	.874	10.14	.112	7.21	.882	7.97	.116	5.80	.889	.116
45.60	22.00	.801	22.51	.118	13.29	.845	14.93	.131	12.04	.852	12.75	.135	10.51	.856	.135
50.67	26.44	.769	26.86	.137	17.80	.815	19.32	.152	16.48	.820	17.13	.157	14.85	.821	.156
55.73	30.61	.735	30.91	.158	22.00	.781	23.37	.176	20.61	.785	21.19	.182	18.82	.783	.181
60.80	34.54	.695	34.70	.183	25.95	.742	27.14	.203	24.43	.743	25.00	.212	22.52	.742	.210
65.86	38.21	.646	38.22	.214	29.67	.691	30.63	.240	28.00	.688	28.46	.252	26.01	.693	.242
70.93	42.16	.557	41.00	.251	33.12	.624	33.65	.292	31.42	.615	31.71	.316	29.26	.624	.295
76.00			43.61	.308											

TABLE 17-19. H_2S—CO_2 CRITICAL CURVE [2, 3]

Compositions and densities along the critical curve where liquid and vapor become identical.

P (bars)	$T(^\circ C)$	Mole fraction CO_2	Density gm cm^{-3}
90.05	100.38	.0000	.349
89.97	93.50	.0630	.364
89.78	84.16	.1614	.379
88.52	74.48	.2608	.392
85.87	64.74	.3759	.406
83.21	56.98	.4728	.417
77.85	43.72	.6659	.437
74.83	35.96	.8292	.453
74.16	33.53	.9009	.459
73.92	31.10	1.0000	.465

TABLE 17-20. H_2O—CO_2 TWO-PHASE REGION [17, 18]

Compositions of coexisting phases are given as mole per cent carbon dioxide. The critical pressure P_c (bars) and critical composition X_c (mole per cent CO_2) are given for each temperature.

Bars	350° C Liquid phase	Gas phase	325° C Liquid phase	Gas phase	300° C Liquid phase	Gas phase
100	..	..	..	..	0.4	8.0
150	..	..	1.0	10.6	1.6	29.0
200	1.5	9.0	2.6	24.6	2.9	39.0
250	4.0	16.2	4.3	32.1	4.1	43.4
300	6.4	16.6	6.1	34.2	5.4	45.4
350			8.2	33.4	6.8	45.6
400	$P_c = 325$ bars		11.2	28.6	8.4	44.8
450	$X_c = 10.5$ per cent				10.4	42.2
500			$P_c = 435$ bars		12.7	38.0
550			$X_c = 18.0$ per cent		17.0	32.0
					$P_c = 575$ bars	
					$X_c = 23.6$ per cent	

Bars	275° C Liquid phase	Gas phase	270° C Liquid phase	Gas phase	260° C Liquid phase	Gas phase
100	1.0	25.6				
150	1.9	42.6				
200	2.8	50.0	2.7	53.0	2.7	57.2
250	3.8	54.0	3.6	57.0	3.5	62.0
300	4.9	55.8	4.6	59.0	4.4	64.0
400	7.2	55.8	6.7	59.0	5.9	64.2
500	9.6	53.0	8.7	57.0	7.3	62.4
600	12.0	49.6	10.6	54.6	8.7	60.4
700	14.4	46.0	12.5	52.0	10.0	58.0
800	17.5	42.0	14.5	49.6	11.3	56.0
900			16.6	46.2	12.5	54.8
	$P_c = 885$ bars					
1000			19.0	42.4	13.5	53.6
	$X_c = 27.0$ per cent					
1100			21.5	38.2	14.5	52.4
1200			25.0	34.0	15.5	51.0
1300					16.0	50.4
1400			$P_c = 1230$ bars		16.5	50.2
1500			$X_c = 28.8$ per cent		17.5	50.0

TABLE 17-20. *Continued*

Bars	250° C Liquid phase	Gas phase	200° C Liquid phase	Gas phase	150° C Liquid phase	Gas phase
100	1.2	41.0	1.3	71.5	1.35	88.0
200	2.7	63.6	2.6	82.0	2.15	91.0
300	4.2	68.0	3.4	82.5	2.60	90.0
400	5.5	67.6	4.1	81.6	2.90	88.2
500	6.4	66.0	4.7	80.0	3.20	86.2
600	7.4	63.6	5.2	78.0	3.45	84.0
700	8.4	61.3	5.6	76.0	3.70	82.4
800	9.4	59.3	5.8	74.5	3.90	80.8
900	10.4	58.0	6.1	73.2	4.05	79.4
1000	11.5	56.7	6.3	72.0	4.20	78.0
1100	12.5	55.5	6.5	71.6	4.40	77.0
1200	13.2	54.8	6.7	70.6	4.50	76.4
1300	13.6	54.2	6.9	70.0	4.60	75.8
1400	14.0	54.0	7.0	69.4	4.70	75.4
1500	14.4	54.0	7.2	69.0	4.80	75.2

Bars	110° C Liquid phase	Gas phase	Bars	110° C Liquid phase	Gas phase
100	1.40	95.6	900	3.45	84.0
200	2.10	95.8	1000	3.60	83.0
300	2.40	94.8	1100	3.70	82.2
400	2.60	93.2	1200	3.75	81.6
500	2.80	91.4	1300	3.85	81.0
600	3.00	89.3	1400	3.90	80.4
700	3.15	87.2	1500	4.00	80.0
800	3.30	85.4			

SECTION 18

IONIZATION CONSTANTS IN AQUEOUS SOLUTIONS

by H. L. BARNES, H. C. HELGESON, AND A. J. ELLIS

CONTENTS

Handbook of Physical Constants—*Revised Edition*

THE GEOLOGICAL SOCIETY OF AMERICA MEMOIR 97, 1966

A large body of information exists on the ionization of electrolytes in water at ambient temperatures. As early as the turn of the century, experiments were devised to obtain ionization constants for weak electrolytes in solutions in equilibrium with vapor at temperatures to 300° C, but only in the last decade have methods been developed for the determination of ionization constants in supercritical aqueous solutions. (The usefulness of these constants as a means of understanding hydrothermal, ionic equilibria has been apparent for some time from successful applications at lower temperatures.) In this relatively new field, there are sufficiently few data to make it possible for this compilation to be, hopefully, complete through 1963 in coverage of constants for water above 0° C and for inorganic compounds in aqueous solutions above the critical point of the solvent. In the subcritical region, constants are given where available for all compounds for which there are supercritical data, as well as for several inorganic acids and bases likely to be of common geologic interest. For ionization constants of other compounds (and commonly only near room temperature), the reader is referred to the exhaustive, but uncritical, compilation of stability constants by Sillén and Martell [53] covering the literature through 1960. Other less complete tabulations of ionization constants of inorganic aqueous species near 25° C include those by Parsons [46] and Yatsimirskiĭ and Vasil'ev [57].

All ionization constants given in the following tables are reported as the logarithms of thermodynamic constants, without dimensions, but are numerically consistent with the usual thermodynamic standard states expressed in molalities and atmospheres. Because these constants are derived from extrapolation of experimental data to infinite dilution, conversion to values consistent with standard states in molalities and atmospheres has been made by appropriate division or multiplication by ρ, the density of pure water in grams per cubic centimeter, at the specific P and T where the constant is given.

Experimental methods, used to determine the ionization constants, are indicated in the tables by the following abbreviations.

cal.	—calorimetric measurements	Raman	—Raman spectral measurements
cond.	—conductivity, including normal and high field strength, and shock wave methods	solub.	—interpretation of the solubility of sparingly soluble salts
e.m.f.	—measurements of cell potentials	spect.	—spectrophotometric measurements
n.m.r.	—nuclear magnetic resonance methods	thermo.	—thermodynamic calculations and literature evaluations of other data
pH	—measurements of hydrogen ion activity with glass electrodes	v. pres.	—vapor pressure measurements.

The most common method, conductivity measurements, requires corrections for activity coefficient variations with concentration. Early investigators [44] extrapolated to infinite dilution using equations satisfactory for weak electrolytes but considerably in error for strong electrolytes [48, p. 63–71], and the resulting values should not be used. Evaluations of recent equations for extrapolation for strong electrolytes are given by Spiro [54] and by Harned and Owen [27, p. 207–211]. At high temperatures, approximate activity coefficients of ions can be evaluated for dilute solutions using the Debye-Hückel equations as discussed by Lietzke and Stoughton [35] and Franck [19]. In the absence of other data and as a last resort, activity coefficients of molecular species in concentrated solutions at elevated temperatures can be approximated by assuming ideality of mixing. This approximation has been shown by Barnes and Ernst [3] to be justified for H_2O (but not NaOH) in NaOH solutions under elevated conditions, although near 25° C, these same solutions exhibit extreme departures from ideal mixing. Critical discussions of many of the other methods of determining ionization constants are included in the volume of the Electrochemical Society Symposium, The Structure of Electrolytic Solutions [25].

The degree of ionization of inorganic species in aqueous solution increases with increasing pressure at constant temperature [23]. Above 400° C, with the only known exception of H_2O, ionization decreases at constant density with increasing temperature. This variation may be expressed as a simple function of temperature and density which is sufficiently regular in behavior among similar species to allow rough graphical approximation of constants at high temperatures, by comparisons starting with data applicable near room temperature. This method requires data on the behavior of an aqueous molecule, complex, or simple ion with similar ligands or central cation that has comparable valence, size, symmetry, and ionization products. Because a good analogy is usually not available, the results of extrapolation from low temperature are questionable. This compilation is limited to ionization constants that have been obtained directly from experiments in the range of temperature and pressure reported.

REFERENCES FOR SECTION 18

1. Ackermann, Zeits. Electrochem. **62**, 411, 1958
2. Arnold, Freitag, and Patterson, Chapt. *in* "Structure of Electrolytic Solutions" edit. by Hamer, Wiley, New York, p. 281, 1959
3. Barnes and Ernst, Am. Jour. Sci. **261**, 129, 1963
4. Barnes and Kullerud, Econ. Geol. **56**, 648, 1961
5. Bates and Pinching, Jour. Am. Chem. Soc. **72**, 1393, 1950
6. Broene and DeVries, Jour. Am. Chem. Soc. **69**, 1644, 1947
7. Buchanan and Hamann, Trans. Faraday Soc. **49**, 1425, 1953
8. Cobble, Jour. Am. Chem. Soc. **86**, 5394, 1964
9. Čůta and Strafelda, Chem. Listy **48**, 1308, 1954
10. David and Hamann, Trans. Faraday Soc. **55**, 72, 1959
11. Davies, Chapt. *in* "Structure of Electrolytic Solutions" edit. by Hamer; Wiley, New York, p. 19, 1959
12. Davies, Jones, and Monk, Trans. Faraday Soc. **48**, 921, 1952
13. Dudziak and Franck, Zeits. Phys. Chem., N.F., in press
14. Ellis, Jour. Chem. Soc., 3689, 1959
15. —— Jour. Chem. Soc., 4300, 1963
16. Ellis and Anderson, Jour. Chem. Soc. 4678, 1961
17. Ellis and Golding, Jour. Chem. Soc. 127, 1959
18. Fogo, Benson, and Copeland, Jour. Chem. Phys. **22**, 212, 1954
19. Franck, Zeits. Phys. Chem., N.F., **8**, 107, 1956
20. Franck, Zeits. Phys. Chem., N.F., **8**, 192, 1956
21. Franck, Angew. Chem. **73**, 309, 1961
22. Gimblett and Monk, Trans. Faraday Soc. **50**, 965, 1954
23. Hamann, Physico-Chemical effects of pressure, Butterworths, London, 1957
24. Hamann and Strauss, Trans. Faraday Soc. **51**, 1684, 1955
25. Hamer, editor, Structure of Electrolytic Solutions, Wiley, New York, 1959
26. Harned and Davis, Jour. Am. Chem. Soc. **65**, 2030, 1943
27. Harned and Owen, Physical chemistry of electrolytic solutions, Reinhold, New York, third edit., 1958
28. Harned and Robinson, Trans. Faraday Soc. **36**, 973, 1940
29. Harned and Scholes, Jour. Am. Chem. Soc. **63**, 1706, 1941
30. Hood, Redlich, and Reilly, Jour. Chem. Phys. **22**, 2067, 1954
31. Kauko and Airola, Zeits. Phys. Chem. **179**, 307, 1937
32. Kerker, Jour. Am. Chem. Soc. **79**, 3664, 1956
33. Kury, Zielen, and Latimer, Jour. Electrochem. Soc. **100**, 468, 1953
34. Lietzke and Stoughton, Jour. Phys. Chem. **63**, 1188, 1959
35. Lietzke and Stoughton, Jour. Phys. Chem. **63**, 1190, 1959
36. Lietzke, Stoughton, and Young, Jour. Phys. Chem. **65**, 2247, 1961
37. Loy and Himmelblau, Jour. Phys. Chem. **65**, 266, 1961
38. Marrony, Electrochim. Acta **1**, 58, 1959
39. McCoubrey, Trans. Faraday Soc. **51**, 743, 1955
40. Muhammad and Sundaram, Jour. Sci. Ind. Res. (India) 20B, 16, 1961
41. Nair and Nancollas, Jour. Chem. Soc., 3706, 1958
42. —— Jour. Chem. Soc., 4144, 1958
43. —— Jour. Chem. Soc., 3934, 1959

44. Noyes et al., Carnegie Inst. of Washington, Pub. 63, 1907
45. Owen and Brinkley, Chem. Rev. **29**, 461, 1941
46. Parsons, Handbook of Electrochemical Constants, Butterworths, London, 1959
47. Pearson, Ph.D. Dissert., U. of S. California, 1960
48. Remy, Treatise on Inorganic Chemistry, Vol. 1, Elsevier, New York, 1956
49. Ringbom, Rept. to Analyt. Sect. of Int. Union Pure and Applied Chem., July 1953
50. Robinson, Trans. Faraday Soc. **32**, 743, 1936
51. Ryzhenko, Geochem. No. 2, 151, 1963
52. —— Geochem. Int., **1**, 8, 1964
53. Sillén and Martell, Chem. Soc. Special Publ. No. 17, 1964
54. Spiro, Trans. Faraday Soc. **55**, 1746, 1959
55. Wissbrun, French, and Patterson, Jour. Phys. Chem. **58**, 693, 1954
56. Wright and Maass, Canad. Jour. Res. **6**, 588, 1932
57. Yatsimirskiĭ and Vasil'ev, Instability constants of complex compounds, Pergamon, New York, 1960
58. Young, Maranville, and Smith, Chapt. *in* "Structure of electrolytic solutions", edit. by Hamer; Wiley, New York, p. 35, 1959
59. Zavodnov and Kryuhov, Izv. Akad. Nauk, S.S.S.R., Otd. Khim. Nauk, 1704, 1960

TABLE 18-1. ACTIVITY PRODUCT OF WATER

$$K_w = (a_{H^+})(a_{OH^-})$$

A. LIQUID WATER IN EQUILIBRIUM WITH VAPOR:

$t°$ C	Log K_w	Ref.	Method
0	$-14.950 \pm .006$	1, 28	cal., e.m.f.
10	$-14.535 \pm .003$	1, 28	cal., e.m.f.
20	$-14.164 \pm .003$	1, 28	cal., e.m.f.
25	$-13.998 \pm .001$	1, 28	cal., e.m.f.
30	$-13.833 \pm .001$	1, 28	cal., e.m.f.
40	$-13.534 \pm .001$	1, 28	cal., e.m.f.
50	$-13.262 \pm .001$	1, 28	cal., e.m.f.
60	$-13.016 \pm .001$	1, 28	cal., e.m.f.
70	-12.80	1	cal.
80	-12.60	1	cal.
90	-12.42	1	cal.
100	-12.27	1, 44	cal., cond.
110	-12.13	1	cal.
120	-12.00	1	cal.
130	-11.90	1, 44	cal., cond.
156	-11.57	44	cond.
218	-11.19	44	cond.
306	-11.46	44	cond.

B. LIQUID WATER UNDER PRESSURE. (Refs. 28, 45; methods: e.m.f., thermo.)

	Log K_w				
Pressure (bars)	5° C	15° C	25° C	35° C	45° C
1	-14.734	-14.346	-13.998	-13.680	-13.396
200	-14.64	-14.258	-13.918	-13.608	-13.33
400	-14.55	-14.173	-13.841	-13.539	-13.27
600	-14.46	-14.09	-13.767	-13.47	-13.21
800	-14.37	-14.01	-13.695	-13.41	-13.15
1000	-14.28	-13.93	-13.63	-13.35	-13.09

C. SUPERCRITICAL AQUEOUS FLUID. (Refs. 10, 20, 21*; methods: cond.)

Applicable from 306–700° C in the density range of .3–.7, where $T = °$ K and $\rho =$ density:

Log $K_w = -(4486/T) - (2.6) + (8 \log \rho_{H_2O})$

Log $K_w =$ about -2, at 772° C, 127,000 atm., $\rho = 1.72$.

Where $K = (a_{H^+})(a_{OH^-})/(a_{H_2O})$:

Log $K = -(4486/T) + (8.0 \log \rho_{H_2O}) - (4.4)$

* Reference 21 has been corrected for a misprint in this equation, on the basis of reference 20, before conversion from a molar to a molal standard state.

TABLE 18-2. IONIZATION CONSTANTS OF HYDROCHLORIC ACID

$$K_{HCl} = \frac{(a_{H^+})(a_{Cl^-})}{(a_{HCl})}$$

A. LOW TEMPERATURE (Liquid in equilibrium with vapor).

$t°$ C	log (K_{HCl})	Ref.	Method
0	+7.3	50	v. pres.
10	+6.8	50	v. pres.
20	+6.4	50	v. pres.
25	+6.1	50, 39	v. pres., thermo.
30	+5.9	50	v. pres.
40	+5.4	50	v. pres.
50	+5.1	50	v. pres.
360	−2.98 (ρ = .525)	47	cond.
370	−3.76 (ρ = .447)	47	cond.
373	−4.21 (ρ = .399)	47	cond.

B. SUPERCRITICAL SOLUTIONS (Ref. 20, 21; method: cond.)

Log (K_{HCl})

Pressures, in bars, are given by italics immediately below each value for Log (K_{HCl}).

$t°$ C	Density					
	.3	.4	.5	.6	.7	.8
400	−4.88	−4.26	−3.66	−2.92	−2.00	−0.60
	290	*320*	*380*	*560*	*1050*	*2100*
500	−5.05	−4.46	−3.89	−3.28	−2.39	−1.47
	550	*690*	*910*	*1290*	*2040*	*(3600)*
600	−5.22	−4.82	−4.24	−3.70	−2.85	
	810	*1070*	*1430*	*1990*	*(4500)*	
700	−5.64	−5.12	−4.55			
	1060	*1460*	*1970*			

TABLE 18-3. IONIZATION CONSTANT OF SULFURIC ACID

$$K_{HSO_4^-} = \frac{(a_{H^+})(a_{SO_4^=})}{(a_{HSO_4^-})}$$

(Liquid in equilibrium with vapor)

A. Temp ° C	Log $K_{HSO_4^-}$	Ref.	Method
0	$-1.68 \pm .02$	42, 52, 58	e.m.f., Raman
15	$-1.80 \pm .01$	12*, 42	e.m.f.
18	$-1.90 \pm .01$	32, 34, 44, 58	cond., Raman
25	$-1.97 \pm .02$	12*, 32, 39, 42, 58	e.m.f., cond., Raman
35	$-2.09 \pm .07$	12, 34, 42, 58	e.m.f., Raman
45	$-2.22 \pm .03$	12, 34, 42, 58	e.m.f., Raman
50	$-2.30 \pm .02$	12, 32, 34, 58	e.m.f., cond., Raman
100	$-3.05 \pm .02$	34, 44, 58	cond., Raman
125	-3.33	36, 52	solub.
150	-3.69	36, 52	solub.
175	-4.09	36, 52	solub.
200	-4.49	36, 52	solub.
225	-4.94	36, 52	solub.
250	-5.29	52	solub.
300	-6.0	52	solub.

* Values from reference 12 have been recalculated for a more precise value of the A term in the Debye-Hückel equation. *See* references 41, 42 and 43.

B.   0° to 50° C (Ref. 12; method: e.m.f.)

$$-Log\ K_{HSO_4^-} = 1.67 + .0127\ t$$

where t = temp. in ° C.

C.   25° to 250° C (Ref. 34, 35, 36; method: Raman, solub.)

$$Log\ K_{HSO_4^-} = \frac{-557.24}{T} + 5.3504 - .018341\ T$$

where T = temp. in ° K.

TABLE 18-4. IONIZATION CONSTANTS OF HYDROFLUORIC ACID

$$K_{HF} = \frac{(a_{H^+})(a_{F^-})}{(a_{HF})} \; ; \quad K_{HF_2^-} = \frac{(a_{HF_2^-})}{(a_{F^-})(a_{HF})}$$

A. Low temperatures, liquid in equilibrium with vapor.
(Ref. 6, 15; method: e.m.f., cond.)

$t°C$	15°	25°	35°	50°	75°	100°	125°	150°	175°	200° C
Log (K_{HF})	−3.10	−3.18	−3.25	−3.40	−3.64	−3.85	−4.09	−4.34	−4.59	−4.89
		±.01		±.01	±.02	±.02	±.02	±.03	±.03	±.04
$(K_{HF_2^-})$		3.4		4.0	4.7	4.8	4.9	5.7	5.8	8.
		±.5		±1.0	±.8	±.8	±.8	±1.5	±1.5	±2.

B. 0°–200° C, liquid in equilibrium with vapor
(Ref. 15; method: cond.)
Log $(K_{HF}) = -2.75-(295/T) + 1.91 \log T-.014 T$

C. Supercritical solutions (Ref. 13, 21; method: cond.)
Log (K_{HF})
Pressures, in bars, are given by italics immediately below each value for Log (K_{HF})

$t°C$	Density					
	.3	.4	.5	.6	.7	.8
450	−7.94	−7.04	−6.34	−5.70	−4.99	−4.72
	420	*500*	*640*	*930*	*1540*	*2800*
550	−8.20	−7.83	−7.13	−6.25	−5.56	
	680	*880*	*1180*	*1640*	*2530*	
650	−8.55	−7.83	−7.38	−6.55	−5.80	
	930	*1270*	*1700*	*2360*	*(6000)*	

TABLE 18-5. IONIZATION CONSTANTS OF NITRIC ACID

$$K_{HNO_3} = \frac{(a_{H^+})(a_{NO_3^-})}{(a_{HNO_3})}$$

(Ref. 58, 30; methods: Raman., n.m.r.)

Liquid in equilibrium with vapor:

$t°C$	0	25	50	75	100	150	200	250	300
Log (K_{HNO_3})	+1.67	+1.43	+1.17	+.91	+.63	+.05	−.55	−1.17	−1.79

0–300° C (Ref. 35, 58; method: Raman.)

$$\text{Log } (K_{HNO_3}) = 6.55_7 - \frac{320.88}{T} - .01359 \, T$$

where T = temperature in ° K.

TABLE 18-6. IONIZATION CONSTANTS OF CARBONIC ACID

A. APPARENT FIRST IONIZATION CONSTANT, $K_a = \dfrac{(a_{H^+})(a_{HCO_3^-})}{(a_{CO_2} + a_{H_2CO_3})(a_{H_2O})}$

which includes the activities of the aqueous molecular forms of both CO_2 and H_2CO_3.

$t°$ C	Log (K_a)	Ref.	Method
At 1 atm. pressure			
0	−6.58	26	e.m.f.
10	−6.46	26	e.m.f.
20	−6.38	26	e.m.f.
25	−6.35	26	e.m.f.
30	−6.33	26	e.m.f.
40	−6.30	26	e.m.f.
50	−6.29	26	e.m.f.
55	−6.30	14	cond.
65	−6.31	14	cond.
At 3000 atm. pressure			
25	−5.09	14	cond.
35	−5.10	14	cond.
45	−5.11	14	cond.
55	−5.16	14	cond.
65	−5.19	14	cond.
Solution in equilibrium with vapor			
100	−6.40	51	cond.
150	−6.72	51	cond.
200	−7.21	51	cond.
250	−7.78	51	cond.
300	−8.43	51	cond.

B. FIRST IONIZATION CONSTANT, $K_1 = \dfrac{(a_{H^+})(a_{HCO_3^-})}{(a_{H_2CO_3})}$ (Ref. 55; method: cond.)

$t°$ C	5	15	25	35	45
Log (K_1):	−3.81	−3.75	−3.76	−3.78	−3.80

C. SECOND IONIZATION CONSTANT, $K_2 = \dfrac{(a_{H^+})(a_{CO_3^{--}})}{(a_{HCO_3^-})}$, where liquid is in equilibrium with vapor.

$t°$ C	Log K_2	Ref.	Method
0	−10.63	29, 31	e.m.f.
10	−10.49	29	e.m.f.
20	−10.38	29	e.m.f.
25	−10.33	29, 31	e.m.f.
30	−10.29	29	e.m.f.
40	−10.22	29	e.m.f.
50	−10.17	29	e.m.f.
60	−10.18	9	pH
70	−10.16	9	pH
80	−10.14	9	pH
90	−10.14	9, 51	pH, cond.
100	−10.11	51	cond.
150	−10.33	51	cond.
200	−10.73	51	cond.
250	−11.24	51	cond.
300	−11.83	51	cond.

Empirical equation for the temperature range 0° to 50° C [29]

$$\text{Log } K_2 = \frac{-2902.39}{T} + 6.4980 - .02379\,T$$

Empirical equation for the temperature range 60° to 90° C [9]

$$\text{Log } K_2 = \frac{-2909.10}{T} + 6.119 - .02272\,T$$

(in both equations, T = temp. in ° K.)

TABLE 18-7. IONIZATION CONSTANTS OF HYDROGEN SULFIDE

A. FIRST IONIZATION CONSTANT $K_1 = \dfrac{(a_{H^+})(a_{HS^-})}{(a_{H_2S})}$.

Temperature dependence (Ref. 56, 37, 53; method: cond., thermo.)

$t°$ C	5	10	15	20	25	30	40	50	60
Log (K_1)	−7.33	−7.24	−7.13	−7.05	−7.00 ± .05	−6.90	−6.79	−6.69	−6.62

0–60° C (?) (Ref. 49; method: thermo.) for t in ° C:
$$\text{Log } (K_1) = -7.05 + .0125 \, (t - 25)$$

Pressure dependence at 25° C (Ref. 16; method: cond.)

P (atm.)	1	500	1000	1500	2000
Log (K_1)	7.00	6.87	6.75	6.64	6.56

B. SECOND IONIZATION CONSTANT, $K_2 = \dfrac{(a_{H^+})(a_{S^{--}})}{(a_{HS^-})}$.

There is a wide variation in values given in the literature, as noted by Cobble [8] and by Sillén and Martell [53], possibly due to the very rapid oxidation of aqueous sulfide solutions in air plus the uncertainty in assigning activity coefficients to the concentrated solutions used experimentally in several methods. For this reason, "best" values cannot be chosen with confidence and only representative values are given below.

$t°$ C	Log (K_2)	Ref.	Method
0	−14.8	38	e.m.f., thermo.
20	−12.9	59	e.m.f.
	−14.0	17	spect.
25	−12.9	33, 4	e.m.f., thermo.
	−13.9	38	e.m.f., thermo.
30	−12.8	59	e.m.f.
	−13.9	40	spect.
40	−12.6	59	e.m.f.
50	−12.4	59	e.m.f.
60	−12.3	59	e.m.f.

0–50° C (?) (Ref. 49; method: thermo.) for t in ° C:
$$\text{Log } (K_2) = -12.9 + .031 \, (t - 25)$$

TABLE 18-8. IONIZATION CONSTANTS OF AMMONIUM HYDROXIDE

$$K_{NH_4OH} = \frac{(a_{NH_4^+})(a_{OH^-})}{(a_{NH_4OH})}$$

A. Subcritical Solutions in equilibrium with vapor.

$t°$ C	Log (K_{NH_4OH})	Ref.	Method
0	−4.862	5, 2, 44	e.m.f., cond.
10	−4.804	5, 2, 44	e.m.f., cond.
20	−4.767	5, 2	e.m.f., cond.
25	−4.751	5, 2, 44	e.m.f., cond.
30	−4.740	5, 2	e.m.f., cond.
40	−4.730	5, 2	e.m.f., cond.
50	−4.723	5, 2, 44	e.m.f., cond.
75	−4.77	44	cond.
100	−4.85	44	cond.
125	−4.95	44	cond.
156	−5.16	44	cond.
218	−5.66	44	cond.
306	−6.87	44	cond.

B. Log (K_{NH_4OH}) (Ref. 7, 24; method: cond.)

Pressure (atm)	1000	2000	3000	4000	5400	6800	8200	9600	11000	12000
25° C	−4.29	−3.91	−3.61							
45° C	−4.32	−3.94	−3.65	−3.32	−2.95	−2.68	−2.42	−2.21	−2.11	−2.00

C. Supercritical Solutions (Ref. 21; method: cond.)

Log (K_{NH_4OH})

$t°$ C	Density	
	.35	.59
640	−7.96 (*1050* bars)	−6.47 (*2220* bars)

TABLE 18-9. IONIZATION CONSTANTS OF ALKALI HYDROXIDES

A. Subcritical Solutions in equilibrium with vapor.

$$K = \frac{(a_{M^+})(a_{OH^-})}{(a_{MOH})} :$$

	5° C	15° C	Log K 25° C	35° C	45° C	Ref.	Method
LiOH	$-.26 \pm .04$	$-.20 \pm .02$	$-.18 \pm .02$	$-.20 \pm .02$	$-.19 \pm .02$	22	e.m.f.
NaOH	$+.60 \pm .3$	$+.60 \pm .3$	$+.70 \pm .2$	$+.70 \pm .2$	$+.70 \pm .2$	22,11	e.m.f, cond.
NaOH		at 360°, density of .525, $-1.8 \pm .3$				47	cond.

$$K = \frac{(a_{M^{++}})(a_{OH^-})}{(a_{MOH^+})}$$

	5° C	15° C	25° C	35° C	45° C	Ref.	Method
MgOH+	..	..	$-2.58 \pm .02$	$-1.40 \pm .02$	..	11	pH
CaOH+		$-1.34 \pm .02$	$-1.37 \pm .02$			22	e.m.f.
SrOH+	$-.78 \pm .02$	$-.80 \pm .02$	$-.82 \pm .02$	$-.86 \pm .02$	$-.89 \pm .02$	22	e.m.f.
BaOH+	$-.62 \pm .02$	$-.60 \pm .02$	$-.64 \pm .02$	$-.69 \pm .02$	$-.72 \pm .02$	11, 22	thermo., e.m.f.

B. Supercritical Solutions. $K_{KOH} = \dfrac{(a_{K^+})(a_{OH^-})}{(a_{KOH})}$ (Ref. 20; method: cond.)

Log (K_{KOH})

Pressures, in bars, are given by italics immediately below each value for Log (K_{KOH})

			Density			
$t°$ C	.3	.4	.5	.6	.7	.8
400	-3.52	-2.80	-2.27	-1.89	-1.68	-1.25
	290	*320*	*380*	*560*	*1050*	*2100*
500	-4.20	-3.15	-2.42	-1.96	-1.68	-1.37
	550	*690*	*910*	*1290*	*2040*	*(3600)*
600	-4.57	-3.37	-2.58	-2.04	-1.72	
	810	*1070*	*1430*	*1990*	*(4500)*	
700	-4.89	-3.52	-2.70			
	1060	*1460*	*1970*			

TABLE 18-10. IONIZATION CONSTANTS OF ALKALI METAL HALIDES, $K = \dfrac{(a_{M^+})(a_{A^-})}{(a_{MA})}$

A. NaCl (method: cond.)

$t°$ C	Ref.	Density (g./cc.)	Log (K)	Pressure (bars)
300	47	.712	$-1.18 \pm .14$	
320	47	.667	$-1.28 \pm .04$	
345	47	.591	$-1.56 \pm .04$	
360	47	.591	$-1.59 \pm .08$	
..	..	.5245	$-1.88 \pm .02$	
370	47	.4473	$-2.29 \pm .02$	
373	47	.591	$-1.57 \pm .08$	
..	..	.5245	$-1.90 \pm .04$	
..	..	.4473	$-2.31 \pm .02$	
..	..	.3990	$-2.52 \pm .03$	
378	47	.591	$-1.59 \pm .12$	
..	..	.5245	$-1.89 \pm .04$	
..	..	.4473	$-2.34 \pm .02$	
..	..	.3990	$-2.62 \pm .02$	
383	47	.591	$-1.66 \pm .07$	
..	..	.5245	$-1.90 \pm .04$	
..	..	.4473	$-2.36 \pm .02$	
..	..	.3990	$-2.66 \pm .03$	
388	18	.40	-3.02	340
..	..	.38	-3.25	
..	..	.36	-3.59	280
..	..	.34	-3.86	
..	..	.32	-4.12	270
..	..	.29	-4.48	
..	..	.26	-4.91	250
..	..	.23	-5.48	
..	..	.20	-6.20	240
550	13, 21	.70	$-.99$	2530
..	..	.60	-1.74	1640
..	..	.50	-2.50	1180
..	..	.40	-3.45	880
..	..	.30	-4.94	680

TABLE 18-10. *Continued*

Log (*K*)

B. Pressure, in bars, are given by italics immediately below each value for Log (*K*).
Density (g./cc.)

Salt	*t*° C	.3	.4	.5	.6	.7	.8	Ref.	Method
LiCl	450	−4.61	−3.12	−2.24	−1.55	−.84	−.70	13, 21	cond.
		420	*500*	*640*	*930*	*1540*	*2800*		
	550	−5.18	−3.52	−2.55	−1.85	−1.20			
		680	*880*	*1180*	*1640*	*2530*			
	650	−5.48	−3.88	−2.83	−2.09	−1.58			
		930	*1270*	*1700*	*2360*	*(6000)*			
	750	−5.58	−4.08						
		1200	*1660*						
KCl	400	..	..	..	−1.46	..	..	20, 21	cond.
		..	..	..	*560*				
	450	−3.92	−2.94	−2.26	..	−1.24			
		410	*500*	*640*	..	*1540*			
	500	..	..	..	−2.00	−1.76	−1.76		
		..	..	..	*1290*	*2040*	*(3600)*		
	550	−4.46	−3.24	−2.52	..	−1.89			
		680	*880*	*1180*	..	*2530*			
	600	..	..	..	−2.32	−2.21			
		..	..	..	*1990*	*(4500)*			
	650	−4.68	−3.44	−2.70					
		930	*1270*	*1700*					
	750	−4.91	−3.52						
		1200	*1660*						
RbCl	450	−4.40	−3.06	−2.27	−1.52	−.84	−.47	13, 21	cond.
and		*420*	*500*	*640*	*930*	*1540*	*2800*		
CsCl	550	−4.58	−3.18	−2.34	−1.63	−1.04			
		680	*880*	*1180*	*1640*	*2530*			
	650	−4.74	−3.32	−2.47	−1.78	−1.23			
		930	*1270*	*1700*	*2360*	*(6000)*			
	750	−4.74	−3.40	−2.52					
		1200	*1660*	*2260*					
NaF	550	−5.02	−3.76	−2.87	−2.32	−1.91	..	13, 21	cond.
		680	*880*	*1180*	*1640*	*2530*			

SECTION 19

SOLUBILITY

By SYDNEY P. CLARK, JR.

CONTENTS

ILLUSTRATIONS

Handbook of Physical Constants—*Revised Edition*

THE GEOLOGICAL SOCIETY OF AMERICA MEMOIR 97, 1966

This section summarizes the small amount of available data on solubility at high temperatures and pressures. Data are given for the solubility of solids in water (or water-rich solutions) and for the solubility of water in silicate melts. Emphasis has been on materials of geological interest, but a few substances which are uncommon in nature have been included. Little of the systematic experimental work has been on systems of a complexity approaching those to be found in nature.

With few exceptions the pressure was measured directly in the work reported here. No measurements of pressure were made in obtaining the data given in Table 19-12 and in some of the data in Table 19-7 [9]. The approximate pressures given in Table 19-13 were calculated from the known volume of the bomb, using the steam tables for P–V–T data for water and the ideal gas law for CO_2. Pressures of the mixture were calculated from Dalton's law. This approximation and the neglect of the effect of dissolved solids on the equations of state can introduce considerable error (See also section 17).

Several methods of determining the solubility of solids in an aqueous phase have been developed. The most accurate are either to withdraw a small sample from the reaction vessel and analyze it chemically, or to determine the loss in weight of a crystal or plate of solid after it has been equilibrated with a known amount of liquid. The first method requires that the sample be extracted in such a way that no loss of material takes place during withdrawal. In the second method, care must be taken to avoid precipitation of material on the sample of solid during cooling and decompression. It is also necessary to take extreme care about thermal gradients when using this method. Otherwise transport of material in the fluid phase, and deposition of solid matter in a part of the reaction vessel which is at a different temperature than the sample may take place. This gives rise to spuriously high apparent solubilities. The first of these methods has been used when dealing with highly soluble materials [2, 8, 13] and the second with less soluble substances [3, 4, 5, 15].

A dynamic method of measuring solubilities has also been used [6, 9]. In it, water is passed slowly over the sample, collected through a throttling valve, and analyzed. The water must move slowly enough so that the solution can come into equilibrium with the solid. Errors due to differential leaching must be avoided, as must clogging of the throttling valve. In practice these considerations seem to restrict the method to materials of low solubility.

The solubility of H_2O in silicate melts is commonly determined by quenching the melt to room temperature at constant pressure, with subsequent analysis of the resulting glass. Although many silica-rich glasses can be prepared in this way, some silicate liquids react with the gas on quenching to form a thin more hydrous layer near the interface; others partially crystallize, and others appear to exsolve all the dissolved H_2O [4] or only part of it. The H_2O in the liquid is estimated by a variety of dehydration techniques that are performed on either the quenched glass or the associated excess H_2O. Serious error may be caused if bubbles in the glass contain water. Bubbles are attributed to failure of initially powdered sample to fuse to a clear homogeneous mass during melting under pressure in some cases [15]; they may also be due to exsolution of water during quenching. A rather different way of determining the water content of glasses has recently been described [3]. In it, glasses are equilibrated with various known amounts of water in sealed capsules. The presence of a second phase is shown by the outline of gas bubbles in the quenched glass. These bubbles are much larger than those formed by exsolution on quenching, and thus are readily distinguished.

A general statement about the accuracy of the data in the tables is difficult to make. The last figure given is always uncertain, but by unknown amounts. The data in Tables

19-5, 19-6, and 19-7 have been read from curves; the error in reading is substantially less than the scatter of the original data. The uncertainty in determinations of the solubility of water in silicate liquids can be estimated from the results of the duplicate determinations given in Table 19-17.

The help of C. Wayne Burnham and David B. Stewart in preparing this section is gratefully acknowledged. They made valuable suggestions about the presentation of the material and contributed many previously unpublished determinations of solubility.

REFERENCES FOR SECTION 19

1. Anderson, G. M. and Burnham, C. W., unpublished
2. Burnham, C. W., unpublished
3. Burnham and Jahns, Am. Jour. Sci. **260**, 721, 1962
4. Goranson, Am. Jour. Sci. **22**, 481, 1931; Am. Jour. Sci. **35A**, 71, 1938; Trans. Am. Geophys. Union, 257, 1936; Am. Jour. Sci. **23**, 227, 1932
5. Hamilton, Burnham, and Osborn, Jour. Petrol. **5**, 21, 1964
6. Keevil, Jour. Am. Chem. Soc. **64**, 841, 1942
7. Kennedy, Econ. Geol. **45**, 629, 1950
8. Kennedy, Wasserberg, Heard, and Newton, Am. Jour. Sci. **260**, 501, 1962
9. Kitahara, Rev. Phys. Chem. Japan **30**, 109, 1960
10. Miller, Am. Jour. Sci. **250**, 161, 1952
11. Morey, Econ. Geol. **52**, 225, 1957
12. Morey and Fenner, Jour. Am. Chem. Soc. **39**, 1173, 1917
13. Morey and Fleischer, Geol. Soc. America Bull. **51**, 1935, 1940
14. Morey and Hesselgesser, Econ. Geol. **46**, 821, 1951
15. —— Am. Jour. Sci., Bowen volume, 343, 1952
16. Morey and Ingerson, Am. Jour. Sci. **35A**, 217, 1938
17. Shaw, Am. Min. **48**, 883, 1963
18. Sourirajan and Kennedy, Am. Jour. Sci. **260**, 115, 1962
19. Spengler, C. J., unpublished Ph.D. Thesis, Pennsylvania State University
20. Spengler, C. J., and Burnham, C. W., unpublished
21. Stewart, Geol. Soc. America Bull. **69**, 1648, 1958
22. —— XXI Internat. Geol. Cong. **17**, 15, 1960
23. Stewart, D. B., unpublished
24. Tuttle and Bowen, Geol. Soc. America Memoir 74, 1958
25. Tuttle and Friedman, Jour. Am. Chem. Soc. **70**, 919, 1948
26. Yoder, Stewart, and Smith, Ann. Rept. Director Geophysical Lab., 206, 1957
27. Morey, Am. Min. **47**, 1456, 1962

TABLE 19-1. VAPOR PRESSURES AND COMPOSITIONS OF
SATURATED SOLUTIONS (3 phase equilibria) [6]

Salt	Temperature (°C)	Pressure (bars)	Solubility (mole fraction of salt)
Na_2CO_3	112	1.29	.070
	183.6	9.85	.053
	225.8	24.69	.042
	247.3	36.04	.034
	305.5	90.6	.014
	334.4	132.9	.005
	368.5	205.4	.0002
Na_2SO_4	158.8	5.5	.051
	209.9	17.2	.054
	227.0	25.4	.055
	258.5	41.5	.050
	292.5	74.0	.029
	323	117.9	.011
	355.5	174.6	.002
	366.8	203.7	.001
NaCl	230.2	19.55	.130
	254.6	27.87	.138
	299.3	56.77	.155
	344.4	97.57	.178
	354.3	107.8	.183
	410.0	181.3	.217
	442.5	233.1	.238
	467.5	272.6	.251
	485.5	298.3	.270
	514.2	339.5	.285
	550.5	375.0	.335
	600.0	393.9	.411
	646.2	373.4	.505
NaI	185.0	2.43	.336
	240.8	8.62	.390
	300.2	17.81	.454
	342	26.71	.502
	372	35.09	.538
	389.5	39.30	.559
	444.0	62.0	.624
	493.0	89.7	.690
	521.4	101.37	.735
KCl	190	8.69	.160
	250	24.74	.185
	300	49.29	.217
	350	84.12	.252
	400	127.25	.295
	450	171.08	.347
	500	207.57	.398
	550	226.75	.461
	600	223	.535
KI	306.3	40.44	.301
	388.0	74.83	.393
	476.5	93.31	.520
	506.5	91.20	.568
	513.0	88.62	.579
	538.0	83.12	.627
	563.0	75.70	.674

TABLE 19-2. SOLUBILITY OF NaCl IN STEAM IN THE GAS-SOLID EQUILIBRIUM REGION FOR
THE SYSTEM NaCl–H_2O [18]

Temperature (°C)	Pressure (bars)	Weight per cent NaCl in steam	Temperature (°C)	Pressure (bars)	Weight per cent NaCl in steam
350	114	.0026*	625	200	.0255
350	100	.0020	625	150	.0200
			625	100	.0145
400	182	.0080*	625	50	.0092
400	150	.0069			
400	100	.0042	650	356	.1600*
			650	300	.0712
450	259	.0157*	650	250	.0527
450	250	.0149	650	200	.0376
450	200	.0134	650	150	.0260
450	150	.0109	650	100	.0178
450	100	.0067	650	50	.0112
			650	20	.0075
500	330	.0243*			
500	300	.0234	675	326	.3815*
500	250	.0209	675	300	.2148
500	200	.0180	675	250	.1200
500	150	.0140	675	200	.0821
500	100	.0090	675	150	.0550
500	50	.0022	675	100	.0352
			675	50	.0213
550	379	.0343*	675	20	.0123
550	350	.0314			
550	300	.0276	700	287	.9416*
550	250	.0240	700	250	.5086
550	200	.0203	700	200	.3004
550	150	.0164	700	150	.1755
550	100	.0109	700	100	.1006
550	50	.0036	700	50	.0531
			700	20	.0260
600	392	.0414*			
600	380	.0377	725	200	1.8235
600	350	.0334	725	150	.9009
600	300	.0293	725	100	.4609
600	250	.0256	725	50	.2052
600	200	.0225	725	20	.0906
600	150	.0184			
600	100	.0124	750	130	7.015
600	50	.0064	750	100	4.526
			750	75	3.206
625	379	.0744*	750	50	2.155
625	350	.0472	750	20	1.282
625	300	.0382			
625	250	.0319			

* Saturated solution

TABLE 19-3. PRESSURE-TEMPERATURE-COMPOSITION DATA IN THE GAS-LIQUID EQUILIBRIUM
REGION IN THE SYSTEM NaCl—H₂O (*Keevil's data, **6**) **[18]**

Pressure (bars)	Weight per cent NaCl Gas phase	Liquid phase	Pressure (bars)	Weight per cent NaCl Gas phase	Liquid phase
	350° C		920	18.26	20.85
165	0	0	918	16.85	22.93
162	..	1.040	913	15.72	24.86
161	..	1.500	907	13.34	26.82
160	..	2.016	902	12.27	
157	..	3.110	897	11.00	
155	..	3.917	858	5.962	
153	..	4.913	806	3.077	
151	..	5.762	766	1.896	
148	..	7.603	710	1.016	
145	..	9.526	656	.5724	
140	..	12.96	603	.3392	
135	..	17.00	559	.2102	
130	..	21.92	503	.1186	
127	..	25.6	460	.0761	
114	.0026	41.5*	392	.0414	69.0*
	400° C			700° C	
285	2.6	2.6	1237	26.4	26.4
283	1.510	3.483	1234	24.30	
281	1.000	4.118	1228	19.61	
274	.5420	5.680	1218	15.82	
265	.2710	7.820	1210	13.94	
248	.1070	12.41	1200	12.06	
240	.0741	14.60	1192	10.91	
232	.0542	17.14	1180	9.613	
218	.0296	23.54	1170	8.804	
182	.0080	46.0*	1150	7.510	
	500° C		1132	6.631	
590	11.5	11.5	1108	5.810	
588	11.18	11.70	1078	5.048	
583	7.068	13.98	1050	4.500	
579	5.423	16.15	1030	4.182	
573	4.324	18.51	1000	3.810	
565	3.198	21.04	970	3.480	
559	2.651	23.02	940	3.200	
553	2.350	23.92	910	2.930	
552	2.246	25.06	860	2.569	
515	.9080		810	2.331	
462	.3090		758	2.103	
413	.1280		705	1.901	
373	.0570		657	1.720	
330	.0243	56.1*	604	1.567	
	600° C		504	1.313	
922	19.6	19.6	403	1.120	
			287	.9416	84.0*

* Saturated solution

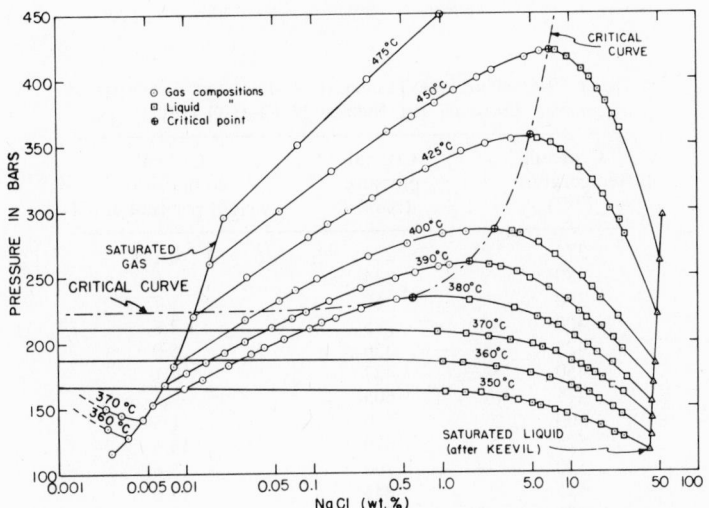

Figure 19-1. Compositions of coexisting gases and liquids in the system NaCl–H₂O,
350–475° C [18]

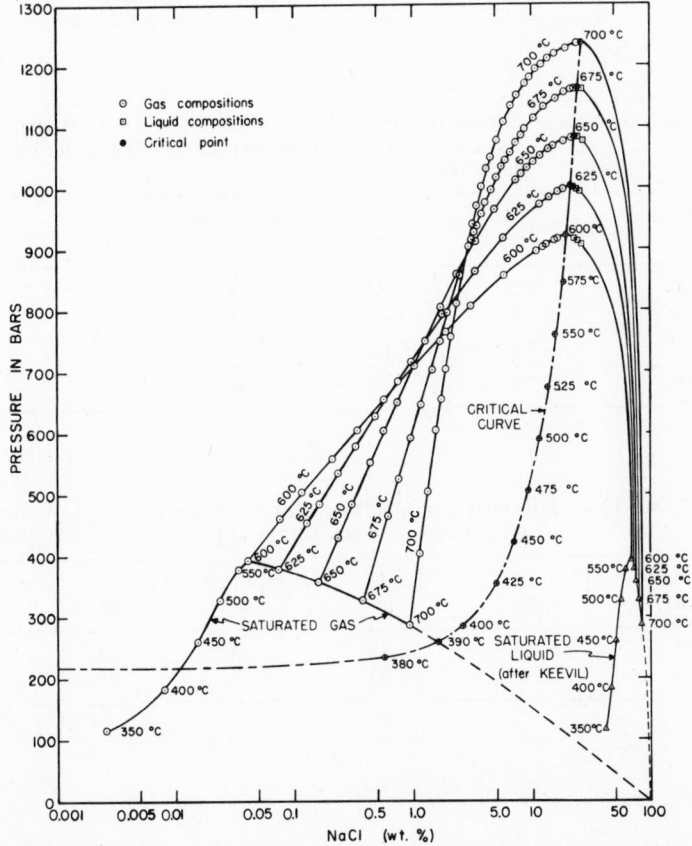

Figure 19-2. Compositions of coexisting gases and liquids in the system NaCl–H₂O,
600–700° C [18]

TABLE 19-4. CRITICAL TEMPERATURE-PRESSURE-COMPOSITION DATA IN THE SYSTEM NaCl–H$_2$O [18]

Critical temperature (°C)	Critical pressure (bars)	Critical composition weight per cent NaCl
374	221	0
380	234	.6
390	260	1.7
400	285	2.6
425	356	5.0
450	422	7.1
475	505	9.3
500	590	11.5
525	670	13.6
550	760	15.6
575	845	17.6
600	922	19.6
625	1002	21.5
650	1082	23.2
675	1163	24.8
700	1237	26.4

TABLE 19-5. SOLUBILITY (in gm/l) OF OPTICAL CALCITE IN WATER AS A FUNCTION OF TEMPERATURE AND PRESSURE OF CO$_2$ [10]

Temperature (°C)	Pressure (bars)				
	1	10	20	50	100
20	.92	1.88	2.33		
40	.54	1.39	1.73	2.23	2.51
60	.35	.97	1.22	1.56	1.80
80	.26	.67	.82	1.08	1.24
100	.20	.52	.61	.77	.88

TABLE 19-6. SOLUBILITY (in gm/l) OF OPTICAL CALCITE IN SEA WATER AS A FUNCTION OF TEMPERATURE AND PRESSURE OF CO$_2$ [10]

Pressure (bars)	Temperature (°C)				
	20	40	60	80	100
1	.88	.56	.40	.28	.17
10	2.60	1.92	1.23	.93	.72

TABLE 19-7. SOLUBILITY (IN WT PER CENT) OF SILICA IN THE QUARTZ-GAS REGION OF THE SYSTEM SILICA-WATER

A. REFERENCE [7]

Temperature (°C)	200	300	400	500	600	750	1000	1250	1750
260							.066		
280							.078		
300	.080	.077		.092		.100	.092		
320	.080	.085		.104		.114	.107		
340	.070	.091	.106	.114		.127	.125		
360		.097	.107	.120	.135	.142	.142		
380		.081	.096	.119	.134	.152	.159		
400		.040	.075	.111	.131	.157	.174	.195	.268
420			.055	.101	.126	.160	.189	.215	.318
440			.044	.090	.114	.161	.203	.237	
460				.078	.107	.162	.217	.257	
480				.069	.103	.163	.229	.277	
500				.062	.101	.164	.238		
520				.059	.100	.165	.245		
540					.099	.166	.250		
560					.098				
580									
600									

B. REFERENCE [9]

Temperature (°C)	Pressure (bars)				
	380	400	420	460	500
250	.051	.041	.042		
300	.078	.069	.066		
350	.091	.089	.085		
400	.099	.101	.100	.055	.058
450	.106	.112	.124	.074	.092
500	.112	.127	.142	.106	.123
600	.121	.137	.156	.134	.156
700				.158	.184
800					
900					

C. REFERENCE [14]

Temperature (°C)	Pressure (bars)			
	360	400	500	600
33		.0001		
67		.0003	.0014	
133		.0005	.0036	
333	.085	.064	.022	.036
667		.126	.135	
1000		.155	.260	.296
1500		.206	.404	.559
2000		.231	.499	.765

TABLE 19-8.   THE LOWER THREE-PHASE REGION, QUARTZ + LIQUID
+ GAS, IN THE SYSTEM SILICA-WATER

Pressure (bars)	Temperature (° C)	Solubility in the liquid phase (weight per cent)
	A. REFERENCE [7]	
6.2	160	.007
11.1	182	.017
15.5	200	.024
25.0	222	.036
33.5	240	.043
51.7	263	.057
64.2	280	.063
85.9	300	.068
106.7	318	.071
128.1	330	.074
156.5	346	.070
186.7	360	.058
205.1	368	.0465
221.0	373	.023
	B. REFERENCE [9]	
6	160	.008
15	200	.026
33	240	.045
63	280	.058
87	300	.062
113	320	.065
145	340	.065
184	360	.053
208	370	.025

TABLE 19-9.   THE UPPER THREE-PHASE REGION, QUARTZ + LIQUID + GAS,
IN THE SYSTEM SILICA-WATER

Pressure (kb)	Temperature ° C	Weight per cent H_2O in liquid	Weight per cent SiO_2 in gas
	A. REFERENCE [8]		
2	1130	4.4	6
4	1100	5.4	10
6	1085	6.3	19
8	1080	8.8	28
9	1080	12.7	47
	B. REFERENCE [23]		
2	1130 ± 5	4 ± .5	
5	1065 ± 5	10 ± 1.0	
10	1055 ± 5	22 ± 2.0	38 ± 2.0

TABLE 19-10. SOLUBILITIES IN PART OF THE SYSTEM Na_2O–SiO_2–H_2O AT 400° C [15]

Pressure (bars)	Gas				Liquid			
	H_2O	Na_2O	SiO_2	$\dfrac{SiO_2}{Na_2O + SiO_2}$	H_2O	Na_2O	SiO_2	$\dfrac{SiO_2}{Na_2O + SiO_2}$
A. COMPOSITION OF GAS AND LIQUID OF THE THREE-PHASE TRIANGLE WITH QUARTZ AT 400° C								
240	.998	.001	.001	.5	.229	.200	.571	.741
400	.992	.003	.005	.58	.242	.195	.563	.743
700	.968	.012	.020	.63	.251	.192	.559	.746
800	.960	.013	.027	.68	.261	.186	.553	.748
1000	.950	.016	.034	.68	.270	.183	.547	.75
1200	.913	.027	.060	.69	.277	.181	.542	.75
1600	.88	.035	.085	.71	.281	.179	.540	.75
2000	.84	.045	.115	.72	.318	.161	.521	.76
2500	.77	.062	.168	.73	.35	.156	.494	.76
B. COMPOSITION OF GAS AND LIQUID OF THE THREE-PHASE TRIANGLE WITH SODIUM DISILICATE AT 400° C								
1. Silica-rich side								
240	.998	.001	.001	.5	.229	.200	.571	.741
400	.987	.006	.007	.56	.242	.202	.556	.733
700	.965	.015	.020	.57	.263	.207	.530	.719
1000	.946	.023	.031	.58	.271	.210	.519	.712
1200	.933	.028	.039	.58	.280	.210	.510	.708
1600	.903	.040	.057	.59	.293	.214	.493	.697
2000	.858	.056	.086	.60	.310	.216	.474	.687
2200	.806	.076	.118	.61	.340	.224	.436	.661
2. Sodium-rich side								
380	.96	.027	.013	.32	.265	.294	.441	.600
700	.932	.044	.024	.35	.272	.281	.447	.614
1000	.907	.054	.039	.42	.292	.266	.442	.624
1600	.836	.077	.087	.53	.315	.247	.438	.640
2000	.823	.077	.100	.58	.333	.231	.436	.654
2200	.806	.074	.120	.61	.340	.224	.436	.661
C. COMPOSITION OF GAS AND LIQUID OF THE THREE-PHASE TRIANGLE WITH SODIUM METASILICATE AT 400° C								
380	.96	.027	.013	.320	.265	.294	.441	.600
500	.94	.040	.020	.336	.289	.290	.421	.594
700	.91	.057	.033	.365	.308	.286	.406	.587
1000	.86	.087	.053	.380	.333	.282	.385	.577
1200	.79	.127	.083	.395	.347	.280	.373	.571
1600	.76	.138	.102	.425	.366	.279	.355	.559
2000	.68	.174	.146	.458	.403	.270	.327	.547
(2500)	.61	.197	.193	(.497)	.427	.268	.305	.532

TABLE 19-11.   COMPOSITION OF GASES IN EQUILIBRIUM WITH CRYSTALLINE
SODIUM METASILICATE AT 400° C [15]

Pressure (bars)	H_2O	Na_2O	SiO_2
400	.871	.115	.014
700	.852	.121	.027
1000	.799	.156	.045
1200	.754	.191	.055
1600	.712	.213	.075
2000	.674	.242	.084

TABLE 19-12.   SOLUBILITY OF QUARTZ IN THE SYSTEM
Na_2O–SiO_2–H_2O

(Pressure is the vapor pressure of the system) [25]

Temperature (° C)	Composition, weight per cent		
	Na_2O	SiO_2	H_2O
250	.98	1.4	97.6
	4.4	10.5	85.1
	10.7	28.3	62.0
	13.0	33.9	53.1
300	.98	1.6	97.4
	1.9	4.2	93.9
	10.4	29.8	59.8
	12.9	35.1	52.0
350	.97	2.5	96.5
	1.9	5.3	92.8
	9.3	27.0	63.7
	12.6	36.1	51.3

TABLE 19-13. LIQUID-GAS EQUILIBRIA IN THE SYSTEM
K_2O-SiO_2-H_2O-CO_2 AT 500° C [13]

H_2O in charge (grams)	K_2O (grams)	Liquid phase SiO_2 (grams)	CO_2 (grams)	H_2O (grams)	Vapor phase CO_2 (grams)	H_2O (grams)	Approximate pressure (bars)
		$K_2O:SiO_2 = 1:1$					
1.068	.778	.496	.292	.110	.435	.976	169
2.169	.778	.496	.295	.313	.432	1.856	280
3.166	.778	.496	.282	.383	.444	2.783	358
4.181	.778	.496	.288	.459	.439	3.722	417
		$K_2O:SiO_2 = 1:1$					
1.951	.950	.606	.286	.297	.158	1.654	215
2.315	.950	.606	.291	.369	.153	1.946	242
2.360	.950	.606	.290	.375	.154	1.985	245
3.109	.950	.606	.291	.466	.153	2.643	301
4.094	.950	.606	.286	.516	.158	3.578	368
		$K_2O:SiO_2 = 1:1$					
2.549	1.069	.682	.241	.444	.009	2.105	246
3.052	1.069	.682	.240	.461	.010	2.591	290
4.034	1.069	.682	.239	.471	.011	3.563	359
		$K_2O:SiO_2 = 1:2$					
3.129	.623	.795	.125	.327	.457	2.802	358
		$K_2O:SiO_2 = 1:3$					
1.177	.520	.994	.113	.187	.373	.990	155
2.078	.520	.994	.081	.198	.405	1.880	252
2.085	.520	.994	.066	.211	.420	1.874	252
2.089	.520	.994	.080	.204	.406	1.885	253
3.141	.520	.994	.061	.238	.425	2.903	338
3.238	.520	.994	.066	.250	.420	2.988	344
4.212	.520	.994	.079	.294	.407	3.918	404
		$K_2O:SiO_2 = 1:3$					
1.498	.592	1.132	.093	.183	.183	1.315	180
1.500	.592	1.132	.088	.162	.189	1.338	182
2.541	.592	1.132	.057	.253	.220	2.288	278
2.557	.592	1.132	.053	.254	.224	2.303	279
3.947	.592	1.132	.056	.311	.220	3.636	372
3.949	.592	1.132	.053	.279	.224	3.679	378
5.128	.592	1.132	.063	.326	.213	4.802	428
		$K_2O:SiO_2 = 1:3$					
1.548	.660	1.263	.015	.235	.062	1.313	173
3.267	.660	1.263	.014	.340	.064	3.267	342
		$K_2O:SiO_2 = 1:4$					
3.497	.446	1.137	.064	.246	.353	3.251	358
3.643	.446	1.137	.067	.259	.350	3.384	367
2.569	.446	1.137	.036	.312	.381	2.257	286
		$K_2O:SiO_2 = 1:4$					
2.517	.498	1.270	.029	.188	.204	2.329	279

TABLE 19-14. SOLUBILITY OF SILICATES IN WATER [14]

Substance and temperature	Pressure (bars)	Total solubility (weight per cent)	Oxide	Molecular ratio of oxides in vapor
Albite, NaAlSi$_3$O$_8$, 500° C	400	.0062	Na$_2$O	1.00
			Al$_2$O$_3$	.71
			SiO$_2$	8.63
	1000	.077	Na$_2$O	1.00
			Al$_2$O$_3$	.90
			SiO$_2$	6.17
	2000	.267$_5$	Na$_2$O	1.00
			Al$_2$O$_3$	.98
			SiO$_2$	6.10
Microcline, KAlSi$_3$O$_8$, 500° C	1000	.076	K$_2$O	1.00
			Al$_2$O$_3$	.96
			SiO$_2$	6.45
	2000	.248	K$_2$O	1.00
			Al$_2$O$_3$	.93
			SiO$_2$	6.76
Enstatite, MgS$_2$O$_3$, 600° C	1000	.063	MgO	1.00
			SiO$_2$	7.65

TABLE 19-15. SOLUBILITY OF OXIDES AND SULFATES IN WATER AT 500° C

Substance	Pressure (bars)	Solubility (weight per cent)	Ref.
Anhydrite, CaSO$_4$	1000	.002	14
Barite, BaSO$_4$	1000	.004	14
Anglesite, PbSO$_4$	1000	.011	14
Na$_2$SO$_4$	67	.0009	14
	133	.0037	
	666	.0249	
	1000	.4307	
Fe$_2$O$_3$	1000	.009	14
UO$_2$	1034	.00002	11
Al$_2$O$_3$	1034	.00018	11
SnO$_2$	1034	.0003	11
NiO	2068	.0020	11
Nb$_2$O$_5$	1034	.0028	11
Ta$_2$O$_5$	1034	.003	11
BeO	1034	.012	11
SiO$_2$	1034	.26	11
GeO$_2$	1034	.87	11

TABLE 19-16. SOLUBILITY OF WATER IN SILICATE MELTS ALONG THE FREEZING CURVE
(3-phase equilibria)

Solid phase	Temperature (°C)	Pressure (bars)	Mole fraction H_2O (per cent)	Ref.
$K_2SiO_3 \cdot H_2O$	200	..	72.7	
	285	4.4	64.8	12
	360	6.2	55.5	
$K_2SiO_3 \cdot 0.5H_2O$	380	7.5	53.7	
	420	10.8	51.2	
	520	10.9	42.0	
K_2SiO_3	942	1.0	14.2	
	976	.0	.0	
$K_2Si_2O_5 \cdot H_2O$	285	29.9	76.0	12
	380	39.5	65.0	
$K_2Si_2O_5$	420	38.2	61.9	
	500	67.0	56.1	
	600	74.9	52.0	
	1034	1.0	7.0	
	1041	.0	.0	
$Na_2Si_2O_5$	874	0	0	16
(Pressures interpolated	800	45		
from graph)	750	113.		

			Per cent H_2O in liquid by weight	
$NaAlSi_3O_8$ (Albite)	1115	0	0	
	1100	67	.5	4
	1050	210	1.75	
	1000	350	3.1	
	950	570	4.5	
	900	920	6.1	
	850	1,700	7.9	
	825	2,660	9.2	
$KAlSi_3O_8$ (Orthoclase)	950	2,600	..	4
	940	3,500	7	

At pressures below 2600 bars, orthoclase melts incongruently to leucite plus liquid.

Stone Mountain granite (Georgia)	1050	0	0	4
(liquidus temperatures)	1035	140	1	
	1005	260	2	
	963	400	3	
	908	550	4	
	840	730	5	
	750	930	6	
	600	1,100	7	
$NaAlSi_3O_8$ (from glass)	835 ± 5	2,000	7.29	22
$NaAlSi_3O_8$ (from gel)	830 ± 5	2,000	7.07	23
$68SiO_2:32CaAl_2Si_2O_8$	1040 ± 10	1,000	4	
$63SiO_2:37CaAl_2Si_2O_8$	922 ± 3	2,000	6	
$58SiO_2:42CaAl_2Si_2O_8$	815 ± 5	5,000	10	21
$52SiO_2:48CaAl_2Si_2O_8$	757 ± 7	10,000	12	
(4-phase equilibria)				

TABLE 19-17. SOLUBILITY OF WATER IN SILICATE MELTS AT HIGH TEMPERATURES AND PRESSURES (Two-phase equilibrium). Abbreviations: Ab, $NaAlSi_3O_8$, albite; An, $CaAl_2Si_2O_8$, anorthite; Or, $KAlSi_3O_8$, orthoclase; Q, SiO_2, quartz

Composition weight per cent	Pressure (bars)	Weight per cent water						Ref.
		800° C	900° C	950° C	1000° C	1100° C	1200° C	
Ab	500	..	4.03	..	3.61	3.21	2.78	4
	1000	..	6.01	..	5.49	4.98	4.44	
	1500	..	7.19	..	6.64	6.10	5.54	
	2000	..	7.97	..	7.42	6.88	6.32	
	2500	..	8.52	..	7.99	7.45	6.91	
	3000	..	8.94	..	8.42	7.88	7.36	
	3500	..	9.26	..	8.75	8.22	7.73	
Or	1500	..	..	..	5.1	..	..	4
	2000	..	..	..	5.7			
	2500	..	..	..	6.2			
	3000	..	..	..	6.5			
	3500	..	..	..	6.8			
	4000	..	..	..	7.1			
Stone Mountain granite melt, Georgia	300	..	2.73	..	..	..	..	4
	500	..	3.76					
	1000	6.06	5.76	..	5.46	5.15	4.85	
	1500	..	7.20					
	2000	..	8.14					
	2500	..	8.58					
	3000	..	8.91					
	3500	..	9.15					
	4000	..	9.35					
$LiAlSi_2O_6$	5000	..	12.6	12.1	11.1	..	..	23
90 per cent $LiAlSi_2O_5$	2000	..	..	..	..	6.5	...	23
10 per cent $NaAlSi_3O_8$	5000	..	12.9	12.7	12.4			

Composition, weight per cent	Temperature (° C)	Pressure (bars)	Weight per cent water	Ref.
Ab	965	490	2.08	14
	920	981	3.76	
	920	981	4.04	
	930	981	3.65	
	850	1,961	6.50	
Ab	870	2,000	6.45 ± .1	3
	810	3,600	8.70 ± .1	
	780	4,900	9.70 ± .1	
	780	5,000	9.90 ± .1	
	690	10,000	16.90 ± .3	
Or	1,010	2,430	5.40 ± .1	20
	965	3,000	5.90 ± .1	
	960	3,930	6.80 ± .4	
	940	5,000	7.80 ± .1	
	960	6,250	8.30 ± .1	
Leucite, $KAlSi_2O_6$	955	4,000	8.30 ± .1	20
	937	4,410	8.50 ± .5	
	931	5,050	9.50 ± .1	
	921	6,150	10.50 ± .5	
$Or_{56}Q_{44}$	850	490	2.49	14
	850	490	2.23	
	825	981	3.59	
	770	1,961	5.65	

TABLE 19-17. *Continued*

Composition, weight per cent	Temperature (°C)	Pressure (bars)	Weight per cent water	Ref.
$Or_{75}Q_{25}$	911	3,000	$6.50 \pm .5$	20
	912	4,960	$7.55 \pm .2$	
$Ab_{64.5}Q_{35.5}$	850	981	4.34	14
	770	1,961	7.29	
$Ab_{55.2}Q_{44.8}$	980	490	2.04	14
$Ab_{65}Q_{35}$ (from gel)	838	2,000	6.9	23
$Ab_{36.8}Or_{26.4}Q_{36.8}$	790	490	2.91	14
	740	490	2.88	
	730	981	4.19	
	730	981	4.78	
	700	1,961	5.86	
	700	1,961	6.66	
	690	2,942	9.96	
$Ab_{47}Or_{23}Q_{30}$	660	3,923	9.36	14
	660	3,923	10.26	
$Ab_{70}Or_{30}$	950	490	2.49	14
	930	490	2.45	
	850	981	4.18	
	810	1,961	6.30	
$Ab_{80}Or_{20}$ to $Ab_{63}Or_{37}$	720	5,000	11	26
$Ab_{78}O_{22}$ to $Ab_{66}Or_{34}$	710	500	11	26
80 per cent Ab 20 per cent $LiAlSiO_4$	780	2,000	8.8	22
Harding Pegmatite	715	1,030	$4.35 \pm .1$	3
	670	2,070	$6.45 \pm .3$	
	670	3,100	$8.50 \pm .1$	
	690	4,100	$10.00 \pm .1$	
	690	5,000	$11.30 \pm .2$	
	680	5,900	$12.05 \pm .1$	
	690	7,400	$14.45 \pm .2$	
	690	10,000	$19.60 \pm .4$	
Mt. Hood	1100	1,034	$4.49 \pm .1$	5
Andesite	1100	2,000	$6.04 \pm .2$	
	1100	3,000	$7.40 \pm .2$	
	1100	5,310	$10.08 \pm .3$	
Columbia River	1100	1,034	$3.09 \pm .1$	5
Basalt	1100	2,000	$4.59 \pm .1$	
	1100	3,000	$5.93 \pm .2$	
	1100	4,000	$7.30 \pm .2$	
	1100	5,340	$8.51 \pm .2$	
	1100	6,070	$9.37 \pm .2$	
$Or_{55}Q_{45}$	880	1,000	4.2	17
	840	2,000	5.3	

TABLE 19-18.　COMPOSITION OF AQUEOUS PHASE IN EQUILIBRIUM WITH HARDING, NEW MEXICO, PEGMATITE* [2]

Weight per cent; n.a.—not analyzed

Pressure Kb	2.9	3.0	3.5	5.5	5.7	5.7	7.9	9.6	9.7	9.9
Temp. °C	650	550	600	550	600	650	650	600	650	700
H_2O/peg.	4.15	3.84	4.55	3.17	3.73	2.39	2.87	2.53	2.03	1.78
SiO_2	1.26	1.18	1.74	1.67	2.72	2.65	5.45	4.84	6.71	9.38
Al_2O_3	.14	.18	.24	.20	.43	.47	1.07	.86	1.29	1.90
CaO	n.a.	n.a.	n.a.	n.a.	.0070	.0088	n.a.	n.a.	n.a.	n.a.
Li_2O	.016	.033	.038	.038	.062	.035	.071	.099	.091	.11
Na_2O	.044	.035	.057	.062	.13	.19	.40	.34	.53	.71
K_2O	.028	.026	.040	.034	.074	.089	.18	.17	.20	.31
Total solute	1.49	1.45	2.12	2.01	3.42	3.45	7.18	6.31	8.82	12.42
H_2O	98.51	98.55	97.88	97.99	96.58	96.55	92.82	93.69	91.18	87.58

* Starting material: SiO_2 = 75.24, Al_2O_3 = 14.42, CaO = .20, Li_2O = .65, Na_2O = 4.23, K_2O = 2.74

TABLE 19-19. COMPOSITION OF AQUEOUS PHASE IN EQUILIBRIUM WITH SPRUCE PINE, NORTH CAROLINA, PEGMATITE* [2]
Weight per cent; sp—Spectrochemical analysis

Pressure Kb	2.0	2.0	2.0	2.2	3.0	4.0	4.0	4.0	5.7
Temp. °C	500	600	650	700	600	500	600	700	700
H_2O/peg.	2.90	5.08	4.15	3.81	2.74	3.48	5.28	2.67	3.89
SiO_2	.58	.79	.90	1.21	1.11	.82	1.50	2.25	3.38
Al_2O_3	.040	.056 sp	.053	.019 sp	.047	.077	.095 sp	.17	.43
CaO	.006	.003 sp	.002	.002 sp	.0007	.005	.002 sp	.004	.005
Na_2O	.014	.017	.015	.008	.020	.032	.044	.064	.19
K_2O	.0093	.013	.011	.005	.016	.020	.032	.055	.15
Total solute	.65	.88	.98	1.24	1.20	.96	1.67	2.54	4.15
H_2O	99.35	99.12	99.02	98.76	98.80	99.04	98.33	97.46	95.85

Pressure Kb	6.0	6.0	6.0	6.0	7.6	7.7	7.8	9.8	10.0
Temp. °C	500	600	650	900	600	650	700	600	650
H_2O/peg.	3.17	4.62	2.90	2.81	3.01	1.97	2.29	2.89	1.72
SiO_2	1.11	2.34	3.31	4.43	2.52	5.34	5.29	4.40	6.38
Al_2O_3	.11	.24	.33	.59	.33 sp	.71	.87	.72	1.18
CaO	.004	.002	.007	.001	.005 sp	.009	.013	.023	.027
Na_2O	.066	.11	.16	.24	.11	.32	.39	.33	.55
K_2O	.032	.076	.11	.22	.10	.23	.29	.21	.34
Total solute	1.31	2.77	3.91	5.48	3.11	6.60	6.85	5.69	8.98
H_2O	98.69	97.23	96.09	94.52	96.89	93.40	93.15	94.31	91.02

* Starting material: SiO_2 = 73.79; Al_2O_3 = 15.11; CaO = .97; Na_2O = 4.71; K_2O = 4.02

TABLE 19-20. COMPOSITION OF AQUEOUS HCl SOLUTIONS IN EQUILIBRIUM WITH SPRUCE PINE, NORTH CAROLINA, PEGMATITE* [1]

Weight per cent; sp.—Spectrochemical analysis, n.a.—not analyzed, n.d.—not detected

Pressure Kb	2.0	2.0	2.0	4.0	4.0	4.0	6.0	6.0	6.0	2.0	4.1	6.1
Temp. °C	500	600	700	500	600	700	500	600	700	600	600	600
Sol'n/peg.	3.06	2.67	2.12	2.90	2.73	3.28	2.75	3.45	2.62	2.64	2.84	2.94
SiO_2	.62	.67	.99	.76	1.05	1.83	.66	1.22	1.82	.72	1.08	1.44
Al_2O_3	.076	.064	.060	.025	.046	.059	.014	.036	.062	.0066	.024	.085
Al_2O_3 sp.	.14	.055	.057	.013	.027	.043	.0064	.018	.036	.0061	.016	.067
Fe_2O_3	n.a.	.037	.087	.015	.024	.024	.016	.016	.019	.00098	.0013	.0019
Fe_2O_3 sp.	.0074	.035	.078	.017	.031	.026	.017	.015	.021	.00086	.0011	n.d.
MnO	.0056	.014	.015	.0058	n.a.	.0063	.0035	n.a.	n.a.	n.d.	n.d.	n.d.
MnO sp.	.022	.015	.017	.0061	.014	.011	.0047	.0081	.0053	.00159	.00038	.00034
MgO	.0042	.0017	.0065	.0016	n.a.	.0073	.0018	n.a.	n.a.	n.d.	.0013	n.d.
MgO sp.	.0047	.0022	.0078	.0031	.0025	.0043	.0028	.0028	.0028	.00031	.00054	.00041
CaO	.15	.14	.051	.18	.097	.060	.14	.11	.052	n.a.	.0073	n.d.
CaO sp.	.19	.13	.083	.18	.11	.084	.14	.13	.055	.0026	.0096	.0064
Na_2O	.79	.87	.81	.98	.90	.96	.81	.84	.93	.11	.14	.18
K_2O	.47	.72	.94	.63	.66	.84	.49	.57	.62	.11	.11	.11
SrO sp.	.0040	.0027	.0018	.0049	.0022	.0024	.0037	.0026	.0014	n.d.	n.d.	n.d.
BaO sp.	.0050	.0011	.0057	.0031	.0011	.0039	.0033	.0015	.0019	n.d.	n.d.	n.d.
Total solute	2.12	2.51	2.95	2.60	2.78	3.78	2.14	2.80	3.50	.95	1.36	1.82
HCl	2.12	2.12	2.12	2.12	2.12	2.12	2.12	2.12	2.12	.21	.21	.21
H_2O	95.76	95.37	94.93	95.28	95.10	94.10	95.74	95.08	94.38	98.84	98.43	97.97

*Starting material: SiO_2 = 73.79; Al_2O_3 = 15.11; Fe_2O_3 = .26; FeO = .16; MnO = .05; MgO = .07; CaO = .97; Na_2O = 4.71; K_2O = 4.02; SrO = .026; BaO = .046;

TABLE 19-21. COMPOSITION OF AQUEOUS PHASE IN EQUILIBRIUM WITH $KAlSi_3O_8$ (SANIDINE) STARTING MATERIAL [19]

Weight per cent

LIQUID

Pressure Kb	3.0	4.0	5.0	5.1	6.2
Temp. °C	965	935	900	900	880
H_2O/sanidine	1.77	3.00	2.33	2.33	2.95
SiO_2	1.13	2.02	2.99	3.14	4.48
Al_2O_3	.18	.40	.78	.85	1.21
K_2O	.17	.38	.75	.82	1.25
Total solute	1.48	2.80	4.52	4.81	6.94
H_2O	98.52	97.20	95.48	95.19	93.06

CRYSTALS

Pressure Kb	2.0	3.0	3.5	4.0	5.0	6.0
Temp. °C	845	840	850	850	830	760
H_2O/sanidine	5.17	3.00	2.95	3.20	3.00	3.00
SiO_2	.46	.67	1.05	1.63	2.50	3.20
Al_2O_3	.02	.10	.19	.34	.60	.89
K_2O	.04	.10	.15	.29	.48	.79
Total solute	.52	.87	1.39	2.26	3.58	4.88
H_2O	99.48	99.13	98.61	97.74	96.42	95.12

TABLE 19-22. COMPOSITION OF AQUEOUS PHASE IN EQUILIBRIUM WITH KAlSi₂O₆ (LEUCITE) STARTING MATERIAL [19]

Weight per cent

	LIQUID					
Pressure Kb	4.0	5.0	6.0	6.0	7.2	7.5
Temp. ° C	935	895	850	915	885	910
H₂O/glass	3.02	3.00	3.00	3.00	3.00	3.00
SiO₂	1.60	3.16	3.97	5.27	6.69	7.03
Al₂O₃	.66	1.36	1.89	2.28	2.96	3.04
K₂O	.67	1.25	2.00	2.01	3.15	3.13
Total solute	2.93	5.77	7.86	9.56	12.80	13.20
H₂O	97.07	94.22	92.14	90.44	87.20	86.80

	CRYSTALS			
Pressure Kb	3.0	4.0	5.0	6.6
Temp. ° C	840	850	795	740
H₂O/crystals	3.00	3.00	3.00	2.79
SiO₂	.79	1.40	2.09	3.71
Al₂O₃	.25	.68	1.55	2.98
K₂O	.24	.72	1.21	2.14
Total solute	1.28	2.80	4.85	8.83
H₂O	98.72	97.20	95.15	91.17

TABLE 19-23. COMPOSITION OF AQUEOUS PHASE IN EQUILIBRIUM WITH LIQUID OF 75 weight per cent $KAlSi_3O_8$-25 weight per cent SiO_2 STARTING COMPOSITION [19] Weight per cent

Pressure Kb	3.0	4.25	5.5	5.9	6.7
Temp. ° C	905	845	855	840	850
H_2O/glass	3.00	3.00	3.00	3.00	3.00
SiO_2	1.85	2.51	3.79	4.95	7.22
Al_2O_3	.09	.21	.54	.69	1.18
K_2O	.08	.24	.61	.79	1.32
Total solute	2.02	2.96	4.94	6.43	9.72
H_2O	97.98	97.04	95.06	93.57	90.28

TABLE 19-24. COMPOSITION OF AQUEOUS PHASE IN EQUILIBRIUM WITH LIQUID $NaAlSi_3O_8$ (Albite) AND $NaAlSiO_4$ (Nepheline) STARTING MATERIAL [2] Weight per cent

	$NaAlSi_3O_8$			$NaAlSiO_4$		
Pressure Kb	7.0	7.6	9.7	4.9	7.6	8.7
Temp. ° C	750	760	700	900	780	750
H_2O/glass	4.55	7.69	2.78	5.00	1.47	.90
SiO_2	3.85	4.60	6.88	1.57	4.87	11.10
Al_2O_3	1.12	1.29	1.87	2.14	7.11	12.30
Na_2O	.73	.81	1.45	1.59	5.02	8.10
Total solute	5.70	6.70	10.20	5.30	17.00	31.50
H_2O	94.30	93.30	89.80	94.70	83.00	68.50

TABLE 19-25. SOLUBILITIES OF CALCITE, MAGNESITE, AND DOLOMITE IN CO_2-FREE WATER. ($P = 200$ BARS; SOLUBILITIES ARE GIVEN IN PARTS PER MILLION.) [27]

Species in solution	Temperature, ° C							
	25	50	100	150	200	250	300	350
				A. CALCITE				
$CaCO_3$	20	20	21	20	18	15	12	7
				B. MAGNESITE				
$MgCO_3$	4	6	12	13	8	..	..	..
$Mg(OH)_2$	..	..	..	..	18	13	3	..
				C. DOLOMITE				
$CaCO_3$	4	6	10	16	18	15	13	6
$MgCO_3$	3	6	8	6	..	..	..	..
$Mg(OH)_2$	..	..	..	..	11	8	4	1

SECTION 20

THERMODYNAMIC PROPERTIES OF MINERALS*

by RICHARD A. ROBIE

CONTENTS

* Publication authorized by the Director, U.S. Geological Survey

Handbook of Physical Constants—*Revised Edition*
THE GEOLOGICAL SOCIETY OF AMERICA MEMOIR 97, 1966

In the 13 years since the publication of the National Bureau of Standards comprehensive tables of thermochemical properties, by Rossini and others [4], a very large body of modern calorimetric and equilibrium data has become available. Because of the complex interrelationships among many thermochemical data and the necessity for internal consistency among these values, a complete revision of this standard reference is required. This is also true of the summaries of thermochemical data for the sulfides [67] and for the oxides [12].

The following tables present critically selected values for the heat and free energy of formation, the logarithm of the equilibrium constant of formation Log K_f, the entropy, and the molar volume, at 298.15° K (25.0° C) and 1 atmosphere for minerals.

Except for the gases, the molar volumes were taken directly from section 5 of this handbook. For a gas, the standard state is the ideal gas at 1 atmosphere pressure, and consequently all ideal gases have the same molar volume, equal to RT, at a given temperature. The volumes given in section 16 are those for the real gas at 298.15° K and 1 atmosphere and are therefore different from those given here.

For all compounds except the silicates, the heat and free energy and Log K_f refer to formation from the *elements* in their standard states. Thermodynamic properties of elements not listed in these tables but used in the calculations were taken from Kelley and King [1] and Stull and Sinke [93].

For the silicates $\Delta H^\circ_{f,298.15}$, $\Delta F^\circ_{f,298.15}$ and Log K_f refer to formation from the oxides in their standard states. This practice was adopted to conform to the more common usage by petrologists and mineralogists, and to correspond with the most commonly measured quantity. Data are given for most oxides so that the conversion to elements as reference states may be carried out for most silicates. Values of $\Delta H_f{}^\circ$ or $\Delta F_f{}^\circ$ for K_2O and Na_2O have not been included because of the large uncertainties in these quantities.

The standard state adopted for sulfur is the orthorhombic solid. Data have been included, however, for $\Delta H^\circ_{f,298.15}$, $\Delta F^\circ_{f,298.15}$ and $S^\circ_{298.15}$ for diatomic sulfur, that is for the reaction

$$2\,S_{\text{rhomb}} \longleftarrow\!\!\!\longrightarrow S_2 \text{ gas}$$

for those who prefer to use S_2 as a reference state in calculations involving sulfides.

Specific heat data at higher temperatures have not been included because of the ready availability of Kelley's excellent modern summary of such data (U.S. Bur. Mines Bull. 584, 1960).

Tables of the change in free energy with pressure at high temperatures were calculated for H_2O and CO_2 from modern PVT data and are here included. These data may also be used to obtain the fugacity of H_2O or CO_2 using the relationship

$$\ln \frac{f}{f^\circ} = \frac{F_{P,T} - F_T{}^\circ}{RT},$$

and where f° is the fugacity of the ideal gas at one atmosphere pressure. Complete thermodynamic functions at high temperatures in the ideal gas state, at one atmosphere, (the standard state for gases) are also given for H_2O, CO_2, and S_2.

The unit of energy is the defined calorie, equal to 4.1840 absolute joules. Zero degrees Celsius is taken as 273.15° K in accordance with the 1954 definition of the thermodynamic temperature scale (Cohen, Crowe and DuMond, *Fundamental constants of physics*, Interscience Publishers, Inc., New York, 1957). These authors' values for the basic physical constants, converted to the chemical scale of atomic weights, were also adopted. The formula weights are based on the International Atomic Weights for 1957 (Wichers, Jour. Am. Chem. Soc. **80**, 4121, 1958). Symbols and constants used in these tables follow:

T	= Temperature in degrees Kelvin
gfw	= Gram formula weight
S_T	= Entropy at temperature T in cal/deg gfw
ΔH_f	= Heat of formation from reference state in cal/gfw
ΔF_f	= Free energy of formation from reference state in cal/gfw
molar volume	= Volume in cm³ of 1 gram formula weight at 1 atmosphere and 298.15° K
°	= Superscript indicates the substance is in its standard state
R	= Gas constant, 1.98726 ± .00008 cal/deg gfw (mole)
	8.31469 ± .00032 joules/deg gfw (mole)
calorie	= Unit of energy, 4.1840 absolute joules
	41.2929 cm³ atmosphere
A	= Avogadro's. number, (6.02322 ± .00016) × 10^{23} molecules/gfw (mole)
f	= Fugacity in atmospheres
P	= Pressure, in atmospheres or bars
Atm	= Atmosphere, 1,013,250 dynes/cm²
bar	= Bar, 1,000,000 dynes/cm²
log	= Logarithm to the base 10
ln	= Logarithm to the base e = 2.71828 ....

For more extensive summaries of thermochemical data, the reader is referred to the following works:

Rossini and others, U.S. Nat. Bur. Stds., Cir. 500, 1952
Richardson and Jeffes, Jour. Iron and Steel Inst. **171**, 167, 1952
Coughlin, U.S. Bur. Mines Bull. 542, 1954
Stull and Sinke, Advances in Chem. **19**, Am. Chem. Soc. 1956
Kelley, U.S. Bur. Mines Bull. 584, 1960
Kelley and King, U.S. Bur. Mines Bull. 592, 1961
Hilsenrath and others, U.S. Nat. Bur. Stds. Cir. 564, 1955
JANAF Interim Thermochemical Tables, the Dow Chemical Company, Midland, Mich., 1960–1962

REFERENCES FOR SECTION 20

1. Kelley and King, U.S. Bur. Mines Bull. 592, 1961
2. DeSorbo, Jour. Chem. Phys. **21**, 876, 1953
3. Desnoyers and Morrison, Phil. Mag. **3**, 42, 1958
4. Rossini and others, U.S. Nat. Bur. Stds. Cir. 500, 1952
5. DeSorbo and Tyler, Jour. Chem. Phys. **21**, 1144, 1953
6. Martin, Canadian Jour. Phys. **38**, 17, 1960
7. Kelley, U.S. Bur. Mines Bull. 406, 1937
8. JANAF Interim Thermochem. Tab., Dow Chemical Co., 1960–1962
9. Coughlin, Jour. Am. Chem. Soc. **80**, 1802, 1958
10. Mah, Jour. Phys. Chem. **61**, 1572, 1957
11. Barany and Kelley, U.S. Bur. Mines, Rept. Invest. 5825, 1961
12. Coughlin, U.S. Bur. Mines Bull. 542, 1954
13. Mah, U.S. Bur. Mines Rept. Invest. 5676, 1961
14. Huber and Holley, Jour. Phys. Chem. **60**, 498, 1956
15. Hatton, Hildenbrand, Sinke, and Stull, Jour. Am. Chem. Soc. **81**, 5028, 1959
16. Halstead and Moore, Jour. Chem. Soc., 3873, 1957
17. Mah, Jour. Am. Chem. Soc. **76**, 3363, 1954
18. Hilsenrath and others, U.S. Nat. Bur. Stds. Cir. 564, 1955
19. Westrum and Beale, Jour. Phys. Chem. **65**, 353, 1961

20. Huber and Holley, Jour. Am. Chem. Soc. **75**, 5645, 1953
21. Boyle, King, and Conway, Jour. Am. Chem. Soc. **76**, 3835, 1954
22. Calculated from data in Barton and Bethke, Am. Jour. Sci. **251A**, 21, 1960
23. Grønvold and Westrum, Jour. Am. Chem. Soc. **81**, 1780, 1959
24. Calculated from data in Darken, and Gurry, Jour. Am. Chem. Soc. **68**, 799, 1946, and reference 25
25. Barany, U.S. Bur. Mines Rept. Invest. 6251, 1963
26. Humphrey, King, and Kelley, U.S. Bur. Mines Rept. Invest. 4870, 1952
27. Giauque, Hornung, Kunzler, and Rubin, Jour. Am. Chem. Soc. **82**, 62, 1960
28. Barron, Berg, and Morrison, Proc. Roy. Soc. **250A**, 70, 1959
29. Calculated from data in Taylor and Wells, Jour. Res. Nat. Bur. Stds. **21**, 133, 1938
30. Evans and Wagman, Jour. Res. Nat. Bur. Stds. **49**, 141, 1952
31. Westrum, E. F., Jr., private communication
32. Good, Jour. Phys. Chem. **66**, 380, 1962
33. Calculated from quartz value and data in Humphrey and King, Jour. Am. Chem. Soc. **74**, 2041, 1952, and Kracek, Ann. Rept. Dir. Geophys. Lab. **52**, 69, 1953
34. Calculated from data in Boyd and England, Jour. Geophys. Res. **65**, 749, 1960
35. Mah, Kelley, Gellert, King, and O'Brien, U.S. Bur. Mines Rept. Invest. 5316, 1957
36. Koehler, Barany, and Kelley, U.S. Bur. Mines Rept. Invest. 5711, 1961
37. Kelley, Todd, and King, U.S. Bur. Mines Rept. Invest. 5059, 1954
38. Egan and Wakefield, Jour. Phys. Chem. **64**, 1953, 1960
39. Garrels, Thompson, and Siever, Am. Jour. Sci. **258**, 402, 1960
40. Robie, and Stout, Jour. Phys. Chem. **67**, 2252, 1963
41. Data in reference 1 corrected for magnetic contribution to entropy
42. Calculated from data of Goldsmith and Graf, Geochim. Cosmochim. Acta **11**, 310, 1957
43. Lander, Jour. Am. Chem. Soc. **73**, 5794, 1951
44. Garrels, Mineral equilibria, Harper and Brothers, New York, 1960
45. Robie, R. A., unpublished calculations based on new data for $SO_4^=$, H_2SO_4, Hg_2SO_4 and $PbSO_4$
46. Dewing and Richardson, Trans. Faraday Soc. **55**, 611, 1959
47. Good, Lacina, and McCullough, Jour. Am. Chem. Soc. **82**, 5589, 1960
48. Gallagher, Brodale, and Hopkins, Jour. Phys. Chem. **64**, 687, 1960
49. Brodale and Giauque, Jour. Am. Chem. Soc. **80**, 2042, 1958
50. Torgeson and Sahama, Jour. Am. Chem. Soc. **70**, 2156, 1948
51. Kracek, Ann. Rept. Dir. Geophys. Lab. **52**, 69, 1953
52. Neuvonen, Bull. Comm. Géol. Finlande **158**, 1952
53. King, Jour. Am. Chem. Soc. **74**, 4446, 1952
54. Kelley, U.S. Bur. Mines Rept. Invest. 5901, 1962
55. Weeks, Jour. Geol. **64**, 456, 1956
56. Todd and Kelley, U.S. Bur. Mines Rept. Invest. 5193, 1956
57. Calculated from data in King, Jour. Am. Chem. Soc. **73**, 656, 1951, reference 1, and Coughlin, and O'Brien, Jour. Phys. Chem. **61**, 767, 1957
58. Jeffes, Richardson, and Pearson, Trans. Faraday Soc. **50**, 364, 1954
59. Kelley, Barany, King, and Christensen, U.S. Bur. Mines Rept. Invest. 5436, 1960
60. Estimated
61. King and Weller, U.S. Bur. Mines Rept. Invest. 5810, 1961
62. Kay and Taylor, Trans. Faraday Soc. **56**, 1372, 1960
63. Grønvold and Westrum, Inorg. Chem. **1**, 36, 1962
64. Kiukkola and Wagner, Jour. Electrochem. Soc. **104**, 379, 1957
65. Goates, Cole, Gray, and Faux, Jour. Am. Chem. Soc. **73**, 707, 1951
66. Rosenqvist, Trans. A.I.M.E. **185**, 451, 1949
67. Richardson and Jeffes, Jour. Iron Steel Inst. **171**, 165, 1952
68. Wagner and Wagner, Jour. Electrochem. Soc. **104**, 509, 1957
69. Brooks, Jour. Am. Chem. Soc. **75**, 2464, 1953
70. Richardson and Antill, Trans. Faraday Soc. **51**, 51, 1955
71. Grønvold, Westrum, and Chou, Jour. Chem. Phys. **30**, 528, 1959
72. Calculated from data in reference 73 and 74
73. Rosenqvist, Jour. Iron Steel Inst. **176**, 37, 1954
74. Alcock and Richardson, Nature **168**, 661, 1951
75. Toulmin and Barton, Abst., Am. Min. **46**, 205, 1962
76. Goates, Cole, and Gray, Jour. Am. Chem. Soc. **73**, 3596, 1951
77. Calculated from data in Dewing and Richardson, Jour. Iron Steel Inst. **195**, 56, 1960
78. Stubbles and Birchenal, Trans. A.I.M.E. **215**, 536, 1959
79. MacAteer and Seltz, Jour. Am. Chem. Soc. **58**, 1936
80. Calculated from data in reference 1, Richards, Trans. Faraday Soc. **51**, 1193, 1955, and Orr and Christensen, Jour. Phys. Chem. **62**, 124, 1958
81. Richards, Jour. Appl. Chem. **9**, 142, 1959
82. Egan, Wakefield, and Luff, Jour. Phys. Chem. **65**, 1265, 1961
83. Rosenqvist, Jour. Iron and Steel Inst. **176**, 37, 1954
84. King and Weller, U.S. Bur. Mines Rept. Invest. 5855, 1961

85. Benz and Wagner, Jour. Phys. Chem. **65**, 1308, 1961
86. Calculated from data in Tuttle and England, Ann. Rept. Dir. Geophys. Lab. **52**, 61, 1953 and from the quartz data
87. Flubacher, Leadbetter, and Morrison, Phil. Mag. **4**, 273, 1959
88. Stubbles and Richardson, Trans. Faraday Soc. **56**, 1460, 1960
89. Chisholmn and Stout, Jour. Chem. Phys. **36**, 972, 1962
90. Koehler and Coughlin, Jour. Phys. Chem. **63**, 605, 1959
91. Grimley and Margrave, Jour. Phys. Chem. **64**, 1763, 1960
92. Wise, Margrave, Feder, and Hubbard, Jour. Phys. Chem. **66**, 381, 1962
93. Stull and Sinke, Advances in Chem. **19**, Am. Chem. Soc., 1956
94. Barany, U.S. Bur. Mines Rept. Invest. 5900, 1962
95. Stout and Robie, Jour. Phys. Chem. **67**, 2248, 1963
96. Huber, Head and Holley, Jour. Phys. Chem. **68**, 3043, 1964

TABLE 20-1. MINERALS

Formula	Name	Formula weight (grams)	Molar volume (cm³)	Entropy $S°_{298.15}$ (cal/gfw deg)	Ref.	$\Delta H°_{f,298.15}$ (cal/gfw)	$\Delta F°_{f,298.15}$ (cal/gfw)	Log K_f	Ref.
	ELEMENTS								
Ag	Silver	107.880	10.274 ±.005	10.20 ±.05	1	0	0		
Au	Gold	197.0	10.216 ±.005	11.32 ±.02	1	0	0		
C	Diamond	12.011	3.4167 ±.0005	.566 ±.003	2, 3	453 ±5	693 ±15	−.508	4
C	Graphite	12.011	5.299 ±.002	1.372 ±.005	5	0	0		
Cu	Copper	63.54	7.114 ±.004	7.95 ±.03	1, 6	0	0		
Fe	α-Iron	55.85	7.093 ±.004	6.49 ±.03	1	0	0		
Ni	Nickel	58.71	6.589 ±.005	7.14 ±.02	1	0	0		
Pt	Platinum	195.09	9.092 ±.005	9.95 ±.05	1	0	0		
S	α-Sulfur	32.066	15.53 ±.02	7.62 ±.04	1	0	0		
S	β-Sulfur	32.066	..	7.78 ±.06	1	70 ±20	15 ±10	−.011	7
S₂	Ideal Gas	64.132	24466.1 ±1.0	54.51 ±.10	8	30840 ±200	19138 ±200	−14.028	8
Pb	Lead	207.21	18.269 ±.005	15.49 ±.05	1	0	0		
Sn	β-Tin	118.70	16.290 ±.010	12.29 ±.06	1	0	0		
Sb	Antimony	121.76	18.18 ±.02	10.92 ±.06	1	0	0		
As	Arsenic	74.91	12.96 ±.05	8.36 ±.20	1	0	0		

	Name	Mol. wt.	V°	S°		ΔG°f	ΔH°f	Cp	
Bi	Bismuth	209.00	21.311 ±.010	13.50 ±.20	1	0	0		
Zn	Zinc	65.38	9.164 ±.005	9.95 ±.05	1	0	0		
Se	Selenium	78.96	16.42 ±.02	10.14 ±.05	1	0	0		
Te	Tellurium	127.61	20.48 ±.02	11.88 ±.10	1	0	0		
O_2	Oxygen (ideal gas)	32.00	24466.1 ±1.0	49.01 ±.01	1	0	0		
Cl_2	Chlorine (ideal gas)	70.914	24466.1 ±1.0	53.29 ±.01	1	0	0		
Si	Silicon	28.09	12.058 ±.006	4.497 ±.009	87	0	0		
HALIDES									
NaCl	Halite	58.448	27.018 ±.007	17.33 ±.10	1	−98,230 ±300	−91,812 ±350	67.30	4
KCl	Sylvite	74.557	37.528 ±.007	19.70 ±.05	1	−104,180 ±200	−97,521 ±250	71.48	4
NaF	Villiaumite	41.991	14.99 ±.01	12.26 ±.07	1	−136,300 ±300	−129,092 ±350	94.62	9
AgBr	Bromyrite	187.796	28.99 ±.01	25.60 ±.10	1	−23,742 ±200	−22,930 ±200	16.81	4
AgCl	Ceragyrite	143.337	25.73 ±.01	23.00 ±.10	1	−30,348 ±250	−26,220 ±200	19.22	4
AgI	Iodyrite	234.79	41.31 ±.02	27.60 ±.40	1	−14,821 ±350	−15,850 ±300	11.62	4
CaF_2	Fluorite	78.08	24.54 ±.01	16.46 ±.08	1	−290,300 ±400	−277,796 ±450	203.62	4
MgF_2	Sellaite	62.32	19.64 ±.02	13.68 ±.07	1	−263,500 ±300	−250,805 ±350	183.84	4
HgCl	Calomel	236.067	32.94 ±.02	23.08 ±.30	1	−31,660 ±300	−25,175 ±200	18.45	4
Na_3AlF_6	Cryolite	209.953	70.86 ±.25	56.98 ±.40	1	−784,700 ±900	−745,413 ±1,000	546.38	9

Table 20-1. *Continued*

Formula	Name	Formula weight (grams)	Molar volume (cm³)	Entropy $S_{298.15}$ (cal/gfw deg)	Ref.	$\Delta H_{f,298.15}$ (cal/gfw)	$\Delta F^{\circ}_{f,298.15}$ (cal/gfw)	Log K_f	Ref.
			HALIDES *Continued*						
$MgCl_2$	Chloromagnesite	95.234	40.95 ±.05	21.42 ±.20	1	−153,400 ±400	−141,570 ±450	103.76	4
HCl	Ideal Gas	36.465	24,466.1 ±1.0	44.64₅ ±.05	8	−21,970 ±150	−22,684 ±180	16.63	8
$MnCl_2$	Sacchite	125.854	42.11 ±.20	28.26 ±.05	89	−115,190 ±120	−105,446 ±300	77.290	90
			OXIDES AND HYDROXIDES						
Al_2O_3	Corundum	101.96	25.57 ±.01	12.18 ±.03	1	−400,400 ±300	−378,073 ±330	277.12	10
AlO(OH)	Boehmite	59.988	19.54 ±.02	11.58 ±.05	1	−235,500 ±3,500	−217,670 ±3,500	159.55	4
$HAlO_2$	Diaspore	59.988	17.76 ±.03	8.43 ±.04	1				
$Al(OH)_3$	Gibbsite	78.004	31.96 ±.04	16.75 ±.10	1	−306,380 ±300	−273,480 ±350	200.46	11
As_2O_3	Arsenolite	197.82	51.12 ±.03	25.6 ±.5	1	−157,000 ±400	−129,170 ±500	94.68	12
BeO	Bromellite	25.013	8.315 ±.005	3.37 ±.02	1	−143,100 ±150	−136,118 ±200	99.77	12
Bi_2O_3	Bismite	466.00	49.73 ±.06	36.2 ±.6	1	−137,160 ±300	−121,040 ±200	88.72	13
CaO	Lime	56.08	16.76 ±.01	9.5 ±.2	1	−151,790 ±300	−144,350 ±350	105.81	14
$Ca(OH)_2$	Portlandite	74.096	33.06 ±.04	19.93 ±.10	1	−235,610 ±450	−214,665 ±500	157.34	15, 16
CdO		128.41	15.59 ±.01	13.1 ±.3	1	−61,200 ±200	−53,037 ±250	38.87	17
CO	Ideal Gas	28.011	24,466.1 ±1.0	47.22 ±.02	18, 8	−26,416 ±60	−32,844 ±80	24.07	8

Formula	Name								
CO₂	Ideal Gas	44.011	24,466.1 ±1.0	51.07 ±.02	18, 8	−94,054 ±30	−94,265 ±50	69.095	8
CeO₂	Cerianite	172.13	23.86 ±.02	14.89 ±.03	19	−260,180 ±350	−245,046 ±450	179.61	20
CoO		74.94	11.64 ±.01	12.66 ±.08	1	−57,100 ±300	−51,428 ±350	37.70	21
Cr₂O₃	Eskolaite	152.02	28.98 ±.05	19.4 ±.3	1	−272,700 ±400	−253,200 ±500	185.59	17
CuO	Tenorite	79.54	12.22 ±.02	10.19 ±.05	1	−37,140 ±300	−30,494 ±350	22.35	22
Cu₂O	Cuprite	143.08	23.44 ±.02	22.4 ±.2	1	−40,400 ±1,500	−35,018 ±1,600	25.67	12
Fe.₉₄₇O	Wüstite	68.89	12.04 ±.04	13.74 ±.10	1	−63,800 ±400	−58,760 ±500	43.07	12
Fe₂O₃	Hematite	159.70	30.28 ±.02	20.89 ±.05	23	−196,750 ±1,100	−177,159 ±1,400	129.85	24
Fe₃O₄	Magnetite	231.55	44.53 ±.02	36.03 ±.10	63	−267,400 ±500	−243,113 ±700	178.20	26
H₂O	Water	18.016	18.069 ±.003	16.715 ±.03	27	−68,317 ±10	−56,688 ±15	41.55	12
H₂O	Ideal Gas	18.016	24,466.1 ±1.0	45.106 ±.01	18	−57,798 ±10	−54,634 ±15	40.06	12
HfO₂	Hafnia	210.50	20.82 ±.01	14.18 ±.10	1	−266,050 ±300	−252,413 ±350	185.01	12
HgO	Montroydite (red)	216.61	19.32 ±.02	16.80 ±.08	1	−21,711 ±90	−13,990 ±50	10.254	12
MgO	Periclase	40.32	11.25 ±.01	6.44 ±.04	28	−143,800 ±100	−136,085 ±150	99.75	12
Mg(OH)₂	Brucite	58.336	24.64 ±.03	15.09 ±.05	1	−221,200 ±500	−199,450 ±550	146.19	29
MnO	Manganosite	70.94	13.22 ±.01	14.27 ±.10	1	−92,050 ±110	−86,708 ±150	63.55	12
MnO₂	Pyrolusite	86.94	16.61 ±.06	12.68 ±.10	1	−124,450 ±200	−111,337 ±250	81.608	12
Mn₂O₃	Bixbyite	157.88	31.38 ±.03	26.40 ±.50	1	−229,200 ±2,000	−210,600 ±2,200	154.36	12

TABLE 20-1. *Continued*

Formula	Name	Formula weight (grams)	Molar volume (cm³)	Entropy $S^{\circ}_{298.15}$ (cal/gfw deg)	Ref.	$\Delta H^{\circ}_{f,\,298.15}$ (cal/gfw)	$\Delta F^{\circ}_{f,\,298.15}$ (cal/gfw)	Log K_f	Ref.
			OXIDES AND HYDROXIDES *Continued*						
Mn_3O_4	Hausmannite	228.82	46.96 ±.08	35.5 ±1.0	1	−331,400 ±400	−305,950 ±800	224.25	12
MoO_3	Molybdite	143.95	30.56 ±.02	18.58 ±.10	1	−178,100 ±100	−154,445 ±150	113.21	10
NiO	Bunsenite	74.71	10.97 ±.01	9.08 ±.04	1	−57,300 ±100	−50,572 ±150	37.07	21
PbO	Litharge (red)	223.21	23.91 ±.02	15.6 ±.2	1	−52,523 ±300	−45,250 ±150	33.17	12
PbO	Massicot (yellow)	223.21	23.15 ±.02	16.1 ±.2	1	−52,174 ±300	−45,050 ±150	33.02	12
SO_2	Ideal Gas	64.066	24,466.1 ±1.0	59.29 ±.10	30	−70,947 ±50	−71,740 ±60	52.58	30
SO_3	Ideal Gas	80.066	24,466.1 ±1.0	61.20 ±.50	1	−94,470 ±70	−88,526 ±100	64.89	30
Sb_2O_3	Valentinite	291.52	50.01 ±.06	29.4 ±.6	1	−168,766 ±1,400	−149,100 ±1,000	109.29	12
SiO_2	α-Quartz	60.09	22.690 ±.005	9.88 ±.02	31	−217,650 ±400	−204,643 ±500	150.00	32, 92
SiO_2	α-Cristobalite	60.09	25.74 ±.02	10.38 ±.02	31	−216,930 ±800	−204,072 ±900	149.58	33
SiO_2	α-Tridymite	60.09	26.53 ±.20	10.50 ±.10	86, 1	−216,900 ±900	−204,077 ±1,000	149.59	33
SiO_2	Coesite	60.09	20.64 ±.05	9.30 ±.50	34				
SnO_2	Cassiterite	150.70	21.55 ±.02	12.5 ±.3	1	−138,820 ±150	−124,270 ±200	91.09	12
TeO_2	Tellurite	159.61	27.75 ±.02	16.8 ±1.0	1	−77,745 ±800	−64,600 ±700	47.35	12
ThO_2	Thorianite	264.05	26.38 ±.01	15.59 ±.05	1	−293,200 ±400	−279,431 ±450	204.82	12

Formula	Mineral								
TiO_2	Rutile	79.90	18.80 ±.02	12.04 ±.04	1	−225,760 ±100	−212,552 ±150	155.80	35
TiO_2	Anatase	79.90	20.49 ±.03	11.93 ±.07	1				12
UO_2	Uraninite	270.07	24.62 ±.01	18.63 ±.10	1	−259,200 ±600	−246,556 ±700	180.72	12
ZnO	Zincite	81.38	14.34 ±.01	10.43 ±.10	1	−83,250 ±200	−76,100 ±200	55.78	
ZrO_2	Baddeleyite	123.22	21.15 ±.06	12.12 ±.08	1	−263,100 ±500	−249,332 ±600	182.76	96
Na_2O	Sodium Oxide	61.982	...	17.99 ±.20	91				
SPINELS, ALUMINATES, AND TITANATES									
$MgAl_2O_4$	Spinel	142.28	39.72 ±.03	19.26 ±.10	1				
$FeAl_2O_4$	Hercynite	173.81	40.82 ±.06	25.4 ±.2	1				
$MgFe_2O_4$	Magnesioferrite	200.02	...	29.6 ±.6	1	−341,171 ±700	−314,573 ±1,000	230.58	36
$NiFe_2O_4$	Trevorite	234.41	43.66 ±.08	31.5 ±.2	1				
$MgCr_2O_4$	Picrochromite	192.34	43.57 ±.06	25.3 ±.2	1				
$FeCr_2O_4$	Chromite	223.87	44.01 ±.10	34.90 ±.40	1				
$CaTiO_3$	Perovskite	135.98	33.72 ±.08	22.4 ±.1	1	−396,900 ±600	−376,507 ±700	275.97	37
$FeTiO_3$	Ilmenite	151.75	31.71 ±.05	25.3 ±.3	1	−295,560 ±600	−277,063 ±700	203.08	37
Fe_2TiO_4	Ulvöspinel	223.60	...	40.36 ±.60	1				
$MgTiO_3$	Geikielite	120.22	30.86 ±.03	17.82 ±.10	1	−375,900 ±400	−354,780 ±500	260.05	37

TABLE 20-1. *Continued*

Formula	Name	Formula weight (grams)	Molar volume (cm³)	Entropy $S^\circ_{298.15}$ (cal/gfw deg)	Ref.	$\Delta H^\circ_{f,298.15}$ (cal/gfw)	$\Delta F^\circ_{f,298.15}$ (cal/gfw)	Log K_f	Ref.
				PHOSPHATES, MOLYBDATES AND TUNGSTATES					
$AlPO_4$	Berlinite	121.955	46.59 ±.05	21.70 ±.05	38				
$Ca_5(PO_4)_3OH$	Hydroxylapatite	502.333	159.66 ±.40	93.30 ±.40	1				
$Ca_5(PO_4)_3F$	Fluorapatite	504.325	157.60 ±.50	92.70 ±.40	1				
$Fe(PO_4)\cdot 2H_2O$	Strengite	186.857	..	40.93 ±.30	82	−451,500 ±1,000	−397,693 ±1,300	291.50	82
				CARBONATES AND NITRATES					
$CaCO_3$	Calcite	100.091	36.94 ±.02	22.2 ±.2	1	−288,086 ±250	−269,820 ±200	197.77	39, 4
$CaMg(CO_3)_2$	Dolomite	184.422	64.35 ±.04	37.09 ±.07	95	−557,567 ±800	−518,676 ±900	380.18	95
$CdCO_3$	Otavite	172.421	34.30 ±.02	23.3 ±.6	1	−179,040 ±600	−149,225 ±1,000	109.40	4
$FeCO_3$	Siderite	115.861	29.38 ±.02	23.9 ±.6	41	−178,200 ±1,200	−161,060 ±800	118.05	4, 41
$MgCO_3$	Magnesite	84.331	28.02 ±.01	15.7 ±.2	1	−266,052 ±400	−246,077 ±450	180.37	95
$Mg_3Ca(CO_3)_4$	Huntite	353.084	122.90 ±.30	..	:	..	−1,007,700 ±1,000	738.63	39
$MnCO_3$	Rhodochrosite	114.951	31.08 ±.01	23.90 ±.50	41	−212,392 ±800	−194,190 ±1,000	142.34	42
$ZnCO_3$	Smithsonite	125.391	28.28 ±.01	19.70 ±.30	1	−194,200 ±700	−174,780 ±1,000	128.11	4
$BaCO_3$	Witherite	197.371	45.81 ±.04	26.8 ±.5	1	−291,300 ±1,100	−272,193 ±1,500	199.51	4
$CaCO_3$	Aragonite	100.091	34.16 ±.02	21.2 ±.3	1	−288,134 ±250	−269,570 ±200	197.59	4, 39

Formula	Name	Mol. wt.			n				Ref.
$PbCO_3$	Cerussite	267.221	40.60 ±.03	31.3 ±.8	1	−167,300 ±700	−149,690 ±1,000	109.72	4
$SrCO_3$	Strontianite	147.641	39.01 ±.03	23.2 ±.4	1	−290,728 ±500	−272,000 ±200	199.37	39, 43
$Cu_2(OH)_2CO_3$	Malachite	221.107	54.86 ±.05	: .	:	:	−216,440 ±200	158.65	44
$Cu_3(OH)_2(CO_3)_2$	Azurite	344.653	91.02 ±.07		:	:	−343,730 ±500	251.95	44
KNO_3	Niter	101.108	48.04 ±.05	31.81 ±.15	1	−117,760 ±300	−93,914 ±500	68.84	4
$NaNO_3$	Soda Niter	84.999	37.60 ±.02	27.85 ±.10	1	−111,540 ±300	−87,461 ±500	64.11	4
SULFATES AND BORATES									
$BaSO_4$	Barite	233.426	52.11 ±.05	31.6 ±.2	1	−351,996 ±2,300	−325,300 ±2,000	238.44	45
$CaSO_4$	Anhydrite	136.146	45.94 ±.05	25.5 ±.4	1	−343,335 ±1,000	−316,475 ±1,000	231.97	45, 46
H_2SO_4	Sulfuric Acid	98.082	53.57 ±.07	37.50 ±.05	27	−194,670 ±100	−165,049 ±150	120.98	47, 27
$PbSO_4$	Anglesite	303.276	47.96 ±.05	35.51 ±.07	48	−220,028 ±300	−194,500 ±200	142.57	45
$SrSO_4$	Celestite	183.696	46.25 ±.05	28.2 ±1.0	1	−346,646 ±1,800	−319,830 ±1,500	234.43	45
$ZnSO_4$	Zinkosite	161.446	41.58 ±.05	27.0 ±1.0	1	−235,488 ±1,500	−209,074 ±900	153.25	45
K_2SO_4	Arcanite	174.266	65.51 ±.07	42.0 ±.4	1	−343,704 ±800	−315,565 ±500	231.30	45
Na_2SO_4	Thenardite	142.048	53.34 ±.06	35.73 ±.07	1	−331,839 ±550	−303,715 ±500	222.62	45
$CaSO_4 \cdot 2H_2O$	Gypsum	172.178	74.31 ±.16	46.36 ±.3	4	−484,000 ±1,100	−430,137 ±1,000	315.28	45
$MgSO_4 \cdot 7H_2O$	Epsomite	246.498	146.85 ±.50	: .	:	−808,700 ±2,000	:	:	4
$Na_2SO_4 \cdot 10H_2O$	Mirabilite	322.208	219.83 ±.40	141.46 ±.15	49	−871,850 ±700	−709,135 ±700	519.78	45

TABLE 20-1. *Continued*

Formula	Name	Formula weight (grams)	Molar volume (cm³)	Entropy $S^\circ_{298.15}$ (cal/gfw deg)	Ref.	$\Delta H_{f,298.15}$ (cal/gfw)	$\Delta F_{f,298.15}$ (cal/gfw)	Log K_f	Ref.
				SULFATES AND BORATES *Continued*					
$CuSO_4 \cdot 5H_2O$	Chalcanthite	249.686	109.08 ±.20	73.0 ±1.0	4	−544,450 ±1,000	−449,300 ±1,200	329.33	4
$Cu_4SO_4(OH)_6$	Brochantite	452.274	113.60 ±1.15	70.2 ±4.0	22	−527,135 ±1,200	−435,311 ±600	319.08	22
$Na_2B_4O_7 \cdot 10H_2O$	Borax	381.422	222.68 ±.40	⋯	⋯	−1,497,200 ±2,000	⋯	⋯	4
				SILICATES					
Al_2SiO_5	Andalusite	162.05	51.54 ±.01	22.28 ±.10	1				
Al_2SiO_5	Kyanite	162.05	44.11 ±.02	20.02 ±.08	1				
Al_2SiO_5	Sillimanite	162.05	49.91 ±.02	22.97 ±.10	1				
$CaSiO_3$	Wollastonite	116.17	39.94 ±.08	19.60 ±.20	1	−21,250 ±700	−21,316 ±800	15.624	50, 85
$CaSiO_3$	Pseudowollastonite	116.17	40.08 ±.08	20.90 ±.20	1				
$CaMg(SiO_3)_2$	Diopside	216.58	66.10 ±.10	34.20 ±.20	1	−36,500 ±1,500	−36,053 ±1,700	26.426	51, 52
$MgSiO_3$	Clinoenstatite	100.41	31.47 ±.07	16.22 ±.10	1	−8,690 ±150	−8,660 ±200	5.028	50
$MnSiO_3$	Rhodonite	131.03	35.32 ±.30	24.50 ±.50	41	−5,920 ±170	−6,024 ±400	4.415	53
$NaAlSi_2O_6$	Jadeite	202.151	60.98 ±.40	31.90 ±.30	1	−36,500 ±1,000	−35,620 ±1,400	26.110	51, 54
$Ca_2Mg_5Si_8O_{22}(OH)_2$	Tremolite	812.496	272.95 ±.90	131.19 ±.30	40	−120,840 ±2,500	−116,138 ±3,000	85.127	55

Formula	Mineral								
CaTiSiO₅	Sphene	196.07	55.70 ±.30	30.88 ±.20	1	−26,850 ±250	−26,689 ±350	19.563	56
γ-Ca₂SiO₄	Calcium Olivine	172.25	58.63 ±.35	28.80 ±.20	1	−32,743 ±600	−32,719 ±700	23.982	57
Fe₂SiO₄	Fayalite	203.79	46.39 ±.08	34.70 ±.40	1	−8,282 ±400	−7,280 ±500	5.336	53
CaAl₂Si₂O₈	Anorthite	278.22	100.73 ±.15	48.45 ±.30	1	−21,810 ±700	−23,900 ±900	17.518*	54, 62
NaAlSi₃O₈	Albite	262.241	100.21 ±.19	50.20 ±.40	1	−35,900 ±1,500	−37,530 ±1,800	27.509	54
KAlSi₃O₈	Orthoclase	278.35	⋮	52.47 ±.60	1	−51,030 ±1,000	⋮	⋮	54
KAlSiO₄	Kaliophillite	158.17	59.90 ±.08	31.85 ±.30	1	−46,200 ±1,500	⋮	⋮	
KAlSi₂O₆	Leucite	218.26	88.39 ±.05	44.05 ±.40	1	−30,900 ±1,000	−32,320 ±1,300	23.690	54
NaAlSiO₄	Nephelite	142.061	54.17 ±.15	29.72 ±.30	1	−32,750 ±700	−34,080 ±900	24.98	54
NaAlSi₂O₆·H₂O	Analcite	220.167	97.50 ±.10	56.03 ±.60	1	−25,580 ±700	−27,690 ±1,000	20.296	94
NaAlSi₂O₆	Dehydrated Analcite	202.151	⋮	41.93 ±.40	84	−16,920 ±600	−18,230 ±800	13.36	54
CaAl₂Si₂O₈	Hexagonal Anorthite	278.22	⋮	45.84 ±.30	84	−37,190 ±600	−31,800 ±800	23.31	94
CaAl₂Si₂O₇(OH)₂·H₂O	Lawsonite	314.252	101.33 ±.15	56.79 ±.50	84	−73,740 ±1,500	−68,075 ±2,000	49.90	94
Ca₂Al₄Si₈O₂₄·7H₂O	Leonhardite	922.91	⋮	220.40 ±1.60	84	−43,830 ±700	⋮	⋮	94
Ca₂MgSi₂O₇	Akermanite	272.68	92.82 ±.15	⋮	⋮		⋮	⋮	52
Mg₂SiO₄	Forsterite	140.73	43.67 ±.08	22.75 ±.20	1	−15,120 ±250	−15,117 ±350	11.081	50
Mn₂SiO₄	Tephroite	201.97	48.62 ±.10	39.00 ±1.00	1	−11,770 ±600	−11,943 ±1,000	8.754	58
CaMgSiO₄	Monticellite	156.49	51.37 ±.15	⋮	⋮	−27,560 ±600	⋮	⋮	52

TABLE 20-1. *Continued*

Formula	Name	Formula weight (grams)	Molar volume (cm³)	Entropy $S_{298.15}$ (cal/gfw deg)	Ref.	$\Delta H^{\circ}_{f,298.15}$ (cal/gfw)	$\Delta F^{\circ}_{f,298.15}$ (cal/gfw)	Log K_f	Ref.
			SILICATES *Continued*						
β-Ca_2SiO_4	Larnite	172.25	51.60 ±.40	30.50 ±.20	1	−30,190 ±250	−30,673 ±350	22.483	57
Be_2SiO_4	Phenacite	110.116	37.20 ±.06	15.37 ±.08	1				
Zn_2SiO_4	Willemite	222.85	52.42 ±.13	31.40 ±.20	1	−6,990 ±140	−7,187 ±400	52.680	57
$ZrSiO_4$	Zircon	183.31	39.27 ±.15	20.20 ±.20	1				
$Mg_3Si_4O_{10}(OH)_2$	Talc	379.336	134.30 ±.80	62.34 ±.15	40	−44,890 ±500	−40,950 ±500	30.02	25, 40
$KMg_3AlSi_3O_{10}F_2$	Fluorphlogopite	421.31	146.38 ±.50	75.90 ±.50	1	−20,880 ±2,000	..	..	59 †
$KMg_3AlSi_3O_{10}(OH)_2$	Phlogopite	417.326	149.66 ±1.00	75.20 ±1.00	60				
$Al_2Si_2O_5(OH)_4$	Kaolinite	258.172	..	48.53 ±.30	61	−7,140 ±500	−1,982 ±700	1.453	11
$Al_2Si_2O_5(OH)_4$	Dickite	258.172	99.31 ±.30	47.10 ±.30	61	−6,840 ±500	−1,390 ±700	1.019	11
$Al_2Si_2O_5(OH)_4$	Halloysite	258.172	..	48.63 ±.30	61	−2,670 ±500	+2,324 ±700	−1.703	11
			SULFIDES, TELLURIDES, AND SELENIDES						
Ag_2S	Acanthite (Argentite)	247.826	34.21 ±.05	34.14 ±.10	63	−7,737 ±300	−9,562 ±200	7.009	64, 65, 66
CaS	Oldhamite	72.146	27.81 ±.02	13.54 ±.30	1	−114,390 ±600	−113,070 ±500	82.878	67
CdS	Greenockite	144.476	29.94 ±.02	16.80 ±.40	1				
CuS	Covellite	95.606	20.43 ±.04	15.93 ±.40	1				
Cu_2S	Chalcocite	127.672	27.47 ±.06	28.86 ±.50	1	−19,148 ±300	−20,728 ±300	15.193	68, 69, 70

Formula	Name	Mol. wt.			ref			log K	ref
FeS	Troilite (Pyrrhotite)	87.916	18.17 ±.05	14.42 ±.04	71	−24,220 ±250	−24,311 ±300	17.820	72,73,74
FeS₂	Pyrite	119.982	23.94 ±.02	12.65 ±.03	63	−41,000 ±400	−38,293 ±450	28.068	75
FeSe₂	Ferroselite	134.81	29.92 ±.08	20.76 ±.06	63				
H₂S	Ideal Gas	34.082	24,466.1 ±1.0	49.13 ±.10	1	−4,815 ±100	−7,890 ±100	5.783	29
HgS	Metacinnabar	232.676	30.17 ±.04	23.00 ±1.00	1	−11,058 ±500	−10,220 ±200	7.491	76
α-MnS	Alabandite	87.006	21.46 ±.01	18.69 ±.40	1	−49,000 ±400	−50,020 ±400	35.169	77
MoS₂	Molybdenite	160.082	32.03 ±.07	14.96 ±.05	63	−60,500 ±1,500	−58,380 ±1,500	42.792	88
NiS	Millerite	90.776	16.89 ±.01	15.80 ±1.00	63	−20,290 ±1,000	−20,600 ±1,000	15.099	83
PbS	Galena	239.276	31.49 ±.01	21.84 ±.30	1	−23,360 ±250	−22,980 ±200	16.844	64,78
PbSe	Clausthalite	286.17	34.61 ±.01	24.48 ±.50	1				
PbTe	Altaite	334.82	40.60 ±.01	26.26 ±.50	1	−16,921 ±500	−16,590 ±300	12.160	79
PtS	Cooperite	227.156	22.15 ±.02	13.16 ±.03	63	−19,700 ±800	−18,370 ±900	13.465	63
SnS	Herzenbergite	150.766	29.01 ±.02	18.36 ±.20	1	−25,400 ±300	−23,950 ±350	17.555	80
WS₂	Tungstenite	247.992	32.07 ±.05	22.70 ±2.0	63				
ZnS	Sphalerite	97.446	23.83 ±.01	13.77 ±.20	1	−49,200 ±1,000	−48,067 ±1,100	35.32	81
S₂	Ideal Gas	64.132	24,466.1 ±1.0	54.51 ±.10	8	30,840 ±200	19,138 ±200	−14.028	8
S₈	Ideal Gas	256.528	24,466.1 ±1.0	103.30 ±.40	8	24,510 ±50	11,919 ±150	−8.736	8

* For the reaction: 2Fe.₉₄₇O + .106Fe + SiO₂ = Fe₂SiO₄

† For the reaction: KF + ½MgF₂ + ⅝MgO + ⅝Al₂O₃ + 3SiO₂ = KMg₃AlSi₃O₁₀F₂

TABLE 20-2.   H₂O, IDEAL GAS

Reference states:
for elements from Stull and Sinke [93]; for H₂O ideal gas 298.15° to 1800° K.

Gram formula weight 18.016 g
Gfw volume 24,466 cm³
ΔH° vaporization 10,518 cal

T Temperature °K	$H_T^\circ - H_{298.15}^\circ$ Heat content cal/gfw	S_T° Entropy cal/deg gfw	$-\dfrac{(F_T^\circ - H_{298.15}^\circ)}{T}$ Free energy function cal/deg gfw	Formation from (reference state)—Elements Heat ΔH_f° cal/gfw	Elements Free energy ΔF_f° cal/gfw	Oxides Heat ΔH_f° cal/gfw	Oxides Free energy ΔF_f° cal/gfw
298.15	*0	45.106 ±.03	45.106	−57,798 ±30	−54,636 ±30		
400	825	47.484	45.422	−58,042	−53,519		
500	1,654	49.334	46.026	−58,277	−52,361		
600	2,509	50.891	46.701	−58,500	−51,156		
700	3,390	52.249	47.406	−58,710	−49,915		
800	4,300	53.464	48.089	−58,905	−48,646		
900	5,240	54.570	48.749	−59,084	−47,352		
1,000	6,209	55.592	49.382	−59,246	−46,040		
1,100	7,210	56.545	49.991	−59,391	−44,712		
1,200	8,240	57.441	50.575	−59,519	−43,371		
1,300	9,298	58.288	51.136	−59,634	−42,022		
1,400	10,384	59.092	51.675	−59,734	−40,663		
1,500	11,495	59.859	52.196	−59,824	−39,297		
1,600	12,630	60.591	52.698	−59,906	−37,927		
1,700	13,787	61.293	53.183	−59,977	−36,549		
1,800	14,964	61.965	53.652	−60,041	−35,170		

* Table modified from Hilsenrath, U.S. Nat. Bur. Stds. Cir. 564, 1955

TABLE 20-3. CO₂, IDEAL GAS

Reference states: for elements from Stull and Sinke [93]; for CO₂, ideal gas 298.15° to 1800° K.	$H_T^\circ - H_{298.15}^\circ$ Heat content (cal/gfw)	S_T° Entropy (cal/deg gfw)	$-\dfrac{(F_T^\circ - H_{298.15}^\circ)}{T}$ Free energy function (cal/deg gfw)	Formation from (reference state) Elements		Oxides	
T Temperature °K				Heat ΔH_f° (cal/gfw)	Free energy ΔF_f° (cal/gfw)	Heat ΔH_f° (cal/gfw)	Free energy ΔF_f° (cal/gfw)
298.15	*0	51.073 (±.05)	51.073	†−94,052 (±10)	−94,259 (±30)		
400	956.9	53.824	51.432	−94,069	−94,317		
500	1985.3	56.116	52.145	−94,090	−94,374		
600	3,085.1	58.119	52.997	−94,123	−94,440		
700	4,243.7	59.904	53.842	−94,165	−94,480		
800	5,451.3	61.516	54.702	−94,216	−94,526		
900	6,699.9	62.986	55.541	−94,269	−94,558		
1,000	7,982.7	64.337	56.354	−94,319	−94,586		
1,100	9,293.9	65.587	57.138	−94,367	−94,622		
1,200	10,630	66.748	57.890	−94,410	−94,616		
1,300	11,986	67.835	58.615	−94,464	−94,656		
1,400	13,360	68.854	59.311	−94,516	−94,683		
1,500	14,748	69.812	59.980	−94,571	−94,682		
1,600	16,150	70.714	60.620	−94,626	−94,676		
1,700	17,563	71.571	61.240	−94,681	−94,681		
1,800	18,985	72.383	61.836	−94,740	−94,675		

Gram formula weight 44.011 g
Gfw volume 24,466 cm³

* Calculated from National Bureau of Standards, Circular 564, 1955
† Coughlin, J. P., U.S. Bur. Mines Bull. 542, 1954

TABLE 20-4. S₂, IDEAL DIATOMIC GAS

Reference states:
for sulfur from JANAF tables [8]; for S₂ ideal diatomic gas 298.15° to 1800° K.

Gram formula weight 64.132 g
Gfw volume 24466 cm³
Transitions in reference states:
$S_{orth} \to S_{mon\,I}$ 368.54° K
$S_{mon\,I} \to S_{mon\,II}$ 374.15° K
$S_{mon\,II}$ M.P.   388.36° K
$S_{liq\,I} \to S_{liq\,II}$ 433.15° K
$S_{liq\,II}$ B.P.   717.75° K

T Temperature °K	$H_T^\circ - H_{298.15}^\circ$ Heat content (cal/gfw)	S_T° Entropy (cal/deg gfw)	$-\dfrac{(F_T^\circ - H_{298.15}^\circ)}{T}$ Free energy function (cal/deg gfw)	Formation from (reference state)- Elements Heat ΔH_f° (cal/gfw)	Free energy ΔF_f° (cal/gfw)	Oxides Heat ΔH_f° (cal/gfw)	Free energy ΔF_f° (cal/gfw)
298.15	*0	54.510 ±.03	54.510	30,840 ±150	19,138 ±200		
400	811	56.848	54.819	29,433	15,233		
500	1,639	58.693	55.416	28,385	11,806		
600	2,486	60.238	56.094	27,518	8,575		
700	3,347	61.564	56.783	26,779	5,525		
800	4,217	62.726	57.455	0	0		
900	5,093	63.758	58.099	0	0		
1,000	5,975	64.687	58.712	0	0		
1,100	6,860	65.531	59.294	0	0		
1,200	7,749	66.304	59.846	0	0		
1,300	8,640	67.017	60.371	0	0		
1,400	9,533	67.679	60.870	0	0		
1,500	10,428	68.296	61.344	0	0		
1,600	11,325	68.875	61.797	0	0		
1,700	12,223	69.420	62.230	0	0		
1,800	13,123	69.934	62.643	0	0		

* Entire table taken from JANAF Interim Thermochem. Tables, Dow Chemical Co., 1960–1962.

TABLE 20-5. H₂O, CHANGE IN FREE ENERGY WITH PRESSURE, $F_{P,T} - F_T°$, calories

Pressure bars	Temperature °K										
	650	700	750	800	850	900	950	1,000	1,100	1,200	1,300
50	4,930	5,338	5,744	6,152	6,553	6,943	7,238	7,718	8,508	9,295	10,048
100	5,719	6,217	6,698	7,184	7,658	8,130	8,596	9,065	9,990	10,923	11,851
150	6,121	6,690	7,238	7,775	8,305	8,820	9,340	9,850	10,865	11,879	12,882
200	6,354	6,994	7,593	8,177	8,745	9,295	9,848	10,395	11,473	12,556	13,623
250	6,474	7,202	7,851	8,472	9,074	9,655	10,238	10,816	11,942	13,070	14,182
300	6,522	7,344	8,046	8,701	9,335	9,943	10,553	11,150	12,320	13,492	14,647
350	6,554	7,438	8,195	8,888	9,547	10,183	10,815	11,432	12,641	13,849	15,042
400	6,590	7,502	8,312	9,039	9,724	10,387	11,033	11,668	12,916	14,153	15,380
450	6,627	7,552	8,406	9,167	9,873	10,559	11,227	11,877	13,155	14,427	15,680
500	6,661	7,596	8,482	9,272	10,002	10,707	11,395	12,058	13,369	14,665	15,945
550	6,693	7,638	8,545	9,365	10,118	10,841	11,543	12,226	13,565	14,880	16,185
600	6,727	7,680	8,604	9,444	10,221	10,960	11,678	12,378	13,738	15,074	16,404
650	6,759	7,718	8,654	9,516	10,310	11,069	11,803	12,515	13,898	15,255	16,603
700	6,792	7,755	8,700	9,580	10,394	11,166	11,915	12,637	14,043	15,425	16,790
750	6,822	7,791	8,748	9,641	10,468	11,255	12,015	12,753	14,179	15,580	16,967
800	6,853	7,828	8,793	9,695	10,538	11,340	12,108	12,860	14,305	15,725	17,129
850	6,885	7,863	8,834	9,747	10,603	11,417	12,200	12,959	14,428	15,864	17,283
900	6,914	7,898	8,875	9,796	10,665	11,491	12,285	13,056	14,539	15,994	17,428
950	6,945	7,930	8,916	9,844	10,721	11,557	12,363	13,144	14,644	16,115	17,565
1,000	6,973	7,963	8,953	9,890	10,762	11,619	12,434	13,226	14,744	16,230	17,696
1,100	7,033	8,030	9,015	9,978	10,877	11,740	12,572	13,380	14,932	16,443	17,936
1,200	7,090	8,095	9,098	10,060	10,975	11,852	12,699	13,520	15,101	16,642	18,159
1,300	7,145	8,154	9,169	10,139	11,062	11,953	12,814	13,647	15,255	16,823	18,362
1,400	7,203	8,215	9,234	10,217	11,143	12,048	12,924	13,771	15,400	16,990	18,548

Calculated from specific volume for H₂O of:

Holser, W. T., and Kennedy, G. C., Am. Jour. Sci. 256, 744, 1958
Holser, W. T., and Kennedy, G. C., Am. Jour. Sci. 257, 71, 1959

TABLE 20-6. CO₂, CHANGE IN FREE ENERGY WITH PRESSURE, $F_{P,T} - F_T^\circ$, calories

Pressure bars	Temperature °K												
	400	450	500	550	600	650	700	750	800	900	1,000	1,100	1,200
*100	3,503	4,002	4,495	4,977	5,456	5,937	6,408	6,878	7,391	8,269	9,190	10,137	11,058
†150	3,780	4,383	4,932	5,465	5,993	6,512	7,030	7,053	8,060	9,083	10,102	11,123	12,118
200	3,959	4,602	5,203	5,777	6,337	6,898	7,447	8,000	8,542	9,622	10,701	11,782	12,844
250	4,085	4,763	5,395	6,002	6,595	7,195	7,762	8,340	8,902	10,038	11,163	12,290	13,407
300	4,188	4,902	5,557	6,191	6,810	7,422	8,021	8,622	9,205	10,385	11,551	12,720	13,874
350	4,277	5,014	5,694	6,351	6,992	7,625	8,247	8,865	9,471	10,678	11,882	13,083	14,270
400	4,357	5,115	5,818	6,494	7,155	7,803	8,445	9,080	9,700	10,938	12,176	13,397	14,616
450	4,436	5,207	5,928	6,622	7,299	7,966	8,623	9,273	9,908	11,169	12,431	13,683	14,927
500	4,510	5,295	6,033	6,741	7,430	8,113	8,785	9,448	10,095	11,380	12,668	13,935	15,203
600	4,643	5,453	6,214	6,949	7,670	8,372	9,065	9,751	10,422	11,755	13,080	14,388	15,698
700	4,773	5,602	6,379	7,133	7,875	8,598	9,312	10,022	10,711	12,082	13,441	14,787	16,126
800	4,895	5,740	6,538	7,305	8,069	8,807	9,541	10,263	10,969	12,370	13,758	15,131	16,502
900	5,010	5,871	6,683	7,472	8,242	9,002	9,747	10,482	11,202	12,629	14,049	15,451	16,846
1,000	5,128	5,998	6,827	7,623	8,406	9,180	9,942	10,685	11,420	12,871	14,317	15,743	17,147
1,100	5,236	6,122	6,958	7,764	8,563	9,348	10,117	10,878	11,624	13,098	14,567	16,019	17,430
1,200	5,346	6,241	7,086	7,909	8,714	9,507	10,288	11,063	11,822	13,316	14,795	16,268	17,703
1,300	5,451	6,355	7,213	8,046	8,861	9,666	10,455	11,233	12,001	13,516	15,018	16,503	17,961
1,400	5,557	6,470	7,340	8,171	9,001	9,813	10,614	11,404	12,184	13,710	15,225	16,723	18,200

* Hilsenrath and others, U.S. Nat. Bur. Stds. Cir. **564**, 1955
† Recalculated from Price, Ind. and Eng. Chem. **47**, 1649, 1955

SECTION 21

THERMAL CONDUCTIVITY

by Sydney P. Clark, Jr.

Contents

Handbook of Physical Constants—*Revised Edition*
The Geological Society of America Memoir 97, 1966

In an isotropic, homogeneous material the conduction of heat depends on a single "constant" of the material, the thermal conductivity; this is actually a function of temperature, pressure, and other variables. The quantity of heat, dQ, conducted in unit time across an element of surface dS is given by

$$dQ = -K \frac{dT}{dn} dS,$$

where K is the conductivity, and dT/dn the thermal gradient in the direction of the normal to dS. The flow of heat in crystals other than those of the cubic system depends on either two or three principal conductivities; the theory of conduction in crystals is given in Kristallphysik by W. Voigt and also Crystal physics by W. A. Wooster.

Two cgs units of heat are in common use, and thermal conductivity is commonly given in either of two units. Units of cal/cm sec ° C are used here; to convert to watts/ cm ° C, the values given in the tables should be multiplied by 4.184. A unit sometimes encountered in engineering work is the British thermal unit per square foot per hour for a temperature gradient of $1°$ F per inch; this unit equals 3.446×10^{-4} cal/cm sec ° C.

Rocks are not homogeneous, and their constituent crystals predominantly are of low symmetry. The fundamental relationship given above is not valid for infinitesimal elements in this case. If no large-scale departures from isotropy exist, however, a single conductivity, determined from a sufficiently large sample, suffices to give the relationship between average heat flow and average thermal gradient. Such factors as bedding, schistosity, and fracturing may introduce marked differences in the conductivity in different directions.

A considerable body of data on the thermal conductivity of rocks at room temperature has accumulated since the first edition of this work, and the table containing these data has been completely revised. Lithologic units represented by less than five samples are not included in this table. Knowledge of the thermal conductivity of soils and loosely compacted deep-sea sediments has also improved recently; the latter material has assumed considerable importance in view of submarine heat-flow investigations.

Since the data given here are intended primarily for geologists and geophysicists, most of the space is devoted to naturally occurring materials. No measurements made at temperatures below $0°$ C are included (with the exception of some frozen soils and ice). The literature on the conductivity of metals at low temperature through 1954 has been reviewed by R. L. Powell and W. A. Blanpied, (Nat. Bur. Standards, Circ. 556), and some more recent measurements are given by H. M. Rosenburg (Phil. Trans., A247, 441, 1955). A review of the thermal conductivity of dielectric crystals at low temperature is given by R. Berman (*Advances in physics*, II, 103, 1959).

Finally, a word of caution about the use of these tables is in order. Even for relatively well-defined substances, measurements by qualified investigators show startling discrepancies; some of them are due to real differences between different samples of what is nominally the same material, but some must be attributed to experimental error. Results obtained by several experimenters for the same material are presented where possible, but preference has been given to recent work. For an exhaustive compilation of older data, *see* K. Schulz, Fortschritte der Mineralogie, 9, 345, 1924.

TABLE 21-1. CONDUCTIVITY OF ROCKS

The measurements were made at a temperature of about 20° C unless otherwise noted. The values are the means of groups of measurements. Only cases in which there are five or more measurements from a single lithologic unit are included (σ = standard deviation).

Rock type and locality	Number of determinations	Conductivity (10^{-3} cal/cm sec ° C) Mean	Range	Ref.
Granite and Quartz Monzonite				
Adams Tunnel, Colo.	59	7.89	6.7– 8.6	2
Granite				
Loetschberg Tunnel, Switzerland	12	7.77	6.2– 9.0	8
Granodiorite				
Steamboat Springs, Nev.	5	6.64	6.2– 6.9	4
Granodiorite				
Grass Valley, Calif.	14	7.61	7.0– 8.3	9
Quartz-Feldspar Porphyry				
Jacoba Bore, Orange Free State, S. Africa (25° C)	5	8.0	7.6– 8.6	5
Syenite and Syenite Porphyry				
Kirkland Lake, Ont.	37	7.66	6.3– 9.5	12
Altered Rhyolite				
Timmins, Ont.	6	8.23	7.4– 8.8	12
Norite				
Sudbury, Ont.	5	6.42	5.5– 7.3	12
Serpentinized Peridotite				
Thetford Mines, Quebec	5	6.34	5.7– 7.0	12
Agglomerate				
Roodepoort Bore, Transvaal, S. Africa	5	7.4	7.1– 8.0	14
Karoo Dolerite				
Kestell Bore, Orange Free State (35° C)	9	4.8	4.0– 5.5	14
Ventersdorp Lava				
Jacoba Bore, Orange Free State (25° C)	9	7.4	6.3– 8.6	5
Ventersdorp Lava				
Roodepoort Bore, Transvaal	15	7.2	6.4– 8.0	14
Portage Lake Lava				
Calumet, Mich.				
Dense Flows	27	5.01	4.1– 6.6	3
Amygdaloidal Tops	10	6.4	5.5– 9.0	3
Porphyrite and Diabase				
Grass Valley, Calif.	21	7.14	6.2– 8.2	9
Quartz Diorite Gneiss				
Adams Tunnel, Colo.	17	7.75	6.6– 8.5	2
Injection Gneiss and Schist				
Adams Tunnel, Colo.	41	7.74	4.0–11.0	2
Gneiss				
Gotthard Tunnel, Switzerland	15	6.68	5.1– 8.0	8
Gneiss				
Simplon Tunnel, Switzerland				
Perpendicular	22	6.34	4.6– 7.7	8
Parallel	8	8.90	6.0–11.4	8
Schistes Lustrées				
Simplon Tunnel, Switzerland				
Perpendicular	8	5.74	4.1– 6.8	8
Parallel	7	7.50	6.8– 8.9	8

TABLE 21-1. *Continued*

Rock type and locality	Number of determi- nations	Conductivity (10⁻³ cal/cm sec ° C)		Ref.
		Mean	Range	
Gneiss				
Chester, Vt.				
Perpendicular	9	6.24	4.9– 8.7	10
Parallel	9	8.33	6.1–10.4	10
Amphibolite				
Homestake Mine, Lead, S.D.	6	6.92	6.1– 9.1	4
Calcareous Mica Phyllite				
Homestake Mine				
Perpendicular	7	7.89	6.5– 9.0	4
Parallel	9	11.83	9.5–14.0	4
Quartzite				
Homestake Mine	6	16.05	14.2–17.6	4
Witwatersrand Quartzite				
Gerhardminnebron Bore,				
Transvaal (25° C)	17	14.3	8.7–19.2	5
	21	14.5	10.4–18.9	14
Witwatersrand Quartzite				
Roodepoort Bore, Transvaal	7	10.1	7.4–12.7	14
Dolomite and Anhydrite				
Loetschberg Tunnel, Switzerland	7	11.93	8.9–13.9	8
Limestone				
Toronto, Canada	6	6.12	4.7– 7.1	12
Dolomite				
Borehole HB15, Transvaal	8	13.2	$\sigma = 1.0$	7
Dolomite				
Gerhardminnebron Bore				
Transvaal (25° C)	7	11.0	9.6–12.0	5.
Karoo Sandstone				
Kestell Bore, Orange Free State				
(35° C)	7	4.7	3.5– 7.7	14
Karoo Shale				
Kestell Bore, Orange Free State				
(35° C)	6	5.7	4.7– 6.9	14
Asmari Limestone				
Masjid-i-Sulaiman, Iran	21	5.2	$\sigma = .9$	11
Argillaceous Limestone				
Resolute Bay, N.W.T.	5	7.3	6.6– 8.0	13
Fars Marl, Shale, etc.				
Masjid-i-Sulaiman, Iran	5	4.9	$\sigma = .3$	11
Shale				
Berry No. 1 Well, Kern Co., Calif.				
1000–5290 feet	14	3.55	2.8– 4.2	1
5290–8780 feet	17	4.20	3.2– 5.6	1
Copper Harbor Conglomerate				
Calumet, Mich.	31	4.98	2.2– 7.9	3
Jacobsville Sandstone				
Calumet, Mich.	8	6.78	5.1–10.2	3
Permian Marl				
Yorkshire, England	5	5.22	4.2– 6.6	6
Carboniferous Sandstone				
Nottinghamshire	6	6.62	6.0– 7.7	6
Carboniferous Shale				
England	11	3.26	3.0– 4.3	6
Millstone Grit				
Nottinghamshire	8	8.85	7.7–11.0	6
Triassic Marl				
Yorkshire	5	3.52	2.2– 5.3	6

REFERENCES FOR TABLE 21-1

1. Benfield, Am. Jour. Sci. **245**, 1, 1947
2. Birch, Geol. Soc. America Bull. **61**, 567, 1950
3. —— Am. Jour. Sci. **252**, 1, 1954
4. —— unpublished
5. Bullard, Proc. Roy. Soc. (London) **A173**, 474, 1939
6. Bullard and Niblett, Mon. Not. Roy. Astr. Soc., Geophys. Suppl. **6**, 222, 1951
7. Carte, Proc. Phys. Soc. (London) **B67**, 664, 1954
8. Clark and Niblett, Mon. Not. Roy. Astr. Soc., Geophys. Suppl. **7**, 176, 1956
9. Clark, Trans. Am. Geophys. Union **38**, 239, 1957
10. Clark, S. P., unpublished
11. Coster, Mon. Not. Roy. Astr. Soc., Geophys. Suppl. **5**, 131, 1947
12. Misener, Thompson, and Uffen, Trans. Am. Geophys. Union **32**, 729, 1951
13. Misener, Trans. Am. Geophys. Union **36**, 1055, 1955
14. Mossop and Gafner, Jour. Chem. Met., Min. Soc., S. Afr. **52**, 61, 1951

TABLE 21-2. CONDUCTIVITY OF MONOMINERALIC AGGREGATES
(*See also* Table 21-3)
The measurements were made at a temperature of about 20° C unless otherwise noted.

Material and locality	Conductivity (10^{-3} cal/cm sec ° C)	Density (gm/cm³)	Ref.
Hortonolite Dunite			
Bushveld, Transvaal	8.7	3.76	4
Pyroxenite			
Cleveland Penin.,			
S. E. Alaska			
(mean of 3)	9.70	3.31	4
Percy Islands			
S. E. Alaska			
(mean of 3)	8.68	3.25	4
Bushveld, Transvaal	11.8	3.29	4
Diopside	10.2	3.24	3
Hornblendite			
Duke Island, S. E. Alaska			
(mean of 4)	6.75	3.22	3
Hornblendite	7.6	3.12	3
Anorthosite			
Bushveld, Transvaal	5.0	2.83	4
Serpentine	5.9	2.65	2
	4.3	2.44	2
Talc	7.1	2.79	2
Chlorite	12.5	2.79	2
Hematite	25	4.1	2
Magnetite	12.6	4.6	2
Soapstone	12.0	2.84	3
Grossularite	12.7	3.49	3
Garnet (Massive, red)	8.5	3.93	3
Anhydrite			
Loetschberg Tunnel			
Switzerland (mean of 3)	13.4	2.91	6
Masjid-i-Sulaiman			
Iran (mean of 3)	11.7	..	5
Cap rock, Louisiana			
(mean of 3)	13.7	2.93	7
Carlsbad, N. Mexico			
(mean of 3)	12.9	2.82	7

TABLE 21-2. *Continued*

Material and locality	Conductivity $(10^{-3} \text{ cal/cm sec}^\circ \text{ C})$	Density (gm/cm^3)	Ref.
Rocksalt			
Oklahoma (mean of 2)	12.75	2.18	7
Carlsbad, N. Mex.			
(mean of 2)	12.75	2.10	7
Wayne Co., Mich.			
(mean of 4)	13.27	..	10
Masjid-i-Sulaiman, Iran	16.2	..	5
Holford, England	17.2	..	1
Polyhalite			
Carlsbad, N. Mexico			
(mean of 2)	3.7	2.76	7
Gypsum			
Masjid-i-Sulaiman, Iran	3.1	..	5
Sulfur, rhombic 20° C	.65	..	9
80° C	.56		
monoclinic 100° C	.37–.39		
liquid 115° C	.31		
210° C	.38		
rhombic 0° C	.70	..	6
Fluorite	9.6	..	8

REFERENCES FOR TABLE 21-2

1. Benfield, Proc. Roy. Soc. (London) **A173**, 428, 1939
2. Birch, Am. Jour. Sci. **252**, 1, 1954
3. —— unpublished
4. Clark, S. P., unpublished
5. Coster, Mon. Not. Roy. Astr. Soc., Geophys. Suppl. **5**, 131, 1947
6. Eucken, Ann. Physik **34**, 185, 1911
7. Herrin and Clark, Geophysics **21**, 1087, 1956
8. Herschel and others, Brit. Assoc. Advancement Sci. Rept., 1881
9. Kaye and Higgins, Proc. Roy. Soc. (London) **A122**, 633, 1929
10. Leney, G. W., and Wilson, J. T., unpublished

TABLE 21-3. CONDUCTIVITY OF SINGLE CRYSTALS

CUBIC CRYSTALS

Crystal	Temperature ($^\circ$ C)	Conductivity (10^{-3} cal/cm sec $^\circ$ C)	Ref.
C (diamond)	0	290–390	6
AgCl, artificial	52	2.71	2
BaF$_2$, artificial	~30	27	1
CaF$_2$	0	24.6	6
	100	19.1	
artificial	36	23.2	2
Fe$_3$O$_4$, magnetite	22	11.9	3
LiF, air grown	36	24.9	2
vacuum grown	34	28.0	2
KBr, artificial	46	11.5	2
KCl	0	16.6	6
	100	11.8	
artificial	12	15.6	2
	72	15.3	
	0	22.1	7
MgAl$_2$O$_4$, artificial	35	33	13
spinel	68	26	
	70	28	17
NaCl	0	16.7	6
	100	11.6	
	30	13.8	11
	29	13.9	9
	8	10.0	16
	19	13.6	12
	30	8.8	5
	75	7.6	
	0	14.6	4
	100	10.1	
	200	7.5	
	300	6.0	
	400	5.0	
artificial	35	14.7	2
	70	13.0	
NaCl, artificial	0	21.3	7
artificial, from solution	0	22.8	7
NaClO$_3$	0	2.7	7
NaAlSi$_2$O$_6$·2H$_2$O analcite	0	8.2	7
FeS$_2$, pyrite	0	90.6	7
ZnS, sphalerite	0	63.6	7
UO$_2$	70	23	17

TABLE 21-3. *Continued*

NONCUBIC CRYSTALS

Absolute values necessary and sufficient to determine the conductivity in any direction have been determined only for crystals of the trigonal and hexagonal systems. For these, two principal conductivities are required; $K \parallel$ is the conductivity parallel to the optic or c axis, and $K \perp$ is the conductivity in any direction perpendicular to this axis. The conductivity in any direction making an angle φ with the optic axis is

$$K\varphi = K \perp \sin^2 \varphi + K \parallel \cos^2 \varphi$$

Crystal	System	Temperature (° C)	$K \parallel$	$K \perp$	Ref.
			(10^{-3} cal/cm sec ° C)		
CaCO₃, calcite	trig.	0	12.9	10.8	7
		0	..	10.3	6
		100	..	8.5	
		~8	9.6	7.9	17
		~30	10.0	8.4	11
		0	9.6	8.3	4
		100	7.2	6.5	
		200	6.1	5.7	
		300	5.5	5.2	
		400	5.1	4.9	
Al₂O₃, artificial	trig.	23	..	55	13
		26	60		
		70	41		
		77	..	40	
(60° from c-axis)		70	..	71	18
Fe₂O₃, hematite	trig.	30	28.9	35.1	10
SiO₂, quartz	trig.	~8	26.3	16.0	17
		0	32.5	17.3	6
		100	21.5	13.3	
		40	24.4	..	8
		68.1	22.2		
		104.3	18.6		
		25	..	14.7	
		70.4	..	12.9	
		105.5	..	11.6	
		~30	29.9	15.8	11
		0	27.3	16.3	4
		100	19.0	11.8	
		200	15.1	9.7	
		300	12.3	8.4	
		400	10.3	7.4	
		28	..	15.1	16
		70	..	14.0	18
TiO₂, rutile	tetr.	36	30	..	13
		44	..	21	
		67	33	17	

TABLE 21-3. *Continued*

. In a few cases, conductivities of noncubic single crystals have been published without information as to the orientation of the test specimen. For some of these crystals, the ratios of the principal conductivities are known to be near unity, so that the indicated values may be taken roughly as mean conductivities. A, B, and C are the principal conductivities along three orthogonal axes; a complete description of the conductivity requires also the orientation of these axes with respect to the crystallographic axes. In the orthorhombic system, these two sets of axes coincide.

Crystal	Temperature ($^\circ$C)	K (orientation unknown) (10^{-3} cal/cm sec $^\circ$ C)	Ref.
BaSO$_4$, barite, rhomb.			
($A/C = 1.13$, $B/C = 1.05$)	0	4.1	14
	100	3.6	
SrSO$_4$, celestite, rhomb.	0	4.5	14
	100	3.7	
CuSO$_4$·5H$_2$O, chalcanthite, tric.	0	5.4	7
MgSO$_4$·7H$_2$O, epsomite, rhomb.	0	5.8	7
Topaz, Al$_2$SiO$_4$ (OH, F)$_2$, rhomb.			
($A/C = .94$, $B/C = .95$)	0	55.9	7
Tourmaline, trig.			
($A/C = B/C = 1.35$)	0	10.8	7
Beryl, hex. ($A/C = B/C = .83$)	0	20.0	7
Orthoclase, mon.			
($A/C = .63$, $B/C = .90$)	0	10.0	7
Andalusite, rhomb.	0	26.3	7

The ratios of the principal conductivities have been determined for a number of minerals for which there appear to be no absolute values. A few of these follow.

Material	System	A/C	B/C
Hornblende	mon.	.50	.64
Ilmenite	trig.	1.23	
Pyrrhotite	hex.	1.14	
Siderite	trig.	1.12	
Magnesite	trig.	1.10	
Anhydrite	rhomb.	.94	.89
Gypsum	mon.	.64	.42
Apatite	hex.	.85	
Dolomite	trig.	1.10	
Mica (muscovite)*	mon.	5.84	6.30

* (For mica, C is about .002 cal/cm sec $^\circ$ C at room temperature [8, 15]; *see also* Table 21-5).

REFERENCES FOR TABLE 21-3

1. Ballard, Combes, and McCarthy, Jour. Opt. Soc. Am. **42**, 84, 1952
2. Ballard, McCarthy, and Davis, Rev. Sci. Instr. **21**, 905, 1950
3. Birch, F., unpublished
4. Birch and Clark, Am. Jour. Sci. **238**, 529 and 613, 1940
5. Bridgman, Am. Jour. Sci. 7, 81, 1924
6. Eucken, Ann. Physik **34**, 185, 1911; Verhandl. deut. physik. Ges. **13**, 829, 1911
7. Eucken and Kuhn, Zeit. physik. Chem. **134**, 193, 1928
8. Griffiths and Kaye, Proc. Roy. Soc. (London) **104**, 71, 1923; Kaye and Higgins, Proc. Roy. Soc. (London) **113**, 335, 1926
9. Herrin and Clark, Geophysics **21**, 1087, 1956

10. Koenigsberger and Weiss, Ann. Physik **35**, 1, 1911
11. Lees, Phil. Trans. Roy. Soc. (London) **183**, 481, 1892; **191**, 899, 1898
12. Leney, G. W., and Wilson, J. T., unpublished
13. McCarthy and Ballard, Jour. Opt. Soc. Am. **41**, 1062, 1951
14. Muller, Phil. Diss. Univ. Jena, 1913
15. Powell and Griffiths, Proc. Roy. Soc. (London) **163**, 189, 1937
16. Ratcliff, Brit. Jour. Appl. Phys. **10**, 22, 1959
17. Tuchschmid, Phil. Diss. Zurich, 1883
18. Weeks and Seifert, Rev. Sci. Instr. **24**, 1054, 1953

TABLE 21-4. EFFECT OF TEMPERATURE ON THE CONDUCTIVITY OF ROCKS

Rock type and locality	Temperature °C	Conductivity (10^{-3} cal/cm sec °C)	Density (gm/cm³)	Ref.
Granite				
Barre, Vt.	0	6.66	2.65	1
	50	6.25		
	100	5.90		
	200	5.50		
Westerly, R.I.				
	0	5.80	2.64	1
	50	5.60		
	100	5.42		
	200	5.12		
Rockport, Mass.				
	0	8.4	2.61	1
	50	7.8		
	100	7.2		
	200	6.5		
	300	5.9		
Granite Gneiss				
Pelham, Mass.	..	..	2.64	
Parallel to foliation	0	7.42	..	1
	100	6.58		
Perpendicular to foliation	0	5.17	..	1
	100	4.82		
Quartz Monzonite				
California	0	7.56	2.64	1
	50	6.98		
	100	6.55		
	200	5.91		
Tonalite				
Calif.	0	6.42	2.74	1
	100	5.90		
	200	5.52		
Syenite				
Ontario	50	5.25	2.80	1
	100	5.08		
	200	4.99		
Albitite				
Pa.	0	4.85	2.61	1
	100	4.80		
	200	4.70		
	300	4.55		
Bronzitite				
Mont.	0	11.0	3.26	1
	100	9.3		
	200	8.7		

TABLE 21-4. *Continued*

Rock type and locality	Temperature ° C	Conductivity (10^{-3} cal/cm sec ° C)	Density (gm/cm³)	Ref.
Dunite				
N.C.	0	12.4	3.26	1
(Mean of 3 samples)	50	10.5		
	100	9.4		
	200	8.1		
Marble				
Proctor, Vt.	..	..	2.69	1
Parallel to bedding	0	7.36		
	100	6.0		
	200	5.2		
Perpendicular to bedding	0	7.2		
	100	5.7		
	200	5.1		
Limestone				
	20	5.7	..	5
	350	3.2		
	0	5.4	..	4
	100	4.9		
Solenhofen, Bavaria	30	5.24	2.61	2
	75	4.52		
	0	7.2	2.61	1
	100	5.5		
	200	4.8		
Carbonaceous				
(Pennsylvania)	..	..	2.69	1
Parallel to bedding	0	8.2		
	100	7.0		
	200	6.5		
Perpendicular to bedding	0	6.1		
	100	5.4		
Dolomite	0	11.9	2.83	1
Pa.	50	10.3		
	100	9.3		
	200	7.95		
Anorthosite	0	4.43	2.74	1
Transvaal	100	4.54		
(Bytownite)	200	4.69		
Quebec	0	4.13	2.70	1
(Labradorite)	100	4.20		
	200	4.34		
	300	4.50		
Montana	0	4.02	2.74	1
(Bytownite)	100	4.10		
	200	4.27		
Diabase				
Md.	0	5.62	3.01	1
	100	5.35		
	200	5.37		
Maine	0	5.23	2.96	1
	100	5.10		
	200	5.03		
	300	4.99		
Mass.	0	5.04	2.96	1
	100	5.01		
	200	5.01		
	300	5.03		
	400	5.06		

Table 21-4. *Continued*

Rock type and locality	Temperature °C	Conductivity (10⁻³ cal/cm sec °C)	Density (gm/cm³)	Ref.
Diabasic Basalt	30	4.04	..	2
	75	4.14		
Gabbro				
Pa.	0	5.55	3.03	1
	100	5.25		
	200	5.13		
Wis.	0	4.75	2.87	1
	100	4.75		
	200	4.76		
	300	4.78		
	400	4.81		
Bronzitite				
Transvaal	0	11.1	3.29	1
	50	9.2		
	100	8.5		
	200	7.8		
	300	7.3		
Quartzite	0	14.9	..	4
	100	12.5		
Quartzitic Sandstone	..	..	2.64	1
Parallel to bedding	0	13.6		
	100	10.6		
	200	9.0		
Perpendicular to bedding	0	13.1		
	100	10.3		
	200	8.7		
Slate				
	0	5.2	..	4
	100	4.7		
Pa.	0	4.6	2.76	1
Perpendicular to bedding	100	4.2		
	200	4.1		
Pyrophyllite				
Transvaal				
Parallel to bedding	0	11.9	..	3
(Values read from curve;	100	10.0		
Conductivity perpen-	200	8.5		
dicular to the bedding is	300	7.5		
about half as large as	400	6.7		
parallel to the bedding.)				

REFERENCES FOR TABLE 21-4

1. Birch and Clark, Am. Jour. Sci. **238**, 529 and 613, 1940
2. Bridgman, Am. Jour. Sci. **7**, 81, 1924
3. Carte, Brit. Jour. Appl. Phys. **6**, 326, 1955
4. Ensor, Proc. Phys. Soc. (London) **43**, 590, 1931
5. Poole, Phil. Mag. **24**, 45, 1912; **27**, 58, 1914

TABLE 21-5. EFFECT OF WETTING AND SIMPLE COMPRESSION ON THE
THERMAL CONDUCTIVITY OF CERTAIN ROCKS

K_0 conductivity of dry, uncompressed rock at 45° C, in 10^{-3} cal/cm sec ° C.
ΔK_w increase of conductivity after soaking in water.
ΔK_p increase of conductivity of dry rock on compressing to 10,000 lbs/in².
ΔK_{wp} increase of conductivity of wet rock on compressing to 10,000 lbs/in².
K_m maximum observed conductivity for compressed, wetted rock.

Rock	Bulk density (gm/cm³)	Porosity (per cent)	K_0	$\dfrac{\Delta K_w}{K_0}$ (per cent)	$\dfrac{\Delta K_p}{K_0}$ (per cent)	$\dfrac{\Delta K_{wp}}{K_0}$ (per cent)	K_m
Marble							
Danby, Vt.*	2.67	1.1	5.80	11	13	2	6.62
Limestone							
Solenhofen*	2.60	3.4	5.03	23	13	..	6.19
Bedford, Ind.*	2.31	13.2	4.40	13	7	1	5.06
Bermuda*	1.55	43	2.11	..	22	..	2.57
Dolomite†							
Crane Co., Texas	2.75	1.7	7.20	7.0	7.0	1.7	7.83
	2.75	1.7	7.10	13.0	8.0	2.0	8.16
	2.73	3.2	7.61	5.7	7.6	9.6	8.40
Calcareous Dolomite							
Upton Co., Texas†	2.72	1.0	6.71	9.0	8.0	1.5	7.48
Sandstone							
Doubling Gap, Pa.*	2.64	.5	9.20	13	18	4	10.9
Owl Canyon, Colo.*	2.17	22	4.43	36	30	6	6.3
Shale							
Sunderland, Mass.*	2.67	..	3.87	..	10	..	4.25
Slate							
Penna.*	2.76	..	4.32	..	4	..	4.50
Anorthosite*	2.72	..	4.13	..	1	..	4.17
Gabbro							
Wis.*	2.87	..	4.51	..	2	..	4.60
Mica, single crystal*	2.83	..	1.67	..	4	..	1.74

* Clark, Trans. Am. Geophys. Union, 543, 1941
† Birch and Clark, Am. Jour. Sci. **243-A**, 69, 1945

TABLE 21-6. CONDUCTIVITY OF POROUS, QUARTZ-RICH SANDSTONES WITH
VARIOUS INTERSTITIAL FLUIDS

Conductivity in units of 10^{-3} cal/cm sec ° C. All measurements at 30° C at atmospheric pressure.

Ref: Woodside and Messmer, Jour. Appl. Phys. **32**, 1699, 1961

Rock type	Porosity (per cent)	(*Vacuo*)	Air	*n*-Heptane	Water
Saturant	..	.00	.063	.307	1.50
Berkeley Sandstone	3	6.94	15.5	17.0	17.7
St. Peters Sandstone	11	5.96	8.50	12.77	15.2
Tensleep Sandstone	15.5	6.26	7.26	10.45	14.01
Berea Sandstone	22	4.02	5.71	8.93	10.7
Teapot Sandstone	29	2.61	3.69	6.34	9.67
Tripolite	59	.53	1.26	2.10	4.86

TABLE 21-7. CONDUCTIVITY OF GLASS

Glass	Temperature ° C	Conductivity (10^{-3} cal/cm sec ° C)	Ref.
Silica	0	3.32	5
(fused quartz, quartz glass)	100	4.59	
	41	2.82	1
	60	3.30	7
	100	3.39	
	200	3.56	
	240	3.63	
	0	2.68	10
	100	3.06	
	300	3.82	
	500	4.59	
	700	5.35	
	900	6.14	
	0	3.25	2
	100	3.54	
	200	3.78	
	300	4.06	
	400	4.42	
	500	4.95	
	0	3.11	6
	100	3.51	
	200	3.94	
	300	4.37	
	400	4.78	
	500	5.21	
	73	4.1	12
	135	5.7	
	0	3.16	9
	50	3.35	
Pyrex	30	2.61	3
	75	2.61	
	25	2.34	11
	150	2.89	
	250	3.13	
Pyrex No. 774 heat	0	2.88	2
resisting chemical glass	100	3.15	
	200	3.45	
	300	3.70	
	400	3.96	
	500	4.38	
Plate glass	0	1.84	4
	100	2.15	
A	80	2.32	8
B	80	2.20	
Borosilicate crown	0	2.80	5
	100	3.25	
Obsidian, Modoc, Calif.	0	3.21	2
	100	3.48	
	200	3.74	
	300	4.00	
	400	4.26	
	500	4.52	
Diabasic glass	0	2.74	2
(artificial)	100	3.00	
	200	3.27	
	300	3.53	

REFERENCES FOR TABLE 21-7

1. Ballard, McCarthy, and Davis, Rev. Sci. Instr. **21**, 905, 1950
2. Birch and Clark, Am. Jour. Sci. **238**, 529 and 613, 1940
3. Bridgman, Am. Jour. Sci. **7**, 81, 1924
4. Ensor, Proc. Phys. Soc. (London) **43**, 590, 1931
5. Eucken, Ann. Physik **34**, 185, 1911
6. Ito, Mazda Res. Rep. **4**, 188, 1929
7. Kaye and Higgins, Proc. Roy. Soc. (London) **113**, 335, 1926
8. Lees and Nancarrow, Phil. Mag. **14**, 811, 1932
9. Ratcliffe, Brit. Jour. Appl. Phys. **10**, 22, 1959
10. Seemann, Phys. Rev. **31**, 119, 1928
11. Stephens, Phil. Mag. **14**, 897, 1932
12. Weeks and Seifert, Jour. Am. Ceram. Soc. **35**, 15, 1952

TABLE 21-8. CONDUCTIVITY OF CERAMIC BODIES AS A FUNCTION OF TEMPERATURE

Both measured values and values corrected to zero porosity are given. Values in parentheses are extrapolated. Reference: Kingery, Francl, Coble, and Vasilos, Jour. Am. Ceram. Soc. 37, 107, 1954

Thermal conductivity (cal sec^{-1} $^{\circ}$C^{-1} cm^{-2} cm) at specified temperature ($^{\circ}$C)

Material	Bulk density	Theoretical density	Porosity (per cent)	100	200	400	600	800	1000	1200	1400	1600	1800
Al$_2$O$_3$	3.69–3.79		4.5–7.3	.0690	.0508	.0300	.0208	.0164	.0140	.0126	.0125	.0138	(.0173)
		3.97	0	.0723	.0538	.0314	.0218	.0172	.0147	.0132	.0131	.0145	(.0181)
BeO	2.7–2.86		4.67–9.95	.500	.398	.211	.107	.0615	.0462	.0393	.0372	.0346	(.0352)
		3.01	0	.525	.417	.222	.112	.0645	.0485	.0412	.0391	.0362	(.0369)
CaO	3.03		8.75	.0333	.0242	.020	.0181	.0174	.0170				
		3.32	0	.0364	.0265	.0219	.0198	.0191	.0186				
Forsterite (Mg$_2$SiO$_4$)	2.22		31.1	.0088	.0074	.0059	.0049	.0044	.0040	.0039	(.0038)		
		3.2	0	.01285	.0108	.00856	.00712	.0064	.00582	.00566	(.00552)		
Graphite	1.55		30.2	.298	.243	.188	.154	.128	(.105)	(.092)			
		2.22	0	.426	.346	.268	.220	.182	(.149)	(.131)			
MgO	3.29–3.48		2.8–8.1	.0823	.0645	.0377	.0263	.0194	.0160	.0140	.0138	.0157	(.0216)
		3.58	0	.0860	.0675	.0394	.0275	.0203	.0167	.0146	.0144	.0164	(.0226)
Mullite (Al$_6$Si$_2$O$_{13}$)	2.79		11.4	.0129	.0117	.0100	.0091	.0086	.0084	.0082	(.0082)		
		3.15	0	.0146	.0132	.0113	.0103	.00972	.0095	.00926	(.00926)		
Mullite (Al$_6$Si$_2$O$_{13}$)	2.21		29.8	(.0097)	.0086	.0074	.0068	.0065	.0064	.0064	(.0064)		
		3.15	0	(.01385)	.0123	.0105	.0097	.0093	.00915	.00915	(.00915)		
NiO	5.05		25.7	.0220	.0176	.0127	.0100	.0082	.0075				
		6.8	0	.0296	.0237	.0171	.0136	.0110	.0107				
Spinel (MgAl$_2$O$_4$)	3.27		7.65	(.033)	.0285	.0225	.0179	.0147	.0128	.0120			
		3.54	0	(.0357)	.0308	.0244	.0194	.0159	.0138	.0130			
UO$_2$	8.00		26.7	(.0175)	.0142	.0103	.0079	.0066	.0061				
		10.9	0	(.0234)	.0190	.0138	.01055	.00885	.00815				
TiO$_2$	4.11		3.5	(.015)	.0115	.0090	.0083	.0078	.0076	.0076			
		4.26	0	(.0156)	.01193	.00935	.00864	.0081	.00790	.0079			
ThO$_2$	8.07		16.75	.0204	.0168	.0119	.0087	.0068	.0061	.0050	.0049		
		9.69	0	.0245	.0204	.0143	.0104	.00814	.0073	.00599	.00586		
Zircon (ZrSiO$_4$)	3.69		18.6		.011	.010	.0090	.0083	.0079	.0076	.0074		
		4.56	0		.0136	.0124	.0111	.0103	.00978	.0094	.00916		
ZnO	3.72		34.0		(.027)	.0177	.011	.0086					
		5.66	0		(.0409)	.0268	.0167	.01305					
ZrO$_2$	5.22–5.35		12.3–14.4	.004	.0041	.0042	.0043	.0045	.0047	.0049	.0050		
		6.1	0	.00466	.00468	.00490	.00501	.00525	.00547	.00571	.00583		

TABLE 21-9. CONDUCTIVITY OF A FEW POLYCRYSTALLINE AND LIQUID METALS

Further data are given by Smithells [10]. These and other data are critically reviewed by R. W. Powell [7], and Jour. Appl. Phys., 19, 995, 1948.

Metal		Temperature ° C	Conductivity (cal/cm sec ° C)	Ref.
Aluminum		25	.538	3
		250	.486	
		450	.454	
		650	.445	
	liquid	740	.143	
		900	.180	
		18	.504	6
		273	.471	
		430	.425	
		605	.360	
	liquid	675	.223	
		800	.214	
Copper		0	.96	9*
		100	.93	
		200	.91	
		300	.89	
		400	.87	
		500	.84	
Iron (Armco)		0	.180	1, 8
		100	.164	
		200	.148	
		400	.117	
		600	.093	
		800	.071	
Nickel		0	.174	5
		100	.156	
		300	.120	
		400	.114	
		500	.121	
		700	.136	
		900	.150	
Potassium		0–100	.22	10
	liquid	200	.107	4
		300	.101	
		500	.090	
		600	.085	
Sodium		0–100	.30	10
		97.7	.27?	7
	liquid	100	.205	4
		200	.195	
		300	.181	
		500	.160	

TABLE 21-9. *Continued*

Metal		Temperature ° C	Conductivity (cal/cm sec ° C)	Ref.
Zinc		0	.280	2†
		100	.262	
		200	.250	
		300	.240	
		400	.231	
	liquid	500	.144	2, 6†
		600	.140	
		700	.135	

* Computed from values of diffusivity read from curve
† Values read from curve

REFERENCES FOR TABLE 21-9

1. Armstrong and Dauphinee, Canadian Jour. Res. **A25,** 357, 1947
2. Bidwell, Phys. Rev. **58,** 561, 1940
3. Bidwell and Hogan, Jour. Appl. Phys. **18,** 776, 1947
4. Ewing, Grand, and Miller, Jour. Am. Chem. Soc. **74,** 11, 1952
5. Hogan and Sawyer, Jour. Appl. Phys. **23,** 177, 1952
6. Konno, Phil. Mag. **40,** 542, 1920
7. Powell, Jour. Iron and Steel Inst. **162,** 315, 1949
8. —— Proc. Phys. Soc. (London) **51,** 407, 1939
9. Sidles and Danielson, Jour. Appl. Phys. **25,** 58, 1954
10. Smithells, *Metals reference book*, New York, Interscience Publishers, Inc., 1955

TABLE 21-10. CONDUCTIVITY OF SOIL, SNOW, ICE

The measurements were made at room temperature unless otherwise noted.

Material	Bulk density (gm/cm³)	Moisture content (per cent of dry weight)	Conductivity (10^{-3} cal/cm sec ° C)	Ref.
Hudson River sand	1.36	.2	.65	9
	1.85	30	3.94	
Fine Quartz flour	.88	..	.40	
	1.82	27	5.31	
Coarse Quartz powder	1.64	..	.91	
	1.87	32	2.70	
Podunk fine sandy loam	1.43	.3	.79	
	1.90	27	5.50	
Leonardtown silt loam	1.21	.8	.88	
	.98	18	2.10	
Muck soil	1.12	4	.35	
	.71	67	.86	
Galveston clay	1.05	1.4	.57	
	1.53	67	3.6	
"Gault"	2.00	..	2.7	10
Barnes loam	1.16	0	.39	11
(mean of 4)	1.12	13	.57	
	1.43	25	1.01	
Chester loam	1.17	0	.37	
(mean of 3)	1.12	13	.84	
	1.37	24	1.11	
Hermon sandy loam	1.59	0	.48	
(mean of 5)	1.36	5	.60	
	1.27	9	.93	
Kalkaska loamy sand	1.46	0	.46	
(mean of 4)	1.50	2	.77	
	1.40	5	1.21	
Russell silt loam (mean of 7)	1.17	0	.37	12
Carrington loam (mean of 6)	1.21	0	.41	
Marshall silt loam (mean of 3)	1.21	0	.43	
Ruston loamy sand (mean of 3)	1.26	0	.44	12
Cecil sandy clay loam (mean of 3)	1.15	0	.39	
Kirvin fine sandy loam (mean of 3)	1.26	0	.42	
Nacodoches fine sandy loam (mean of 3)	1.15	0	.37	
Columbiana clay (mean of 6)	.96	0	.33	
Volcanogeneous soil, Memuro	.90	0	.32	4
	..	20	.60	
	..	40	.97	
	..	60	1.40	
	..	80	1.47	
	..	100	1.47	
Black cultivated soil (frozen, $-20°$ C)	1.09	0	.42	5
	..	20	.83	
	..	40	1.61	
	..	60	2.71	

TABLE 21-10. *Continued*

Material	Bulk density (gm/cm³)	Moisture content (per cent of dry weight)	Conductivity (10⁻³ cal/cm sec ° C)	Ref.
Brown subsoil	1.04	0	.20	
(frozen, −20° C)	..	20	.42	
	..	40	.85	
	..	60	1.59	
	..	80	2.88	
Yellow brown subsoil	.80	0	.25	
(frozen, −20° C)	..	20	.55	
	..	40	1.15	
	..	60	1.96	
Pumice	..	Dry	.60	3
	..	Wet	1.2	
Snow, densely packed	.54	..	1.1	6
Ice, 0° C	..	..	5.3	7
−130° C	..	..	9.6	
0° C	..	..	5.0	2
−130° C	..	..	6.1	
−4° C	..	..	4.8	8
−5° C	..	..	5.3	1

REFERENCES FOR TABLE 21-10

1. Arzybychew and Jushakow, Ann. Hydrograph., 213, 1939
2. Van Dusen, Int. Crit. Tables 5, 216, 1929; *based on* Lees, Phil. Trans. Roy. Soc. London **A204**, 433, 1905
3. Herschel and others, Brit. Assoc. Advance. Sci., Rept., 1881
4. Higashi, Jour. Fac. Sci. Hokkaido Univ. **4**, 95, 1952
5. —— Trans. Am. Geophys. Union **34**, 737, 1953
6. Ingersoll and Koepp, Phys. Rev. **24**, 92, 1924
7. Jakob and Erk, Zeit. tech. Physik **10**, 623, 1929
8. Landauer and Plumb, Snow, Ice, and Permafrost Res. Establ., U.S. Army Corps of Engineers Research Rept. 16, 1956
9. Patten, U.S. Dept. Agric., Bur. Soils Bull. 59, 1909
10. Brit. Assoc. Advance. Sci., Rept., 271, 1938
11. Smith, Soil Sci. America Proc. **4**, 32, 1939
12. Smith and Bayers, Soil Sci. America Proc. **3**, 13, 1938

TABLE 21-11. CONDUCTIVITY OF DEEP-SEA SEDIMENTS

These measurements show a close correspondence between conductivity and water content, and little dependence on type of sediment. *See* discussion by Ratcliffe [4].

Sediment type	Water content (per cent of wet weight)	Density (gm/cm³)	Conductivity (10⁻³ cal/cm sec ° C)	Ref.
Red Clay	52	1.43	1.93	3
	54	1.39	1.93	
	56.5	1.38	1.93	
	50	1.47	2.17	
	50	1.47	2.20	
	42.5	1.58	2.37	
	43.5	1.57	2.43	
	52.5	1.41	1.91	
	52	1.40	1.96	
	69.5	1.20	1.68	
	61.8	1.27	1.73	
Mud	55	1.32	1.91	
	52.5	1.36	1.90	
	56.5	1.31	1.88	
	51.5	1.37	1.94	
	46	1.47	2.06	
Globigerina Ooze and Glacial Clay	41.3	1.58	2.31	1
	39.8	1.62	2.40	
	44.7	1.52	2.24	
	43.8	1.56	2.23	
	40.5	1.55	2.52	
	37.5	1.61	2.60	
	31.5	1.83	2.72	
	50.0	1.44	2.04	
	47.0	1.50	2.19	
	43.1	1.55	2.27	
	20.2	2.14	3.24	
	38.2	1.59	2.54	
	43.7	1.46	2.27	
	40.3	1.56	2.44	
	32.2	1.72	2.68	
Globigerina Ooze	37.8	1.54	2.33	2
	43.8	1.47	2.07	
	43.4	1.47	2.22	
	36.9	1.55	2.55	
	38.5	1.54	2.52	
Dark Mud	46.8	1.43	2.08	
	45.7	1.45	2.17	
	44.4	1.47	2.24	
	44.6	1.47	2.24	
	42.6	1.49	2.24	
	38.0	1.57	2.39	
	37.8	1.57	2.30	
	38.9	1.56	2.44	

REFERENCES FOR TABLE 21-11

1. Bullard, Proc. Roy. Soc. (London) A222, 408, 1954
2. —— unpublished
3. Butler, D. W., unpublished
4. Ratcliffe, Jour. Geophys. Research 65, 1535, 1960

TABLE 21-12. CONDUCTIVITY OF POWDERS WITH VARIOUS INTERSTITIAL GASES AT VARIOUS PRESSURES

Conductivity in units of 10^{-3} cal/cm sec ° C. Numbers in parentheses are pressures in mm Hg. Reference: Kannuluik and Martin, Proc. Roy. Soc. (London) A141, 144, 1933

Magnesium oxide			Glass			No. 40		Carborundum No. 280			No. 600		
H_2	Air	CO_2	He	Air	H_2	Air	CO_2	H_2	Air	CO_2	H_2	Air	CO_2
.466 (762)	.175 (757)	.149 (728)	.862 (574)	.383 (763)	2.53 (761)	.555 (760)	.434 (750)	1.71 (757)	.629 (748)	.435 (704)	1.28 (760)	.432 (754)	.327 (769)
.427 (503)	.162 (404)	.144 (482)	.834 (279)	.381 (524)	2.36 (345)	.538 (442)	.415 (411)	1.42 (406)	.561 (383)	.405 (370)	.955 (361)	.375 (434)	.294 (401)
.368 (273)	.142 (177)	.130 (213)	.747 (113)	.372 (303)	1.97 (131)	.498 (137)	.385 (129)	.860 (124)	.398 (96.5)	.328 (116)	.435 (81.7)	.218 (96)	.195 (101)
.276 (104)	.126 (100)	.116 (97.3)	.581 (35.2)	.341 (99.7)	1.68 (53.5)	.422 (40.8)	.312 (26.6)	.321 (21.9)	.168 (9.80)	.198 (21.8)	.129 (9.31)	.073 (7.18)	.116 (27.8)
.149 (18.8)	.112 (61.6)	.100 (51.5)	.361 (10.0)	.302 (32.4)	1.16 (19.6)	.321 (11.4)	.267 (12.5)	.110 (4.55)	.118 (3.56)	.139 (7.6)	.082 (2.44)	.050 (1.46)	.054 (3.2)

TABLE 21-13. CONDUCTIVITY OF COAL, COKE, GRAPHITE

Material	Temperature (°C)	Conductivity (10^{-3} cal/cm sec ° C)	Ref.
Coal		.43	3
Newcastle		6.0	4
Cannel, Blaydon		11.0	
Anthracite			
(density 1.3)		.50	2
(density 1.4)		.67	
Coke, gas (density .91–.95)	30	1.72	2
(low-temperature distillation)			
(density .655)		.33	
(density .700)		.41	
Graphite, Acheson	0	400	5
	500	220	
	1000	130	
	1500	70	
	2000	30	
	2500	30	
Acheson, parallel to extrusion axis	0	420	1
	100	350	
perpendicular to extrusion axis	0	270	
	100	220	
parallel to extrusion axis	70	605	7
perpendicular to extrusion axis	70	367	
Canadian natural	77	1000	6
perpendicular to c-axis. Values read from curve.			

REFERENCES FOR TABLE 21-13

1. Buerschaper, Jour. Appl. Phys. **15**, 452, 1944
2. Fritz and Diemke, Physik. Z. **40**, 361, 1939
3. Hecht, Ann. Phys. **14**, 1008, 1904
4. Herschel and others, Brit. Assoc. Advance. Sci. Rept., 1881
5. Powell and Schofield, Proc. Phys. Soc. (London) **51**, 153, 1939
6. Smith, Phys. Rev. **95**, 1095, 1954
7. Weeks and Seifert, Rev. Sci. Instr. **24**, 1054, 1953

TABLE 21-14. CONDUCTIVITY OF WATER AS FUNCTION OF PRESSURE AND TEMPERATURE
Units of 10^{-3} cal/cm sec ° C

| T ° C | P kg/cm² | | | | |
	1	1000	2500	4000	8000
0	1.34*				
10	1.39*				
20	1.43*				
30	1.47*	1.46	1.55	1.69	1.80	2.04
40	1.50*				
50	1.53*	1.52	1.62	1.76	1.88	2.12
60	1.56*				
70	1.58*	1.56	1.67	1.82	1.94	2.20
80	1.60*				
90		1.59	1.72	1.87	1.99	2.26
110		1.62	1.75	1.91	2.05	2.31
130			1.78	1.95	2.10	2.36

* From Powell, Adv. in Physics 7, 276, 1958. (All other values from Lawson, Lowell, and Jain, Jour. Chem. Phys. 30, 643, 1959.)

TABLE 21-15. EFFECT OF HYDROSTATIC PRESSURE ON THE
THERMAL CONDUCTIVITY OF SOLIDS

The conductivity at a pressure P kg/cm², within the pressure range 1 to 12,000 kg/cm², is given by $K_0(1 + \alpha P)$, where K_0 is the conductivity at normal pressure, and α the coefficient given in the following table.

Metals, 30° C	α	Ref.
Lead	$+17.3 \times 10^{-6}$	1
Tin	$+12.2$	1
Cadmium	$+7.4$	1
Gold	$+4.0$	3
Silver	$+4.5$	3
Copper	$+3.0$	3
Bismuth	-31.0	1
Antimony	-21.0	1

Values for zinc, iron, copper, silver, nickel, and platinum are also given [1]; these measurements have been critically reviewed [3].

Nonmetals	α	Ref.
Pyrex glass, 30° and 75° C	$+3.8 \times 10^{-6}$	2
Basalt, 30° C	$+4.7$	2
75° C	$+2.2$	2
Limestone, Solenhofen, 30° C	$+1$	2
75° C	$+6.7$	2
Talc, 30° C	$+15.7$	2
Rocksalt, 30° and 75° C	$+36$	2
Pipestone, 30° C	$+30$	2

REFERENCES FOR TABLE 21-15

1. Bridgman, Proc. Am. Acad. 57, 77, 1922
2. —— Am. Jour. Sci. 7, 81, 1924
3. Starr, Phys. Rev. 54, 210, 1938

SECTION 22

HEAT FLOW AND VOLCANIC TEMPERATURES

by W. H. K. LEE AND SYDNEY P. CLARK, JR.

CONTENTS

Handbook of Physical Constants—*Revised Edition*
THE GEOLOGICAL SOCIETY OF AMERICA MEMOIR 97, 1966

Measurements of terrestrial heat flow have been made only in recent years. The first determinations of heat flow in the continents were published in 1939 by Bullard [37], and by Benfield [73], and results of oceanic heat-flow measurements were first given in 1952 by Revelle and Maxwell [26]. At present, about 2000 heat-flow observations are available and have been recently reviewed and analyzed by Lee and Uyeda [115]. The following list of data is based mostly on this work. (For a review of heat-flow measurement *see* [115].)

In early oceanic heat-flow measurements, temperature gradients were measured with metal probes equipped with temperature sensors that penetrated a few meters into the ocean bottom sediment. Conductivities were measured from cores taken at or near the the site of temperature measurement. Recently, temperature sensors have been attached as outriggers to coring tubes. This technique combines coring (usually piston coring) and temperature-gradient measurement in one operation and offers deeper penetration. Although some thermal conductivities are estimated from the water or chlorine content of the bottom sediment, most of them are measured directly on cores, using a needle probe technique [116]. For a deep ocean station, it is common to correct conductivities measured in the laboratory by -4 per cent to bring them to ambient sea-bottom conditions. Since thermal conductivity of ocean sediments varies only slightly, some oceanic heat-flow values are determined by using the thermal conductivity of nearby stations. These values are enclosed in parentheses in the tables. Occasionally, a probe has not achieved full penetration into the sediments. Heat-flow values which are derived from these less reliable temperatures gradients are marked by an asterisk. A single oceanic determination, that at Eniwetok atoll, depends on temperature measurements in a borehole at depths between 3580 and 3980 feet [95]. At the Preliminary Mohole Site, 75 km east of Guadalupe Island, the measured heat flow is almost constant to a depth of 154 m, and the results agree well with nearby measurements made with a probe [20].

On the continents, annual and diurnal temperature fluctuations invalidate measurements of underground temperatures at very shallow depths, and relatively deep borings or workings are required for determination of heat flow. Other disturbances, which may penetrate to great depths, may be caused by circulation of ground water. It should be remarked that the validity of the oceanic measurements depends on the assumption that these types of disturbances do not affect the sea floor.

Some of the early measurements of heat flow were corrected by a large amount in order to take account of Pleistocene climatic fluctuations. A rediscussion of the problem by Birch [101] led to the conclusion that this correction should barely be perceptible at middle and low latitudes, and that the corrections which had been made previously were much too large. No correction for climatic change has been made in these tables.

In mountainous regions account must be taken of the effects of local topographic features. The geothermal gradient may also be affected by recent uplift and erosion. Corrections for these effects have been considered to be important in parts of the western United States, in the Alps, and in Australia and Tasmania.

A number of published measurements of heat flow on land have been omitted from the tables either because they have been superseded by later, more accurate work or because their accuracy was thought to be too low to merit inclusion. However, these omitted data can be found in Lee and Uyeda [115]. The references contain almost all articles reporting heat-flow observations, whether or not they are referred to in the tables.

Where the accuracy is in doubt or the heat flow seems to be disturbed, the value has been marked by a question mark. The reliability of the remaining entries in the table is difficult to assess. The best values may be in error by less than 10 per cent, but it is not clear which determinations fall in this category. Disturbance of temperatures by circulating ground water may go undetected, and the estimate of conductivity may be in error because of inadequate and biased sampling. This latter difficulty is extreme where the local lithology is characterized by short-range fluctuations between units with sharply contrasting conductivities, a situation that is commonly encountered in coal-mining regions, for example. Oceanic heat-flow values may be affected by submarine slumping, local relief of the sea floor, and local variations in sediment thickness. Objective criteria for assessing reliability under these circumstances do not exist, and the reader is referred to the original literature in order to form his own opinion.

Estimates for the conductive part of heat flow in areas of thermal activity are given in Table 22-10. These values, although rough, show clearly that very high heat flow may occur locally on land, as well as at sea.

The temperatures recorded in Table 22-11 are the highest observed in volcanoes which emit lavas of a broadly basaltic character. As such, they are the highest sustained temperatures produced by nature at the earth's surface. More siliceous lavas, such as dacites, may emerge at temperatures hundreds of degrees lower than those given here.

In assessing these results, it must be remembered that observing conditions are far from ideal in the immediate vicinity of an active volcano. This circumstance inevitably affects the accuracy of the measurements.

Most of the satisfactory data on volcanic temperatures have been obtained with optical pyrometers. Temperatures measured in this way in daylight may be systematically too high [105]. Results are also dependent on the magnifying power of the pyrometer, since with higher magnification the instrument may be focused more precisely on the hottest part of the lava [107]. Pyrometric measurements must be corrected for the emissivity of the lava and for atmospheric absorption. The former correction has been found to amount to a few tens of degrees [113] and the latter can be determined if measurements can be made at several distances from the source.

The notation for Tables 22-1 to 22-10 are as follows:

Lat.   = Station latitude in degrees and minutes
Long. = Station longitude in degrees and minutes
Elev. = Station elevation on land in meters
Depth = Station depth at sea in meters
∇T = Temperature gradient in 10^{-3} ° C/cm
K = Thermal conductivity in 10^{-3} cal/cm sec °C
Q = Heat flow in 10^{-6} cal/cm^2 sec
No   = Number of heat-flow values averaged together
Ref   = Reference number in the References
Yr   = Year of publication; e.g., 39 = 1939
( )   = Heat-flow value derived from estimated conductivity
*   = Heat-flow value obtained when penetration of the temperature-gradient probe is partial
?   = Heat-flow value is questionable

REFERENCES FOR SECTION 22

1. Von Herzen and Langseth, Physics and chemistry of the earth, *edited by* L. H. Ahrens and others 6, Pergamon Press, in press, 1965
2. Burns, Jour. Geophys. Res. 69, 4918, 1964
3. Lister and Reitzel, Jour. Geophys. Res. 69, 2151, 1964

4. Reitzel, Jour. Geophys. Res. **68**, 5191, 1963
5. Birch, F. S., M.Sc. Thesis, Univ. Wisconsin, 1964
6. Bullard and Day, Geophys. Jour. **4**, 282, 1961
7. Reitzel, Jour. Geophys. Res. **66**, 2267, 1961
8. Gerard, Langseth, and Ewing, Jour. Geophys. Res. **67**, 785, 1962
9. Vacquier and Von Herzen, Jour. Geophys. Res. **69**, 1093, 1964
10. Nason and Lee, Jour. Geophys. Res. **69**, 4875, 1964
11. Lister, Jour. Geophys. Res. **68**, 5569, 1963
12. —— Geophys. Jour. **7**, 571, 1963
13. Langseth and Grim, Jour. Geophys. Res. **69**, 4916, 1964
14. Nason and Lee, Nature **196**, 975, 1962
15. Bullard, Proc. Roy. Soc. London **222A**, 408, 1954
16. Bullard, Maxwell, and Revelle, Advan. Geophys. **3**, 153, 1956
17. Reitzel, J. S., Ph.D. Thesis, Harvard Univ. 1961
18. Uyeda and Horai, Jour. Geophys. Res. **69**, 2121, 1964
19. Von Herzen, Marine Geology **1**, 225, 1964
20. Von Herzen and Maxwell, Jour. Geophys. Res. **69**, 741, 1964
21. Von Herzen, Science **140**, 1207, 1963
22. —— Nature **183**, 882, 1959
23. Foster, Jour. Geophys. Res. **67**, 2991, 1962
24. Von Herzen and Uyeda, Jour. Geophys. Res. **68**, 4219, 1963
25. Maxwell, A. E., Ph.D. Thesis, Univ. California, 1958
26. Revelle and Maxwell, Nature **170**, 199, 1952
27. Von Herzen, R. P., Ph.D. Thesis, Univ. California, 1960
28. Langseth, Grim, and Ewing, Jour. Geophys. Res. **70**, 367, 1965
29. Rhea, Northrop, and Von Herzen, Marine Geology **1**, 220, 1964
30. Lister, C. R. B., Ph.D. Thesis, Cambridge Univ., 1962
31. Horai and Uyeda, Nature **199**, 364, 1963
32. Maxwell and Revelle, Publ. Bur. Cent. Seism., Intern. Trav. Sci. **19**, 395, 1956
33. Birch, Trans. Am. Geophys. Union **28**, 792, 1947
34. Uyeda, Horai, Yasui, and Akamatsu, Jour. Geophys. Res. **67**, 1186, 1962
35. Lachenbruch, and Marshall, Trans. Am. Geophys. Union **45**, 123, 1964, also in press, 1965
36. Yasui, Horai, Uyeda, and Akamatsu, Oceanog. Mag. **14**, 147, 1963
37. Bullard Proc. Roy. Soc. London **A173**, 474, 1939
38. Carte, Proc. Phys. Soc. B, **LXVII**, 664, 1954
39. Gough, D. I., Proc. Roy. Soc. **A272**, 207, 1963
40. Von Herzen, R. P., Private communication, 1964
41. Spicer, Jour. Wash. Acad. Sci. **31**, 495, 1941
42. Clark, Trans. Am. Geophys. Union **38**, 239, 1957
43. Benfield, Am. Jour. Sci. **245**, 1, 1947
44. Birch and Clark, Am. Jour. Sci. **243A**, 69, 1945
45. Herrin and Clark, Geophysics **21**, 1087, 1956
46. Birch, Am. Jour. Sci. **245**, 733, 1947
47. Birch, Geol. Soc. America Bull. **61**, 567, 1950
48. Lovering, Econ. Geol. **43**, 1, 1948
49. Birch, Am. Jour. Sci. **252**, 1, 1954
50. Joyner, Geophysics **25**, 1229, 1960
51. Diment and Robertson, Jour. Geophys. Res. **68**, 5035, 1963
52. Diment and Werre, Jour. Geophys. Res. **69**, 2143, 1964
53. Roy, R. F., Ph.D. Thesis, Harvard Univ., 1963
54. Diment and Weaver, NAS-NRC Publication 1188, 75, 1964
55. Lachenbruch, Greene, and Marshall, in press, 1965
56. Misener, Thompson, and Uffen, Trans. Am. Geophys. Union **32**, 729, 1951
57. Leith, Trans. Am. Geophys. Union **33**, 435, 1952
58. Misener, Trans. Am. Geophys. Union **36**, 1055, 1955
59. Lachenbruch, Geol. Soc. America Bull. **68**, 1515, 1957
60. Saull, Clark, Doig, and Butler, Can. Min. Met. Bull. **65**, 63, 1962
61. Garland and Lennox, Geophys. Jour. **6**, 245, 1962
62. Beck, Nature **195**, 368, 1962
63. Beck and Logis, Nature **201**, 383, 1963
64. Newstead and Beck, Australian Jour. Phys. **6**, 480, 1953
65. Jaeger and Sass, Geofis. Pura Appl. **54**, 53, 1963
66. Beck, A. E., Ph.D. Thesis, Australian National Univ., 1956
67. Howard and Sass, Jour. Geophys. Res. **69**, 1617, 1964
68. Le Marne and Sass, Jour. Geophys. Res. **67**, 3981, 1962
69. Sass and Le Marne, Geophys. Jour. **7**, 477, 1963
70. Sass, Jour. Geophys. Res. **69**, 299, 1964
71. —— Jour. Geophys. Res. **69**, 3889, 1964
72. Bodvarsson, Timarit Verkfraeoingafelags Islands **39**, 1, 1955

73. Benfield, Proc. Roy. Soc. London **A173,** 428, 1939
74. Anderson, Proc. Roy. Soc. Edinburgh **60,** 192, 1940
75. Bullard and Niblett, Monthly Notices Roy. Astron. Soc. Geophys. Suppl. **6,** 222, 1951
76. Chadwick, Nature **178,** 105, 1956
77. Mullins and Hinsley, Trans. Inst. Mining Engineers **117,** 379, 1957–1958
78. Clark and Niblett, Monthly Notices Roy. Astron. Soc. Geophys. Suppl. **7,** 176, 1956
79. Clark, Geophys. Jour. **6,** 45, 1961
80. Boldizsar, Nature **202,** 1278, 1964
81. —— Geofis. Pura Appl. **56,** 115, 1963
82. Schossler and Schwarzlose, Freiberger Forschungsh., **C75,** Geophysik, 120 p., 1959
83. Stenz, Geophysica Polonica **2,** 159, 1954
84. Langseth, M. G., Private communication, 1964
85. Grim, P., Private communication, 1964
86. Yasui, M. and others, Private communication, 1964
87. Sisoev, Okeanologiya **1,** 886, 1961
88. Sclater, J., Private communication, 1964
89. Coster, Monthly Notices Roy. Astron. Soc. Geophys. Suppl. **5,** 131, 1947
90. Verma, R. K., Private communication, 1964
91. Boldizsar, Acta Techn. Acad. Scientiarum Hungaricae **47,** 293, 1964
92. Boldizsar and Gozon, Acta Techn. Acad. Scientiarum Hungaricae **43,** 467, 1963
93. Boldizsar, Publ. Fac. Mining, Sopron **20,** 27, 1959
94. Lubimova, Lusova, and Firsov, Geothermal Research, USSR, Academy of Sciences, Moscow, **5,** 1964
95. Birch, Geol. Soc. America Bull. **67,** 941, 1956
96. Kraskovski, Izv. Akad. Nauk SSSR, Ser. Geofiz., 247, 1961
97. Diment, Marine, Neiheisel, and Siple, Jour. Geophys. Res., in press, 1965
98. Diment, Raspet, Mayhew, and Werre, Jour. Geophys. Res. **70,** 923, 1965
99. Spicer, Bollettino Di Geofisica Teorica ed Applicata **6,** 263, 1964
100. Lubimova, Lusova, Firsov, Starikova, and Shushpanov, Ann. Geofis. Rome, 157, 1961
101. Birch, Am. Jour. Sci. **246,** 729, 1948
102. Benseman, Jour. Geophys. Res. **64,** 1057, 1959
103. Bodvarsson, Jokull **7,** 1, 1957
104. Day and Sheperd, Geol. Soc. America Bull. **24,** 601, 1913
105. Finch and Macdonald, U.S. Geol. Survey Bull. 996-B, 75, 1953
106. Jagger, Jour. Wash. Acad. Sci. **7,** 398, 1917
107. Macdonald, U.S. Geol. Survey Bull. 1021-B, 87, 1955
108. Macdonald and Eaton, Volcano Letter **529,** 6, 1955, and Macdonald, Private communication
109. Minakami, Bull. Earthquake Res. Inst. **29,** 491, 1951
110. Parsons and Mulford, Cranbrook Inst. Sci., News Letter **28,** 17, 1958
111. Sahama and Meyer, Expl. du Parc National Albert, Fasc. 2, 15, 1958
112. Tsuya, Morimoto, and Ossaka, Bull. Earthquake Res. Inst. **32,** 59, 1954
113. Verhoogen, Expl. du Parc National Albert, Fasc. 1, 134, 1948
114. Zies, Trans. Am. Geophys. Union **27,** 178, 1946
115. Lee, *Editor,* Am. Geophys. Union, Geophys. Monograph 8, 1965
116. Von Herzen and Maxwell, Jour. Geophys. Res. **64,** 1557, 1959
117. Dawson and Fisher, New Zealand Jour. Geol. Geophys. **7,** 144, 1964

TABLE 22-1.   HEAT FLOW IN AFRICA

Station	Lat.	Long.	Elev.	∇T	K	Q	No.	Ref.	Yr.
Jacoba	27°18′ S	26°24′ E	1310	.128	7.46	.95	1	37	39
Doornhoutrivier	27°18′ S	26°24′ E	1300	.131	7.40	.97	1	37	39
Gerhardminnebron	26°30′ S	27°12′ E	1520	.095	13.5	1.28	1	37	39
Doornkloof	26°18′ S	27°30′ E	1660	.089	13.5	1.20	1	37	39
Reef-nigel	26°18′ S	28°18′ E	1565	.103	10.0	1.03	1	37	39
Dubbeldevlei	30°30′ S	21°30′ E	990	.223	6.80	1.52	1	37	39
HB 15	26°48′ S	26°54′ E	1310	.105	10.0	1.05	1	38	54
Roodepoort	26°54′ S	26°36′ E	1300	.119	7.2	.86	1	38	54
Messina	22°18′ S	30°06′ E	518	.269	5.1	1.37	1	38	54
Kestell	28°18′ S	28°42′ E	1980	.248	5.2	1.29	1	38	54
Sambokkraal	32°42′ S	21°18′ E	737	.183	7.6	1.39	1	39	63
Koegelfontein	33°00′ S	21°18′ E	726	.182	7.9	1.45	1	39	63
Bothadale	32°48′ S	22°36′ E	952	.178	7.1	1.28	1	39	63
Kalkkop	32°42′ S	24°24′ E	654	.196	6.1	1.21	1	39	63
Lake Nyasa	11°27′ S	34°29′ E	460	.62	1.6	1.0	20	40	65

TABLE 22-2.   HEAT FLOW IN AMERICA

Station	Lat.	Long.	Elev.	∇T	K	Q	No.	Ref.	Yr.
United States									
Grass Valley, Calif.	39°12′N	121°03′W	667	.092	6.	.6	1	42	57
Bakersfield, Calif.	35°28′N	119°45′W	207	.350	3.7	1.29	1	43	47
Reeves Co., Texas	31°10′N	103°14′W	700	.083	13.	1.1	1	45	56
Regan County, Texas	31°15′N	101°28′W	700	.083	13.	1.1	12	45	56
Well 103	31°15′N	101°28′W	700	.090	13.	1.2	1	45	56
Well 115	31°15′N	101°28′W	700	.076	13.	1.0	1	45	56
Well 118	31°15′N	101°28′W	700	.079	13.	1.0	1	45	56
Well 119	31°15′N	101°28′W	700	.083	13.	1.1	1	45	56
Well 126	31°15′N	101°28′W	700	.083	13.	1.1	1	45	56
Well 127	31°15′N	101°28′W	700	.086	13.	1.1	1	45	56
Upton Co., Texas	31°23′N	101°48′W	700	.083	13.	1.1	1	45	56
Midland Co., Texas	31°39′N	102°15′W	700	.094	13.	1.2	1	45	56
Eddy Co., N. Mex.	32°29′N	104°03′W	700	.085	12.6	1.1	5	45	56
Sand. + Mills	32°38′N	104°14′W	700	.103	11.8	1.2	1	45	56
Superior No. 1	32°14′N	104°07′W	700	.101	11.8	1.2	1	45	56
N.M. Prod. Ref.	32°24′N	104°16′W	700	.073	13.	.9	1	45	56
Marland, Ohio	32°18′N	103°45′W	700	.077	13.	1.0	1	45	56
Getty No. 7	32°31′N	104°09′W	700	.080	13.	1.0	1	45	56
Lea Co., N. Mex.	32°47′N	103°48′W	1000	.092	13.	1.2?	1	45	56
Colorado Springs, Colo.	38°49′N	104°49′W	1885	.2	7.	1.4?	1	46	47
Griffin, Lagrange, Ga.	33° N	84° W	300	.143	7.	1.0?	2	51	63
Front Range, Colo.	40°15′N	105°40′W	2500	.22	7.8	1.7	1	47	50
San Manuel, Ariz.	32°37′N	110°39′W	970	.15	8.	1.2?	1	48	48
Calumet, Mich.	47°17′N	88°28′W	360	.186	5.0	.93	1	49	54
Butler, Penn.	40°59′N	80°08′W	200	.29	4.2	1.2?	1	50	60
Potter, Penn.	41°54′N	77°56′W	200	.37	3.8	1.4?	2	50	60
Doddridge, West Va.	39°17′N	80°46′W	200	.29	4.2	1.22?	1	50	60
Marion, West Va.	39°25′N	80°05′W	200	.34	3.5	1.20?	1	50	60
Harrison, West Va.	39°18′N	80°14′W	200	.37	3.4	1.26?	1	50	60
Oak Ridge, Tenn.	35°55′N	84°19′W	240	.12	6.1	.73	1	51	63
Washington, D.C.	39° N	77° W	30	.157	7.13	1.12	1	52	64
Boss, Mo.	37°39′N	91°10′W	375	.17	7.6	1.29	1	53	63
Bourbon, Mo.	38°09′N	91°15′W	290	.15	8.1	1.22	1	53	63
Delaware, Mich.	47°24′N	88°01′W	389	.16	5.3	.95	1	53	63
White Pine, Mich.	46°44′N	89°34′W	281	.16	6.7	1.07	3	53	63
DDH N55	46°45′N	89°34′W	279	.16	6.7	1.07	1	53	63
DDH N65	46°44′N	89°34′W	305	.16	6.6	1.06	1	53	63
DDH E27	46°44′N	89°36′W	260	.16	6.9	1.10	1	53	63
Metaline, Wash.	48°54′N	117°21′W	686	.20	11.6	2.31	4	53	63
DDH CS2	48°55′N	117°20′W	671	.24	11.	2.67	1	53	63
DDH CS9	48°53′N	117°21′W	734	.21	11.	2.31	1	53	63
DDH R1	48°54′N	117°21′W	664	.20	12.	2.38	1	53	63
DDH R4	48°54′N	117°20′W	675	.19	12.	2.25	1	53	63
Gov't Canyon, Utah	39°52′N	112°04′W	1860	.40	4.7	1.9	1	53	63
Eureka, Utah	39°57′N	112°03′W	1702	.80	4.4	3.51?	1	53	63
Yerington, Nevada	38°55′N	119°04′W	1034	.27	8.7	2.36	3	53	63
DDH L2	38°55′N	119°04′W	1459	.27	8.4	2.26	1	53	63
DDH L5	38°56′N	119°04′W	1410	.28	8.5	2.39	1	53	63
DDH L13	38°56′N	119°04′W	1434	.21	9.1	1.9	1	53	63
Barstow, Calif.	34°39′N	116°21′W	1245	.24	8.8	2.1	2	53	63
DDH M10	34°39′N	116°41′W	1246	.24	6.6	1.59	1	53	63
DDH M11	34°39′N	116°21′W	1245	.24	8.8	2.10	1	53	63
Alberta, Va.	36°52′N	77°54′W	116	.18	7.8	1.4	1	98	65
Aiken, S.C.	33°17′N	81°40′W	100	.15	6.7	1.0	6	97	65
Salt Valley, Utah	38°55′N	109°50′W	1500	.385	3.43	1.2	5	99	64
Reeder 1	38°55′N	109°50′W	1500	.374	3.54	1.32	1	99	64
Crescent	38°55′N	109°50′W	1500	.386	3.38	1.30	1	99	64
Brendell	38°55′N	109°50′W	1500	.394	3.38	1.33	1	99	64
Balsley	38°46′N	109°38′W	1500	.314	3.51	1.10	1	99	64
Hyde	38°51′N	109°30′W	1500	.194	5.23	1.01	1	99	64
Puerto Rico									
Mayaguez	18°09′N	67°10′W	30	.10	6.0	.6	1	54	64

TABLE 22-2.   *Continued*

Station	Lat.	Long.	Elev.	∇T	K	Q	No.	Ref.	Yr.
Canada									
Toronto	43°42′ N	79°25′ W	100	.160	6.4	1.03	1	56	51
Sudbury	46°30′ N	81°01′ W	200	.158	6.4	1.01	1	56	51
Thetford	46°06′ N	71°18′ W	200	.157	6.7	1.05	1	56	51
Calumet Island	45°49′ N	74°41′ W	50	.156	8.5	1.32?	1	56	51
Kirkland Lake	48°10′ N	80°02′ W	200	.130	7.7	1.00	3	56	51
Lake Shore	48°10′ N	80°02′ W	200	.130	7.5	.97	1	56	51
Teck-Hughes	48°10′ N	80°02′ W	200	.130	7.9	1.03	1	56	51
Wright-Hargreave	48°10′ N	80°02′ W	200	.130	7.7	.99	1	56	51
Malartic	48°09′ N	78°09′ W	200	.101	6.8	.69	1	56	51
Larder Lake	48°06′ N	79°44′ W	200	.097	9.1	.88	1	56	51
Timmins	48°30′ N	81°20′ W	200	.091	8.0	.73	2	56	51
Delnite	48°30′ N	81°20′ W	200	.092	8.0	.73	1	56	51
McIntyre	48°30′ N	81°20′ W	200	.090	8.0	.73	1	56	51
Montreal	45°15′ N	73°57′ W	50	.062	12.0	.74	1	60	62
Ste. Rosalie	45°38′ N	72°40′ W	49	.159	5.06	.81	1	60	62
Lounan-Cartier	46°05′ N	73°08′ W	22	.269	3.03	.82	1	60	62
Leduc	53°23′ N	113°48′ W	700	.43	3.7	1.6	1	61	62
Redwater	53°59′ N	113°07′ W	700	.30	4.9	1.46	1	61	62
Norman Wells	65°18′ N	126°51′ W	100	.65	3.1	2.00	1	61	62
Flin Flon	54°47′ N	101°51′ W	200	.12	6.7	.8	1	62	62
Brent Crater	46°05′ N	78°29′ W	335	.133	5.6	.75	1	63	63

Table 22-3. Heat Flow in Australia

Station	Lat.	Long.	Elev.	∇T	K	Q	No.	Ref.	Yr.
Great Lake, Tasmania	41°58′ S	146°11′ E	1027	.4	5.	2.	6	65	63
DDH 5001	41°58′ S	146°11′ E	1027	.43	4.7	2.04	1	64	53
DDH 5084	41°58′ S	146°11′ E	1000	.338	5.4	1.9	1	65	63
DDH 5154	41°58′ S	146°11′ E	1000	.338	5.4	1.9	1	65	63
Storey Creek, Tasmania	42° S	146° E	900	.308	12.2	3.8	1	65	63
Rosebery, Tasmania	41°46′ S	145°34′ E	320	.29	8.6	2.5	1	65	63
Snowy Mountains	36°30′ S	148° E	1000	.226	8.6	2.	2	67	64
DDH 5010	36°30′ S	148° E	1000	.213	8.8	1.9	1	66	56
Eucumbene-Tumut	36°30′ S	148° E	1000	.239	8.4	2.0	1	67	64
Cobar	31°32′ S	145°50′ E	250	.205	10.6	2.18	1	68	62
Broken Hill	31°57′ S	141°28′ E	300	.199	9.70	1.93	18	69	63
DDH BH1205	31°57′ S	141°28′ E	300	.197	9.87	1.94	1	69	63
DDH BH1126	31°57′ S	141°28′ E	300	.200	9.53	1.91	1	69	63
DDH BH1093	31°57′ S	141°28′ E	300	.196	9.84	1.93	1	69	63
DDH BH1040	31°57′ S	141°28′ E	300	.193	10.4	2.01	1	69	63
DDH BH950	31°57′ S	141°28′ E	300	.198	10.5	2.07	1	69	63
DDH BHW1	31°57′ S	141°28′ E	300	.187	10.3	1.93	1	69	63
DDH BH305	31°57′ S	141°28′ E	300	.199	9.49	1.89	1	69	63
DDH BH678	31°57′ S	141°28′ E	300	.198	9.51	1.88	1	69	63
DDH G969	31°57′ S	141°28′ E	300	.200	10.1	2.03	1	69	63
DDH P814	31°57′ S	141°28′ E	300	.188	9.61	1.81	1	69	63
DDH P820	31°57′ S	141°28′ E	300	.193	9.93	1.92	1	69	63
DDH P831	31°57′ S	141°28′ E	300	.198	9.58	1.90	1	69	63
DDH P835	31°57′ S	141°28′ E	300	.189	9.84	1.86	1	69	63
DDH C834	31°57′ S	141°28′ E	300	.202	9.61	1.94	1	69	63
DDH 57LBH1	31°57′ S	141°28′ E	300	.211	9.47	2.00	1	69	63
DDH 57LBH6	31°57′ S	141°28′ E	300	.203	9.61	1.95	1	69	63
DDH 59P8	31°57′ S	141°28′ E	300	.206	9.61	1.98	1	69	63
DDH 55C6	31°57′ S	141°28′ E	300	.216	8.40	1.81	1	69	63
Kalgoorlie	30°45′ S	121°30′ E	380	.088	10.1	.89	1	67	64
Kalgoorlie	30°55′ S	121°33′ E	380	.098	10.1	.96	4	70	64
DDH SE10	30°55′ S	121°33′ E	380	.107	9.7	1.04	1	70	64
DDH SE12	30°55′ S	121°33′ E	380	.105	10.4	1.09	1	70	64
DDH SE6	30°55′ S	121°33′ E	380	.084	9.9	.83	1	70	64
DDH SE4	30°55′ S	121°33′ E	380	.096	9.2	.83	1	70	64
Coolgardie	30°57′ S	121°10′ E	423	.124	7.3	.90	2	67	64
DDH BV1	30°57′ S	121°10′ E	423	.142	7.7	1.09	1	70	64
DDH MLS1	30°57′ S	121°10′ E	423	.105	6.9	.72	1	70	64
Norseman	32°20′ S	121°37′ E	305	.119	7.5	.89	1	67	64
Norseman	32°20′ S	121°37′ E	305	.143	7.1	1.01	3	70	64
DDH C79	32°20′ S	121°37′ E	305	.151	6.9	1.04	1	70	64
DDH C80	32°20′ S	121°37′ E	305	.154	6.8	1.05	1	70	64
DDH PRS105	32°20′ S	121°37′ E	305	.125	7.5	.94	1	70	64
Rum Jungle	13° S	131° E	60	.19	10.5	2.0?	3	67	64
Tennant Creek	19°34′ S	134°13′ E	328	.225	10.2	2.3	1	67	64
Mount Isa	21° S	139° E	300	.189	9.5	1.8	1	67	64
Cue	27°27′ S	117°52′ E	454	.108	8.8	.95?	1	67	64
Mount Magnet	28° S	118° E	460	.113	11.4	1.3	1	67	64
Bullfinch	31°14′ S	119°19′ E	360	.139	8.8	1.2	1	67	64
Radium Hill	32°30′ S	140°30′ E	305	.230	7.8	1.8	1	67	64
Ravensthorpe	33°40′ S	120° E	180	.116	8.2	.95	1	67	64
Cabawin	27°30′ S	150°12′ E	300	.25	4.6	1.16?	1	71	64
Moonie	27°44′ S	150°13′ E	300	.22	4.6	1.01?	1	71	64
Canberra	35°17′ S	149°08′ E	560	.252	8.15	2.06	1	71	64
Whyalla	33°10′ S	137°30′ E	60	.21	10.3	2.16	1	71	64
Kanmantoo	35°05′ S	139°15′ E	150	.194	10.9	2.11	1	71	64
Stawell	37°03′ S	142°47′ E	300	.271	10.5	2.84	1	71	64
Castlemaine	37°03′ S	144°13′ E	165	.242	11.9	2.88	1	71	64

TABLE 22-4. HEAT FLOW IN ASIA

Station	Lat.	Long.	Elev.	∇T	K	Q	No.	Ref.	Yr.
India									
Kolar Gold Fields	12°55′ N	78°15′ E	600	.104	6.28	.66	1	90	65
Iran									
Masjid-i-Sulaiman	31°59′ N	49°18′ E	413	.151	5.8	.87	18	89	47
T171	31°59′ N	49°18′ E	580	.164	6.2	1.01	1	89	47
T230	31°59′ N	49°18′ E	565	.147	4.4	.65	1	89	47
K178	31°59′ N	49°18′ E	550	.123	6.5	.80	1	89	47
SH95	31°59′ N	49°18′ E	440	.113	4.7	.53	1	89	47
B162	31°59′ N	49°18′ E	350	.133	4.8	.64	1	89	47
B187	31°59′ N	49°18′ E	310	.114	7.3	.83	1	89	47
B212	31°59′ N	49°18′ E	335	.128	7.2	.93	1	89	47
T232	31°59′ N	49°18′ E	440	.125	6.4	.80	1	89	47
CS23	31°59′ N	49°18′ E	435	.127	8.9	1.13	1	89	47
B211	31°59′ N	49°18′ E	335	.106	6.2	.66	1	89	47
Q250	31°59′ N	49°18′ E	555	.180	5.1	.92	1	89	47
Q225	31°59′ N	49°18′ E	420	.214	5.7	1.22	1	89	47
C209	31°59′ N	49°18′ E	335	.181	5.2	.94	1	89	47
C229	31°59′ N	49°18′ E	315	.166	5.4	.90	1	89	47
C222	31°59′ N	49°18′ E	320	.155	6.0	.92	1	89	47
C240	31°59′ N	49°18′ E	335	.150	5.7	.85	1	89	47
A244	31°59′ N	49°18′ E	305	.186	5.2	.96	1	89	47
C235	31°59′ N	49°18′ E	510	.198	5.3	1.05	1	89	47
Japan									
Haboro	44°21′ N	141°52′ E	100	.45	4.12	1.87	1	18	64
Shimokawa	44°14′ N	142°41′ E	350	.30	5.63	1.71	1	18	64
Konomai	44°08′ N	143°21′ E	100	.40	6.41	2.54	1	18	64
Akabira	43°32′ N	142°02′ E	100	.25	4.31	1.07	1	18	64
Ashibetsu	43°33′ N	142°12′ E	100	.30	4.38	1.35	1	18	64
Yabase	39°44′ N	140°06′ E	10	.48	4.19	2.01	1	18	64
Innai	39°16′ N	139°58′ E	10	.48	3.11	1.49	1	18	64
Osarizawa	40°11′ N	140°45′ E	300	.33	6.70	2.24	1	18	64
Noda-Tamagawa	40°04′ N	141°50′ E	0	.14	8.28	1.14	1	18	64
Kamaishi	39°16′ N	141°42′ E	770	.09	5.66	.52	1	18	64
Hitachi	36°38′ N	140°38′ E	350	.11	6.62	.71	1	18	64
Katsuta	36°24′ N	140°30′ E	0	.30	3.02	.91	1	18	64
Kashima	35°57′ N	140°41′ E	0	.21	3.57	.76	1	18	64
Mobara	35°24′ N	140°20′ E	0	.18	2.94	.54	1	18	64
Tokyo	35°42′ N	139°46′ E	20	.22	3.36	.74	1	18	64
Ashio	36°39′ N	139°27′ E	700	.36	6.25	2.23	1	18	64
Chichibu	36°01′ N	138°48′ E	1020	.19	7.06	1.34	1	18	64
Sasago	35°37′ N	138°48′ E	650	.27	7.61	2.06	1	18	64
Kamioka	36°21′ N	137°19′ E	650	.28	6.49	1.80	1	18	64
Nakatatsu	35°52′ N	136°35′ E	600	.29	6.71	1.95	1	18	64
Kune	35°05′ N	137°50′ E	262	.20	8.14	1.60	1	18	64
Nako	35°03′ N	137°52′ E	285	.22	6.65	1.44	1	18	64
Minenosawa	35°	137°51′ E	300	.29	6.13	1.79	1	18	64
Ikuno	35°10′ N	134°50′ E	370	.19	7.33	1.38	1	18	64
Nakaze	35°21′ N	134°57′ E	300	.34	6.51	2.21	1	18	64
Yanahara	34°57′ N	134°04′ E	100	.20	5.89	1.20	1	18	64
Isotake	35°11′ N	132°26′ E	100	.40	8.65	3.49 ?	1	18	64
Tsumo	34°34′ N	132° E	350	.18	6.08	1.09	1	18	64
Kawayama	34°15′ N	132°59′ E	350	.17	5.85	1.00	1	18	64
Naka	34°15′ N	135°25′ E	197	.30	5.90	1.79	1	18	64
Hidaka	33°57′ N	135°05′ E	0	.29	7.40	2.12	1	18	64
Kiwa	33°50′ N	135°53′ E	80	.18	7.06	1.31	1	18	64
Besshi	34°01′ N	133°09′ E	160	.25	4.89	1.22	1	18	64
Izuhara	34°13′ N	129°14′ E	150	.29	7.41	2.17	1	18	64
Takamatsu	33°52′ N	130°43′ E	450	.31	6.27	1.92	1	18	64
Taio	33°07′ N	130°52′ E	600	.17	6.16	1.05	1	18	64
Makimine	32°38′ N	131°27′ E	120	.26	6.95	1.79	1	18	64

TABLE 22-5. HEAT FLOW IN EUROPE

Station	Lat.	Long.	Elev.	∇T	K	Q	No.	Ref.	Yr.
Great Britain									
Balfour	56°08′ N	3°07′ W	0	.23	3.0	.68	1	73	39
Holford	53°20′ N	2°30′ W	30	.13	5.7	.74	1	73	39
Blythswood	55°53′ N	4°20′ W	20	.36	3.4	1.24	1	73	39
South Balgary	55°53′ N	4°20′ W	20	.46	3.3	1.53	1	73	39
Hankham	50°55′ N	0°15′ W	20	.234	3.0	.71	1	73	39
Cambridge	52°12′ N	0°00′ E	30	.13	9.8	1.28	1	76	56
Nottinghamshire	53°08′ N	0°53′ W	70	.38	4.1	1.57	6	75	51
Eakring 5	53°09′ N	0°59′ W	83	.743	3.7	2.73?	1	75	51
Eakring 6	53°09′ N	1°00′ W	86	.786	3.5	2.75?	1	75	51
Eakring 64	53°08′ N	0°59′ W	91	.573	3.4	1.97?	1	75	51
Eakring 141	53°09′ N	1°00′ W	79	.718	4.0	2.87?	1	75	51
Kelham Hills	53°07′ N	0°52′ W	52	.364	4.0	1.47	1	75	51
Caunton	53°08′ N	0°54′ W	30	.391	4.2	1.67	1	75	51
Yorkshire	54°34′ N	1°03′ W	39	.24	4.9	1.16	2	75	51
Kirckleatham	54°35′ N	1°05′ W	21	.209	5.5	1.15	1	75	51
Tocketts	54°33′ N	1°01′ W	57	.277	4.3	1.18	1	75	51
Bawtry	53°25′ N	1°00′ W	50	.36	5.3	1.91	4	77	57
Misson	53°25′ N	1°00′ W	50	.38	5.3	2.03	1	77	57
Ranby Camp	53°25′ N	1°00′ W	50	.36	5.5	1.98	1	77	57
Ranby Hall	53°25′ N	1°00′ W	50	.34	5.4	1.84	1	77	57
Scaftworth	53°25′ N	1°00′ W	50	.35	5.1	1.79	1	77	57
Nottingham	53°00′ N	1°10′ W	50	.32	5.0	1.61	2	77	57
Goosedale	53°00′ N	1°10′ W	50	.31	4.9	1.52	1	77	57
Papplewick	53°00′ N	1°10′ W	50	.34	5.0	1.69	1	77	57
Switzerland									
Gotthard tunnel	46°25′ N	8°35′ E	1154	.209	6.70	1.4	1	78	56
Simplon tunnel	46°25′ N	8°05′ E	705	.328	6.70	2.2	1	78	56
Loetschberg tunnel	46°35′ N	7°45′ E	1243	.244	7.77	1.9	1	78	56
Austria									
Arlberg tunnel	46°55′ N	10°10′ E	1300	.173	11.0	1.9	1	79	61
Tauern tunnel	46°50′ N	13°05′ E	1200	.230	7.83	1.8	1	79	61
Hungary									
Hosszuheteny	46°10′ N	18°22′ E	270	.41	6.1	2.49	2	80	64
Komlo-Zobak	46°12′ N	18°18′ E	300	.45	7.3	3.31	2	80	64
Bakonya	46°07′ N	18°04′ E	300			2.4	1	80	64
Nagylengyel	46°46′ N	16°45′ E	200	.46	4.4	1.9	1	80	64
Hajduszoboszlo	47°26′ N	21°23′ E	100			2.4	1	80	64
Szentendre	47°41′ N	19°05′ E	200			2.0	1	80	64
Czechoslovakia									
Banska Stiavnica	48°27′ N	18°53′ E	1000			2.6	1	80	64
Poland									
Ciechocinek	52°53′ N	18°47′ E	100	.23	5.3	1.23?	1	83	54
U.S.S.R.									
Krivoi Rog	48°02′ N	33°20′ E	100	.104	7.5	.78	3	94	64
KR 7554	48°02′ N	33°20′ E	100	.104	7.13	.74	1	94	64
KR 8123	47°55′ N	33°20′ E	100	.091	8.53	.78	1	94	64
KR 8500	47°55′ N	33°20′ E	100	.10	7.1	.71	1	94	64
Belaya Tserkov	49°50′ N	30°10′ E	100	.092	7.2	.66	1	94	64
Uman	48°45′ N	30°13′ E	200	.11	5.8	.63	1	94	64
Yakovlevsky	50°30′ N	36°30′ E	300	.15	9.7	1.45?	1	94	64
Mazesta-Hosta	43°35′ N	39°48′ E	500	.15	6.7	1. ?	2	94	64

TABLE 22-6. HEAT FLOW IN THE ATLANTIC OCEAN (INCLUDING BLACK SEA, CARIBBEAN SEA, AND MEDITERRANEAN SEA)

Station	Lat.	Long.	Depth	∇T	K	Q	No.	Ref.	Yr.
Black Sea	..	..	2269	.48	4.0	1.9?	7	87	61
CH21-1	29°51′ N	54°36′ W	5610	.50	2.08	1.04	1	3	64
CH21-4	28°56′ N	46°44′ W	4370	.30	2.24	.67	1	3	64
CH21-5	28°47′ N	44°55′ W	3940	.51	2.22	1.13	1	3	64
CH21-10	29°04′ N	43°12′ W	3080	.4	1.96	<.8	1	3	64
CH21-12	28°51′ N	42°49′ W	3520	.38	2.11	.81	1	3	64
CH21-13	29°02′ N	41°10′ W	4060	..2	1.94	.4	1	3	64
CH19-C	20°13′ N	66°35′ W	5810	.56	2.27	1.28	1	3	64
CH19-7-1	20°14′ N	66°35′ W	5770	.75	2.05	1.54	1	3	64
A-282-3	23°20′ N	70°02′ W	5480	.54	2.09	1.12	1	4	63
A-282-5	23°28′ N	72°18′ W	5300	.66	1.77	1.17	1	4	63
A-282-6	25°14′ N	73°16′ W	5310	.53	2.03	1.08	1	4	63
A-282-7	26°59′ N	72°13′ W	5150	.58	1.86	1.09	1	4	63
A-282-9	25°18′ N	69°01′ W	5580	.55	2.11	1.17	1	4	63
A-282-10	23°37′ N	67°54′ W	5650	.53	2.00	1.06	1	4	63
A-282-11	21°47′ N	68°51′ W	5560	.61	2.10	1.27	1	4	63
A-282-12	20°22′ N	67°23′ W	5410	.87	2.01	1.76	1	4	63
A-282-13	21°54′ N	66°37′ W	5640	.61	1.94	1.19	1	4	63
A-282-14	23°40′ N	65°37′ W	5800	.59	1.92	1.13	1	4	63
A-282-15	25°29′ N	64°34′ W	5680	.57	1.92	1.09	1	4	63
A-282-17	25°26′ N	66°40′ W	5580	.64	1.90	1.22	1	4	63
A-282-18	27°05′ N	67°56′ W	5200	.57	1.88	1.07	1	4	63
A-282-20	28°44′ N	69°05′ W	5330	.58	2.06	1.18	1	4	63
A-282-21	28°51′ N	66°50′ W	5240	.62	1.93	1.19	1	4	63
A-282-22	28°54′ N	64°39′ W	4900	.61	1.80	1.11	1	4	63
A-282-23	30°27′ N	67°58′ W	5230	.55	1.91	1.05	1	4	63
AII-1-1	32°02′ N	74°09′ W	4870	.40	2.05	.81	1	4	63
AII-1-3	30°56′ N	74°36′ W	3430	.47	1.99	.94	1	4	63
AII-1-5	29°10′ N	76°22′ W	4990	.46	2.51	1.17	1	4	63
C-36-1	21°08′ N	65°02′ W	5696	.53	1.82	.96	1	5	64
C-36-3	19°24′ N	61°30′ W	5468	.73	1.89	~1.37	1	5	64
C-36-5	16°45′ N	57°38′ W	5853	.12	2.28	>.27	1	5	64
C-36-6	16°47′ N	57°49′ W	5853	.15	2.0	>.3	1	5	64
C-36-7	16°34′ N	57°52′ W	4330	.54	1.96	1.06	1	5	64
C-36-8	16°35′ N	57°54′ W	4330	.54	1.93	1.05	1	5	64
C-36-9	16°57′ N	58°24′ W	5890	.22	2.01	>.44	1	5	64
C-36-10	16°18′ N	58°37′ W	5599	.60	1.86	1.11	1	5	64
ATS296-4	39°32′ N	65°50′ W	4330	.47	2.29	>1.08	1	5	64
ATS296-6	39°33′ N	66°17′ W	4325	.56	2.37	>1.33	1	5	64
ATS296-7	39°47′ N	65°16′ W	4467	.48	2.22	1.07	1	5	64
ATS296-8	39°26′ N	65°09′ W	4757	.54	2.10	1.14	1	5	64
ATS296-9	39°46′ N	66°28′ W	3922	.56	2.11	<1.18	1	5	64
C-39-1	29°00′ N	59°11′ W	5811	.47	1.96	.92	1	5	64
C-39-2	25°18′ N	55°44′ W	5932	.72	1.93	~1.39	1	5	64
C-39-3	24°04′ N	55°14′ W	5984	.33	1.82	.60	1	5	64
C-39-5	28°30′ N	57°59′ W	5800	.48	1.98	.95	1	5	64
C-39-6	29°56′ N	60°33′ W	5715	.72	1.84	1.33	1	5	64
C-39-7	29°47′ N	62°12′ W	4865	.66	1.81	1.19	1	5	64
B-D-6	39°36′ N	12°13′ W	3020	.46	2.30	1.06*	1	6	61
B-D-7	35°59′ N	9°59′ W	4534	.37	2.31	.87	1	6	61
B-D-8	35°58′ N	4°34′ W	1251	.57	2.13	1.22	1	6	61
B-D-9	45°28′ N	5°47′ W	4592	.33	2.26	.75	1	6	61
B-D-10	46°32′ N	13°04′ W	4413	.50	2.17	1.09	1	6	61
B-D-11	46°30′ N	22°58′ W	4084	.57	2.25	1.29	1	6	61
B-D-12	46°37′ N	27°18′ W	4109	3.15	2.07	6.52*	1	6	61
B-D-13	36°20′ N	21°00′ W	4844	.54	2.12	1.14	1	6	61
B-D-14	35°36′ N	19°02′ W	5375	.67	2.01	1.34*	1	6	61
B-D-15	35°34′ N	18°56′ W	5380	.46	2.01	.93*	1	6	61

TABLE 22-6. *Continued*

Station	Lat.	Long.	Depth	∇T	K	Q	No.	Ref.	Yr.
B-D-16	36°39′ N	17°21′ W	5146	.53	2.13	1.14	1	6	61
B-D-17	44°55′ N	10°45′ W	4844	.64	2.18	1.39	1	6	61
B-D-18	40°59′ N	15°09′ W	5305	.49	2.32	1.14*	1	6	61
B-D-19	42°18′ N	11°53′ W	3063	.36	2.18	.78	1	6	61
B-D-20	41°27′ N	14°40′ W	5260	.55	2.18	1.21*	1	6	61
B-D-21	43°42′ N	12°39′ W	5030	.51	2.29	1.16	1	6	61
CHAIN-1	35°35′ N	61°08′ W	4590	.62	1.92	1.20	1	7	61
CHAIN-2	35°35′ N	61°15′ W	4680	.68	1.92	1.31	1	7	61
CHAIN-3	51°18′ N	29°35′ W	3260	3.7	1.7	>6.2	1	7	61
CHAIN-4	53°53′ N	24°05′ W	3350	.73	2.10	1.54	1	7	61
V-15-3	00°59′ S	38°10′ W	4137	.66	2.31	1.52	1	8	62
V-15-4	00°12′ N	39°54′ W	4111	.48	2.23	1.07	1	8	62
V-15-5	02°30′ N	40°55′ W	4285	.63	2.19	1.38	1	8	62
V-15-6	05°04′ N	41°01′ W	4544	.83	2.23	1.85	1	8	62
V-15-7	06°59′ N	41°04′ W	4636	.90	2.25	2.03	1	8	62
V-15-8	10°45′ N	41°21′ W	5002	1.51	2.23	3.37	1	8	62
V-15-10	14°14′ N	57°06′ W	5002	.73	2.19	1.60	1	8	62
V-15-12	17°21′ N	65°11′ W	4169	.52	2.23	1.16	1	8	62
V-15-13	20°49′ N	66°25′ W	5227	.68	2.23	1.52	1	8	62
V-15-14	23°14′ N	66°36′ W	5605	.61	2.23	1.36	1	8	62
V-15-16	21°34′ N	67°06′ W	5115	.75	2.23	1.67	1	8	62
V-15-19	19°50′ N	65°53′ W	7934	.52	2.23	1.16	1	8	62
V-15-23	32°35′ N	74°24′ W	4521	.46	2.23	1.03	1	8	62
V-15-24	32°47′ N	74°49′ W	4462	.47	2.22	1.04	1	8	62
LSDA-55	33°45′ S	15°00′ E	4170	.77	2.45	1.88	1	9	64
LSDA-56	33°15′ S	11°59′ E	4630	.43	2.37	(1.01)	1	9	64
LSDA-57	32°30′ S	09°01′ E	5040	.40	2.01	.8*	1	9	64
LSDA-58B	32°00′ S	06°06′ E	5210	.55	2.01	(1.1)*	1	9	64
LSDA-59	31°37′ S	02°47′ E	4215	.04	2.18	(.09)	1	9	64
LSDA-60	31°21′ S	01°58′ E	4190	1.00	2.18	2.17	1	9	64
LSDA-61	30°52′ S	00°56′ W	3810	.41	2.18	(.90)	1	9	64
LSDA-63	30°16′ S	04°21′ W	4890	.46	2.15	.99	1	9	64
LSDA-64	30°06′ S	05°45′ W	4340	.34	2.19	(.74)	1	9	64
LSDA-65	29°43′ S	07°16′ W	4150	.22	2.23	.48	1	9	64
LSDA-66	29°48′ S	08°24′ W	4155	.12	2.23	(.27)	1	9	64
LSDA-67	29°51′ S	09°25′ W	3940	.21	2.32	.48	1	9	64
LSDA-68	29°49′ S	10°18′ W	3735	.51	2.28	(1.16)	1	9	64
LSDA-69	29°51′ S	11°07′ W	3690	.50	2.28	(1.15)	1	9	64
LSDA-70	29°55′ S	11°54′ W	3400	.18	2.28	(.41)	1	9	64
LSDA-71	29°51′ S	12°46′ W	3200	.50	2.24	1.12	1	9	64
LSDA-72B	29°45′ S	14°11′ W	3385	.48	2.24	(1.08)	1	9	64
LSDA-73	29°50′ S	14°51′ W	3735	.15	2.24	(.34)	1	9	64
LSDA-74	29°50′ S	15°33′ W	3405	.32	2.24	(.72)	1	9	64
LSDA-75	27°22′ S	12°34′ W	3520	.99	2.27	(2.24)	1	9	64
LSDA-76	27°27′ S	10°56′ W	3580	.59	2.27	1.34	1	9	64
LSDA-77	26°47′ S	13°54′ W	2480	.78	2.27	(1.7)*	1	9	64
LSDA-78	25°58′ S	14°51′ W	3785	.44	2.27	(1.0)*	1	9	64
LSDA-79	24°03′ S	15°32′ W	4100	.05	2.18	.10	1	9	64
LSDA-80	23°47′ S	14°27′ W	4000	.41	2.18	(.9)	1	9	64
LSDA-81	23°42′ S	12°12′ W	3580	.51	2.18	(1.12)	1	9	64
LSDA-82	22°43′ S	13°07′ W	3605	3.44	2.27	(7.8)*	1	9	64
LSDA-83	21°21′ S	11°35′ W	2515	3.58	2.27	8.14	1	9	64
LSDA-85	21°15′ S	10°39′ W	3535	.45	2.18	(.97)	1	9	64
LSDA-86	20°10′ S	11°30′ W	2925	3.35	2.18	(7.3)*	1	9	64
LSDA-87	19°53′ S	12°26′ W	2710	1.73	2.18	(3.78)	1	9	64
LSDA-88	19°44′ S	12°55′ W	3500	.48	2.18	1.04	1	9	64
LSDA-89	18°58′ S	12°49′ W	3125	.51	2.18	(1.11)	1	9	64
LSDA-90	18°58′ S	12°00′ W	2510	2.14	2.27	(4.85)	1	9	64

TABLE 22-6.   *Continued*

Station	Lat.	Long.	Depth	∇T	K	Q	No.	Ref.	Yr.
LSDA-91	18°32′ S	10°15′ W	3395	.21	2.15	.45	1	9	64
LSDA-92	18°08′ S	11°15′ W	3305	.34	2.18	(.75)	1	9	64
LSDA-93	17°39′ S	12°22′ W	3440	.74	2.18	(1.61)	1	9	64
LSDA-94	17°15′ S	13°20′ W	3340	.22	2.18	(.47)	1	9	64
LSDA-95	16°46′ S	14°30′ W	3455	.62	2.18	(1.35)	1	9	64
LSDA-96	16°15′ S	15°45′ W	3435	.20	2.18	(.43)	1	9	64
LSDA-97	15°48′ S	16°50′ W	3820	1.07	2.18	(2.33)	1	9	64
LSDA-98	15°23′ S	17°54′ W	4390	.23	2.18	(.51)	1	9	64
LSDA-99	14°55′ S	19°22′ W	4230	.19	2.24	.43	1	9	64
LSDA-100	10°00′ S	15°26′ W	3595	.13	2.23	.29	1	9	64
LSDA-101	09°11′ S	13°20′ W	2690	.04	2.16	.08	1	9	64
LSDA-102	09°03′ S	10°29′ W	3550	.18	2.23	(.40)	1	9	64
LSDA-103	06°43′ S	13°27′ W	3245	.12	2.18	(.26)	1	9	64
LSDA-104	05°41′ S	11°12′ W	2905	1.18	2.18	2.58	1	9	64
LSDA-105	04°57′ S	09°28′ W	3500	.53	2.18	(1.15)	1	9	64
LSDA-106	00°56′ S	10°37′ W	4040	.50	2.12	(1.07)	1	9	64
LSDA-107	00°28′ S	10°51′ W	4350	.42	2.12	(.89)	1	9	64
LSDA-108	00°03′ N	11°02′ W	4125	.68	2.12	1.45	1	9	64
LSDA-109	00°26′ N	11°14′ W	4215	.85	2.12	(1.80)	1	9	64
LSDA-110	00°52′ N	11°28′ W	4950	.07	2.12	(.15)	1	9	64
LSDA-111	02°38′ N	12°12′ W	4735	.76	1.81	1.37	1	9	64
LSDA-112	05°01′ N	12°45′ W	4390	.82	1.91	1.56	1	9	64
LSDA-113	07°24′ N	17°08′ W	4800	.71	1.95	1.39	1	9	64
LSDA-114	06°47′ N	19°18′ W	4360	.46	2.09	.96	1	9	64
LSDA-115	06°21′ N	20°49′ W	3590	.58	2.12	(1.22)	1	9	64
LSDA-116	05°07′ N	25°15′ W	4360	.92	2.16	1.99	1	9	64
LSDA-117	03°21′ N	30°52′ W	2590	.16	2.34	.37	1	9	64
LSDA-118	03°18′ N	31°00′ W	2820	1.16	2.31	(2.68)	1	9	64
LSDA-119	03°15′ N	31°35′ W	2415	1.00	2.31	(2.3)*	1	9	64
LSDA-120	03°57′ N	34°04′ W	3340	.82	2.28	1.87	1	9	64
LSDA-121	05°42′ N	32°51′ W	2955	2.23	2.28	(5.08)	1	9	64
LSDA-122	05°59′ N	32°28′ W	3300	2.26	2.31	(5.22)	1	9	64
LSDA-124	08°26′ N	34°23′ W	4790	.76	2.04	1.56	1	9	64
LSDA-125	09°39′ N	37°40′ W	4045	.11	2.16	(.23)	1	9	64
LSDA-126	09°34′ N	39°32′ W	3340	.57	2.28	(1.31)	1	9	64
LSDA-127	09°41′ N	40°49′ W	2315	.74	2.28	(1.7)*	1	9	64
LSDA-128	09°45′ N	41°18′ W	3295	.74	2.28	(1.70)	1	9	64
LSDA-130	11°35′ N	44°03′ W	2755	1.05	2.28	(2.4)*	1	9	64
LSDA-131	11°34′ N	44°48′ W	3830	.40	2.12	.84	1	9	64
LSDA-132	11°34′ N	45°33′ W	4105	1.11	2.08	(2.30)	1	9	64
LSDA-133	12°17′ N	46°13′ W	4515	.22	2.08	(.46)	1	9	64
LSDA-134	14°59′ N	58°10′ W	3535	.32	2.22	.72	1	9	64
LSDA-135	15°04′ N	59°58′ W	4480	.32	2.20	.71	1	9	64
LSDA-136	15°04′ N	60°30′ W	2335	.93	2.15	2.0*	1	9	64
LSDA-137	15°02′ N	62°15′ W	2720	.93	2.15	(2.0)	1	9	64
LSDA-139	15°00′ N	63°50′ W	2082	.66	2.06	1.36	2	9	64
ZEP-4	13°36′ N	71°59′ W	4232	.72	2.0	1.4	1	10	64
ZEP-5	13°43′ N	68°38′ W	5042	.58	1.9	1.1	1	10	64
ZEP-8	14°22′ N	62°19′ W	2877	.70	1.9	1.3*	1	10	64
ZEP-9	16°24′ N	57°39′ W	4647	.39	1.8	.7?	1	10	64
ZEP-11	19°10′ N	52°03′ W	5344	.81	1.7	1.4	1	10	64
ZEP-12	20°12′ N	49°01′ W	4632	.30	1.5	.5	1	10	64
ZEP-13	21°06′ N	46°30′ W	3912	.16	1.9	.3	1	10	64
ZEP-14	21°04′ N	44°57′ W	3255	.84	2.1	1.8	1	10	64
ZEP-15	21°56′ N	45°46′ W	3372	3.24	2.0	6.5	1	10	64
ZEP-16	23°06′ N	45°39′ W	3983	1.48	2.0	3.0	1	10	64
ZEP-17	23°34′ N	44°14′ W	4960	.81	2.0	1.6	1	10	64
ZEP-18	23°57′ N	44°59′ W	3493	1.34	2.1	2.8*	1	10	64

TABLE 22-6. *Continued*

Station	Lat.	Long.	Depth	∇T	K	Q	No.	Ref.	Yr.
ZEP-19	23°36′ N	42°28′ W	4113	.23	2.1	.5*	1	10	64
ZEP-20	24°16′ N	39°06′ W	5439	.19	1.9	.4	1	10	64
ZEP-22	25°05′ N	34°13′ W	5602	.36	1.9	.7	1	10	64
ZEP-23	26°14′ N	26°27′ W	5210	.59	2.0	1.2	1	10	64
ZEP-25	26°57′ N	19°58′ W	4298	.46	2.1	1.0	1	10	64
ZEP-26	31°12′ N	11°50′ W	3210	.50	2.2	1.1*	1	10	64
ZEP-27	33°35′ N	9°43′ W	4340	.45	2.2	1.0	1	10	64
ZEP-32	40°37′ N	5°50′ E	2720	.56	2.2	1.2?	1	10	64
D 4775	29°02′ N	25°27′ W	5342	..	..	1.39	1	11	63
D 4777	28°60′ N	25°26′ W	5344	..	..	1.20	1	11	63
D 4778	29°03′ N	25°33′ W	5342	..	..	1.13	1	11	63
D 4784	29°04′ N	25°27′ W	5339	..	..	1.21	1	11	63
D 4788	29°05′ N	25°15′ W	5299	..	..	1.29	1	11	63
D 4809	28°51′ N	25°27′ W	4871	..	..	1.11	1	11	63
D 4813	28°50′ N	25°24′ W	4862	..	..	1.05	1	11	63
D 4817	29°34′ N	25°18′ W	5400	..	..	1.03	1	11	63
D 4821	29°35′ N	25°23′ W	5297	..	..	1.23	1	11	63
D 4822	29°08′ N	24°19′ W	5281	..	..	1.33	1	11	63
D 4528	45°19′ N	11°27′ W	4143	..	..	1.13	1	12	63
D 4531	45°19′ N	11°28′ W	4125	..	..	1.00	1	12	63
C19-6-17	31°54′ N	64°44′ W	4262	..	..	.97	1	12	63
CH21-8	29°04′ N	44°11′ W	..	..	..	+ ?	1	12	63
CH21-14	34°00′ N	15°51′ W	3810	..	..	.57	1	12	63
CH21-16	34°06′ N	14°24′ W	4315	..	..	.94	1	12	63
CH21-18	39°31′ N	05°26′ E	2826	..	..	>.87	1	12	63
CH21-19	42°14′ N	07°09′ E	2731	..	..	2.5	1	12	63
D 4790	27°10′ N	21°06′ W	4702	..	..	1.06	1	12	63
D 4794	27°10′ N	21°00′ W	4682	..	..	∼1.2	1	12	63
D 4795	27°13′ N	21°05′ W	4707	..	..	.92	1	12	63
D 4805	29°35′ N	23°52′ W	5240	..	..	1.13	1	12	63
D 4824	43°06′ N	19°50′ W	5959	..	..	1.30	1	12	63
V18-151	19°51′ N	84°56′ W	4564	.7	2.0	(1.4)	1	13	64
V18-153	26°35′ N	88°49′ W	2582	.22	2.3	.5	1	13	64
V18-155	26°28′ N	68°25′ W	5284	.55	2.0	1.1	1	13	64
V18-158	38°45′ N	67°33′ W	4184	.55	1.8	1.0	1	13	64
V18-159	39°11′ N	65°26′ W	4730	.55	2.0	(1.1)	1	13	64
V19-1	34°50′ N	70°15′ W	4716	.42	1.9	(.8)	1	13	64
V19-2	32°36′ N	71°19′ W	5392	.63	1.9	(1.2)	1	13	64
V19-3	28°20′ N	68°06′ W	5261	.68	1.9	1.3	1	13	64
V19-4	27°28′ N	68°27′ W	2858	.47	1.9	.9	1	13	64
V19-5	24°16′ N	67°11′ W	5562	.63	1.9	(1.2)	1	13	64
V19-6	16°06′ N	66°29′ W	4520	.6	2.0	1.2	1	13	64
C7-2	13°06′ N	63°09′ W	1060	.55	2.0	(1.1)	1	13	64
C7-3	12°34′ N	66°18′ W	4529	.4	2.0	(.8)	1	13	64
C7-4	13°59′ N	71°43′ W	3948	.75	2.0	(1.5)	1	13	64
C7-5	12°04′ N	74°54′ W	3611	.5	2.0	(1.0)	1	13	64
C7-6	14°11′ N	76°32′ W	4087	.6	2.0	(1.2)	1	13	64
C7-9	14°50′ N	73°50′ W	3460	.5	2.0	(1.0)	1	13	64
C7-10	15°23′ N	73°17′ W	3324	.75	2.0	(1.5)	1	13	64
C7-11	16°08′ N	72°48′ W	2893	.55	2.0	(1.1)	1	13	64
C7-12	14°36′ N	70°57′ W	3525	.5	2.0	(1.0)	1	13	64
Bullard 1	49°46′ N	12°30′ W	2032	.426	2.59	1.10	1	15	54
Bullard 2	49°58′ N	18°33′ W	4017	.548	2.58	1.42	1	15	54
Bullard 3	49°09′ N	17°38′ W	4532	.237	2.43	.58	1	15	54
Bullard 4	48°14′ N	16°58′ W	4670	.254	2.28	.58	1	15	54
Bullard 5	48°52′ N	15°00′ W	4710	.455	2.64	1.20	1	15	54

TABLE 22-7. HEAT FLOW IN THE INDIAN OCEAN (INCLUDING ANDAMAN SEA, GULF OF ADEN, AND RED SEA)

Station	Lat.	Long.	Depth	∇T	K	Q	No.	Ref.	Yr.
MSN-12	9°14′ S	127°30′ E	3300	.81	2.09	1.69	1	1	65
MSN-15	7°46′ S	121°14′ E	4840	.84	2.02	1.7	1	1	65
MSN-16	11°58′ S	115°26′ E	5010	.63	1.77	1.12	1	1	65
MSN-17	12°48′ S	115°24′ E	5400	.64	1.65	1.05	1	1	65
MSN-18	10°11′ S	115°19′ E	4330	.24	1.63	.39	1	1	65
MSN-20	13°19′ S	109°34′ E	4630	.80	1.85	1.48	1	1	65
MSN-21	11°39′ S	109°35′ E	4605	1.00	1.87	1.87	1	1	65
MSN-23	8°49′ S	109°36′ E	3300	.26	1.88	.48	1	1	65
MSN-24	12°21′ S	101°25′ E	4745	.78	1.99	1.56	1	1	65
MSN-28	16°59′ S	93°29′ E	5230	.61	1.63	1.0	1	1	65
MSN-29	18°14′ S	86°42′ E	4455	.89	1.83	1.63	1	1	65
MSN-30	15°51′ S	81°10′ E	5000	1.01	1.71	1.73	1	1	65
MSN-32	14°05′ S	72°15′ E	5200	.77	1.55	1.20	1	1	65
MSN-33	14°56′ S	70°13′ E	4460	.07	2.06	.14	1	1	65
MSN-34	16°25′ S	66°01′ E	3660	1.40	1.99	2.78	1	1	65
MSN-35	16°58′ S	64°46′ E	4055	1.10	1.99	(2.19)	1	1	65
MSN-36	17°48′ S	62°40′ E	3740	.15	2.26	.34	1	1	65
MSN-38	26°22′ S	74°08′ E	4130	2.48	1.98	4.91	1	1	65
MSN-40	33°20′ S	72°37′ E	4220	.42	2.19	.91	1	1	65
MSN-41	37°44′ S	71°47′ E	4260	.66	2.08	1.38	1	1	65
MSN-42	42°09′ S	70°37′ E	4200	.80	2.08	1.67	1	1	65
MSN-43	39°50′ S	75°03′ E	3780	..	2.0	..?	1	1	65
MSN-44	38°26′ S	79°34′ E	3410	.25	2.0	(.5)	1	1	65
MSN-45	37°50′ S	85°22′ E	3600	.35	2.0	(.7)	1	1	65
MSN-46	37°18′ S	90°42′ E	3855	.65	2.0	(1.3)	1	1	65
MSN-47	36°19′ S	98°41′ E	4375	.39	1.93	.76	1	1	65
MSN-48	39°18′ S	119°52′ E	4895	.58	1.78	1.04	1	1	65
MSN-49	49°31′ S	132°14′ E	3500	.72	1.8	(1.3)	1	1	65
Z-1	12°27′ N	47°07′ E	1820	2.95	2.03	5.98	1	1	65
Z-2	12°57′ N	48°16′ E	2205	1.88	1.92	(3.62)	1	1	65
Z-3	13°17′ N	49°15′ E	2425	1.78	1.81	3.22	1	1	65
Z-4	12°54′ N	49°38′ E	2200	1.29	1.92	(2.47)	1	1	65
Z-5	12°25′ N	50°33′ E	2420	1.53	2.02	3.09	1	1	65
Z-6	9°08′ N	54°42′ E	3705	.79	2.11	1.66	1	1	65
Z-7	9°09′ N	57°30′ E	3265	.68	2.01	(1.37)	1	1	65
Z-8	9°16′ N	59°00′ E	3200	.91	1.91	1.74	1	1	65
Z-9	9°34′ N	59°52′ E	3895	.84	2.01	(1.68)	1	1	65
Z-10	9°32′ N	61°24′ E	4580	.45	2.10	.95	1	1	65
Z-11	9°34′ N	63°06′ E	4505	.10	2.25	(.23)*	1	1	65
Z-12	9°40′ N	66°19′ E	4450	.35	2.30	.8*	1	1	65
Z-13	9°48′ N	69°15′ E	4550	.69	2.17	1.49	1	1	65
Z-14	9°50′ N	71°50′ E	2370	.58	2.21	1.29	1	1	65
Z-15	9°56′ N	73°08′ E	1925	.81	2.09	1.70	1	1	65
Z-16	9°59′ N	74°50′ E	2285	.82	1.92	1.57	1	1	65
LSDA-1	8°13′ N	70°39′ E	4145	.71	2.03	1.44	1	1	65
LSDA-2	3°57′ N	70°49′ E	4130	.84	1.91	1.6*	1	1	65
LSDA-3	0°05′ S	71°50′ E	4200	.51	2.15	1.1*	1	1	65
LSDA-4	2°40′ S	73°16′ E	2980	.79	2.28	1.8*	1	1	65
LSDA-5	5°21′ S	75°08′ E	5220	.92	1.64	1.51	1	1	65
LSDA-6	5°23′ S	72°47′ E	2530	.84	2.28	1.92	1	1	65
LSDA-7	5°40′ S	70°17′ E	3935	.30	1.88	.57	1	1	65
LSDA-8	5°52′ S	66°36′ E	4370	.16	1.90	(.30)	1	1	65
LSDA-9	5°34′ S	63°42′ E	4210	.87	1.91	1.67	1	1	65
LSDA-10	5°26′ S	59°14′ E	3980	1.19	1.97	2.35*	2	1	65
LSDA-11	5°30′ S	57°56′ E	2525	.61	2.02	1.23	1	1	65
LSDA-12	9°56′ S	57°07′ E	4045	.76	2.03	(1.55)	2	1	65

TABLE 22-7. *Continued*

Station	Lat.	Long.	Depth	∇T	K	Q	No.	Ref.	Yr.
LSDA-13	10°21′ S	58°31′ E	3575	.46	2.02	.92	1	1	65
LSDA-14	10°34′ S	59°51′ E	2315	.71	2.04	1.44	1	1	65
LSDA-15	13°42′ S	59°42′ E	3900	.50	2.00	1.00	1	1	65
LSDA-16	17°20′ S	57°42′ E	4145	.60	2.21	1.32	1	1	65
LSDA-17	22°01′ S	57°34′ E	4750	.51	1.77	.90	1	1	65
LSDA-18	24°34′ S	57°26′ E	5000	.77	1.57	1.21	1	1	65
LSDA-19	26°53′ S	58°12′ E	5540	.58	1.58	.91	1	1	65
LSDA-20	29°53′ S	61°52′ E	4620	.41	1.70	.7	1	1	65
LSDA-21B	31°25′ S	61°56′ E	4420	.24	1.73	.42	1	1	65
LSDA-22	32°55′ S	62°25′ E	4745	.43	1.59	.68	1	1	65
LSDA-23B	39°44′ S	63°56′ E	4810	1.70	2.18	(3.7)*	1	1	65
LSDA-24	44°36′ S	70°57′ E	3580	.79	1.89	1.49	1	1	65
LSDA-25	35°47′ S	73°37′ E	4380	.20	1.93	.38	1	1	65
LSDA-26	36°52′ S	76°22′ E	3925	.94	2.17	2.03	1	1	65
LSDA-30	31°28′ S	114°24′ E	3740	.52	2.04	1.05	2	1	65
LSDA-32	29°42′ S	111°30′ E	5340	.82	2.18	(1.79)	1	1	65
LSDA-33	25°03′ S	104°12′ E	5100	.71	1.63	1.15	1	1	65
LSDA-34	16°25′ S	89°19′ E	5625	.85	1.64	1.39	1	1	65
LSDA-35	13°48′ S	90°50′ E	5200	.82	1.59	1.30	1	1	65
LSDA-36	13°09′ S	93°13′ E	5230	1.83	1.64	3.0*	1	1	65
LSDA-37	14°56′ S	108°09′ E	5580	.68	1.70	1.15	1	1	65
LSDA-38	13°46′ S	115°32′ E	5680	.69	1.65	1.14	1	1	65
LSDA-39	13°31′ S	118°29′ E	5680	.57	1.64	.93	1	1	65
LSDA-50	30°08′ S	37°47′ E	4990	.51	1.97	1.00	1	1	65
LSDA-51	31°04′ S	36°40′ E	4535	.98	2.26	(2.22)	1	1	65
LSDA-52	31°39′ S	35°57′ E	2545	.34	2.40	.82	1	1	65
LSDA-53	32°14′ S	34°16′ E	2660	.63	2.30	(1.45)	1	1	65
LSDA-54	32°22′ S	32°47′ E	3560	.02	2.12	.04	1	1	65
LSDH-1	9°07′ N	72°59′ E	2135	.77	2.08	1.61	1	1	65
LSDH-2	9°03′ N	73°10′ E	2110	.57	2.08	1.18	1	1	65
LSDH-3	7°24′ N	70°40′ E	4110	.66	2.19	1.44*	1	1	65
LSDH-4	5°22′ S	74°17′ E	4780	1.15	1.64	1.88	1	1	65
LSDH-5	5°40′ S	69°40′ E	3815	.00	2.00	.00	1	1	65
LSDH-6	5°53′ S	65°57′ E	4260	.61	1.90	1.16	1	1	65
LSDH-7	5°31′ S	63°04′ E	4255	1.16	1.94	(2.26)	1	1	65
LSDH-8	5°28′ S	60°02′ E	4100	.78	1.97	(1.54)	1	1	65
LSDH-9	5°26′ S	59°29′ E	3952	1.96	2.02	3.95*	2	1	65
LSDH-11	4°10′ S	57°15′ E	3765	.94	2.03	1.9*	1	1	65
LSDH-13	9°49′ S	56°28′ E	3885	.13	2.03	.27	1	1	65
LSDH-14	10°05′ S	57°53′ E	3935	.64	2.02	(1.29)	1	1	65
LSDH-15	10°30′ S	59°23′ E	2858	.66	1.94	1.28	2	1	65
LSDH-18	31°14′ S	62°58′ E	5062	.14	1.60	.22	2	1	65
LSDH-20	33°16′ S	61°43′ E	4695	1.13	1.56	1.77	1	1	65
LSDH-21	39°54′ S	67°53′ E	4065	.00	2.18	.00	1	1	65
LSDH-22	40°47′ S	72°46′ E	4000	.17	2.30	.40	1	1	65
LSDH-23	40°58′ S	75°08′ E	4030	.25	2.16	.54	1	1	65
LSDH-24	40°19′ S	76°32′ E	3020	.94	2.25	2.12	1	1	65
LSDH-25	36°05′ S	75°59′ E	3290	.80	2.17	(1.74)	1	1	65
LSDH-26	37°21′ S	76°35′ E	3380	.44	2.10	.92	1	1	65
LSDH-27	32°58′ S	96°02′ E	4030	.01	2.1	(.01)	1	1	65
LSDH-28	32°06′ S	100°20′ E	2450	1.22	2.37	2.9*	1	1	65
LSDH-29	32°45′ S	102°45′ E	4760	.54	1.71	.93	1	1	65
LSDH-30	32°59′ S	103°33′ E	5130	.75	1.70	1.27	1	1	65
LSDH-32	33°01′ S	111°11′ E	4390	2.34	2.26	(5.3)*	1	1	65
LSDH-33	32°17′ S	113°58′ E	4190	.44	2.26	.99	1	1	65
LSDH-34	29°16′ S	110°42′ E	5550	.92	2.18	2.0*	1	1	65

TABLE 22-7.   *Continued*

Station	Lat.	Long.	Depth	∇T	K	Q	No.	Ref.	Yr.
LSDH-35	25°40′ S	105°22′ E	4830	.69	1.63	(1.13)	1	1	65
LSDH-36	24°33′ S	103°39′ E	5400	.64	1.63	(1.04)	1	1	65
LSDH-37	20°11′ S	96°22′ E	4910	.66	1.59	1.05	1	1	65
LSDH-38	14°12′ S	89°50′ E	5315	.66	1.63	1.07	1	1	65
LSDH-39	13°39′ S	91°31′ E	5150	.93	1.59	(1.48)	1	1	65
LSDH-40	13°23′ S	92°32′ E	5200	1.85	1.73	3.20	1	1	65
LSDH-43	14°06′ S	101°22′ E	5110	1.11	1.63	1.81	1	1	65
LSDH-44	14°56′ S	107°16′ E	5805	.79	1.74	1.37	1	1	65
LSDH-45	14°58′ S	109°12′ E	5630	.65	1.74	(1.13)	1	1	65
LSDH-46	14°13′ S	114°54′ E	5670	.63	1.62	1.02	1	1	65
LSDH-47	13°09′ S	116°29′ E	5670	.69	1.60	1.11	1	1	65
LSDH-48	13°41′ S	117°23′ E	5715	.58	1.62	(.94)	1	1	65
V18-54	36°55′ S	23°24′ E	5064	.63	2.42	1.53	1	1	65
V18-55	38°59′ S	29°56′ E	4202	.62	2.52	1.57	1	1	65
V18-58	31°12′ S	48°05′ E	4395	.74	2.23	1.65	1	1	65
V18-59	26°42′ S	50°28′ E	5266	1.08	1.68	1.81	1	1	65
V18-60	23°59′ S	51°11′ E	4928	.87	1.92	1.67	1	1	65
V18-61	21°26′ S	51°37′ E	4959	.73	1.99	1.46	1	1	65
V18-63	20°35′ S	63°32′ E	3296	.16	2.67	.43	1	1	65
V18-67	25°29′ S	85°09′ E	4559	.96	2.74	>2.64	1	1	65
V18-69	25°47′ S	93°43′ E	4435	.74	1.75	1.30	1	1	65
V18-70	25°46′ S	95°58′ E	4937	.75	1.81	1.35	1	1	65
V18-71	25°41′ S	99°04′ E	5365	.68	1.76	1.20	1	1	65
V18-72	25°41′ S	101°56′ E	4720	.85	1.82	1.54	1	1	65
V18-73	27°59′ S	108°40′ E	5148	.63	2.00	1.26	1	1	65
V18-74	36°07′ S	118°47′ E	4590	.47	2.19	1.02	1	1	65
V18-76	37°27′ S	133°40′ E	5570	.52	2.22	>1.15	1	1	65
V19-54	7°43′ S	103°15′ E	6411	.96	2.03	1.95	1	1	65
V19-55	7°16′ S	102°02′ E	5663	.91	1.89	1.72	1	1	65
V19-57	14°31′ S	101°21′ E	5363	.71	1.69	1.20	1	1	65
V19-58	16°20′ S	100°33′ E	5906	.60	1.86	1.12	1	1	65
V19-59	18°11′ S	99°24′ E	5754	.70	1.81	1.26	1	1	65
V19-60	19°02′ S	97°15′ E	5500	.89	1.91	1.70	1	1	65
V19-61	20°56′ S	91°12′ E	4840	.83	1.87	1.55	1	1	65
V19-64	18°23′ S	82°08′ E	5224	.85	1.63	1.38	1	1	65
V19-65	16°11′ S	82°06′ E	5380	.37	1.77	.66	1	1	65
V19-66	14°11′ S	82°08′ E	4798	.74	1.84	1.36	1	1	65
V19-67	12°44′ S	82°01′ E	..	1.20	1.68	~2.02	1	1	65
V19-68	10°13′ S	81°37′ E	5107	.97	1.63	1.58	1	1	65
V19-69	7°54′ S	81°25′ E	5229	.58	1.76	1.02	1	1	65
V19-70	7°04′ S	80°46′ E	5045	.77	1.79	1.38	1	1	65
V19-72	7°07′ N	76°33′ E	1770	.49	2.22	1.09	1	1	65
V19-73	7°35′ N	74°13′ E	2769	.80	2.15	1.72	1	1	65
V19-74	8°07′ N	73°15′ E	2186	.71	2.32	1.65	1	1	65
V19-75	8°09′ N	70°38′ E	4128	.76	2.36	1.80	1	1	65
V19-76	8°09′ N	69°15′ E	4650	.90	2.11	1.90	1	1	65
V19-78	8°07′ N	62°47′ E	4325	.49	2.32	1.13	1	1	65
V19-79	7°26′ N	61°04′ E	3605	1.19	2.50	2.98	1	1	65
V19-80	6°42′ N	59°20′ E	2857	.28	2.30	.64	1	1	65
V19-82	7°04′ N	60°55′ E	2680	.61	2.02	1.23	1	1	65
V19-83	6°52′ N	60°42′ E	3356	.25	2.41	.61	1	1	65
V19-84	6°37′ N	59°48′ E	2923	.91	2.33	2.12	1	1	65
V19-85	6°10′ N	57°10′ E	4128	.50	2.31	1.16	1	1	65
V19-87	4°43′ N	52°05′ E	5111	.54	1.96	1.05	1	1	65
V19-88	2°29′ N	51°28′ E	5095	.63	1.78	1.12	1	1	65
V19-89	0°29′ S	53°41′ E	4857	.93	1.92	1.78	1	1	65

TABLE 22-7.　*Continued*

Station	Lat.	Long.	Depth	∇T	K	Q	No.	Ref.	Yr.
V19-90	2°40′ S	54°45′ E	4186	.74	2.30	1.71	1	1	65
V19-91	3°34′ S	51°51′ E	5056	.88	1.89	(1.66)	1	1	65
V19-92	3°24′ S	48°46′ E	4987	.58	1.99	∼1.15	1	1	65
V19-93	3°11′ S	45°49′ E	4607	.61	1.90	1.15	1	1	65
V19-94	3°43′ S	43°52′ E	4089	.56	2.32	1.30	1	1	65
V19-95	4°13′ S	41°33′ E	2722	.52	2.44	1.27	1	1	65
V19-96	5°20′ S	40°26′ E	1863	.74	2.34	1.72	1	1	65
V19-97	6°59′ S	41°11′ E	3369	.62	2.39	1.48	1	1	65
V19-98	9°28′ S	43°19′ E	3643	.69	2.18	1.50	1	1	65
V19-100	13°08′ S	44°09′ E	3548	.65	2.10	1.37	1	1	65
V19-101	14°53′ S	42°51′ E	3250	.58	2.30	1.33	1	1	65
V19-102	16°56′ S	41°06′ E	2548	.29	2.51	.72	1	1	65
V19-103	17°54′ S	39°30′ E	2314	.50	2.23	1.12	1	1	65
V19-106	22°57′ S	42°10′ E	3175	.64	2.18	1.40	1	1	65
V19-107	22°58′ S	41°22′ E	3885	..	..	..?	1	1	65
V19-108	23°11′ S	39°58′ E	3345	.70	2.19	1.54	1	1	65
V19-109	23°22′ S	38°51′ E	3087	.61	2.36	1.44	1	1	65
V19-110	23°31′ S	37°51′ E	2903	.80	1.99	1.60	1	1	65
V19-111	25°20′ S	36°47′ E	2203	.56	2.34	1.32	1	1	65
V19-112	31°42′ S	38°10′ E	5018	.59	2.03	1.20	1	1	65
V19-114	34°24′ S	31°25′ E	4124	.67	2.23	∼1.50	1	1	65
V19-115	35°30′ S	29°57′ E	4565	.53	2.49	1.32	1	1	65
V19-116	35°55′ S	27°45′ E	4656	.63	2.67	1.68	1	1	65
AND-1	10°01′ N	93°45′ E	4206	3.1	1.70	5.27	1	2	64
AND-2	11°01′ N	93°42′ E	2562	1.3	1.83	2.38	1	2	64
AND-3	11°56′ N	93°22′ E	1390	.5	1.79	.90	1	2	64
AND-4	12°44′ N	93°58′ E	2151	1.1	1.76	1.94	1	2	64
DIS 5116	5°35′ N	61°57′ E	3560	.663	2.02	1.34	1	88	65
DIS 5122	5°35′ N	61°56′ E	3560	.642	2.01	1.29	1	88	65
DIS 5125	2°45′ N	60°15′ E	4806	.265	1.70	.45	1	88	65
DIS 5135	2°55′ N	59°53′ E	4697	.412	1.77	.73	1	88	65
DIS 5139	1°54′ N	56°10′ E	4812	.728	1.73	1.26	1	88	65
DIS 5144	1°41′ S	42°13′ E	2255	.700	2.00	1.40	1	88	65
DIS 5149	2°24′ S	43°24′ E	3552	.643	1.96	1.26	1	88	65
DIS 5152	2°32′ S	44°56′ E	4160	.618	1.86	1.15	1	88	65
DIS 5155	2°48′ S	47°03′ E	4812	.610	1.77	1.08	1	88	65
DIS 5160	3°30′ S	49°40′ E	5042	.723	1.77	1.28	1	88	65
DIS 5165	3°33′ S	51°29′ E	5100	.418	1.70	.71	1	88	65
DIS 5171	2°10′ S	57°25′ E	4402	.221	2.26	.50?	1	88	65
DIS 5177	2°12′ S	57°20′ E	4402	.519	2.12	1.10	1	88	65
DIS 5180	6°39′ S	54°16′ E	3824	.748	2.06	1.54	1	88	65
DIS 5190	2°51′ S	47°00′ E	4800	.659	1.82	1.20	1	88	65
DIS 5194	2°34′ S	44°53′ E	4180	.597	1.91	1.14	1	88	65
DIS 5201	1°42′ S	42°15′ E	2046	.613	2.04	1.25	1	88	65
DIS 5204	3°31′ S	48°23′ E	4940	.761	1.80	1.37	1	88	65
DIS 5207	3°34′ S	50°29′ E	5082	.710	1.83	1.30	1	88	65
DIS 5215	2°25′ S	54°45′ E	4360	.750	2.00	(1.50)	1	88	65
DIS 5226	11°07′ N	54°03′ E	4028	.745	2.09	1.55	1	88	65
DIS 5227	11°39′ N	47°50′ E	1900	1.80	2.14	3.85	1	88	65
DIS 5229	12°29′ N	47°02′ E	2197	2.69	2.29	6.15	1	88	65
DIS 5230	12°56′ N	46°36′ E	1600	1.50	2.16	3.25	1	88	65
DIS 5231	15°58′ N	41°31′ E	1735	1.81	2.31	4.18	1	88	65
DIS 5232	18°24′ N	39°47′ E	1480	.404	2.62	1.06	1	88	65
DIS 5234	20°27′ N	37°55′ E	0870	..	2.75	+ ?	1	88	65

TABLE 22-8. HEAT FLOW IN THE PACIFIC OCEAN (INCLUDING JAPAN SEA, BERING SEA, AND GULF OF CALIFORNIA)

Station	Lat.	Long.	Depth	∇T	K	Q	No.	Ref.	Yr.
Eniwetok	11°30′ N	162°15′ E	0	.18	5.	.9	1	95	56
E1	38°09′ N	142°58′ E	1710	.130	2.10	.27	1	34	62
E2	37°59′ N	143°58′ E	7345	.542	2.11	1.14	1	34	62
E6	38°12′ N	147°55′ E	5631	1.05	1.95	2.05	1	34	62
F20	33°39′ N	161°39′ E	5605	.681	2.00	(1.36)	1	18	64
F23	34°23′ N	142°15′ E	7490	.630	2.21	1.39	1	18	64
F24	34°04′ N	142°56′ E	5110	.598	2.07	1.24*	1	18	64
F25	33°53′ N	145°26′ E	5770	.549	1.81	.99*	1	18	64
Akko 7	39°22′ N	150°03′ E	5480	1.74	1.90	3.30*	1	18	64
Akko 8	39°30′ N	143°28′ E	2800	.546	2.16	~1.18	1	18	64
MYJ 1	34°32′ N	139°46′ E	1710	.574	2.54	1.46*	1	18	64
Akko 11	29°53′ N	137°56′ E	3960	.397	2.06	.82	1	18	64
Akko 12	32°35′ N	138°06′ E	3970	1.20	2.42	2.88*	1	18	64
G1	40°02′ N	142°31′ E	810	.702	1.75	1.26*?	1	18	64
G12	43°26′ N	148°15′ E	5175	.407	1.53	.62	1	18	64
G202	40°28′ N	142°59′ E	1550	.464	2.16	1.00*?	1	18	64
G*2	39°42′ N	145°25′ E	5315	.610	1.82	1.11	1	18	64
G*5	40°24′ N	145°40′ E	5215	.344	1.67	.58	1	18	64
G*10	41°52′ N	145°09′ E	4435	.356	1.80	.64*	1	18	64
G*11	41°02′ N	146°00′ E	5495	.568	2.44	1.38	1	18	64
Akko M1	38°11′ N	133°45′ E	0970	1.08	1.98	2.13?	1	86	65
Akko M2	40°47′ N	132°04′ E	3080	.35	1.78	.63	1	86	65
Akko M3	40°48′ N	134°24′ E	3400	1.30	1.79	2.33	1	86	65
Akko M4	38°01′ N	135°57′ E	2550	1.39	1.75	2.44	1	86	65
Akko M5	40°13′ N	136°52′ E	2525	.80	1.70	1.40	1	86	65
Akko M6	40°59′ N	137°24′ E	3422	.96	2.08	1.98	1	86	65
Akko M7	40°23′ N	139°11′ E	2670	1.18	1.95	2.02	1	86	65
Akko M8	39°29′ N	137°59′ E	2508	.72	1.81	1.30	1	86	65
EN 1	39°00′ N	139°10′ E	0720	.83	1.67	1.4?	1	86	65
EN 2	38°32′ N	139°10′ E	0320	.26	1.82	.5?	1	86	65
H 11	39°50′ N	153°52′ E	5560	.50	1.74	.88	1	86	65
H 12	40°05′ N	152°01′ E	5475	.51	1.68	.86	1	86	65
H 14A	40°02′ N	146°02′ E	5150	.59	1.59	.94*	1	86	65
Makko 1	37°21′ N	134°07′ E	2440	1.45	1.83	2.66	1	86	65
Makko 2	39°10′ N	133°02′ E	2720	1.18	1.57	1.84	1	86	65
Saiko 3	40°01′ N	132°29′ E	3330	1.36	1.65	2.24	1	86	65
Saiko 4	41°01′ N	131°54′ E	3470	1.34	1.59	2.13	1	86	65
Saiko 5	41°20′ N	132°48′ E	3600	1.21	1.56	1.89*	1	86	65
Makko 3	41°34′ N	133°35′ E	3650	1.29	1.56	2.08	1	86	65
Makko 4	39°55′ N	134°50′ E	1450	1.09	1.65	1.80?	1	86	65
Makko 5	38°58′ N	135°25′ E	3180	1.23	1.69	2.08	1	86	65
Makko 6	38°02′ N	135°57′ E	2740	1.35	1.65	2.23	1	86	65
Makko 7	38°13′ N	137°52′ E	1970	1.25	1.80	2.25?	1	86	65
Makko 8	39°13′ N	132°25′ E	2340	1.06	1.96	2.07	1	86	65
Makko 9	40°08′ N	136°44′ E	2650	1.47	1.78	2.62	1	86	65
Makko 10	41°03′ N	136°06′ E	3450	1.25	1.55	1.95	1	86	65
Makko 11	42°00′ N	138°10′ E	3670	1.33	1.88	2.51	1	86	65
Makko 12	41°59′ N	139°23′ E	1480	1.41	1.92	2.70?	1	86	65
Makko 13	43°32′ N	140°20′ E	0700	1.15	1.62	1.87?	1	86	65
Makko 14	43°59′ N	139°20′ E	1710	1.22	1.80	2.19?	1	86	65
Makko 15	44°31′ N	138°26′ E	2430	1.13	1.72	1.94	1	86	65
Makko 16	44°59′ N	137°29′ E	1630	1.34	1.73	2.32?	1	86	65
Makko 17	45°00′ N	138°36′ E	2150	.45	1.80	.79*	1	86	65
Makko 18	45°02′ N	139°37′ E	0885	1.00	1.92	1.92?	1	86	65
Makko 19	45°05′ N	140°44′ E	0330	1.31	2.04	2.66*?	1	86	65

TABLE 22-8. *Continued*

Station	Lat.	Long.	Depth	∇T	K	Q	No.	Ref.	Yr.
Tokko-1	31°58′ N	140°29′ E	..	1.58	2.10	<3.2*	1	86	65
Tokko-3	33°44′ N	139°34′ E	..	1.54	1.60	2.46*	1	86	65
Tokko-4	33°55′ N	139°14′ E	..	1.12	1.60	1.79	1	86	65
Men-2A	33°45′ N	119°31′ W	1900	.72	2.00	1.43	1	19	64
Men-3	33°58′ N	122°34′ W	4200	.30	1.89	.57	1	19	64
Men-4	34°02′ N	125°15′ W	4640	.60	1.81	1.08	1	19	64
Men-5	36°04′ N	125°04′ W	4450	.50	1.87	.94	1	19	64
Men-6	38°25′ N	126°09′ W	4230	1.70	2.03	3.45	1	19	64
Men-7	39°47′ N	126°21′ W	4140	.96	2.04	1.96	1	19	64
Men-8	40°33′ N	126°31′ W	3150	1.89	2.06	3.9*	1	19	64
Men-9	40°56′ N	126°31′ W	3120	2.35	1.96	4.60	1	19	64
Men-10	41°30′ N	126°32′ W	2960	3.06	1.89	5.79	1	19	64
Men-11	40°36′ N	127°25′ W	3280	2.84	1.96	5.56	1	19	64
Men-12	40°07′ N	128°10′ W	4510	.98	1.92	1.88	1	19	64
Men-13	40°40′ N	129°13′ W	3220	2.01	2.05	4.12	1	19	64
Men-14	40°00′ N	131°00′ W	4520	.60	1.90	1.14	1	19	64
Men-15	42°02′ N	133°07′ W	3870	.40	1.87	.75	1	19	64
Men-16	40°25′ N	133°06′ W	4070	.36	2.00	.72	1	19	64
Men-17	39°30′ N	133°05′ W	4750	.17	2.07	.35	1	19	64
Men-18	41°06′ N	135°32′ W	4060	.48	2.08	1.00	1	19	64
Men-19	41°07′ N	151°22′ W	5100	.91	2.03	1.84	1	19	64
Men-20	39°21′ N	149°56° W	5500	.19	2.04	.39	1	19	64
Men-21	40°38′ N	149°01′ W	4840	.91	2.07	1.88	1	19	64
Men-22	40°47′ N	146°00′ W	4720	.50	2.11	1.05	1	19	64
Men-23	40°41′ N	142°52′ W	4730	.61	1.96	1.19	1	19	64
Men-24	40°44′ N	139°22′ W	4520	.91	2.06	1.88	1	19	64
Men-26	38°40′ N	142°36′ W	5290	.63	2.02	1.27	1	19	64
Men-27	39°05′ N	139°26′ W	5290	.87	2.05	1.78	1	19	64
Men-28	38°02′ N	137°58′ W	5380	.86	1.97	1.69	1	19	64
Men-29	39°33′ N	135°59′ W	5140	.49	2.00	(.98)	1	19	64
Men-30	38°00′ N	134°00′ W	4810	.85	2.02	1.72	1	19	64
Men-31	39°32′ N	133°05′ W	4740	.05	2.07	.10	1	19	64
Men-33	39°30′ N	131°47′ W	4510	.23	2.02	.46	1	19	64
Men-34	40°44′ N	131°45′ W	3640	.49	1.95	.95	1	19	64
Men-36	39°36′ N	129°31′ W	4540	.59	1.90	(1.12)	1	19	64
Men-37	38°01′ N	128°46′ W	4750	.83	2.03	(1.68)	1	19	64
Men-38	32°36′ N	118°06′ W	2010	.99	1.97	1.96	1	19	64
Men-39	32°32′ N	117°31′ W	1240	1.1	1.83	2.03	1	19	64
GU-1	32°32′ N	117°31′ W	1230	1.41	1.83	(2.58)	1	19	64
GU-2	32°29′ N	118°03′ W	1890	1.47	1.89	2.78	1	19	64
GU-3	32°14′ N	118°27′ W	1630	.95	1.88	1.78	1	19	64
GU-4	32°03′ N	118°50′ W	1480	.95	1.99	1.89	1	19	64
GU-5	31°50′ N	119°06′ W	1690	1.15	1.88	2.16	1	19	64
GU-6	31°37′ N	119°35′ W	3720	.44	1.93	.84	1	19	64
GU-7	31°26′ N	120°04′ W	3970	.89	1.87	1.66	1	19	64
GU-8	31°14′ N	120°32′ W	3840	.87	1.88	1.64	1	19	64
GU-9B	31°01′ N	120°55′ W	3970	1.30	1.98	2.58	1	19	64
GU-10	30°48′ N	121°31′ W	4100	1.20	2.02	2.42	1	19	64
GU-11	29°03′ N	121°04′ W	4160	.15	2.10	.31	1	19	64
GU-12	29°09′ N	120°35′ W	3910	.83	1.97	1.64	1	19	64
GU-13	29°16′ N	120°04′ W	3830	2.30	1.93	4.43	1	19	64
GU-14	29°22′ N	119°35′ W	3710	1.20	1.99	2.39	1	19	64
GU-15B	29°35′ N	118°56′ W	3800	.81	2.02	1.64	1	19	64
GU-16	29°37′ N	118°27′ W	3570	.19	2.06	.39	1	19	64
GU-17	29°33′ N	117°59′ W	3580	1.29	2.02	2.61	1	19	64
GU-18	28°59′ N	117°28′ W	3542	1.48	1.94	2.87	6	19	64

TABLE 22-8.   *Continued*

Station	Lat.	Long.	Depth	∇T	K	Q	No.	Ref.	Yr.
GU-19	28°52′ N	117°26′ W	3550	2.11	1.94	(4.09)	1	19	64
GU-20	28°58′ N	117°21′ W	3550	.92	1.94	(1.79)	1	19	64
GU-21	29°06′ N	117°28′ W	3620	.97	1.94	(1.89)	1	19	64
GU-22	29°54′ N	117°36′ W	2840	1.12	2.08	2.34	1	19	64
SB-1	31°16′ N	117°45′ W	1930	1.06	2.12	2.25	1	19	64
SB-2	31°15′ N	117°46′ W	1950	1.58	2.12	3.35	1	19	64
SB-3	30°54′ N	117°53′ W	2050	.92	2.03	1.87	1	19	64
SB-4	30°53′ N	117°53′ W	2040	.98	2.03	1.99	1	19	64
SB-5	30°18′ N	117°31′ W	3250	1.42	2.04	2.90	1	19	64
SB-6A	29°18′ N	117°29′ W	3950	1.58	2.03	3.20	1	19	64
SB-8	28°57′ N	117°31′ W	3480	1.14	2.07	2.37	1	19	64
SB-9	29°09′ N	116°43′ W	4060	1.29	2.08	2.69	1	19	64
SB-10	29°08′ N	116°42′ W	4070	1.33	2.08	2.77	1	19	64
SB-11	30°30′ N	116°30′ W	2840	1.50	2.04	3.07	1	19	64
SB-12	30°31′ N	116°33′ W	2840	1.39	2.04	2.84	1	19	64
H-1	31°27′ N	120°59′ W	3835	.53	1.89	1.01	1	19	64
H-2	29°41′ N	121°36′ W	4000	.96	1.95	(1.88)	1	19	64
T-1	32°35′ N	117°31′ W	1225	1.12	1.83	(2.05)	1	19	64
T-2	32°33′ N	117°31′ W	1220	1.08	1.83	(1.98)	1	19	64
EHF-1	31°11′ N	119°16′ W	3690	.63	2.04	1.28	1	19	64
Mohole	28°59′ N	117°30′ W	3570	1.38	2.04	2.81	1	20	64
V-1	27°08′ N	111°38′ W	1840	1.58	1.77	2.80	1	21	63
V-2	27°17′ N	111°22′ W	1870	1.78	1.65	2.94	1	21	63
V-3	27°38′ N	111°44′ W	1775	2.55	1.64	4.19	1	21	63
V-4	26°46′ N	111°04′ W	1750	1.68	1.75	2.95	1	21	63
V-5	24°09′ N	108°55′ W	3020	2.13	1.99	4.24	1	21	63
V-6	22°58′ N	108°04′ W	2900	.34	1.81	.62	1	21	63
V-7	21°59′ N	107°41′ W	3055	2.96	1.86	5.51	1	21	63
V-8	21°00′ N	107°04′ W	3300	2.11	1.89	3.98	1	21	63
V-9	20°55′ N	106°25′ W	4450	1.07	2.00	2.14	1	21	63
V-10	20°10′ N	107°43′ W	3290	.71	1.76	1.25	1	21	63
V-11	19°45′ N	108°28′ W	2600	.79	1.82	1.43	1	21	63
V-12	20°48′ N	109°34′ W	2910	1.33	1.81	2.40	1	21	63
V-13	22°33′ N	109°29′ W	2860	2.96	2.08	6.15	1	21	63
D-1	1°23′ S	131°31′ W	4450	.06	2.29	.14	1	22	59
D-2	14°59′ S	136°01′ W	4510	.35	1.86	∼.65	1	22	59
D-3	21°40′ S	147°41′ W	4760	.56	1.74	.97	1	22	59
D-4	40°37′ S	132°52′ W	5120	.61	1.80	1.1	1	22	59
D-5	42°16′ S	125°50′ W	4620	.08	1.71	.14	1	22	59
D-6	46°44′ S	123°18′ W	4140	.35	2.09	.73	1	22	59
D-7	44°27′ S	110°44′ W	3180	.92	2.24	2.06	1	22	59
D-8	43°43′ S	107°33′ W	3180	1.34	2.28	3.06	1	22	59
D-9	43°44′ S	104°25′ W	3850	1.03	2.03	2.09	1	22	59
D-10	42°44′ S	96°03′ W	4580	1.48	1.55	2.30	1	22	59
D-11	41°06′ S	86°38′ W	3310	.51	2.0	1.0	1	22	59
D-12	23°23′ S	72°10′ W	4110	.49	1.82	>.89	1	22	59
D-13	23°28′ S	72°58′ W	3750	.41	1.96	.80	1	22	59
D-14	21°33′ S	79°09′ W	4550	.89	1.82	1.62	1	22	59
D-15	20°49′ S	81°08′ W	2340	.35	2.26	.79	1	22	59
D-16	20°48′ S	81°09′ W	2400	.68	2.26	1.54	1	22	59
D-17	13°35′ S	79°09′ W	4440	.79	1.84	1.46	1	22	59
D-18	12°49′ S	77°53′ W	2260	1.35	2.02	2.72	1	22	59
D-19	12°54′ S	78°06′ W	3700	.56	1.91	1.07	1	22	59
D-20	12°38′ S	78°38′ W	5950	.08	2.09	.17	1	22	59
D-21	12°59′ S	78°21′ W	5900	.08	1.94	.17	1	22	59
D-22	18°26′ S	78°16′ W	4220	.14	1.86	.26	1	22	59

TABLE 22-8. *Continued*

Station	Lat.	Long.	Depth	∇T	K	Q	No.	Ref.	Yr.
D-23	18°20′ S	79°21′ W	3090	.46	2.14	.98	1	22	59
D-24	19°01′ S	81°29′ W	4230	.55	1.86	1.02	1	22	59
D-25	27°04′ S	88°53′ W	3880	1.04	2.04	2.12	1	22	59
D-26	28°00′ S	96°20′ W	3200	.10	2.25	.23	1	22	59
D-27	27°55′ S	106°57′ W	2910	2.10	2.16	4.54	1	22	59
D-28	23°15′ S	117°48′ W	3500	.92	1.90	~1.76	1	22	59
D-29	14°44′ S	112°06′ W	3060	3.45	2.22	7.66	1	22	59
D-30	13°30′ S	108°31′ W	3580	.43	2.34	1.01	1	22	59
D-31	11°39′ S	109°48′ W	3280	3.61	2.24	8.09	1	22	59
D-32	9°55′ S	110°39′ W	2840	3.90	2.04	7.95	1	22	59
D-33	5°56′ S	112°29′ W	4040	.44	2.00	.87	1	22	59
D-34	3°40′ S	114°13′ W	4330	.94	1.82	1.71	1	22	59
D-35	1°28′ N	116°04′ W	3810	.28	1.97	.56	1	22	59
D-36	4°06′ N	115°41′ W	4200	.20	2.13	.43	1	22	59
LFG-1	33°13′ N	118°36′ W	1300	1.00	1.8	1.8	1	23	62
LFG-2	36°40′ N	123°03′ W	3320	1.1	2.0	2.2	1	23	62
LFG-3	36°39′ N	123°16′ W	3470	1.10	2.1	2.3	1	23	62
LFG-5	36°34′ N	123°41′ W	3770	1.10	2.1	(2.3)	1	23	62
LFG-7	44°17′ N	138°36′ W	4220	.45	2.2	1.0	1	23	62
LFG-8	48°20′ N	157°22′ W	5220	.25	2.0	.5	1	23	62
LFG-11	52°33′ N	175°09′ W	3240	.59	1.7	1.0	1	23	62
LFG-12	54°17′ N	176°15′ W	3740	.60	1.5	.9	1	23	62
LFG-13	55°41′ N	177°40′ W	4160	.81	1.6	1.3	1	23	62
LFG-14A	56°05′ N	176°10′ W	3690	.69	1.6	1.1	1	23	62
LFG-14B	56°13′ N	176°18′ W	3670	.62	1.6	1.0	1	23	62
LFG-16	53°23′ N	163°20′ W	4230	.21	1.9	.4	1	23	62
LFG-17	54°08′ N	156°52′ W	5680	1.42	1.9	(2.7)	1	23	62
LFG-19	57°11′ N	149°38′ W	2950	.55	2.0	1.1	1	23	62
LFG-20	57°34′ N	147°37′ W	4880	.50	2.4	(1.2)	1	23	62
LFG-22	59°05′ N	145°05′ W	4220	.92	2.4	2.2	1	23	62
LFG-24	59°07′ N	144°20′ W	4000	.56	2.7	1.5	1	23	62
LFG-25	59°09′ N	143°39′ W	3920	.74	2.3	1.7	1	23	62
LFG-27	59°14′ N	142°50′ W	2670	.62	2.1	1.3	1	23	62
LFG-28	58°11′ N	139°31′ W	2910	.68	2.2	1.5	1	23	62
LFG-29	57°42′ N	140°08′ W	3310	.72	1.8	1.3	1	23	62
LFG-30	56°58′ N	139°12′ W	3340	.92	2.4	2.2	1	23	62
LFG-35	54°27′ N	134°41′ W	2560	1.86	2.2	(4.1)	1	23	62
LFG-37	54°13′ N	135°27′ W	2900	1.35	2.0	2.7	1	23	62
LFG-38	54°07′ N	135°51′ W	2740	1.22	1.8	2.2	1	23	62
LFG-39	53°07′ N	133°27′ W	2900	.94	1.7	1.6	1	23	62
LFG-40	53°15′ N	133°30′ W	2910	.61	1.8	1.1	1	23	62
LFG-41	50°04′ N	132°25′ W	3100	.30	2.3	.7	1	23	62
LFG-42	48°19′ N	131°38′ W	3050	.52	2.3	1.2	1	23	62
LFG-43	46°15′ N	131°59′ W	3290	.36	2.2	.8	1	23	62
LFG-44	43°51′ N	130°55′ W	3320	1.45	2.2	3.2	1	23	62
LFG-45	42°19′ N	130°39′ W	3430	.24	2.1	.5	1	23	62
LFG-46	40°36′ N	130°26′ W	3760	.05	2.0	.1?	1	23	62
LFG-47	40°35′ N	129°22′ W	3240	1.71	2.1	3.6	1	23	62
LFG-48	38°35′ N	127°45′ W	4630	.30	2.0	.6	1	23	62
LFG-50	36°19′ N	125°56′ W	4620	1.11	1.8	2.0	1	23	62
MSN-2	23°15′ N	130°46′ W	4930	.11	2.04	.22	1	24	63
MSN-3	20°02′ N	135°11′ W	5180	.75	2.08	1.56	1	24	63
MSN-64	10°34′ S	151°05′ W	5070	.73	1.62	1.18	1	24	63
MSN-65	8°17′ S	151°36′ W	5190	.87	1.65	1.44	1	24	63
MSN-66	5°55′ S	149°39′ W	5160	.47	1.59	.75	1	24	63
MSN-67	4°22′ S	149°29′ W	4600	.44	1.69	.74	1	24	63

TABLE 22-8.   *Continued*

Station	Lat.	Long.	Depth	∇T	K	Q	No.	Ref.	Yr.
MSN-68	5°20′ N	146°13′ W	5090	.64	1.62	1.03	1	24	63
MSN-69	7°02′ N	145°38′ W	5100	.91	1.66	1.51	1	24	63
MSN-70	8°07′ N	145°24′ W	5000	.80	1.67	1.34	1	24	63
MSN-71	9°06′ N	145°18′ W	5300	.79	1.77	1.40	1	24	63
MSN-72	10°59′ N	142°37′ W	4890	2.77	1.61	(4.46)	1	24	63
MSN-73	11°03′ N	142°28′ W	5000	.66	1.61	1.06	1	24	63
MSN-74	13°04′ N	138°59′ W	5000	.41	1.58	.64	1	24	63
MSN-75	15°11′ N	136°52′ W	4990	.70	1.83	1.28	1	24	63
MSN-76	24°18′ N	126°30′ W	4750	.43	2.10	.90	1	24	63
MSN-77	29°07′ N	121°03′ W	4080	.10	2.00	.19	1	24	63
MSN-78	31°01′ N	119°04′ W	3620	1.43	1.91	2.73	1	24	63
RIS-1	28°02′ N	117°12′ W	3900	1.22	2.07	2.52	1	24	63
RIS-2	26°11′ N	117°18′ W	4000	.91	2.14	1.95	1	24	63
RIS-3	24°12′ N	117°23′ W	3935	.62	2.02	1.26	1	24	63
RIS-4	22°13′ N	117°21′ W	3890	1.29	2.08	2.69	1	24	63
RIS-5	20°18′ N	117°27′ W	4010	.33	1.83	.60	1	24	63
RIS-6	18°46′ N	117°14′ W	4090	1.20	1.80	2.16	1	24	63
RIS-8	14°26′ N	117°12′ W	4110	1.60	1.76	2.82	1	24	63
RIS-9	12°54′ N	117°24′ W	4230	.24	1.69	.41	1	24	63
RIS-10	11°28′ N	117°38′ W	4310	.52	1.90	.99	1	24	63
RIS-11	9°43′ N	117°32′ W	4230	.33	1.63	.54	1	24	63
RIS-12	8°06′ N	117°51′ W	3880	.59	1.95	1.15	1	24	63
RIS-13	6°45′ N	117°51′ W	4000	.41	1.87	.76	1	24	63
RIS-14	5°20′ N	117°52′ W	4355	.38	1.88	.71	1	24	63
RIS-15	3°54′ N	118°08′ W	4110	.35	1.99	.69	1	24	63
RIS-16	4°03′ N	117°01′ W	4160	.46	1.99	(.91)	1	24	63
RIS-17	4°03′ N	115°53′ W	4120	.78	2.13	(1.66)	1	24	63
RIS-18	4°03′ N	115°36′ W	4170	.19	2.13	(.40)	1	24	63
RIS-19	4°13′ N	114°58′ W	4210	.34	2.06	(.70)	1	24	63
RIS-20	4°25′ N	113°41′ W	3980	.30	1.98	.60	1	24	63
RIS-21	4°34′ N	112°31′ W	3950	.54	1.98	(1.07)	1	24	63
RIS-22	4°44′ N	111°33′ W	4060	.65	1.87	1.21	1	24	63
RIS-24B	5°04′ N	109°11′ W	3980	1.25	2.06	2.57	1	24	63
RIS-25	5°13′ N	107°59′ W	3760	.98	2.04	(1.99)	1	24	63
RIS-26	5°14′ N	106°33′ W	3820	1.15	2.02	2.32	1	24	63
RIS-27	5°24′ N	105°41′ W	3645	.79	1.95	(1.55)	1	24	63
RIS-28	5°37′ N	104°27′ W	3570	.86	1.87	1.61	1	24	63
RIS-29	5°43′ N	103°29′ W	3305	2.26	1.76	(3.98)	1	24	63
RIS-30	5°37′ N	104°03′ W	3400	.87	1.87	(1.63)	1	24	63
RIS-31	5°34′ N	103°08′ W	3300	.90	1.76	1.58	1	24	63
RIS-32B	5°41′ N	102°36′ W	3130	2.76	1.76	(4.86)	1	24	63
RIS-33	5°39′ N	102°06′ W	3175	4.24	1.75	7.42	1	24	63
RIS-34B	5°42′ N	101°43′ W	3440	.36	1.84	(.67)	1	24	63
RIS-35	5°36′ N	101°09′ W	3250	.92	1.93	1.78	1	24	63
RIS-36	5°41′ N	100°50′ W	3405	.64	1.94	(1.25)	1	24	63
RIS-37	5°44′ N	101°56′ W	3285	.69	1.75	(1.20)	1	24	63
RIS-38	5°43′ N	99°55′ W	3420	.58	1.94	1.12	1	24	63
RIS-39	6°05′ N	98°47′ W	3470	.54	1.74	(.94)	1	24	63
RIS-40	6°41′ N	97°25′ W	3520	.21	1.74	.37	1	24	63
RIS-41	6°58′ N	96°06′ W	3785	.05	1.67	(.08)	1	24	63
RIS-42	6°57′ N	94°58′ W	3740	.73	1.60	1.17	1	24	63
RIS-43	5°05′ N	93°56′ W	3540	.66	1.72	(1.13)	1	24	63
RIS-44	4°07′ N	92°09′ W	3150	.28	1.95	.55	1	24	63
RIS-45	3°16′ N	90°42′ W	2360	.44	2.00	(.87)	1	24	63
RIS-46	2°17′ N	89°28′ W	2160	.24	2.09	.51	1	24	63
RIS-47B	1°13′ N	88°32′ W	2480	2.79	1.89	5.27	1	24	63

TABLE 22-8. *Continued*

Station	Lat.	Long.	Depth	∇T	K	Q	No.	Ref.	Yr.
RIS-48B	0°15′ N	86°23′ W	2760	2.52	1.85	(4.66)	1	24	63
RIS-49	0°09′ S	85°58′ W	2750	.36	1.81	.65	1	24	63
RIS-50	1°41′ S	85°33′ W	2440	3.11	1.91	(5.94)	1	24	63
RIS-51	1°45′ S	85°31′ W	2385	1.00	1.98	(1.98)	1	24	63
RIS-52	2°44′ S	85°29′ W	3220	1.53	1.98	3.03	1	24	63
RIS-53	3°52′ S	84°50′ W	3395	1.22	1.98	(2.42)	1	24	63
RIS-54	9°07′ S	81°33′ W	4700	.50	1.75	.87	1	24	63
RIS-55	8°51′ S	80°53′ W	6280	.46	2.00	(.91)	1	24	63
RIS-56	8°47′ S	80°35′ W	2975	.54	2.00	(1.07)	1	24	63
RIS-57	12°34′ S	78°35′ W	5940	.12	2.09	(.26)	1	24	63
RIS-58	12°46′ S	80°00′ W	4630	.64	1.79	(1.14)	1	24	63
RIS-59	12°59′ S	81°32′ W	4800	1.21	1.68	2.04	1	24	63
RIS-60	13°04′ S	82°58′ W	4990	1.51	1.70	(2.56)	1	24	63
RIS-61	13°11′ S	84°25′ W	4740	.86	1.72	1.48	1	24	63
RIS-62B	13°24′ S	86°15′ W	4500	.21	1.69	(.36)	1	24	63
RIS-63	13°32′ S	87°26′ W	4240	.29	1.66	.48	1	24	63
RIS-64	13°33′ S	89°05′ W	4080	.58	1.80	(1.05)	1	24	63
RIS-65	13°43′ S	90°30′ W	3900	.08	1.93	.15	1	24	63
RIS-66	13°40′ S	92°00′ W	3830	.78	2.01	(1.57)	1	24	63
RIS-67	13°35′ S	93°28′ W	3880	1.55	2.08	3.22	1	24	63
RIS-68	13°37′ S	94°58′ W	3720	1.00	2.08	(2.08)	1	24	63
RIS-69	13°37′ S	96°44′ W	4150	1.10	1.86	2.04	1	24	63
RIS-70	13°32′ S	97°48′ W	3740	.62	2.05	1.28	1	24	63
RIS-71	13°26′ S	99°11′ W	3950	.87	1.91	(1.66)	1	24	63
RIS-72	13°23′ S	100°30′ W	4210	.22	1.77	.39	1	24	63
RIS-73	13°16′ S	101°24′ W	4300	1.74	1.80	(3.14)	1	24	63
RIS-74B	13°18′ S	102°18′ W	4430	.79	2.22	1.75	1	24	63
RIS-75	13°11′ S	103°30′ W	4170	.78	2.10	(1.63)	1	24	63
RIS-76	13°03′ S	104°41′ W	3720	.40	1.98	.79	1	24	63
RIS-77	12°59′ S	105°31′ W	3910	.64	2.13	(1.37)	1	24	63
RIS-78	12°54′ S	106°29′ W	3720	1.33	2.27	3.02	1	24	63
RIS-79	12°50′ S	107°31′ W	3710	.41	2.22	(.92)	1	24	63
RIS-80	12°48′ S	107°59′ W	3550	.50	2.16	1.09	1	24	63
RIS-81	12°43′ S	108°32′ W	3550	.98	2.17	(2.13)	1	24	63
RIS-82	12°44′ S	109°02′ W	3415	.91	2.17	(1.97)	1	24	63
RIS-83	12°40′ S	109°30′ W	3405	1.06	2.17	(2.31)	1	24	63
RIS-84	12°39′ S	110°01′ W	3255	1.34	2.18	2.93	1	24	63
RIS-85	12°35′ S	110°29′ W	3180	2.17	2.18	(4.74)	1	24	63
RIS-86	12°35′ S	110°15′ W	3165	1.36	2.18	(2.96)	1	24	63
RIS-87	12°33′ S	110°47′ W	3010	1.20	1.82	(2.18)	1	24	63
RIS-88B	12°33′ S	111°13′ W	3105	1.52	1.82	2.76	1	24	63
RIS-89	12°32′ S	111°29′ W	3030	1.64	1.88	(3.08)	1	24	63
RIS-90	12°33′ S	112°01′ W	3075	3.27	1.94	(6.35)	1	24	63
RIS-91	12°32′ S	112°16′ W	3175	1.75	2.00	(3.50)	1	24	63
RIS-92	12°30′ S	112°37′ W	3170	.98	2.05	2.00	1	24	63
RIS-93	12°26′ S	113°05′ W	3230	1.43	2.05	(2.94)	1	24	63
RIS-94	12°25′ S	113°31′ W	3325	.87	2.05	(1.79)	1	24	63
RIS-95	13°02′ S	113°17′ W	3240	2.10	1.90	(4.00)	1	24	63
RIS-96	13°36′ S	112°42′ W	3025	1.85	1.75	3.24	1	24	63
RIS-97	14°02′ S	112°20′ W	2960	1.48	1.75	(2.59)	1	24	63
RIS-98	14°47′ S	112°32′ W	3020	.60	2.22	(1.34)	1	24	63
RIS-99	14°47′ S	112°54′ W	3065	.92	2.09	(1.93)	1	24	63
RIS-100	14°41′ S	113°30′ W	3010	3.62	1.96	7.10	1	24	63
RIS-101	14°40′ S	113°45′ W	3170	4.10	1.96	(8.04)	1	24	63
RIS-102	14°38′ S	114°02′ W	2975	2.38	1.95	(4.65)	1	24	63
RIS-103	14°15′ S	113°11′ W	3045	3.14	1.85	(5.80)	1	24	63

TABLE 22-8.   *Continued*

Station	Lat.	Long.	Depth	∇T	K	Q	No.	Ref.	Yr.
RIS-104	14°15′ S	113°33′ W	3020	2.07	1.95	(4.03)	1	24	63
RIS-105	14°15′ S	113°50′ W	3045	.43	1.94	.84	1	24	63
RIS-106	14°15′ S	114°09′ W	3015	1.69	1.94	(3.27)	1	24	63
RIS-107	14°17′ S	114°32′ W	3120	.96	1.94	(1.87)	1	24	63
RIS-108	14°17′ S	114°59′ W	3210	.57	2.04	(1.17)	1	24	63
RIS-109	14°18′ S	115°37′ W	3440	.45	2.14	.97	1	24	63
RIS-110	14°15′ S	116°23′ W	3280	.79	2.17	(1.72)	1	24	63
RIS-111	14°14′ S	117°35′ W	3440	.45	2.20	1.00	1	24	63
RIS-112	13°59′ S	118°33′ W	3380	.32	2.19	(.70)	1	24	63
RIS-113	14°00′ S	119°39′ W	3270	.06	2.19	.13	1	24	63
RIS-114B	14°04′ S	120°16′ W	3600	.69	2.13	(1.48)	1	24	63
RIS-115	14°03′ S	121°17′ W	3680	.31	2.13	(.67)	1	24	63
RIS-116	14°01′ S	122°28′ W	3935	.03	2.07	.07	1	24	63
RIS-117	14°07′ S	123°47′ W	3860	.67	2.07	(1.39)	1	24	63
RIS-118	13°33′ S	121°48′ W	3640	.75	2.13	(1.60)	1	24	63
RIS-119	13°33′ S	121°50′ W	3665	.12	2.13	(.25)	1	24	63
RIS-120	13°52′ S	125°20′ W	3680	.47	2.20	1.04	1	24	63
RIS-121	14°02′ S	127°07′ W	3930	.09	2.05	(.18)	1	24	63
RIS-122	14°02′ S	128°25′ W	3995	.54	1.90	1.02	1	24	63
RIS-123	14°02′ S	129°48′ W	4120	1.49	1.74	(2.60)	1	24	63
RIS-124	14°03′ S	130°18′ W	4090	.47	1.74	(.82)	1	24	63
RIS-125	14°03′ S	131°44′ W	4010	.30	1.58	.48	1	24	63
RIS-127	14°02′ S	133°45′ W	4290	.50	1.57	(.79)	1	24	63
RIS-128	14°02′ S	134°55′ W	4220	.75	1.56	1.17	1	24	63
RIS-129	14°03′ S	136°34′ W	4290	.36	1.56	(.57)	1	24	63
RIS-130	14°09′ S	138°06′ W	4040	1.10	1.55	1.70	1	24	63
RIS-131	14°03′ S	139°35′ W	3925	.86	1.94	1.67	1	24	63
RIS-132	14°55′ S	141°34′ W	2610	.84	2.15	(1.8)	1	24	63
RIS-133	15°15′ S	142°26′ W	3725	.52	2.15	1.12	1	24	63
RIS-134	16°30′ S	145°07′ W	1440	.79	2.14	~1.70	1	24	63
RIS-135	16°52′ S	145°49′ W	2750	.66	2.05	1.35	1	24	63
RIS-136	17°05′ S	147°13′ W	4190	.12	1.72	.21	1	24	63
RIS-137	16°46′ S	148°52′ W	4200	.09	1.75	(.16)	1	24	63
RIS-138	16°34′ S	148°30′ W	4250	.65	1.75	1.13	1	24	63
RIS-140	14°43′ S	145°40′ W	2770	.54	2.20	1.20	1	24	63
RIS-141	13°37′ S	145°03′ W	4390	.17	1.72	.29	1	24	63
RIS-142	13°03′ S	144°03′ W	4960	.58	2.24	1.29	1	24	63
RIS-143	12°46′ S	143°34′ W	4480	.64	1.71	(1.10)	1	24	63
RIS-144	11°58′ S	142°27′ W	4520	.73	1.62	1.19	1	24	63
RIS-145	11°05′ S	140°57′ W	4270	.22	2.11	(.46)	1	24	63
RIS-146	10°30′ S	139°59′ W	4140	.18	2.11	.37	1	24	63
RIS-147	8°38′ S	138°18′ W	4080	.83	2.01	1.67	1	24	63
RIS-148	7°27′ S	137°11′ W	4400	.43	1.82	~.78	1	24	63
RIS-149	6°23′ S	136°11′ W	4350	.80	1.64	1.31	1	24	63
RIS-151	4°06′ S	133°59′ W	4445	.63	1.95	1.22	1	24	63
RIS-152	2°46′ S	132°58′ W	4350	.82	1.98	(1.63)	1	24	63
RIS-153	1°40′ S	131°52′ W	4345	.31	2.01	.63	1	24	63
RIS-154	1°21′ S	131°31′ W	4510	.11	2.01	(.23)	1	24	63
RIS-155	1°25′ S	131°04′ W	4480	.37	2.01	(.74)	1	24	63
RIS-156	1°27′ S	130°34′ W	4580	.20	2.01	(.40)	1	24	63
RIS-157	0°47′ S	131°42′ W	4425	.39	2.01	(.78)	1	24	63
RIS-158	0°18′ N	132°00′ W	4410	.41	1.96	(.80)	1	24	63
RIS-159	2°04′ N	132°32′ W	4305	.22	1.91	.42	1	24	63
RIS-160	3°36′ N	133°00′ W	4375	.00	2.00	(.01)?	1	24	63
RIS-161	3°58′ N	133°09′ W	4375	.10	2.00	(.19)	1	24	63
RIS-162	5°38′ N	133°26′ W	4390	.21	2.08	.44	1	24	63

TABLE 22-8. *Continued*

Station	Lat.	Long.	Depth	∇T	K	Q	No.	Ref.	Yr.
RIS-163	7°14′ N	133°47′ W	4410	.82	2.08	(1.7)	1	24	63
RIS-164	9°03′ N	133°40′ W	4980	1.08	1.67	1.80	1	24	63
RIS-165	10°57′ N	133°56′ W	4910	.85	1.67	(1.42)	1	24	63
RIS-166	12°56′ N	133°36′ W	4810	.64	1.67	(1.07)	1	24	63
RIS-167	14°58′ N	133°42′ W	4775	.74	1.82	1.34	1	24	63
RIS-169	18°15′ N	133°06′ W	5190	1.05	1.91	2.00	1	24	63
RIS-170	19°59′ N	133°03′ W	5060	.64	1.91	(1.23)	1	24	63
RIS-172	23°30′ N	132°43′ W	4880	.61	2.02	(1.23)	1	24	63
RIS-173	25°19′ N	132°37′ W	4530	.38	2.13	.80	1	24	63
RIS-174	27°15′ N	132°28′ W	4815	.49	2.10	(1.02)	1	24	63
RIS-175	28°26′ N	135°54′ W	4740	.77	2.07	1.59	1	24	63
RIS-176	28°29′ N	134°35′ W	4660	.36	2.00	(.71)	1	24	63
RIS-177	28°18′ N	133°21′ W	4385	.74	1.92	1.43	1	24	63
RIS-178	27°54′ N	132°37′ W	3700	.51	1.92	(.98)	1	24	63
RIS-180	28°10′ N	131°04′ W	4550	1.10	1.96	(2.16)	1	24	63
RIS-181	28°17′ N	129°36′ W	4740	.52	2.00	1.05	1	24	63
RIS-182	28°21′ N	127°59′ W	4660	.97	1.98	(1.92)	1	24	63
RIS-183	28°27′ N	126°37′ W	4500	.88	1.96	1.73	1	24	63
RIS-184	28°35′ N	125°00′ W	4445	1.13	1.96	(2.22)	1	24	63
RIS-185	28°47′ N	123°37′ W	4370	.94	1.77	1.66	1	24	63
RIS-186	28°56′ N	122°27′ W	4220	1.10	1.96	(2.16)	1	24	63
RIS-187	29°33′ N	121°44′ W	4005	1.15	2.05	(2.36)	1	24	63
MP-21	20°48′ N	159°42′ W	4500	.65	1.79	1.16	1	25	58
MP-32	18°18′ N	173°23′ W	3900	.35	2.05	.72	1	25	58
MP-35-2	19°28′ N	174°35′ W	4900	.62	2.07	1.29	1	25	58
MP-36	16°45′ N	176°24′ W	5040	.66	1.80	1.19	1	25	58
MP-38	19°02′ N	177°19′ W	4750	.69	1.57	1.09	1	25	58
STN-1	32°35′ N	122°30′ W	4000	.67	1.90	(1.27)	1	25	58
CAP-2B	0°40′ N	169°17′ E	4310	.76	2.48	1.88	1	25	58
CAP-5B	9°04′ S	174°51′ E	5000	.72	1.87	1.35	1	25	58
CAP-9B	18°59′ S	177°36′ E	2700	.63	2.40	1.51	1	25	58
CAP-10B	21°56′ S	178°33′ E	3900	1.25	2.07	2.58	1	25	58
CAP-31B	17°28′ S	158°40′ W	4880	.86	1.83	1.58	1	25	58
CAP-33B	12°48′ S	143°33′ W	4300	.21	1.71	.36	1	25	58
CAP-40B	14°45′ S	112°11′ W	3020	2.15	2.44	5.25	1	25	58
CAP-48B	5°52′ N	123°55′ W	4100	.73	2.26	1.65	1	25	58
CAP-50B	14°59′ N	124°12′ W	4350	1.24	1.96	2.43	1	25	58
ACA-B5-1	13°08′ N	91°57′ W	6170	.24	1.92	.47	1	25	58
ACA-B6	11°55′ N	91°37′ W	3600	.46	1.67	.76	1	25	58
ACA-B8	9°49′ N	93°02′ W	3730	.14	1.76	.25	1	25	58
ACA-B9	12°14′ N	98°44′ W	3500	.40	1.72	.69	1	25	58
ACA-B11	10°52′ N	105°04′ W	3300	1.83	1.95	>3.57	1	25	58
ACA-B11B	10°54′ N	104°25′ W	2950	1.40	1.95	(2.73)	1	25	58
ACA-B13	12°12′ N	111°04′ W	3600	.48	1.95	(.93)	1	25	58
ACA-B13A	20°44′ N	115°42′ W	3910	.59	2.02	1.19	1	25	58
GUA-P6	25°01′ N	123°04′ W	4300	.48	2.30	1.11	1	25	58
GUA-P7	24°54′ N	123°05′ W	4200	.49	2.30	1.13	1	25	58
V18-100	09°42′ S	136°28′ W	4329	.96	1.72	1.65	1	28	65
V18-101	08°00′ S	133°50′ W	4696	1.24	1.56	1.93	1	28	65
V18-102	07°20′ S	133°03′ W	4477	.99	1.52	1.50	1	28	65
V18-105	05°19′ S	130°22′ W	4661	.57	1.65	.94	1	28	65
V18-107	03°37′ S	127°41′ W	4564	.23	1.66	.38	1	28	65
V18-108	02°51′ S	126°12′ W	4612	.36	1.78	.59	1	28	65
V18-109	01°06′ S	124°37′ W	4550	.28	2.16	.60	1	28	65
V18-110	01°14′ S	122°55′ W	4389	.48	2.33	1.12	1	28	65
V18-111	01°03′ N	120°46′ W	4371	.36	2.31	.83	1	28	65

TABLE 22-8.   *Continued*

Station	Lat.	Long.	Depth	∇T	K	Q	No.	Ref.	Yr.
V18-112	02°12′ N	119°40′ W	4332	1.52	2.30	(3.50)	1	28	65
V18-113	03°10′ N	118°28′ W	4217	.71	2.13	1.51	1	28	65
V18-114	04°14′ N	117°00′ W	4161	.42	2.19	.82	1	28	65
V18-116	06°23′ N	113°32′ W	4104	.15	1.85	.28	1	28	65
V18-118	08°01′ N	109°18′ W	4065	1.92	1.67	3.21	1	28	65
V18-119	08°46′ N	107°09′ W	3488	1.74	1.83	3.18	1	28	65
V18-122	10°16′ N	103°05′ W	3190	1.91	1.55	2.96	1	28	65
V18-125	11°54′ N	100°44′ W	3360	1.22	1.65	2.01	1	28	65
V18-126	12°38′ N	99°27′ W	3426	1.78	1.64	2.62	1	28	65
V18-127	12°54′ N	98°52′ W	3342	.96	1.80	(1.73)	1	28	65
V18-128	12°49′ N	97°47′ W	3720	.42	1.72	.46	1	28	65
V18-129	13°09′ N	97°07′ W	3590	.64	1.80	(1.15)	1	28	65
V18-130	13°19′ N	96°51′ W	2757	5.78	1.85	10. ?	1	28	65
V18-131	14°31′ N	96°18′ W	3890	1.55	1.91	2.96	1	28	65
V18-134	12°47′ N	96°17′ W	3987	.76	1.82	1.38	1	28	65
V18-135	08°49′ N	97°16′ W	3793	.66	1.61	1.06	1	28	65
V18-140	06°37′ N	88°24′ W	3247	1.91	1.60	3.06	1	28	65
V18-141	06°44′ N	86°30′ W	2892	.56	1.82	1.02	1	28	65
V18-142	06°04′ N	85°43′ W	1819	1.53	1.97	3.01	1	28	65
V18-143	05°42′ N	85°16′ W	1840	1.41	2.15	3.03	1	28	65
V18-144	05°18′ N	84°45′ W	3005	1.40	1.78	2.50	1	28	65
V18-145	05°34′ N	83°24′ W	3064	1.95	1.76	3.43	1	28	65
V18-146	06°06′ N	82°05′ W	3031	1.91	1.80	(3.44)	1	28	65
V18-148	06°42′ N	80°42′ W	3424	1.70	1.80	(3.06)	1	28	65
V19-8	07°04′ N	78°59′ W	3345	1.63	1.69	2.75	1	28	65
V19-9	04°56′ N	78°16′ W	3819	2.83	2.16	6.11	1	28	65
V19-10	03°12′ N	80°08′ W	1711	.91	2.08	1.89	1	28	65
V19-11	02°28′ N	81°42′ W	2398	1.12	1.79	2.00	1	28	65
V19-14	02°22′ S	84°39′ W	2724	.07	1.78	.12	1	28	65
V19-15	03°35′ S	83°56′ W	3153	1.17	1.67	1.95	1	28	65
V19-19	11°59′ S	81°31′ W	4749	1.21	1.53	1.85	1	28	65
V19-23	13°13′ S	92°53′ W	3647	.83	2.19	1.82	1	28	65
V19-26	16°21′ S	104°48′ W	4199	.78	2.42	1.8	1	28	65
V19-27	17°01′ S	108°52′ W	3624	.76	2.49	1.9	1	28	65
V19-28	17°01′ S	110°23′ W	3449	.71	2.1	(1.5)	1	28	65
V19-29	17°00′ S	110°51′ W	3438	.58	2.23	1.3	1	28	65
V19-30	17°00′ S	111°12′ W	3537	.44	2.06	.9	1	28	65
V19-31	17°01′ S	111°33′ W	3320	.57	2.1	(1.2)	1	28	65
V19-32	17°02′ S	111°53′ W	3256	.67	2.1	(1.4)	1	28	65
V19-33	17°02′ S	112°12′ W	3184	1.57	2.1	(3.3)	1	28	65
V19-34	17°01′ S	112°34′ W	2981	1.10	2.1	(2.3)	1	28	65
V19-35	17°01′ S	112°55′ W	3175	.81	2.1	(1.7)	1	28	65
V19-36	17°01′ S	113°31′ W	3056	.86	2.1	(1.8)	1	28	65
V19-37	17°02′ S	113°54′ W	2830	1.67	2.1	(3.5)	1	28	65
V19-38	17°00′ S	114°11′ W	3177	.76	2.1	(1.6)	1	28	65
V19-39	17°00′ S	114°32′ W	3139	1.00	2.1	(2.1)	1	28	65
V19-40	17°00′ S	114°53′ W	3157	.76	2.1	(1.6)	1	28	65
V19-41	16°58′ S	115°12′ W	3270	.24	2.1	(.5)	1	28	65
V19-42	16°58′ S	115°33′ W	3300	3.38	2.1	(7.1)	1	28	65
V19-43	16°58′ S	115°56′ W	3336	1.00	2.1	(2.1)	1	28	65
V19-44	16°57′ S	116°18′ W	3407	.71	2.1	(1.4)	1	28	65
V19-45	16°58′ S	116°48′ W	3374	1.05	2.1	(2.2)	1	28	65
V19-46	16°59′ S	117°53′ W	3422	.76	2.1	(1.6)	1	28	65
V19-48	16°39′ S	124°23′ W	3760	.43	2.1	(.9)	1	28	65
H-4	28°14′ N	127°38′ W	4580	.710	2.07	1.47	1	29	64
H-5	24°46′ N	134°30′ W	4530	.632	1.97	1.25	2	29	64

TABLE 22-8. *Continued*

Station	Lat.	Long.	Depth	∇T	K	Q	No.	Ref.	Yr.
H-7	23°03′ N	137°55′ W	5295	.935	2.00	(1.87)	1	29	64
H-8	23°00′ N	143°58′ W	4850	1.32	2.10	2.78	1	29	64
H-9	22°58′ N	148°24′ W	5470	.726	1.90	(1.38)	1	29	64
H-10	23°00′ N	150°38′ W	5580	.763	1.86	1.42	1	29	64
H-11	22°59′ N	152°59′ W	5060	.860	1.86	1.6*	1	29	64
H-12	22°29′ N	154°26′ W	4390	.758	1.98	(1.5)*	1	29	64
H-15	19°08′ N	157°20′ W	4610	1.04	1.68	1.74*	1	29	64
H-17	23°36′ N	156°07′ W	4260	.695	1.87	1.30	1	29	64
H-18	21°56′ N	154°48′ W	4660	.353	2.01	.71	1	29	64
H-19	23°07′ N	156°07′ W	4260	.742	1.90	1.41	1	29	64
LSDH-68	20°15′ N	154°13′ W	5480	.527	1.67	.88*	1	29	64
LSDH-69	19°59′ N	151°09′ W	5305	.773	1.85	1.43	1	29	64
LSDH-70	20°06′ N	145°16′ W	5410	.774	1.90	1.47	1	29	64
LSDH-71	21°26′ N	140°23′ W	5200	.672	2.04	1.37	1	29	64
LSDH-72	22°12′ N	138°57′ W	5100	.721	2.08	1.50	2	29	64
LSDH-73	23°10′ N	130°58′ W	4870	.659	2.07	1.36	2	29	64
LSDH-74	27°30′ N	125°47′ W	4483	.441	2.02	.89	2	29	64

TABLE 22-9. HEAT FLOW IN THE ARCTIC OCEAN

Station	Lat.	Long.	Depth	∇T	K	Q	No.	Ref.	Yr.
FL-1	82°30′ N	156°26′ W	3747	.683	2.13	1.45	1	35	65
FL-2	82°12′ N	156°24′ W	3742	.674	2.07	1.40	1	35	65
FL-3	82°31′ N	156°54′ W	3741	.672	2.20	1.48	1	35	65
FL-6	82°42′ N	158°04′ W	3740	.625	2.11	1.32	1	35	65
FL-8	82°39′ N	157°28′ W	3742	.665	2.19	1.46	1	35	65
FL-9	82°46′ N	156°51′ W	3743	.634	2.16	1.37	1	35	65
FL-10	82°57′ N	155°54′ W	3507	.496	2.72	1.35	1	35	65
FL-11	83°00′ N	156°07′ W	3520	.547	2.60	1.42	1	35	65
FL-12	83°06′ N	156°01′ W	3473	.552	2.67	1.47	1	35	65
FL-13	83°08′ N	156°47′ W	3577	.540	2.60	1.40	1	35	65
FL-14	83°08′ N	157°18′ W	3216	.394	2.76	1.09	1	35	65
FL-15	82°60′ N	158°16′ W	3137	.295	2.63	.78	1	35	65
FL-16	83°01′ N	159°03′ W	2247	.338	2.68	.91	1	35	65
FL-17	82°60′ N	159°02′ W	2215	.296	2.61	.77	1	35	65
FL-19	83°03′ N	162°52′ W	3417	.440	2.43	1.07	1	35	65
FL-21	83°01′ N	163°37′ W	3494	.478	2.66	1.27	1	35	65
FL-22	82°53′ N	163°17′ W	3750	.666	2.14	1.43	1	35	65
FL-23	82°39′ N	162°49′ W	3748	.676	2.18	1.47	1	35	65
FL-24	82°22′ N	162°07′ W	3743	.570	2.52	1.44	1	35	65
FL-25	82°26′ N	160°40′ W	3760	.631	2.10	1.32	1	35	65

TABLE 22-10. HEAT FLOW IN GEOTHERMAL AREAS

Station	Lat.		Long.		Elev.	∇T	K	Q	No.	Ref.	Yr.
Iceland	65°	N	18°	W	500	.9	5.	∼4.5	1	72	55
Italy											
Larderello	43°12′ N		10°54′ E		300	3.4	3.2	10.6	9	81	63
Japan											
Matsukawa Area	40°	N	141°	E	500	..	..	15.	1	18	64
Shirane Volcano	36°37′ N		138°34′ E		1600	2.47	4.48	10.8	1	18	64
Toyoha	42°54′ N		141°05′ E		500	1.13	5.	5.6	1	18	64
New Zealand											
Orakei Korako											
Area	37°30′ S		175°	E	300	30.	3.	100.	1	102	59
Wairakei Area	38°30′ S		177°	E	300	25.	1.6	40.	1	120	64

TABLE 22-11. MAXIMUM OBSERVED TEMPERATURES OF BASALTIC LAVAS

Locality and rock type	Temperature (°C)	Remarks	Ref.
Halemaumau, 1912, basalt, Lava lake	1210	Optical pyrometer; 25-degree correction for emissivity included; measured in daylight	104
Halemaumau, 1917, basalt, Lava lake	1120–1170	Seger cones in iron pipe 3.8 cm in internal diameter. Immersed for 8 minutes to depths from 8 to 13 m in Lava lake. Correction of 200° for failure of cones to attain temperature of lava included	106
Nyamuragira, 1938, Leucite basalt, fountains	1095	Optical pyrometer; 25-degree correction for emissivity included; measured in daylight	113
Paricutin, 1944, basalt	1200–1250 1110	Optical pyrometer; measured in daylight; no correction for emissivity Thermocouple in porcelain tube, 10 cm into lava; 3 miles from source of flow	114
Mauna Loa, 1950, basalt dome fountain throat of spatter cone	1085–1105 1115–1135	Optical pyrometer; 25-degree correction for emissivity included; measured at night	105
Mihara, 1950, basalt, fountain	1240	Optical pyrometer; 30-degree correction for emissivity included; measured in daylight	112
Mihara, 1951, basalt, flow	1125	Platinum/platinum-rhodium thermocouple, hot junction unprotected	109
Kilauea, 1952, basalt, fountains	1145	Glowing-filament optical pyrometer; 25-degree correction for emissivity included; measured at night	107
Kilauea, 1955, basalt, fountains	1110	Glowing-filament optical pyrometer; 25-degree correction for emissivity included. Extrapolated from distance of 200–300 feet to correct for atmospheric absorption; measured at night	108
Nyiragongo, 1956, Nephelinite fountain in Lava lake	980	Optical pyrometer; 20-degree correction for emissivity included; measured at night	111
Capelinhos, Azores, 1957, basalt, fountains	1005	Optical pyrometer; 20-degree correction for emissivity included; measured at night	110

SECTION 23

RADIOACTIVE DECAY CONSTANTS AND ENERGIES

by GEORGE W. WETHERILL

CONTENTS

Handbook of Physical Constants—*Revised Edition*

THE GEOLOGICAL SOCIETY OF AMERICA MEMOIR 97, 1966

The decay constant of a radioactive nuclide is defined by the relationship $\dfrac{dN}{dt} = -\lambda N$

where N is the number of atoms of the nuclide under consideration. Because radio-active decay is statistical in nature this relationship is approximate. However, geo-chronological work always involves the decay of a sufficient number of atoms of the parent nuclide to produce measurable quantities of the daughter; in this case the statistical fluctuations are of negligible importance. The decay constant is related to the half-life $t_{1/2}$ by the equation:

$$t_{1/2} = \frac{\ln 2}{\lambda} = \frac{.6932}{\lambda},$$

and therefore any experimental method which determines the decay constant also determines the half-life. If the parent nuclide decays in two or more alternative ways (branching decay) there are as many decay constants as there are branches, and the relationship may be written

$$-\frac{dN}{dt} = (\lambda_1 + \lambda_2 + \cdots \lambda_n)N.$$

The only branching decay of major importance in geochronology is that of K^{40} which decays into Ca^{40} (β^- decay) and into Ar^{40} (electron capture).

A discussion has been published [1] of the exact way in which the decay constants enter into the age equations, the errors in the calculated age resulting from possible errors in the decay constants, and experimental problems encountered in measuring the various decay constants.

Historically, geochronological measurements preceded counting techniques in determining good values for the decay constants of U^{235} [2], K^{40} [3], Rb^{87} [4], and Re^{187} [5, 6]. However, at the present time, with the exception of Re^{187}, the counting methods should be superior, and only results obtained by counting experiments will be discussed.

Values of the decay constants are tabulated in Table 23-1. The choice of constants

TABLE 23-1.   SELECTED VALUES OF THE NATURAL
RADIOACTIVE DECAY CONSTANTS

Nuclide	Decay constant
K^{40}	$\lambda_e = 5.85 \times 10^{-11}$ yr^{-1}
	$\lambda_\beta = 4.72 \times 10^{-10}$ yr^{-1}
Rb^{87}	1.390×10^{-11} yr^{-1}*
Re^{187}	1.61×10^{-11} yr^{-1}
Th^{232}	4.99×10^{-11} yr^{-1}
U^{235}	9.72×10^{-10} yr^{-1}
U^{238}	1.540×10^{-10} yr^{-1}

* With considerable justification many authors have adopted the value 1.47×10^{-11} yr^{-1}. *See* text.

is to some extent arbitrary, as with any experimentally determined quantity there will be always some uncertainty in the experimental result. A brief discussion of the reasons lying behind the choice of these constants follows.

K^{40}. A tabulation of experimental values of the decay constant for electron capture (λ_e) and that for beta decay (λ_β) have been published [1]. Ages in that publication and in most subsequent publications have been calculated using $\lambda_e = 5.85 \times 10^{-11}$ yr^{-1} and $\lambda_\beta = 4.72 \times 10^{-10}$ yr^{-1} or values sufficiently close to these that the differences are negligible.

A. For reasons discussed in the publication cited [1], earlier values of λ_e had experimental errors of about 10 per cent, because of the difficulty of determining the absolute efficiency of the counting device used at the energy of the K^{40} γ-ray which occurs in the electron-capture branch. This error can be minimized by the use of a γ-ray scintillation spectrometer, and therefore values of λ_e obtained in this way can be regarded as intrinsically superior to older techniques. Measurements using this technique are given in Table 23-2.

TABLE 23-2. MEASUREMENTS OF THE SPECIFIC GAMMA ACTIVITY OF
POTASSIUM USING SCINTILLATION SPECTROMETERS

Investigators	Activity γ/g sec
McNair, Glover, and Wilson [7]	3.33 ± .15
Wetherill [8]	3.39 ± .12

Engelkemeir and others [10] have made an important contribution by detecting the positrons in the electron-capture branch, and they measure the ratio of positrons to beta particles as $1.12 \pm .14 \times 10^{-5}$. This permits a calculation of the number of electron captures which go directly to the ground state of Ar^{40} without the production of a γ-ray. The result is that about 1.6 per cent of the electron capture proceeds by this mode. Considering the experimental errors and the confusion resulting from a change in decay constants there is probably no reason to calculate ages with the slightly different value resulting from inclusion of this effect.

B. The absolute measurement of the K^{40} beta activity is not essentially difficult, but the measurements tabulated in [1] did not make the greatest possible use of presently existing techniques, for reasons discussed therein. Recently Flynn, Engelkemeir, and Glendenin [9] have measured the absolute activity using 4π geometry and enriched K^{40} under conditions where self absorption should be negligible. They obtained a result of 28.2 β/g sec. This is 2 per cent higher than the value used in [1] which has been in common use. The advantage of a higher counting rate obtained by the use of enriched potassium is partially offset by the fact that age calculations made with this decay constant are dependent on the isotopic composition of natural K and the enriched source. Since the difference between ages calculated with the two values will be less than 1 per cent together with experimental uncertainties there is no reason to change the decay constant used in age calculations.

Rb^{87}. The principal difficulty in counting the absolute beta activity of Rb^{87} has been that of measuring the unusually large fraction of low energy beta particles in its spectrum. Recent advances in determining this constant have resulted from the use of very thin sources in 4π geometry or by chemically incorporating the Rb within the counting medium. Measurements made with thin sources and 4π geometry or with liquid scintillators are given in Table 23-3.

Because it is difficult to understand how the investigators whose work is reported in Table 23-3 could have been apparently counting too many beta particles, it seems most likely that for some unknown reason solid scintillators fail to count some of the low-energy particles.

TABLE 23-3. MEASUREMENTS OF THE Rb[87] HALF-LIFE USING THIN SOURCES IN 4π COUNTERS OR WITH LIQUID SCINTILLATORS

Measurements made with solid scintillators, given in Table 23-4, appear to be systematically higher.

Investigators	Half life (10^{10} yrs.)
Flynn and Glendenin [11]	4.70 ± .10
Rausch and Schmidt [12]	4.72 ± .08
McNair and Wilson [13]	5.25 ± .10

TABLE 23-4. MEASUREMENTS OF THE Rb[87] HALF-LIFE USING SOLID SCINTILLATORS

Investigators	Half-life (10^{10} yrs.)
Lewis [14]	5.93 ± .3
Egelkraut and Leutz [15]	5.82 ± .1
Beard and Kelly [16]	5.53 ± .1
Leutz, Wenninger and Ziegler [35]	5.80 ± .12

Ages were calculated in [1] using a decay constant of 1.390×10^{-11} yr^{-1} corresponding to a half-life of 4.99×10^{10} yrs. Recently some workers have calculated ages based on the work of Flynn and Glendenin [11], which corresponds to a decay constant of 1.474×10^{-11} yr^{-1}. This is in complete agreement with that of Rausch and Huster whose work appears to have minimized the self-absorption problem more completely than that of McNair and Wilson. It seems likely that the 4.7×10^{10} yr. half-life is more nearly the correct one; however, it may be wise to wait until refined measurements now in progress are completed before recalculating measured ages.

Re[187]. The extremely low energy of the Re[187] beta-particle (8 Kev) has made it very difficult to measure its decay constant by counting methods. Measured values are given in Table 23-5. Because of the difficulty in obtaining a reliable value of the Re[187]

TABLE 23-5. MEASUREMENTS OF THE Re[187] HALF-LIFE

Investigators	Half-life 10^{11} year	Maximum beta energy Kev	Detection method
Naldrett and Libby [17]	40 ± 10	43	solid sample G-M
Sugarman and Richter [18]	50	..	solid sample G-M
Suttle and Libby [19]	1	8	solid sample G-M
Dixon, McNair, and Curran [20, 21]	130,000	1	solid sample proportional
Walton [22]	2.1 ± .5	2.4 ± .5	gas-counting
Naldrett [23]	3.2 ± .7	20	solid sample G-M
Wolf and Johnston [24]	1.2 ± .4	3 ± 1	gas counting

beta-activity by counting techniques it is probably still best to use a value based on geochronological comparisons. These have been given as $6.2 \pm {}^{.6}_{.7} \times 10^{10}$ yrs. [6] and more recently as $4.3 \pm .5 \times 10^{10}$ yrs. [25].

Th^{232}. Measurements of the decay constant for alpha decay of Th^{232} are given in [1], and ages are calculated using a decay constant of 4.99×10^{-11} yr^{-1} corresponding to a half-life of 1.39×10^{10} yrs. A new determination of $1.401 \pm .007 \times 10^{10}$ yrs. has been made by Le Roux and Glendenin [26] using liquid scintillation methods. This is in complete agreement with earlier values.

TABLE 23-6. DECAY CONSTANTS OF C^{14} AND H^3

C^{14}	1.203×10^{-4} yr^{-1}	[29]
	1.199×10^{-4}	[30]
	1.245×10^{-4}	[34]
H^3	5.653×10^{-2}	[31]
	5.563×10^{-2}	[32]

U^{235}. Measurements of the decay constant for alpha decay of U^{235} are given in [1]. It was judged that the result of Fleming, Ghiorso, and Cunningham [27] of $7.13 \pm .16 \times 10^8$ years (corresponding to a decay constant of 9.72×10^{-10} yr^{-1}) was the most reliable, and this value was used to calculate ages in that publication. No new work has been published since the last review, and this value still seems the best to use.

Regularities of discordant uranium-lead zircon age [28] seem to indicate that zircons from an orogenic belt appear to be about 5 per cent older than micas and feldspars from the same orogenic belt dated by the K-Ar and Rb-Sr methods. This

TABLE 23-7. DECAY ENERGIES OF U, Th, AND K [33]

Isotope	Mev/atom	Energy ergs/gm sec	cal/gm yr
U^{238}	47.4	.94	.71
U^{235}	45.2	5.7	4.3
U (ordinary)	..	.97	.73
Th^{232}	39.8	.27	.20
K^{40}	.71	.28	.21
K (ordinary)	..	36×10^{-6}	27×10^{-6}

effect may be of geological origin, but could also be caused by using a U^{235} decay constant which is about 3 per cent too low. This possibility cannot be excluded by present measurements. It would be of considerable interest if this question could be resolved by a more accurate measurement of the U^{235} half-life.

U^{238}. Measurements of the U^{238} half-life are tabulated in [1]. These results agreed very well at 4.50×10^9 yrs. corresponding to a decay constant of 1.540×10^{-10} yr^{-1}. No new determinations have been published, and this value is still adopted.

The accepted half-life of C^{14} is 5568 ± 30 years, as given by Libby [34]. Recent redeterminations [29, 30], lead to values of 5760 and 5780 years respectively.

TABLE 23-8. THE GEOLOGIC TIME SCALE

Several versions of the geologic time scale are given herein. Uncertainties, where given, are the author's estimates, which are necessarily subjective. Since rocks dated radioactively never fall exactly at the boundary between two geologic periods, some interpolation between measured ages is necessary. No great accuracy can be claimed for such a process. Particular uncertainty may be attached to the age of the base of the Cambrian, as discussed elsewhere [36, 37].

| | Ages in 10^6 years | | | |
	(a)	(b)	(c)	(d)
Pleistocene				
	..	..	1	1
Pliocene				
	12	..	11	13
Miocene				
	26	..	25	25
Oligocene				
	38	..	40	36
Eocene				
	..	..	60	58
Paleocene				
	58	60	70 ± 2	63
Cretaceous				
	127	130	135 ± 5	135
Jurassic				
	152	155	180 ± 5	181
Triassic				
	182	185	225 ± 5	(230)
Permian				
	203	210	270 ± 5	280
Carboniferous				
	255	265	350 ± 10	345
Devonian				
	313	320	400 ± 10	405
Silurian				
	350	360	440 ± 10	(425)
Ordovician				
	430	440	500 ± 15	500
Cambrian				
	510	520	600 ± 20	(600)
Precambrian				

(a) Holmes, Trans. Geol. Soc. Glasgow 21, 117, 1947
(b) Holmes (Holmes-Marble scale), Rept. Comm. Geologic Time, (1946–1947), J. P. Marble, Chairman, Nat. Res. Council, p. 39–46, 1948
(c) Holmes, Trans. Edinburgh Geol. Soc. 17, 183, 1960
(d) Kulp, Science 133, 1105, 1961

REFERENCES FOR SECTION 23

1. Aldrich and Wetherill, Ann. Rev. Nucl. Sci. 8, 257, 1958
2. Nier, Phys. Rev. 55, 150, 1939
3. Wetherill, Wasserburg, Aldrich, Tilton, and Hayden, Phys. Rev. 103, 987, 1956
4. Aldrich, Wetherill, Tilton, and Davis, Phys. Rev. 103, 1045, 1956
5. Herr, Hintenberger, and Voshage, Phys. Rev. 95, 1691, 1954
6. Herr and Merz, Z. Naturforsch 13A, 231, 1958
7. McNair, Glover, and Wilson, Phil. Mag. 1, 199, 1956

 8. Wetherill, Science **126,** 545, 1957
 9. Glendenin, L. E., Annals of the New York Academy of Sciences **91,** 166, 1961
10. Engelkemeir, Flynn, and Glendenin, Phys. Rev. **126,** 1818, 1962
11. Flynn and Glendenin, Phys. Rev. **116,** 744, 1959
12. Rausch, W., and Huster, E., private communication, 1961
13. McNair and Wilson, Phil. Mag. **6,** 563, 1961
14. Lewis, Phil. Mag. **43,** 1070, 1952
15. Egelkraut and Leutz, Z. Physik **161,** 13, 1961
16. Beard and Kelly, Nuclear Phys. **28,** 570, 1961
17. Naldrett and Libby, Phys. Rev. **73,** 487, 1948
18. Sugarman and Richter, Phys. Rev. **73,** 1411, 1948
19. Suttle and Libby, Phys. Rev. **95,** 866, 1954
20. Dixon and McNair, Phil. Mag. **45,** 1099, 1954
21. Dixon, McNair, and Curran, Jour. Phys. Radium **16,** 538, 1955
22. Walton, J. R., Ph.D. Dissertation, Purdue University, 1957
23. Naldrett, New York Acad. Sci. **72,** 215, 1958
24. Wolf, C. J., and Johnston, W. H., Phys. Rev. **125,** 307, 1962
25. Hirt, Tilton, Herr, and Hoffmeister, Helv. Phys. Acta **35,** 320, 1962
26. Le Roux, L. J., and Glendenin, L. E., private communication, 1961
27. Fleming, Ghiorso, and Cunningham, Phys. Rev. **88,** 642, 1952
28. Tilton, Jour. Geophy. Res. **65,** 2933, 1960
29. Mann, Marlow, and Hughes, Internat. Jour. Appl. Radiation and Isotopes **11,** 57, 1961
30. Watt, Ramsden, and Wilson, Internat. Jour. Appl. Radiation and Isotopes **11,** 68, 1961
31. Jones, Phys. Rev. **100,** 124, 1955
32. Jenks, Sweeton, and Ghormley, Phys. Res. **80,** 990, 1950
33. Birch *in* Faul, Editor, Nuclear geology, John Wiley & Sons, New York, 1954
34. Libby, Radiocarbon dating, Univ. of Chicago Press, 1958
35. Leutz, H., Wenninger, H. and Ziegler, K., zeit. f. Physik **169,** 409, 1962
36. Wetherill, G. W., Nature **187,** 34, 1960
37. Holmes, A., Nature **187,** 1960

SECTION 24

ABUNDANCES OF URANIUM, THORIUM, AND POTASSIUM*

by Sydney P. Clark, Jr., Zell E. Peterman, and Knut S. Heier

Contents

Illustrations

* Publication authorized by the Director, U.S. Geological Survey

Handbook of Physical Constants—*Revised Edition*
THE GEOLOGICAL SOCIETY OF AMERICA MEMOIR 97, 1966

This section contains data on the abundances of uranium, thorium, and potassium in geological materials. These elements are singled out for special attention because their radioactivity gives them unique importance to the thermal budget of the earth and the other terrestrial planets. The concentrations given here can be converted to rates of heat production by use of the data in Table 23-7.

Uranium and thorium are trace elements; their concentrations rarely exceed a few tens of parts per million. Potassium, on the other hand, is a major element in many rocks, and its concentration is given in any complete chemical analysis. This difference in abundance, by a factor of the order of 10^4, has meant that commonly potassium has been determined by different methods and for different purposes than have uranium and thorium. Determinations of all three elements on the same sample are still regrettably rare. Because of this, it proves desirable to tabulate potassium separately in many cases.

Analyses of the concentrations of these elements in rocks have been made for many years, but it is now clear that most of the older determinations led to results that were too large, sometimes by orders of magnitude. The errors were most serious in materials where the concentrations are low, such as ultramafic rocks and meteorites. The presence of systematic errors in old uranium and thorium analyses has been known for some time, but it is only recently that errors in potassium values have been demonstrated. The latter errors appear to be serious only in materials with concentrations of potassium of a few tenths of a per cent or less.

Analytical difficulties have meant that there are few reliable analyses of meteorites and ultramafic rocks and eclogites. Hence individual tabulation of the data is feasible, and the analytical method can be specified. For more silicic igneous rocks, data are so numerous that they must be summarized; they are presented below as histograms, with medians and means given. Such a procedure inevitably involves combination of data obtained by different methods, but the types of rocks represented by the histograms contain sufficiently high concentrations of uranium and thorium to make several reliable methods of analysis available. Much of the material in this section is condensed from the extensive compilations of Peterman [85].

Abbreviations used to specify analytical method are as follows:

α—total alpha and alpha-pair counting   *i*—isotope dilution

γ—gamma-ray spectrometry   *n*—neutron activation.

d—distillation of alkali chloride

URANIUM, THORIUM, AND POTASSIUM IN METEORITES

Data are given in Tables 24-1, 24-2, and 24-3. Virtually all the uranium and thorium values listed in Table 24-1 were obtained by neutron activation. This method gives the most reliable results. Potassium has been determined by a distillation method [32], by isotope dilution, and by gamma-ray spectrometry. Ordinary chondrites form a reasonably homogeneous group with respect to potassium content, and a fairly large number of meteorites have been analyzed by each of the three methods. Hence a comparison between the methods is possible (Table 24-2); the results are in good agreement. The three studies have been lumped together to give an overall summary (5th entry of Table 24-2, and Fig. 24-1). If a given meteorite had been included in more than one study, the results were averaged, and the average was given unit weight. Results for carbonaceous chondrites will be found in Table 24-2, and for achondrites in Table 24-3.

TABLE 24-1.   URANIUM AND THORIUM IN METEORITES

Meteorite	U 10^{-8}g/g	Th 10^{-8}g/g	Th/U	Method	Ref.
Irons					
Sikhote-Alin	<.002	..	..	*n*	35
Tamarugal	.0003–.0035	..	..	*n*	87
Carbo	.0003–.007	..	..	*n*	87
Thunda	.0005–.032	..	..	*n*	87
Arispe I	..	.0018⎫			
	..	.0016⎬	..	*n*	17
	..	.0011⎭			
Arispe II	..	.00061⎫			
	..	.00059⎬	..	*n*	17
	..	.00053⎭			
Sandia Mts.	..	.0010 ⎫			
	..	.0011 ⎬	..	*n*	17
	..	.00089⎭			
Toluca					
(metal)	<.03, <.015	..	..	*n*	38
(troilite)	1.0 ± .1	..	..	*n*	38
	<1.3	..	..	*n*	88
Canyon Diablo	.0005–.0014	..	..	*n*	87
(metal)	<.06	..	..	*n*	38
(troilite)	.4	..	..	*n*	88
	.35 ± .04	..	..	*n*	38
Grant					
(metal)	<.05	..	..	*n*	38
(troilite)	.65 ± .07	..	..	*n*	38
Sardis					
(troilite)	.65 ± .11	..	..	*n*	38
Soroti					
(troilite)	1.7 ± .2	..	..	*n*	38
Pallasite					
Brenham					
(metal)	.0005–.012	..	..	*n*	87
(olivine)	..	1.1	..	*n*	15
Type I carbonaceous chondrites					
Orgueil	.8*	..	..	*n*	88
	1.95 ± .05	5.95 ± .15⎫	2.7	*n*	71
	2.88 ± .04	7.00 ± .18⎭			
Type II carbonaceous chondrites					
Mighei	1.6*	..	..	*n*	88
	2.1, .8	..	..	*n*	38
Murray	1.8, 2.8, 1.5	..	..	*n*	38
Olivine-hypersthene chondrites					
Akaba	.82	..	..	*n*	30
	.9	..	..	*n*	49
Bruderheim	1.1, 1.7, 1.8	..	..	*n*	38
Ergheo	2.1	..	..	*n*	38
Holbrook	1.40, 1.12	..⎫		*n*	43
	1.2, 1.6, 1.6, 2.1*	..⎬	2.8	*n*	88
	..	3.79, 3.81⎭		*n*	16
Mocs	1.1	..	..	*n*	38
Modoc	1.08, 1.08	..⎫		*n*	43
	1.1, 1.2, 1.5, 1.8*	..⎪	3.3	*n*	88
	1.04	..⎬		*n*	59
	..	4.5⎪		*n*	15
	..	3.90, 3.94⎭		*n*	16

TABLE 24-1. *Continued*

Meteorite	U $10^{-8}g/g$	Th $10^{-8}g/g$	Th/U	Method	Ref.
Olivine-bronzite chondrites					
Beardsley	.9, 1.1, 1.7*	.. ⎫		n	88
	1.13	.. ⎪	3.9	n	59
	..	4.3 ⎬		n	15
	..	4.77 ⎭		n	16
Beddgelert	2.1	..	..	n	49
Breitscheid	1.5	..	..	n	49
	1.23	..	..	n	30
	1.24	..	..	n	59
Forest City	.99, 1.06	.. ⎫		n	43
	1.4, 1.6*	.. ⎪	3.2	n	88
	..	4.0, 4.7 ⎬		n	15
	..	3.87 ⎭		n	16
Plainview	1.3, 1.2	..	..	n	38
Pultusk	1.20	..	..	n	30
	1.23	..	..	n	59
Richardton	1.30, 1.13	.. ⎫		n	43
	1.3	.. ⎬	3.1	n	38
	..	3.96, 3.64 ⎭		n	16
Ställdalen	1.1	..	..	n	38
Olivine-pigeonite chondrites					
Mokoia	1.44 ± .04	6.02 ± .18 ⎫	4.3	n	71
	1.35 ± .04	6.08 ± .18 ⎭			
Karoonda	1.25 ± .03	5.99 ± .21 ⎫	4.1	n	71
	1.48 ± .04	5.33 ± .15 ⎭			
Enstatite chondrites					
Abee	1.0, 1.1, 1.1*	..	..	n	88
	1.2, 1.7	..	..	n	38
Hvittis	.615 ± .024	2.92 ± .08 ⎫	5.1	n	71
	.622 ± .027	3.29 ± .10 ⎭			
Indarch	1.6*	..	..	n	88
	.8, .8, 1.1	..	..	n	38
St. Marks	.9	..	..	n	38
Achondrites (angrite)					
Angra dos Reis	19.9 ± .5	98.0 ± 2.7 ⎫	4.9	n	80
	19.8 ± .5	95.5 ± 2.3 ⎭			
Achondrites (aubrites)					
Bishopville	.467 ± .10	4.54 ± .1 ⎫	8.6	n	80
	.568 ± .06	4.38 ± .2 ⎭			
Norton County	1.0	..	..	i	84
Achondrites (diogenites)					
Ellemeet	.146 ± .012	.374 ± .030 ⎫	2.5	n	80
	.156 ± .010	.383 ± .048 ⎭			
Johnstown	1.28 ± .04	2.99 ± .09 ⎫	2.6	n	80
	1.03 ± .03	3.05 ± .09 ⎭			
	.19, .24	..	..	n	59
	..	.587	..	n	16
	1.1	..	..	n	14
	..	.55	..	n	15
Achondrites (eucrites)					
Juvinas	..	60 ± 4	..	γ	84
Moore County	1.96 ± .07	6.39 ± .2 ⎫	3.2	n	80
	1.96 ± .07	6.01 ± .2 ⎭			
Nuevo Laredo	14.4 ± .3	60.7 ± .9 ⎫			
	13.3 ± .3	63.8 ± 1.2 ⎪	4.5	n	80
	14.5 ± .3	69.1 ± 1.0 ⎬			
	14.6 ± .3	64.5 ± .5 ⎭			

TABLE 24-1.   *Continued*

Meteorite	U 10^{-8}g/g	Th 10^{-8}g/g	Th/U	Method	Ref.
Achondrites *Continued*					
	12.6, 12.6	..	..	*n*	43
	14, 17*	..	..	*n*	88
	..	54	..	*n*	15
	..	45.6, 49.6	..	*n*	16
	..	47 ± 22	..	γ	92
Pasamonte	5.42	..	..	*n*	59
	..	52 ± 4	..	γ	92
Sioux County	6.30	..	..	*n*	59
	..	35 ± 4	..	γ	92
Stannern	..	50 ± 4	..	γ	92
Achondrites (howardite)					
Binda	2.26 ± .06	6.41 ± .17	2.8	*n*	80
	2.28 ± .06	6.20 ± .16			
Achondrites (nakhlite)					
Nakhla	4.78 ± .12	19.1 ± .5	3.9	*n*	80
	5.07 ± .13	19.0 ± .5			
Tektites					
Mean of 15	201 ± 47	..		α, γ	21, 22
range	130–278	..	5.8		
Mean of 23	..	1151 ± 267		α, γ	21, 22, 92
range	..	810–1570			

* Authors consider that these values may be too high by 30 per cent.

TABLE 24-2.   POTASSIUM IN CHONDRITES

	Number of determinations	Mean ppm	Median ppm	Method	Ref.
Ordinary chondrites	33	832	830	γ	92
	43	864	870	*d*	31, 32
	38	841	836	*i*	57
	37*	859	837	*i*	57
	83†	841	840		
Carbonaceous chondrites (water and carbon free basis)					
Type I					
Ivuna	1	750	..	*d*	31
Orgueil	1	730	..	*d*	31
Type II					
Haripura	1	730	..	*d*	31
Mighei	1	530	..	*d*	31
Cold Bokkeveld	1	520	..	*d*	31
Ornans	1	410	..	*d*	31
Murray	1	380	..	*d*	31
Type III					
Felix	1	420	..	*d*	31
Warrenton	1	430	..	*d*	31
Mokoia	1	380	..	*d*	31

* Same as third entry with one value of 199 ppm omitted
† Composite of first three entries. *See* text

TABLE 24-3. POTASSIUM IN ACHONDRITES

Achondrite	K (per cent)	Method	Ref.
Aubrites			
Bishopville	.083, .123	*d*	31, 32
	.0199	*i*	57
	.126	*γ*	92
Bustee	.003	*d*	31
Cumberland Falls	.014	*d*	31
Norton County	.0067, .0074, .0068	*i*	57
	.007	*i*	57
	.012	*γ*	92
Pena Blanca Spring	.0296	*i*	57
	.0	*γ*	92
Pesyanoe	.0363	*i*	57
Shallowater	.036	*d*	31
Diogenites			
Johnstown	.0008	*d*	32
Tatahouine	.020	*i*	57
Eucrites			
Juvinas	.038	*d*	32
	.0236	*i*	57
	.048	*γ*	92
Macibini	.039	*i*	57
Moore County	.0187	*i*	57
	.021	*i*	57
	.017	*γ*	92
Nuevo Laredo	.047	*d*	31
	.050	*γ*	92
	.0376, .0358	*i*	57
Pasamonte	.057, .052	*d*	31
	.043	*i*	57
	.0436, .0413	*i*	57
	.038	*γ*	92
Petersburg	.046	*d*	31
Shergotty	.151	*i*	57
Sioux County	.0322, .0347	*i*	57
	.0326	*i*	57
	.024	*γ*	92
Stannern	.060, .069	*d*	31, 32
	.076	*γ*	92
Howardites			
Frankfort	.021	*d*	31
	.013	*i*	57
Kapoeta	.0165	*i*	57
Pavlovka	.017	*d*	31
Nakhlite			
Nakhla	.102	*d*	31
Ureilite			
Goalpara	.006	*d*	31

URANIUM, THORIUM, AND POTASSIUM IN IGNEOUS ROCKS

Because of the low concentration of these elements in ultramafic rocks and eclogites, there are few reliable analyses. Individual results are tabulated in Table 24-4. The possibility that these rocks are contaminated in the sense that their present content of uranium, thorium, and potassium differs from their "original" contents must be borne in mind. Almost any other geological materials brought into contact with these types of rocks are potentially capable of radically increasing their concentrations of radioactive elements through exchange of material. Specimens which occur as nodules in basalts or kimberlites are especially susceptible to contamination, and the eclogites from kimberlites may have had radioactive elements added from the kimberlite matrix.

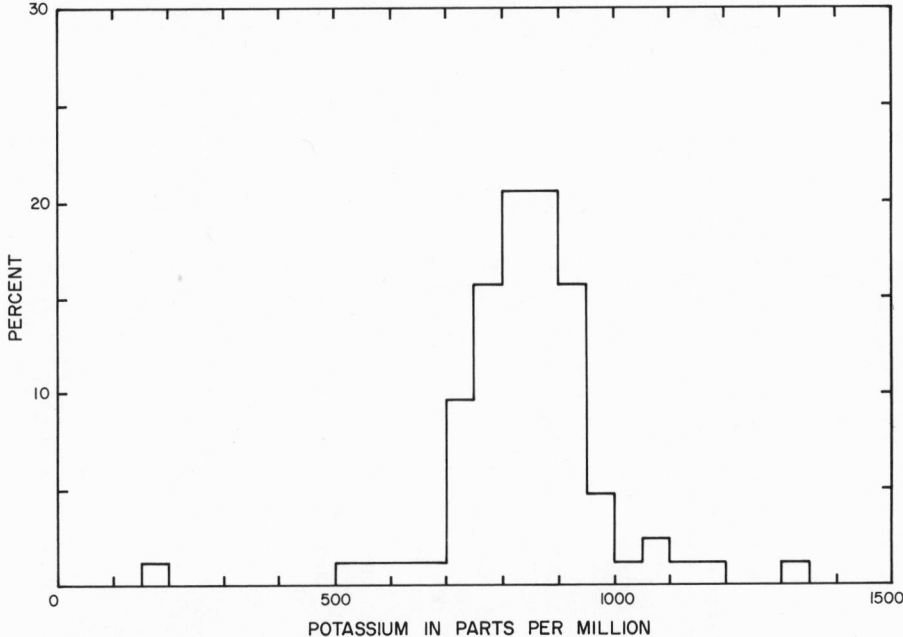

Figure 24-1. Histogram of potassium contents of ordinary chondrites. Data are the same as in fifth entry of Table 24-2 (83 determinations)

Data are far more abundant for the more silicic igneous rocks. Uranium and thorium concentrations are shown as histograms in Figures 24-2 through 24-9. Mean and median values are given in the figure captions. Three types of data went into the construction of the histograms: individual analyses of individual samples, averages of such analyses, and individual analyses of composites representing many samples. For the histograms and medians these data were treated equally as individual values. For comparative purposes, means were calculated, with the averages and analyses of composites weighted according to the number of samples represented. Data for potassium are given in Table 24-6. The specimens analyzed and the scheme of petrological classification in the table both differ from the histograms. Further data for potassium, based on old measurements, are given in Table 1-1. Table 24-5 contains estimates of the ranges of concentrations of uranium and thorium in minerals of igneous rocks. The strong concentration of these elements in certain accessory minerals is noteworthy.

TABLE 24-4. URANIUM, THORIUM AND POTASSIUM IN ULTRAMAFIC ROCKS AND ECLOGITES

Rock	U ppm	Th ppm	K ppm	Th/U	Method	Ref.
Dunites						
Twin Sisters, Wash.	.016	..		..	i	106
	≥.0004	..	12 ± 4	..	n	106
	.0012		..	..	n	43
	.016	.05	..	3.1	i	28
	.0013, .0076	.0010, .0054	..	.71, .77	n	69
St. Paul's Rock	.015	..	..	..	n	106
Olivine nodules and peridotite inclusions						
Hualalai, Hawaii	.005, .009	..	..	..	i	106
	.004	..	..	..	n	106
	.005	..	..	..	i	28
Dreiser Weiher, Germany	.007	..	..	..	i	106
	.05	..	..	..	n	106
Gila, Arizona	.003, .005	..	..	..	i	106
	.009	..	..	..	n	106
San Bernardino, Calif.	.0041, .0051	.012, 0.15	..	2.9	n	69
	.007	..	..	..	i	28
Pyroxenite						
Oslo district, Norway	.70	2.5	7600	3.6	γ	47
Eclogites, metamorphic environment						
Hareidland, Norway	.24, .17	.24, .33	120, 4300	1.0, 1.9	γ	46
Wüstüben, Münchberg	.66	1.7	2400	2.6	γ	46
Mittenbachgraben, Austria	.19	.58	450	3.1	γ	46

Eclogites, Kimberlites*						
Roberts Victor mine, S. Africa	.15, .80, .20 .35, .43, .20	.29, .44 .73, .90, .42	3100, 3300 4500, 6700, 3000	.5–2.1	γ	46
Jägersfontein mine, S. Africa	.07	.17	1000	2.4	?	46
Bulfontein mine, S. Africa	.07	.31	1300	4.4	?	46
Kimberley, S. Africa	.10, .25	.26, .44	700, 1100	2.6, 1.8	?	46
Dodoma, Tanganyika	.17	.45	1300	2.6	?	46
Eclogites, inclusions in basalts						
Salt Lake Crater, Oahu	.05	.09	200	1.8	γ	46
	.041, .043	.10, .10		2.4	n	70
total rocks	.041	..	..	..	i	106
total rock minus spinel	.043	..	527	..	i	106
pyroxene-rich eclogite sol. in HCl	.015	..	..	..	i	106
rock minus sol. in HCl	.030	.102	190	3.4	i	106
Eclogite, N.S.W.	.051, .053	.19, .18	..	3.6	n	70
Hornblende eclogite, N.S.W.	.072, .074	.28, .30	..	3.9	n	70
Olivine eclogite, N.S.W.	.042, .044	.15, .15	..	3.5	n	70
Orange Free State	.041, .041	.24, .24	..	5.8	n	70
Crustal eclogites						
Healdsburg quadrangle, Calif.	.18, .21 .23, .25, .25	.43, .43 .58, .58, .64	..	2.2 2.5	n	70
Silberbach Hof, Germany	.053, .064	.27, .30	..	4.8	n	70
Hof Bavarra, Germany	.026, .025	.009, .020	..	.6	n	70
Tessin River, Switzerland	.024, .013	.011, .024	..	1.0	n	70
Madras, India					n	70

* There is a distinct possibility that these samples were contaminated by the kimberlite matrix during emplacement of the rock. *See* text.

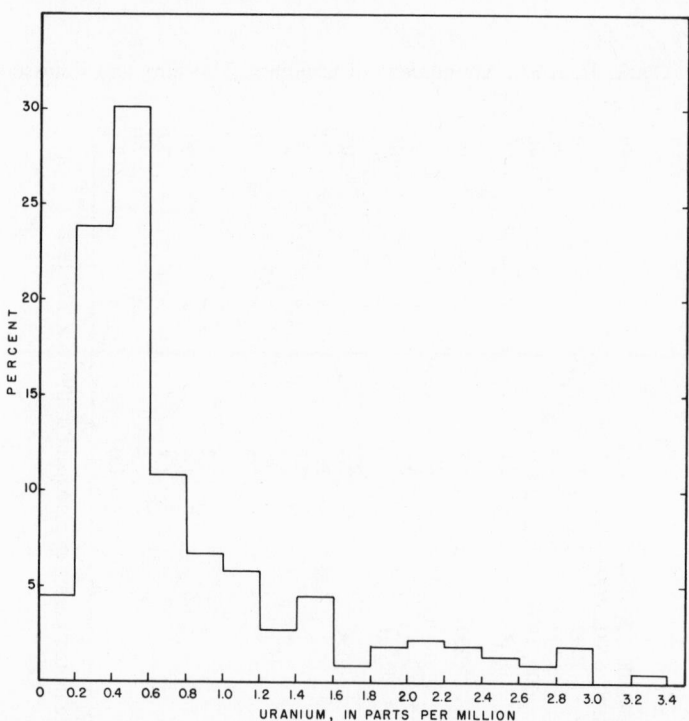

Figure 24-2. Histogram of uranium contents of mafic igneous rocks. Plot represents 125 individual analyses and 14 average values for volcanic rocks, and 81 individual analyses and 16 average values for plutonic and hypabyssal rocks. Mean uranium = .9 ppm, median = .5 ppm. Data from: **1, 2, 3, 7, 8, 19, 33, 36, 39, 40, 41, 42, 44, 45, 47, 50, 52, 56, 64, 65, 66, 69, 74, 89, 90, 94, 95, 98, 102, 107, 108**

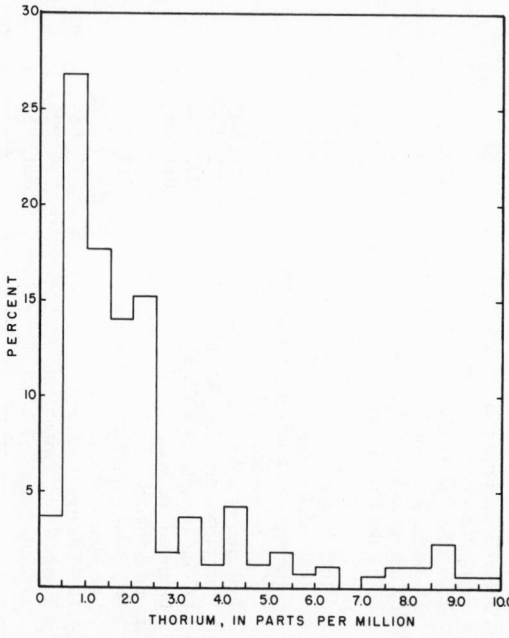

Figure 24-3. Histogram of thorium contents of mafic igneous rocks. Plot represents 107 individual analyses for volcanic rocks and 53 individual analyses and 9 average values for plutonic and hypabyssal rocks. Mean thorium = 2.7 ppm, median = 1.6 ppm. Data from: **1, 2, 7, 19, 33, 39, 40, 41, 42, 47, 52, 56, 64, 65, 69, 74, 90, 95, 107, 108**

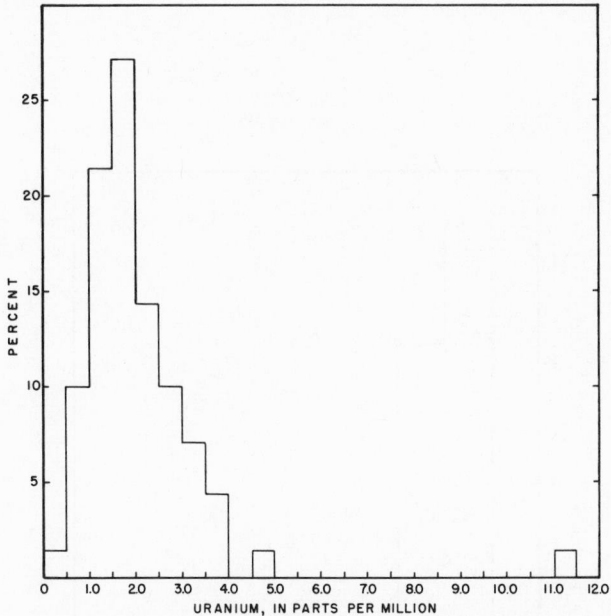

Figure 24-4. Histogram of uranium content of diorites and quartz diorites. Plot represents 59 individual analyses and 10 average values. Mean uranium = 2.0 ppm, median = 1.7 ppm. Data from: **1, 2, 7, 8, 53, 64, 65, 72, 90, 98, 108**

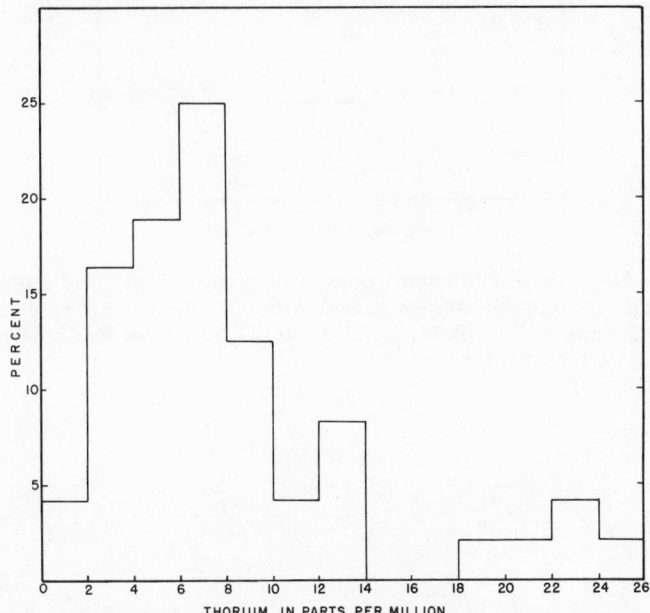

Figure 24-5. Histogram of thorium content of diorites and quartz diorites. Plot represents 39 individual analyses and 8 average values. Mean thorium = 8.5 ppm, median = 7.0 ppm. Data from: **1, 2, 7, 64, 65, 72, 90, 98, 108**

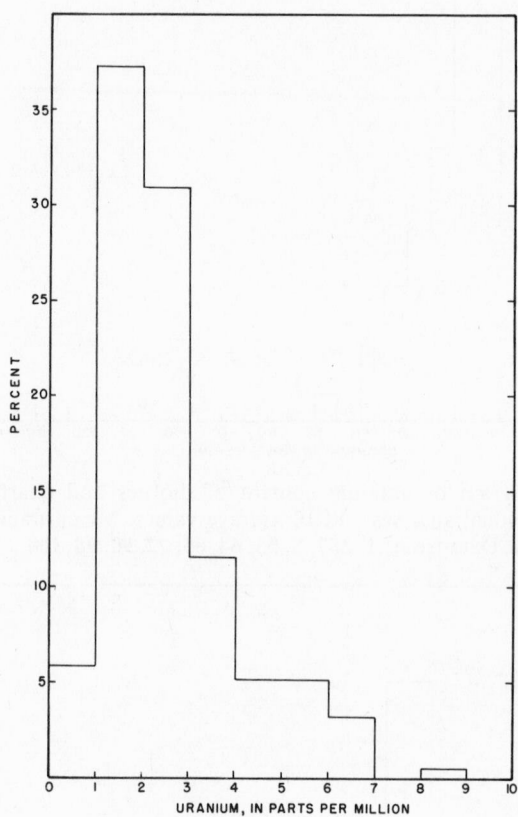

Figure 24-6. Histogram of uranium contents of granodiorites. Plot represents 126 individual analyses and 30 average values. Mean uranium = 2.6 ppm, median = 2.3 ppm. Data from: **1, 7, 8, 10, 11, 29, 33, 34, 41, 47, 50, 53, 54, 56, 63, 64, 65, 72, 74, 82, 89, 90, 93, 98, 102, 107, 108**

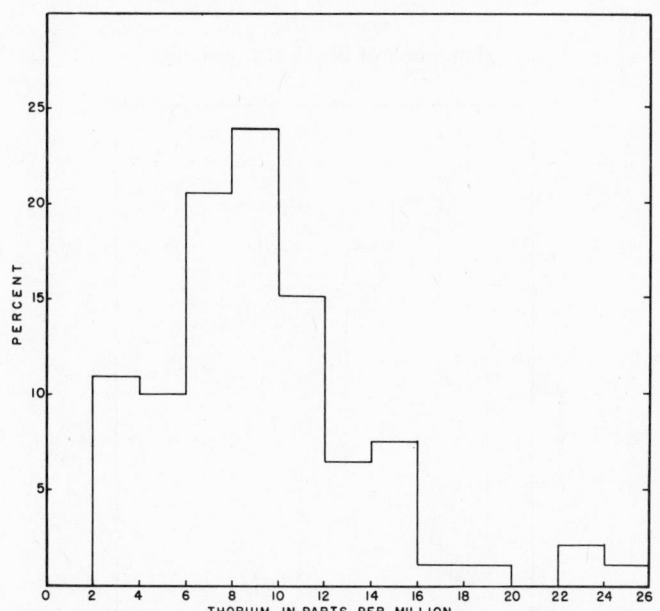

Figure 24-7. Histogram of thorium contents of granodiorites. Plot represents 75 individual analyses and 17 average values. Mean thorium = 9.3 ppm, median = 9.0 ppm. Data from: **1, 7, 10, 11, 33, 34, 41, 47, 56, 64, 65, 72, 74, 90, 93, 98, 107, 108**

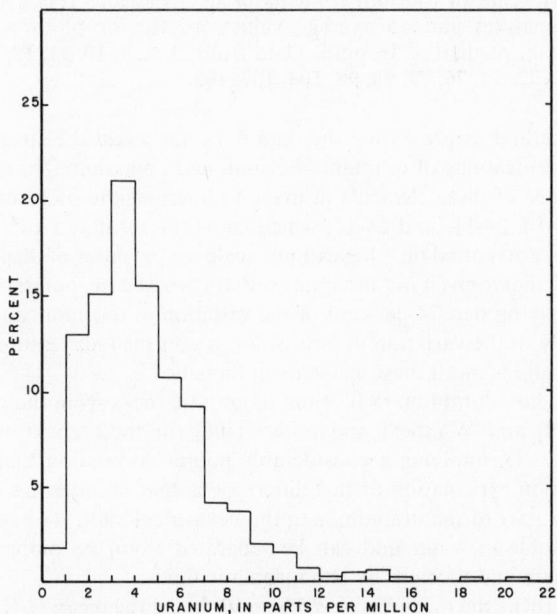

Figure 24-8. Histogram of uranium contents of silicic igneous rocks. Plot represents 242 individual analyses and 3 average values for volcanic rocks, and 194 individual analyses and 96 average values for plutonic and hypabyssal rocks. Mean uranium = 4.7 ppm, median = 3.9 ppm. Data from: **1, 2, 7, 8, 10, 11, 18, 20, 24, 25, 27, 29, 33, 34, 36, 39, 40, 41, 44, 47, 50, 51, 53, 54, 55, 56, 60, 63, 64, 65, 66, 67, 68, 72, 73, 74, 76, 77, 89, 90, 98, 101, 102, 104, 107, 108**

533

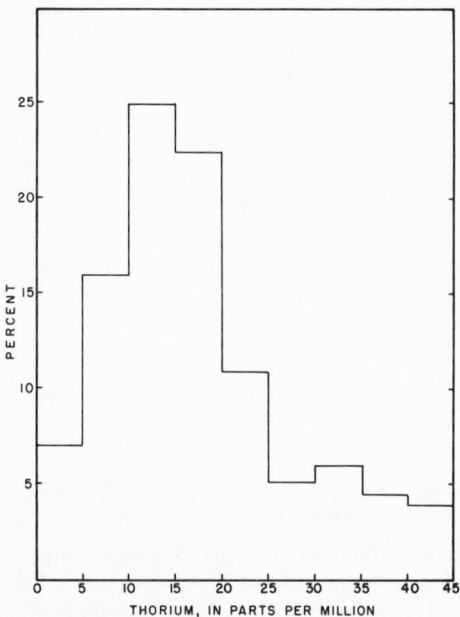

Figure 24-9. Histogram of thorium contents of silicic igneous rocks. Plot represents 111 individual analyses and 45 average values mostly for plutonic rocks. Mean thorium = 20 ppm, median = 16 ppm. Data from: **1, 2, 7, 10, 11, 18, 33, 34, 41, 47, 56, 60, 64, 65, 67, 72, 74, 76, 77, 90, 98, 104, 107, 108**

The above method of presenting the data does not reveal the strong correlations between the concentrations of uranium, thorium, and potassium. An idea of the geochemical coherence of these elements in mafic to intermediate rocks can be obtained from Figures 24-10, 24-11, and 24-12, which show the results of two recent studies [**47, 48**]. The data are plotted on a logarithmic scale for purposes of display. The linear correlation coefficient is given in the captions. In the worst case, potassium *vs* thorium, it equals .86, implying that 74 per cent of the variation in thorium concentration can be related directly to the variation in potassium. A conspicuous feature of the data is the low concentrations of all these elements in tholeiites.

Figure 24-13 shows uranium *vs* thorium in granitic rocks from the data of Rogers and Ragland [**90**] and Whitfield and others [**108**]. In these rocks the correlation coefficient is only .73, implying a considerably poorer correlation than in the mafic rocks. The common explanation of this difference is that granites are more oxidized than basalts, and part of the uranium is in the hexavalent state. The resulting uranyl ion is highly soluble in water and can be separated from the more tightly bound tetravalent uranium and thorium by late magmatic fluids.

In "granitic" rocks the mean Th/K is 5.0×10^{-4}, and the mean U/K is 1.3×10^{-4}. In basaltic rocks the ratios are 2.8×10^{-4} and $.6 \times 10^{-4}$ respectively [**47**].

URANIUM, THORIUM, AND POTASSIUM IN SEDIMENTARY ROCKS AND SEDIMENTS

The coherence between uranium and thorium is to some extent destroyed in the sedimentary cycle. Uranium is partially oxidized to the hexavalent state, producing the

TABLE 24-5. URANIUM AND THORIUM IN THE MINERALS OF IGNEOUS ROCKS [4]

Mineral	U, ppm	Th, ppm
Accessory minerals		
Allanite {accessory	30–700	500–5,000
Allanite {pegmatite	?–100	1,000–20,000
Apatite {accessory	5–150	20–150
Apatite {coarse aggregate	10–50 (?)	50–250 (?)
Epidote	20–50	50–500
Ilmenite	1–50	
Magnetite	1–30	.3–20
Monazite	500–3,000	25,000–200,000
Sphene	100–700	100–600
Xenotime	500–35,000	low
Zircon {accessory	300–3,000	100–2,500
Zircon {pegmatite	100–6,000	50–4,000
Major minerals		
Biotite	1–40	.5–50
Hornblende	1–30	5–50
Potassium feldspar	.2–3	3–7
Muscovite	2–8	
Olivine	.01	low
Plagioclase	.2–5	.5–3
Pyroxene	.01–40	2–25
Quartz {	.1–5	.5–6
Quartz {beach sands	.7	2.0

TABLE 24-6. POTASSIUM IN IGNEOUS ROCKS

Plutonic rocks	K (per cent)	Ref.	Volcanic rocks	K (per cent)	Ref.
Olivine gabbro	.33	81	Tholeiitic basalt	.28	62, 48
Gabbro	.46	81	High-alumina basalt	.32	62
Quartz gabbro	1.31	81	Alkali olivine basalt	.94	62
Diorite	1.10	81	Quartz basalt	1.16	81
Granodiorite	2.55	81	Nepheline basalt	1.72	81
Monzonite	3.89	81	Andesite	.92	81
Alkali granite	4.26	81	Dacite	1.16	81
Nepheline syenite	4.43	81	Rhyodacite	2.50	81
Alkali syenite	4.91	81	Alkali rhyolite	3.93	81
			Trachyandesite	3.68	81
			Alkali trachyte	4.59	81

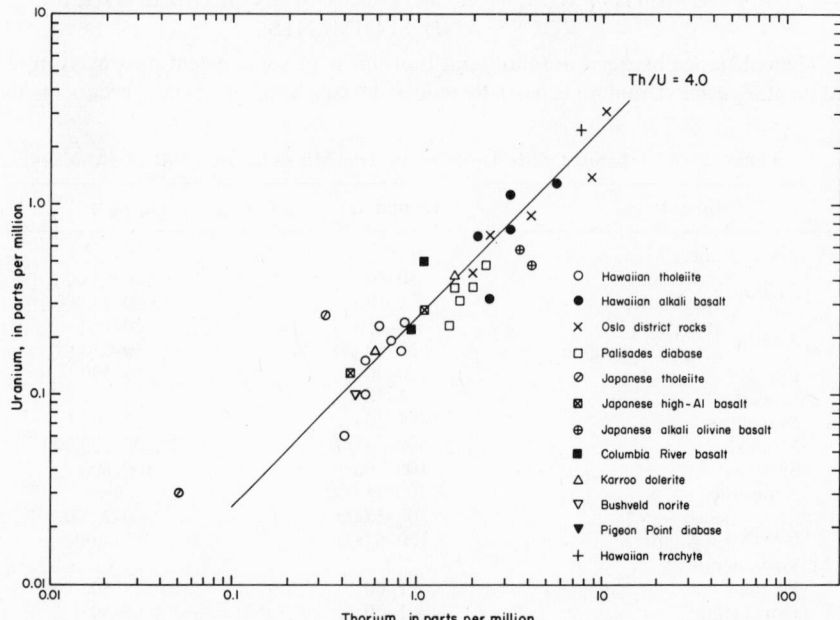

Figure 24-10. Uranium *vs* thorium in mafic and intermediate rocks. The correlation coefficient is .93. Data from: **47, 48**

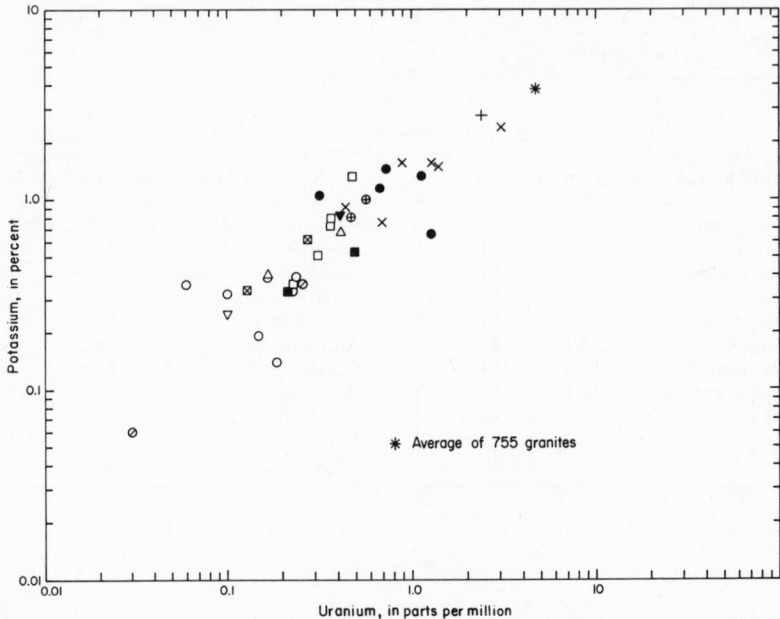

Figure 24-11. Potassium *vs* uranium in mafic and intermediate rocks. Symbols as in Figure 24-10. The correlation coefficient is .89. Data from: **47, 48**.

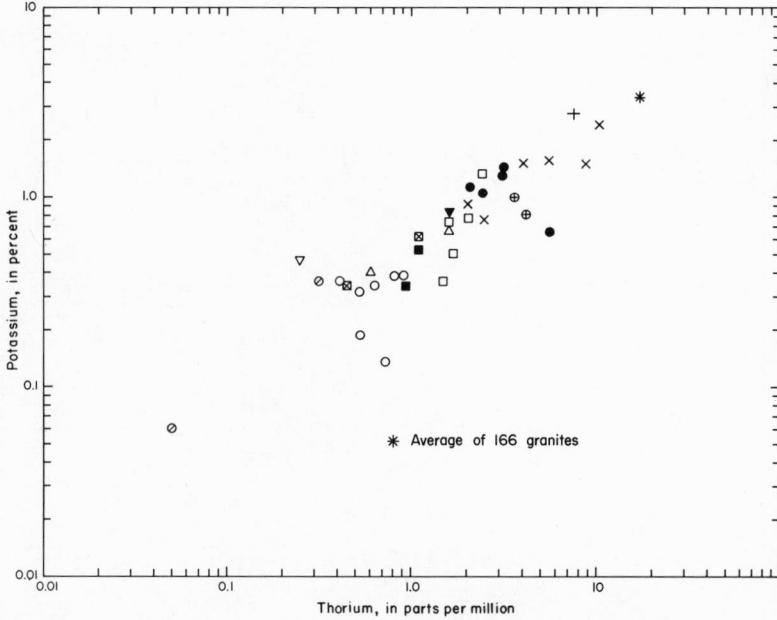

Figure 24-12. Potassium *vs* thorium in mafic and intermediate rocks. Symbols as in Figure 24-10. The correlation coefficient is .86. Data from: **47, 48**.

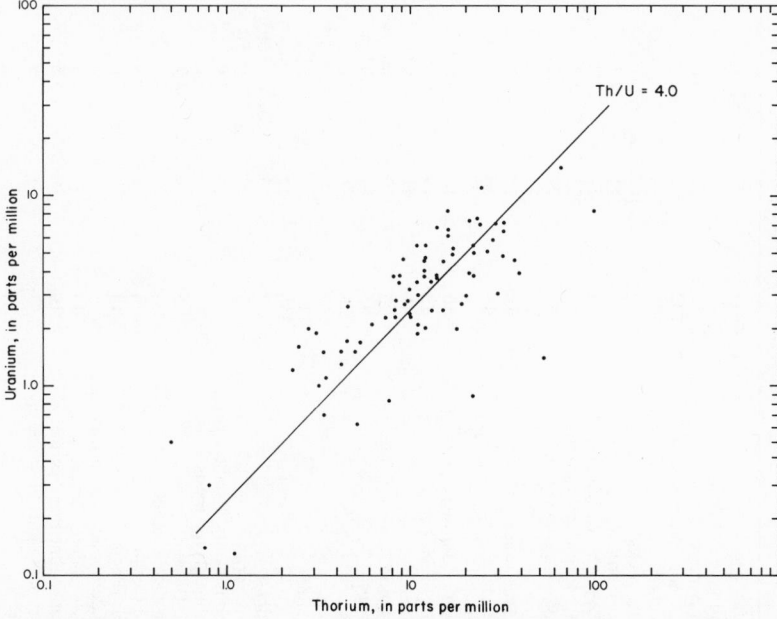

Figure 24-13. Uranium *vs* thorium in granitic rocks. The correlation coefficient is .73. Data from: **90, 108**

TABLE 24-7. URANIUM AND THORIUM IN SEDIMENTARY ROCKS, SEDIMENTS, AND SEA WATER

	Number of samples	Number of determinations	U, ppm		Th, ppm		Th/U		Ref.
			Mean	Range	Mean	Range	Mean	Range	
"Common" shales*	4847	75	3.7 ± .5	1–13	12 ± 1	2–47	3.8	1–12	4
Gray and green shales, North America	52	52	3.2	1.2–12	13.1	.1–47	4.9	.1–11	6
Mancos Shale, Western U.S.	102	102	3.7	.9–12	10.2	5.3–23	3.1	.5–10	86
Russian clays	4795	178	4.1	3.2–5.9	11	7.7–14.2	2.7	2.0–4.1	13
Carbonate rocks*	6045	103	2.2 ± .1	.1–9	1.7 ± .7	.1–7	1.0	.1–6.5	4
Russian carbonates	5475	128	2.1	..	2.4	..	1.1	..	13
North American carbonates	54	54	2.2	.1–18	1.7	0–6.5	1.2	..	6
North American carbonates	516	25	2.2	.65–8.8	1.1	0–2.8	.7	..	6
California limestones	27	27	1.29	.03–4.87	..	..	.8†	..	109
	21	21	..	..	1.08	.07–10.78			83
Florida limestones	10	10	2	.5–6	1.5	.2–4	.75†	..	4
Orthoquartzites	18	18	.45 ± .05	.2–6	1.7 ± .1	.7–2	4.0	1.8–5.8	5
Beach sands (U.S.)									
W. Gulf of Mexico	10	10	.80	..	2.78	..	..	..	
E. Gulf of Mexico	19	19	.41	..	.86	..	..	..	
S. Atlantic	41	41	3.97	..	11.27	..	..	..	
N. Atlantic	13	13	.80	..	2.07	..	..	..	
Average	83	83	2.97	..	6.42	..	..	..	
Bauxites	26	26	8.0	3–27	42	8–132	6.9	1.5–22	4
Bentonites	69	69	5.0	1–21	24	6–44	5.8	1.0–21	4
Black shales	350	..	8	3–250	..	..	..	.07–12	100
Halite rocks	7	7	.013 ± .005	14–80	<.2	all <.2	..	..	4
Anhydrite rocks	3	3	.37 ± .10	.25–.43	<.2	all <.2	..	..	78
Terrigenous sands, Pacific Ocean	5	5	3.0	1.0–4.8	1.2	1.0–1.6	.4†	.2–1.6	78
Terrigenous clayey muds, Pacific Ocean	6	6	2.7	1.2–3.6	4.8	2.2–6.6	1.8†	.9–4.3	12
Biogenic clayey muds, Pacific Ocean	6	6	3.4	1.5–5.0	2.5	1.4–3.6	.7†	.3–2.4	12
Red clays, Pacific Ocean	13	13	4.0	1.8–8.0	6.8	1.4–15.0	1.7†	.3–4.2	12
North Atlantic and Caribbean deep-sea clays (3 cores)	18	18	2.1	..	11	..	5.2†	..	91
Baltic sea sediments (3 cores)	10	10	5.5	2.2–10.3	..	..	..	..	58
Black Sea sediments (4 cores)	44	44	3.9	.3–12.0	7.3	.6–14.0	3.3	.2–11	99, 111
Sea water	..	..	..	.001–.003	..	$4 \times 10^{-7} - 5 \times 10^{-6}$	..	..	103
	..	..	..	..	..		..	..	79

* Grand averages which include data for these types of rock from other entries listed in this table
† Mean Th/Mean U. Other entries in this column are means of individual Th/U values.

TABLE 24-8. POTASSIUM IN SEDIMENTARY ROCKS AND SEDIMENTS

	Number of determinations	K per cent	Ref.
Shales	..	2.7	23
Sandstones	..	..	75
Quartzites	57	.93	
Arkoses	27	2.3	
Graywackes (High rank)	41	1.4	
Graywackes (Low rank)	43	1.4	
Weighted average	168	1.4	
Limestones	345	.27	23
Deep-sea clays (including interstitial salt)	..	2.5	37
Beach sands (U.S.)	..	..	5
West Gulf of Mexico	10	1.2	
East Gulf of Mexico	19	.046	
South Atlantic	41	.27	
North Atlantic	13	.30	
Average	83	.33	
Modern carbonate shells	..	.0069	110

soluble uranyl ion. Thorium tends to be carried by suspended matter rather than in solution, and any dissolved thorium is soon fixed by clays and secondary resistates. As a result the Th/U ratio varies widely in sediments, depending in large part on whether deposition takes place in an oxidizing or a reducing environment.

Data for uranium and thorium in sedimentary rocks and sediments are given in Table 24-7. Two main types of sedimentary rocks not listed are arkoses and graywackes. To a first approximation the arkoses may be represented by the orthoquartzites or the beach sands, and the graywackes and impure sandstone by some mixture of orthoquartzite and shale. Graywacke might be represented by 1 part orthoquartzite and 2 parts shale, subgraywacke by 4 parts orthoquartzite and 1 part shale. More data will be necessary before a meaningful average of the uranium and thorium contents of sandstones as a group can be given. Corals, oölites, and aragonitic muds have about 2 ppm uranium, and contemporary calcareous tests except corals have about .02 ppm uranium. All contemporary carbonate deposits contain less than .2 ppm thorium.

Table 24-8 gives concentrations of potassium in various sedimentary rocks and sediments. On the basis of a 10 per cent clay contribution and including interstitial sea water the potassium content of "typical Globigerina ooze" is estimated to be .29 per cent.

In rocks such as evaporites and impure sandstones, the bulk of the radioactive elements may be contained in clay impurities, and a strong correlation between the concentrations of uranium, thorium, and potassium may exist. If appreciable potassium is contributed by feldspar, or evaporite minerals such as sylvite, the correlation would be largely destroyed.

URANIUM, THORIUM, AND POTASSIUM IN METAMORPHIC ROCKS

Data on the distribution of radioactive elements in metamorphic rocks are insufficient to merit tabulation. It appears that metamorphism does not seriously alter the concentrations of these elements at the lower grades, so that the concentrations expected in the original sedimentary or igneous rocks can be used for the metamorphosed equivalents. At higher grades, changes in composition may take place, and there is evidence that rocks in the granulite facies are impoverished in uranium and thorium. The basement gneisses which probably make up much of the "granitic" crustal layer of seismologists may be significantly less radioactive than granites, and estimates of crustal abundances based on some combination of data for granites and basalts may give too large a value for the radioactivity of the crust [112].

REFERENCES FOR SECTION 24

1. Abdulkabirova, Akad. Nauk Kazakn.SSSR Izvest. Ser. Geol. **2**, 78, 1958
2. Abramovich, Geochemistry **4**, 442, 1959
3. Adams, Geochim. Cosmochim. Acta **8**, 74, 1955
4. Adams, Osmond, and Rogers, Physics and chemistry of the Earth, Pergamon Press, London **3**, 298, 1959
5. Adams, Mahdavi, and Rogers, Geol. Soc. America Spec. Paper **76**, 2, 1964
6. Adams and Weaver, Am. Assoc. Pet. Geol. Bull. **42**, 387, 1958
7. Afanas'yev and Tseytlin, Akad. Nauk SSSR Izvest., Ser. Geol. **3**, 12, 1958
8. Asayama, Kyoto Tech. Univ., Faculty Indus. Arts, Mem. **2B**, 53, 1953
9. —— Kyoto Tech. Univ., Faculty Indus. Arts, Mem. **3B**, 25, 1954
10. Atrashenok and Krylov, Radiokhimii **5-2**, 170, 1963
11. Baranov and Tu, Geochemistry **12**, 1180, 1961
12. Baranov and Khristianova, Khim. zemnoi. Kory, Akad. Nauk SSSR, Tr. Geokhim. Konf. **1**, 401, 1963
13. Baranov, Ronov, and Kunoshova, Geochemistry **3**, 226, 1956
14. Bate and Huizenga, Geochim. Cosmochim. Acta **27**, 345, 1963
15. Bate, Huizenga, and Potratz, Science **126**, 612, 1957
16. —— Geochim. Cosmochim. Acta **16**, 88, 1959
17. Bate, Potratz, and Huizenga, Geochim. Cosmochim. Acta **14**, 118, 1958
18. Begemann, Helv. Phys. Acta **27**, 451, 1954
19. Butler, U.S. Geol. Survey Prof. Paper 424-B, B67, 1961
20. Chentsov, Petrog., Mineral., i Geokhim., Trudy **28**, 142, 1959
21. Cherry, Nature **195**, 1184, 1962
22. Cherry and Adams, Geochim. Cosmochim. Acta **27**, 1089, 1963
23. Clarke, U.S. Geol. Survey Bull. **770**, 841, 1924
24. Coates, U.S. Geol. Survey Prof. Paper **300**, 75, 1956
25. Coulomb, Publ. Comm. a l'energie Atomique, Rapport CEA, 1173, 85 p., 1959
26. Davis, Am. Jour. Sci. **248**, 107, 1950
27. Davis and Hess, Am. Jour. Sci. **247-12**, 856, 1949
28. Davis, Aldrich, Tilton, Wetherill, and Jeffery, Carnegie Inst. Wash. Year Book **55**, 167, 1956
29. K. R. Dawson, unpublished
30. Ebert, König, and Wänke, Zeit. Naturforsch **12a**, 763, 1957
31. Edwards, Geochim. Cosmochim. Acta **8**, 285, 1955
32. Edwards and Urey, Geochim. Cosmochim. Acta **7**, 154, 1955
33. Evans and Goodman, Geol. Soc. America Bull. **52**, 459, 1941
34. Filippov and Komlev, Geochemistry **5**, 535, 1959
35. Fireman and Fisher, Nature **192**, 644, 1961
36. Gast, Jour. Geophys. Res. **65**, 1287, 1960
37. Goldberg and Arrhenius, Geochim. Cosmochim. Acta **13**, 183, 1958
38. Goles and Anders, Geochim. Cosmochim. Acta **26**, 723, 1962
39. Gottfried, U.S. Geol. Survey, TEI 750, 95, 1958
40. —— U.S. Geol. Survey, TEI 751, 102, 1959
41. —— U.S. Geol. Survey Prof. Paper 450-E, 85, 1963
42. Gottfried, D., unpublished
43. Hamaguchi, Reed, and Turkevich, Geochim. Cosmochim. Acta **12**, 337, 1957
44. Hamilton, Medd. Grønland **162**, 34 p., 1959
45. —— Medd. Grønland **162**, 38 p., 1960
46. Heier, Geochim. Cosmochim. Acta **27**, 849, 1963
47. Heier and Rogers, Geochim. Cosmochim. Acta **27**, 137, 1963
48. Heier, McDougall, and Adams, Nature **201**, 254, 1964
49. Hernegger and Wänke, Zeit. Naturforsch **12a**, 795, 1957
50. Hida, Shimazu, and Igarashi, Japan Geol. Survey Rept. 190, 78, 1961
51. Hussein, Sciences de la Terre **7**, 7, 1961
52. Hurley, Geol. Soc. America Bull. **67**, 395, 1956

53. Igarashi and Shimazu, Japan Geol. Survey Rept. 190, 43, 1961
54. Ishihara, Japan Geol. Survey Rept. 190, 92, 1961
55. Jurain, Sciences de la Terre, Mémoire 1, 352 p., 1962
56. Keevil, Am. Jour. Sci. 242, 309, 1944
57. Kirsten, Krankowsky, and Zähringer, Geochim. Cosmochim. Acta 27, 13, 1963
58. Koczy, Tomic, and Hecht, Geochim. Cosmochim. Acta 11, 86, 1957
59. König and Wänke, Zeit. Naturforsch 14a, 866, 1959
60. Krylov, Geochemistry 3, 240, 1958
61. —— Akad. Nauk SSSR, Izvest. Ser. geol. 11, 8, 1959
62. Kuno, Jour. Petrol. 1, 121, 1960
63. Larsen, U.S. Geol. Survey TEI-700, 249, 1957
64. Larsen and Gottfried, Am. Jour. Sci., Bradley Vol., 151, 1960
65. —— U.S. Geol. Survey Bull. 1070-c, 63, 1961
66. Larsen, Gottfried, and Molloy, U.N. 2d Int. Conf. on the Peaceful Uses of Atomic Energy 2, 509, 1958
67. Leible, Zeit. Erzbergbau u. Metallhuttenw. 12, 234, 1959
68. Leonova, Geochemistry 10, 999, 1961
69. Lovering and Morgan, Nature 199, 479, 1963
70. —— Nature 197, 138, 1963
71. —— Jour. Geophys. Res. 69, 1979, 1964
72. Lyons, U.S. Geol. Survey Prof. Paper 424-B, B69, 1961
73. Marinelli, Soc. toscana Sci. Nat. 68, 117, 1962
74. Meliksetyan, Izvest. Akad. Nauk Armyan SSR, Geol. i Geograf. Nauk 14, 21, 1961
75. Middleton, Geol. Soc. America Bull. 71, 1011, 1960
76. Mineyeva and Aver'yanova, Sovetskia Geologia 5, 83, 1962
77. Monich, Acad. Sci. USSR 33, 262, 1941
78. Moore, U.S. Geol. Survey Open-File report, Menlo Park, Calif., 1957
79. Moore and Sackett, Am. Geophys. Union Trans. 45, 119, 1964
80. Morgan and Lovering, Jour. Geophys. Res. 69-10, 1989, 1964
81. Nockolds, Geol. Soc. America Bull. 65, 1007, 1954
82. Nozawa and Takahashi, Japan Geol. Survey Bull. 11, 1, 1960
83. Osmond, in The natural radiation environment, U. of Chicago Press, in press 1965
84. Patterson, Brown, Tilton, and Inghram, Phys. Rev. 92, 1234, 1953
85. Peterman, unpublished
86. Pliler and Adams, Geochim. Cosmochim. Acta 26, 1115, 1962
87. Reed, Hamaguchi, and Turkevich, Geochim. Cosmochim. Acta 13, 248, 1958
88. Reed, Kigoshi, and Turkevich, Geochim. Cosmochim. Acta 20, 122, 1960
89. Rekharskii and Krutetskaya, Akad. Nauk SSSR Izvest. Ser. Geol. 7, 45, 1961
90. Rogers and Ragland, Geochim. Cosmochim. Acta 25, 99, 1961
91. Rosholt, Emiliani, Geiss, Koczy, and Wangersky, Jour. Geol. 69, 162, 1961
92. Rowe, Van Dilla, and Anderson, Geochim. Cosmochim. Acta 27-10, 983, 1963a
93. Senftle and Keevil, Am. Geophys. Union Trans. 28, 733, 1947
94. Shavrova, Akad. Nauk SSSR, Lab. Vulkanol., Byull. Vulkanol. Stantsii 24, 65, 1956
95. —— Akad. Nauk SSSR, Lab. Vulkanol., Byull. Vulkanol. Stantsii 27, 51, 1958
96. —— Akad. Nauk SSSR, Lab. Vulkanol., Byull. Vulkanol. Stantsii 31, 28, 1961
97. —— Akad. Nauk SSSR, Byull. Vulkanol, Stantsii 33, 67, 1962
98. Smyslov, Geochemistry 3, 248, 1958
99. Starik, Kuznetsov, Nikolaev, Legin, Lazarev, Grashenko, and Kolyadin, Dokl. Akad. Nauk SSSR 129, 1142, 1959
100. Swanson, U.S. Geol. Survey Prof. Paper 356-C, 1961
101. Tauson, Geochemistry 3, 236, 1956
102. Tauson, Zlobin, and Leonova, Geochemistry 7, 653, 1956
103. Thurber, Am. Geophys. Union Trans. 45, 119, 1964
104. Tilton, Geol. Soc. America Bull. 66, 1131, 1955
105. —— Geochim. Cosmochim. Acta 14, 323, 1958
106. Tilton and Reed, Earth science and meteoritics, Amsterdam, North-Holland Pub. 31, 1963
107. Turovskii, Geochemistry 2, 199, 1957
108. Whitfield, Rogers, and Adams, Geochim. Cosmochim. Acta 17, 248, 1959
109. Wollenberg and Smith, Univ. Calif., UCRL-10475, 29, 1962
110. Zartman, Wasserburg, and Reynolds, Jour. Geophys. Res. 66, 277, 1961
111. Starik, Nikolaev, Kuznetsov, and Legin, Dokl. Akad. Nauk SSSR 39, 1456, 1961
112. Heier and Adams, Geochim. Cosmochim. Acta 29, 53, 1965

SECTION 25

MAGNETIC PROPERTIES OF ROCKS AND MINERALS*

by D. H. LINDSLEY, G. E. ANDREASEN, AND J. R. BALSLEY

CONTENTS

ILLUSTRATIONS

* Publication authorized by the Director, U.S. Geological Survey

Handbook of Physical Constants—*Revised Edition*
THE GEOLOGICAL SOCIETY OF AMERICA MEMOIR 97, 1966

The magnetism of rocks is the vector sum of *induced* magnetization—dependent on an external field—and *remanent* magnetization—independent of any external field. The magnetization induced by an external field is a function of the magnetic susceptibility of the rock.

MAGNETIC SUSCEPTIBILITY OF ROCKS AND MINERALS

DEFINITIONS: The magnetic susceptibility, k, of a substance is the ratio of intensity of magnetization, I, to the magnetizing field, H; $k = I/H$, defined with respect to unit volume. The specific susceptibility, χ, and specific intensity of magnetization, J, are defined with respect to unit mass.

Most minerals are paramagnetic or diamagnetic with positive or negative susceptibilities of the order of 10^{-6} c.g.s units. The susceptibility of such minerals is essentially independent of the applied field.

For ferromagnetic materials like iron and nickel, the intensity of magnetization reaches a maximum value within a finite strength of applied field; the susceptibility approaches or exceeds unity. There is for each such substance a characteristic temperature, the Curie point, at and above which the high susceptibility vanishes. The ferromagnetic properties of rocks, which are of prime interest from a geophysical standpoint, are due to the presence of a small percentage of ferrimagnetic minerals. Ferrimagnetism is distinguished from ferromagnetism (all atomic spin moments parallel) and antiferromagnetism (two equal but opposite sets of spins with zero net moment) in that there are two opposite but unequal sets of spins. For example, in magnetite the spins of $8Fe^{+3}$ ions per unit cell in the tetrahedral positions are antiparallel to the spins of $8Fe^{+3}$ and $8Fe^{+2}$ ions in octahedral positions. The moments contributed by the trivalent ions are virtually self-cancelling, leaving a resultant moment contributed by the Fe^{+2} ions. This magnetism should properly be called ferrimagnetism, but its properties are similar to those of ferromagnetism, and the latter term is frequently applied in a broad sense to include ferrimagnetism.

FACTORS INFLUENCING THE MAGNETIC SUSCEPTIBILITY OF ROCKS

The magnetic susceptibility of a rock varies with the strength of the inducing field, the type, composition, and amount of ferrimagnetic minerals, grain size, fabric, temperature, and pressure.

STRENGTH OF INDUCING FIELD: Figure 25-1 shows a magnetization curve typical of a lava, illustrating the magnetic hysteresis characteristic of ferromagnetic and ferrimagnetic minerals. Because susceptibility depends on field strength for ferrimagnetic minerals, only susceptibilities measured in weak fields (equivalent to the earth's) are of importance from the standpoint of exploration geophysics.

TYPE AND COMPOSITION OF FERRIMAGNETIC MINERALS: The main ferrimagnetic minerals of rocks are the iron-titanium oxides, magnetite (Fe_3O_4) being the most important because of its high susceptibility and common occurrence. Important solid solution series in this group are the magnetite-ulvöspinel (Fe_2TiO_4) and hematite-ilmenite (αFe_2O_3–$FeTiO_3$) binaries, which form complete solid solutions above 600° and 950° respectively [52, 10]. Perfect crystals of the hematite-ilmenite series should have two antiparallel sublattices and thus be antiferromagnetic. Ilmenite is indeed antiferromagnetic, with a Néel point of 68° K [5]. However, some hematite and hematite-ilmenite solid solutions are ferrimagnetic (or antiferromagnetic with a parasitic ferromagnetism), with variations in magnetic properties probably due to varying degrees of ordering of Fe and Ti ions [50]. The Curie temperatures of much of the hematite-ilmenite series depend linearly on the mole fraction x_{ilm} of $FeTiO_3$ in solid solution:

$$\theta \,°K = 943 - 1143x_{ilm}, \qquad 0 \leq x_{ilm} \leq .8 \,[34].$$

The Curie points of quenched samples of the magnetite-ulvöspinel binary can be expressed by:

$$\theta \,°K = 851 - 580x_{usp} - 150x_{usp}^2, \qquad 0 \leq x_{usp} \leq 1 \,[3],$$

where x_{usp} is the mole fraction of Fe_2TiO_4. These data show a Curie point of 121° K for pure Fe_2TiO_4, as opposed to the theoretical value of 0° K for ulvöspinel with a

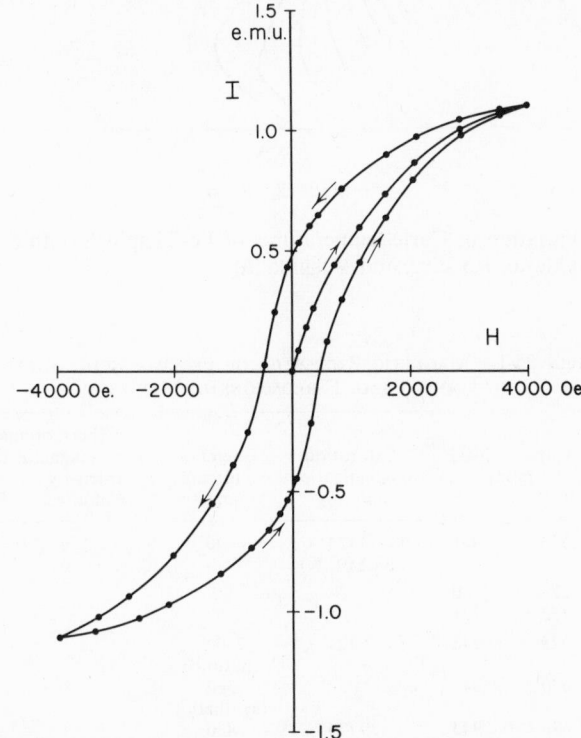

Figure 25-1. Magnetization curve typical of a lava. Sample was not completely saturated at 4000 oe. *After* Nagata [33]

perfect inverse spinel structure; apparently some disordered structure was retained upon quenching. Cation-deficient Fe–Ti spinels deviating in composition from the magnetite-ulvöspinel join toward the hematite-ilmenite join can be made by oxidizing magnetite-ulvöspinel solid solutions, and are found in many lavas. Curie point data for these spinels are shown in Figure 25-2. A special case of this oxidation process is the conversion of magnetite to maghemite (γFe_2O_3). Many of these cation-deficient spinels are strongly ferrimagnetic.

Below 600° or 950° respectively, a single phase of intermediate composition in the magnetite-ulvöspinel or hematite-ilmenite series may exsolve into two phases closer in composition to the end members [52, 10]. Likewise, magnetite-ilmenite intergrowths may form by breakdown of cation-deficient Fe–Ti spinels or by direct oxidation of

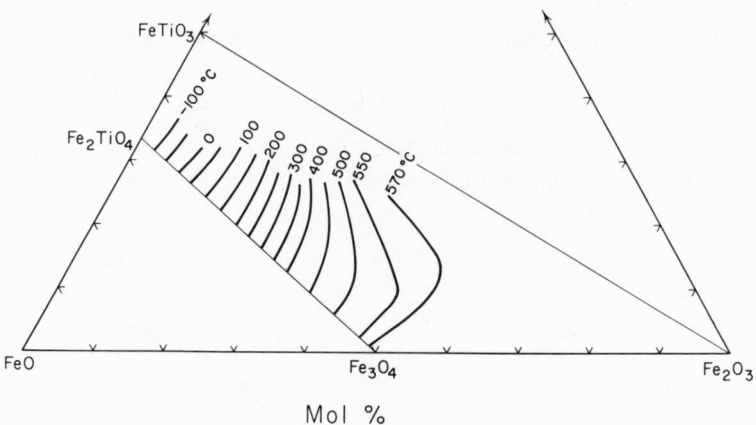

Mol %

Figure 25-2. Variation of Curie temperatures of Fe–Ti spinels with composition (*see* text). *After* Akimoto, Katsura, and Yoshida [3]

TABLE 25-1. MAGNETIC PROPERTIES OF FERRIMAGNETIC MINERALS AND THREE FERROMAGNETIC METALS

Mineral	Curie or Néel point θ °C	θ °K	Saturation magnetization e.m.u./g	Coercive force oe.	Thermoremanent magnetization Intensity e.m.u./cc	External field in oe.	Ref.
Magnetite Fe_3O_4	578	851	92–93 (24° C) 98.2 (0° K)	20	..	..	33
Ulvöspinel Fe_2TiO_4	−273 −152	0 121	.. ..	.. ..	.. ..	.. ..	33 3
Hematite Fe_2O_3	675	948	.5 (24° C)	7600 (natural)	..	..	33
	670	943	..	360 (synthetic)	.34	2.0	50
	670	943	.39 (24° C)	430 (synthetic)	..	..	34
Ilmenite $FeTiO_3$	−205	68	..	..	..	..	5
Hem_{40}–Ilm_{60}	230	503	20 (24° C)	117 (synthetic)	−1.94 (self-reversing)	2.0	50
Maghemite Fe_2O_3	675	948	83.5 (24° C)	..	..	..	33
Pyrrhotite $Fe_{1-x}S$	300–325	573–598	62 (24° C) ..	15–20 ..	.. .04–.23	.. .5	33 50
Iron	770	1043	21,500	1.8	..	..	8
Nickel bar powder	358	631	6,100	.7	.. 3.0 3.8	.. .5 2.0	8 50 50
Cobalt	1120	1393	17,900	10	..	..	8

magnetite-ulvöspinel solid solutions [31]. Thus it is possible by partial exsolution to convert a single magnetic mineral into two separate magnetic phases whose Curie points bracket that of the original mineral.

The iron-titanium oxides in rocks are seldom pure; most contain small amounts of magnesium, manganese, aluminum, vanadium, and chromium. The main magnetic effect of these minor components is a lowering of the Curie points; for example, the effect of Al as $FeAl_2O_4$ (hercynite) on the Curie point of magnetite is:

$$\theta \; °K = 851 - 480x_{hc}, \qquad 0 \le x_{hc} \le .3,$$

where x_{hc} is the mole fraction of hercynite [38].

Pyrrhotite ($Fe_{1-x}S$) is ferrimagnetic, but is present in very small amounts in most rocks, and thus contributes little to their magnetic properties.

Significant magnetic data on ferrimagnetic minerals and three ferromagnetic metals are given in Table 25-1.

AMOUNT OF FERRIMAGNETIC MINERALS: The magnetic susceptibility of most rocks is proportional to magnetite content. Figure 25-3 shows the relationship between susceptibilities of a variety of rock types and their magnetite content; the values for magnetite content for the Adirondack rocks are calculated from chemical analyses of separated magnetic oxides, and are probably close to the modal magnetite content of the rocks. It is noteworthy that some rocks with very low contents of ferrimagnetic minerals may have susceptibilities as low as 10^{-6} c.g.s units; the true ferrimagnetic character of these latter rocks is shown by detection of a Curie point and a hysteresis curve [33].

Because magnetite is an accessory mineral (<10 per cent) in most rocks, its content can vary significantly from a magnetic viewpoint without affecting the rock classification. It is therefore impossible to make a rigorous correlation between susceptibility and rock type. In general, however, mafic igneous rocks have higher susceptibilities than do more silicic igneous rocks (Table 25-2). The data in Table 25-2 were compiled by P. M. Hurley for the first edition of this Handbook.

GRAIN SIZE OF FERRIMAGNETIC MINERALS: Several investigators [2, 14, 19, 30, 37] have shown that the magnetic susceptibility of ferrimagnetic minerals is related to grain size. Susceptibility decreases with decreasing grain size (Figure 25-4). Exsolution of ilmenite lamellae from a titaniferous magnetite may subdivide the host magnetite so that the effective grain size and hence susceptibility are decreased.

FABRIC: In general rocks with anisotropic structures show anisotropic magnetic susceptibilities. The long and intermediate dimensional axes of ferrimagnetic minerals tend to lie in the bedding planes of detrital sediments and in the foliation planes of metamorphic rocks; this orientation results in a plane of maximum susceptibility parallel to these planar structures [4, 20, 22]. Hargraves [18] found a distinct plane of maximum susceptibility parallel to the crystallographic basal plane in coarse-grained hemo-ilmenite from Allard Lake, Quebec. In some metamorphic rocks there is also a direction of maximum susceptibility parallel to lineation. The degree of susceptibility anisotropy of banded Adirondack rocks is illustrated by the extent of the vertical lines in Figure 25-3.

TEMPERATURE: The relationship of magnetic susceptibility to temperature has been determined for many rocks and ferrimagnetic minerals. Plots of susceptibility-temperature relationships have several distinctive forms, which are figured and reviewed by Nagata [33]. For many igneous and metamorphic rocks, and most sedimentary rocks, susceptibility first changes slowly with increasing temperature, and then decreases rapidly to zero as the Curie point is approached. In the absence of physical or chemical changes attendant upon heating the sample, the curve is reversible upon cooling.

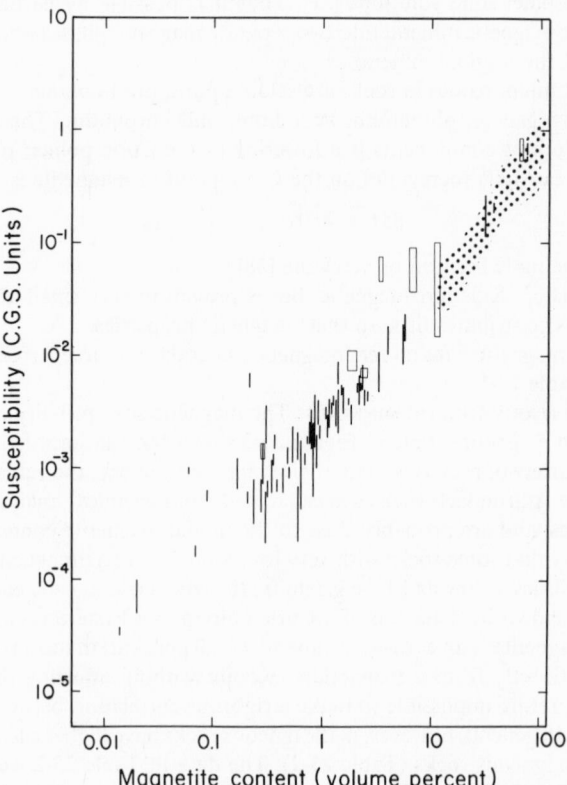

Magnetite content (volume percent)

Figure 25-3. Relationship between magnetic susceptibility and magnetite content for a variety of rocks and ores. Vertical lines and boxes from Balsley and Buddington [4]; stippled area shows range of data from Werner [53]. Vertical extent of lines shows susceptibility anisotropy in individual specimens. Width of boxes shows variation in magnetite content for two or more analyzed specimens from the same rock unit

TABLE 25-2.   RANGE OF MAGNETIC SUSCEPTIBILITY IN MAJOR ROCK TYPES
Summary of literature under references **6, 7, 12, 17, 27, 28, 29, 32, 39, 40, 41, 42, 43, 46, 47, 49, 54**
Susceptibility in cgs emu per cm³

Rock type	Number of samples	Percentage of samples with susceptibility			
		Less than 10^{-4}	Between 10^{-4} and 10^{-3}	Between 10^{-3} and 4×10^{-3}	Greater than 4×10^{-3}
Mafic effusive rocks	97	5	29	47	19
Mafic plutonic rocks	53	24	27	28	21
Granites and allied rocks	74	60	23	16	1
Gneisses, schists, slates	45	71	22	7	0
Sedimentary rocks	48	73	19	4	4

Irreversibility may be caused by such changes as the oxidation of magnetite or the inversion of maghemite to hematite. Rocks containing two or more ferrimagnetic minerals typically display composite susceptibility-temperature curves, showing a break in slope at each Curie point [25]. In cases where two ferrimagnetic minerals are in intimate contact (as in exsolution textures), heating of the sample may homogenize the two phases, and the cooling curve may be a simple smooth curve, usually showing a Curie point intermediate between those of the original minerals.

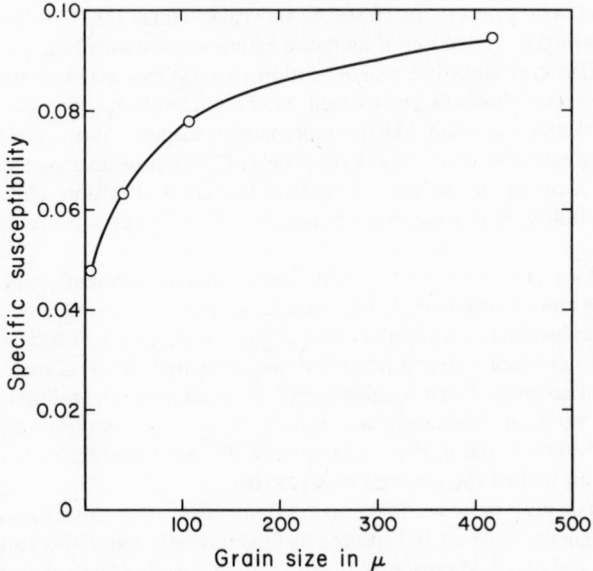

Figure 25-4. Specific susceptibility of rock-forming titaniferous magnetites as a function of particle size. External field 1.35 oe. *After* Nagata [33]

PRESSURE: Kalashnikov and Kaptitsa [24] have shown that the magnetic susceptibility of rocks varies in response to mechanical stress. In general, compression of rock specimens produces a decrease in susceptibility measured in a field parallel to the direction of stress. Susceptibility measured perpendicular to the compression axis may increase or decrease with compression. These results suggest that the susceptibility measured from a core sample from a drill hole may differ from that of the sample in place because of differences in mechanical stress.

Adams and Green [1] found no significant difference in the Curie point of magnetite at 1 atm. and 2000 atm. The data of Patrick [36] on metals and alloys substantiates the conclusion that the change of Curie point with pressure is nil or very slightly negative up to 9000 bars.

REMANENT MAGNETIZATION OF ROCKS

The remanent (permanent) magnetization of rocks depends on the quantity and composition of ferrimagnetic minerals they contain, and their previous history in terms of time, heat, pressure, and the chemical environment to which they have been exposed since their formation. The total remanent magnetization of a rock is termed its natural remanent magnetization. The types of remanent magnetization acquired by rocks are summarized below.

THERMOREMANENT MAGNETIZATION: Thermoremanent magnetization is that magnetization acquired by a ferromagnetic or ferrimagnetic substance upon cooling at temperatures below the Curie point in a magnetic field. This magnetization typically has a high coercive force and is usually more intense than the magnetization induced by the same field at room temperature. Most igneous and high-temperature metamorphic rocks have acquired thermoremanent magnetization upon cooling. Intensities of thermoremanent magnetizations acquired by several ferrimagnetic minerals in fields roughly equivalent to the geomagnetic field are shown in Table 25-1.

CRYSTALLIZATION OR CHEMICAL MAGNETIZATION: Haigh [16] has demonstrated that magnetite formed by reduction of hematite acquires a remanent magnetization, which has been called crystallization magnetization or chemical magnetization. During recrystallization new domains are formed whose moments are aligned by an external field. This new magnetization, like thermoremanent magnetization, may have a coercive force much greater than the magnetizing field. Crystallization magnetization may be acquired by rocks upon oxidation or reduction, recrystallization, chemical precipitation, or exsolution of ferrimagnetic minerals at temperatures below the appropriate Curie points.

DEPOSITIONAL MAGNETIZATION: During deposition of sediments, previously magnetized particles tend to become aligned parallel to an external magnetic field. In a low-turbulence depositional environment this alignment may be retained in the deposited sediments and produce a strong remanent magnetization. Because many ferrimagnetic mineral grains are magnetized roughly parallel to their long dimensional axes, and these axes tend to lie in the bedding plane, the resulting magnetization may have a lower inclination (dip) than that of the orienting field. The azimuth (declination) is, however, coincident with that of the external field [23, 26].

ISOTHERMAL REMANENT MAGNETIZATION AND VISCOUS MAGNETIZATION: Isothermal remanent magnetization may be acquired by ferrimagnetic material at constant temperature when placed in a field greater than the smallest coercive force of any domain in the material. The intense magnetic fields of a lightning strike may produce a strong component of isothermal remanent magnetization in rocks. Long exposure to the geomagnetic field may bias a Boltzmann-type fluctuation of domain walls and produce so-called viscous magnetization in some rocks. Rocks may acquire viscous and isothermal remanent magnetizations sufficiently intense to bias or even to obscure primary components of thermoremanent, crystallization, or depositional magnetization. However, in many cases it is possible to destroy components of viscous and isothermal remanent magnetizations by suitable heating or alternating field demagnetization techniques without seriously affecting the primary magnetizations.

EFFECT OF MINERALOGY ON REMANENT MAGNETIZATION: In general the acquisition of thermoremanent magnetization by a single phase ferrimagnetic mineral is straightforward, the mineral being magnetized in the direction of the external field. However, Néel [35] and Verhoogen [51] have proposed mechanisms by which some single-phase minerals might acquire a remanent magnetization opposite to that which is induced by the same field, and Uyeda [50] has pointed out that some intermediate members of the hematite-ilmenite series possess this property, which is termed self-reversal.

Intimate mixtures of ferrimagnetic minerals, such as those due to exsolution, may acquire complex magnetizations, as components with lower Curie points become magnetized in a combination of the original external field plus the demagnetizing field of components with higher Curie points. Néel has proposed that magnetostatic interactions of this sort might give rise to self-reversal in rocks [35], although Cox and Doell [13] point out that there are stringent requirements on the geometrical arrangement of the two magnetic phases for the process to be effective. No cases of self-reversal by magnetostatic interaction have been proved in rocks.

EFFECTS OF TEMPERATURE ON REMANENT MAGNETISM: The natural remanent magnetization of a rock may be sensitive to temperature changes. Heating to 200°–300° C may destroy viscous and isothermal remanent magnetizations. Thellier [48] has shown that thermoremanent magnetization is additive, so that a component of thermoremanent magnetization acquired by cooling over a given temperature interval is destroyed by heating over the same interval. Furthermore, exsolution textures and order-disorder relationships in ferrimagnetic minerals are temperature sensitive, and it is therefore possible to change the remanent magnetization of a rock by altering the mineralogy upon heating.

VARIATION OF REMANENT MAGNETIZATION WITH PRESSURE: It has long been known that magnetostriction plays an important role in the magnetization of metals; preliminary experiments have shown a measurable effect on some rocks [15]. Differential stress of up to 2000 p.s.i. produces appreciable shifts of the direction of remanent magnetization of rocks containing magnetite, but has no effect on rocks containing members of the hematite-ilmenite series.

PALEOMAGNETIC INTERPRETATIONS: Many recent sediments and lavas faithfully reflect the direction of the local geomagnetic field at the time of their formation [11, 33, 55]. It has been argued that from the remanent magnetization of older rocks one can reconstruct the geomagnetic field during geologic time; from such attempts at reconstruction have come arguments supporting hypotheses of polar wandering and continental drift. The data and conclusions of a voluminous literature have been summarized in reviews [13, 21, 44, 45].

Many sequences of sedimentary and volcanic rocks, especially Tertiary basalt formations, consist of several alternating units magnetized roughly parallel and antiparallel to the field of an assumed axial dipole. Where no systematic mineralogical differences (which might suggest self-reversals) are found between units with "normal" and "reverse" magnetizations, periodic reversals of the earth's field may be indicated. The course of one such reversal is apparently recorded in a sequence of 13 Tertiary basalts from Iceland [9].

REFERENCES FOR SECTION 25

1. Adams and Green, Phil. Mag. **12**, 361, 1931
2. Akimoto, Jour. Geomag. Geoelect. **3**, 47, 1951
3. Akimoto, Katsura, and Yoshida, Jour. Geomag. Geoelect. **9**, 165, 1957
4. Balsley and Buddington, Econ. Geol. **53**, 777, 1958
5. Bizette and Tsai, Compt. rend. **242**, 2124, 1956
6. Bohurin (*in* Angenheister's Handbuch der Experimentallphysik, article by Reich) Bull. Inst. Pract. Geophys. Leningrad **3**, 1927
7. Booth and Rayner, Jour. Roy. Soc. N. South Wales **67**, 118, 1933
8. Bozorth, Ferromagnetism, New York, Van Nostrand, 1951, 968 p.
9. Brynjólfsson, Adv. Phys. **6**, 247, 1957
10. Carmichael, Proc. Roy. Soc. **263A**, 508, 1961
11. Chevallier, Ann. phys. **4**, 5, 1925
12. Collingswood, Bull. Am. Assoc. Petrol. Geol. **14**, 1187, 1930
13. Cox and Doell, Geol. Soc. America Bull. **71**, 645, 1960
14. Gottschalk and Wartman, Bur. Mines Rept. Inv. **3268**, 67, 1935
15. Graham, Buddington, and Balsley, Jour. Geophys. Research **62**, 465, 1957
16. Haigh, Phil. Mag. **3**, 267, 1958
17. Hallimond and Herroun, Proc. Roy. Soc. **141A**, 302, 1933
18. Hargraves, Jour. Geophys. Research **64**, 1565, 1959
19. Herroun, Proc. Phys. Soc. (London) **55**, 338, 1943
20. Howell, Martinesz, and Statham, Geophysics **23**, 285, 1958

21. Irving, Roy. Astron. Soc. Geophys. Jour. **2**, 51, 1959
22. Ising, Arkiv för Matematik, Astronomi, och Fysik **29A**, 1, 1943
23. Johnson, Murphy, and Torreson, Terr. Mag. and Atm. Elec. **53**, 349, 1948
24. Kalashnikov and Kaptitsa, Doklady Akademii Nauk S.S.S.R. **86**, 521, 1952
25. Kawai, Kume, and Sasajima, Proc. Japan Acad. **30**, 588, 1954
26. King, Monthly Notices Roy. Astron. Soc., Geophys. Supp. **7**, 115, 1955
27. Koenigsberger, Beitr. z. Geophys. **23**, 248, 1929
28. —— Terr. Mag. and Atm. Elec. **34**, 209, 1929
29. —— Terr. Mag. and Atm. Elec. **35**, 145, 1930
30. —— Beitr. Angew. Geophys. **4**, 385, 1932
31. Lindsley, D. H., Carnegie Inst. Wash. Year Book **61**, p. 100, 1962
32. Malamphy, DeAmaral, and Odonne, Am. Inst. Min. Eng., Contrib. **96**, 1936
33. Nagata, Rock magnetism, Tokyo, Maruzen and Co., 225 p., 1953
34. Nagata and Akimoto, Geofisica pura e appl. **34**, 36, 1956
35. Néel, Ann. Geophys. **7**, 90, 1951
36. Patrick, Phys. Rev. **93**, 384, 1954
37. Petrova, Akad. Nauk S.S.S.R., Izv. Ser. Geog. i Geofiz. **12**, 549, 1948
38. Pickart and Turnock, Jour. Phys. and Chem. of Solids **10**, 242, 1959
39. Pockels, Ann. de Phys. **63**, 195, 1897
40. Puzicha, Zeit. f. prakt. Geol. **38**, 161, 1930
41. Rothe, Compt. rend. **196**, 1443, 1934
42. Rucker, Proc. Roy. Soc. **48**, 505, 1890
43. Rucker and White, Proc. Roy. Soc. **63**, 460, 1898
44. Runcorn, Adv. Phys. **4**, 244, 1955
45. —— Science **129**, 1002, 1959
46. Slichter, Am. Inst. Min. Eng. Geophys. Prosp. **238**, 1929
47. Takagi and Ishiwara, Sci. Rep. Tohoku Imp. Univ. **3**, 127, 1914
48. Thellier, Jour. Phys. Rad. **12**, 205, 1951
49. Turcev, Bull. Acad. Sci. Leningrad **7**, 89, 1928
50. Uyeda, Jap. Jour. Geophys. **2**, 1, 1958
51. Verhoogen, Jour. Geophys. Res. **61**, 201, 1956
52. Vincent, Wright, Chevallier, and Mathieu, Min. Mag. **31**, 624, 1957
53. Werner, Sveriges Geol. Undersokning **39**, no. 5, 79 p., 1945
54. Wilson, Phil. Trans. Roy. Soc. **A219**, 83, 1919
55. Yukutake, Bull. Earthquake Res. Inst. **39**, 467, 1961

SECTION 26

ELECTRICAL PROPERTIES OF ROCKS AND MINERALS*

by GEORGE V. KELLER

CONTENTS

* Publication authorized by the Director, U.S. Geological Survey

Handbook of Physical Constants—*Revised Edition*
THE GEOLOGICAL SOCIETY OF AMERICA MEMOIR 97, 1966

INTRODUCTION

The electrical properties of a material define its behavior when an electric field is applied. The two principal electrical properties are the *dielectric constant*, which is a measure of the electrical polarization that takes place when an electric field is applied, and the *conductivity*, which is a measure of the conduction current developed by an electric field.

In accordance with modern usage, the MKS unit for conductivity, the mho per meter, is used in these tables. More commonly the reciprocal of conductivity, the resistivity, measured in ohm-meters, is used. In the case of dielectric constant, the tables are compiled in terms of the ratio:

$$\text{dielectric constant} = \frac{\text{specific capacity of material}}{\text{specific capacity of vacuum}}.$$

To obtain the specific capacity of a material from the data listed in these tables, it is necessary to multiply the values listed by the specific capacity of a vacuum, 8.85×10^{-12} farads per meter.

ELECTRICAL RESISTIVITY

Materials are classified in a general way as conductors, semiconductors or insulators. A material with a resistivity of 10^{-5} ohm-meters or less is classed as a conductor; materials with a resistivity greater than 10^8 ohm-meters are classed as insulators; materials in the intermediate range are semiconductors.

Resistivities which have been reported in the literature for individual materials are listed in Table 26-1. These data were obtained at ambient room temperatures, ranging probably between 15° and 30° C, and at a sufficiently low frequency that these may be classed as D.C. measurements.

The minerals listed in Table 26-1 are all conductors or semiconductors. They are such rarely occurring minerals as the native metals and various sulfosalts. No data are available for the common rock-forming silicates, presumably because such minerals are insulators. Except in the case of the native metals, the range in resistivities reported for a particular mineral is several orders of magnitude. This wide variation represents not only the effects of impurities and of departure from stoichiometric proportions, but also the effect of structure in the mineral grains on which the measurements were made. Harvey [23] has pointed out that microscopic crevices and oxidized surfaces within individual grains will cause considerable variation in measured resistivities.

A summary of normal resistivities for water-bearing rocks is given in Table 26-2. These data again are given for low frequencies and temperatures near 20° C. Unless unusually large concentrations of conducting minerals, such as those listed in Table 26-1, are present in a rock, the electrical conductivity of a rock at ordinary temperatures is determined by the amount of water present, the salinity of the water, and the manner in which the water is distributed through the rock.

Measurements of resistivity made as a function of frequency indicate that radio-frequency resistivities are generally lower than the D.C. values. Figure 26-1 shows a summary of resistivity measurements made on a series of sandstone samples as a function of frequency and water content. It should be noted that:

(1) At low frequencies the resistivity decreases with increasing water content.

(2) All curves show a relaxational character with the relaxation time decreasing with increase in water content. Hence they overlap at the higher frequencies.

Most rocks are electrically anisotropic. In the case of microanisotropy, orientation of elongate or flat grains in the rock may result in differences in resistivity as a function of the direction of current flow. Macroanisotropy is observed when a section of rock is made up of layers with different resistivities. In such a case, the resistivity measured along the bedding direction (the longitudinal resistivity) is less than the resistivity measured across the bedding (the transverse resistivity). The square root of the ratio of these two resistivities (transverse to longitudinal) is defined as the coefficient of macroanisotropy. Table 26-3 lists values of longitudinal resistivity, transverse resistivity and coefficient of macroanisotropy calculated from several electric logs. Table 26-4 lists general ranges of anisotropy reported by Dakhnov [14] with no indication of the source of the data.

In water-bearing rocks, resistivity, ρ, may usually be correlated with water content, using an empirical equation first presented by Archie [2]:

$$\rho = a\rho_w\phi^{-m}S^{-n} \tag{1}$$

where ρ_w is the resistivity of the water contained in the rock,

ϕ is the fractional pore volume,

S is the fraction of the pore volume filled with water, and

a, m, and n are arbitrary parameters.

The parameter m assumes values as low as 1.3 for unconsolidated sand and as high as 2.5 for well-cemented granular rocks. Values of m greater than 2.5 have been reported but do not appear to be reliable. Table 26-5 lists the values for the parameters a and m which have been reported in the literature.

The value for n in equation 1 usually is very close to 2.0 for water saturation of more than 30 per cent of pore space. In the case of a rock in which the water does not wet the grains the value of n may be as large as 10 [26].

Values for ground-water resistivity are listed in Table 26-6. Some caution must be used in determining the conductivity of the water in a rock from its salinity. Three factors may alter the conductivity of water in a fine pore structure:

(1) ion exchange between the pore water and the solid minerals in the rock;

(2) surface conductance over the individual grains;

(3) change in viscosity of the water held in the double layer on the grain surfaces.

Very few quantitative data are available on the importance of these phenomena, although there have been several theoretical discussions published [14, 31].

The resistivity of a rock depends also on the temperature at which it is measured. For water-bearing rocks, the effect of temperature on the resistivity of the rock is essentially the same as the effect of temperature on the resistivity of water content for temperatures between the freezing point and boiling point of water. The variation in resistivity caused by temperature changes in an electrolytic solution is given approximately by the equation:

$$\rho_T = \rho_{20°}e^{-0.022(T-20)} \tag{2}$$

where ρ_T is the resistivity at a temperature, T; and $\rho_{20°}$ is the resistivity at 20° C.

Table 26-7 lists the conductivity of crystalline ice as a function of temperature and frequency. Water in the pore spaces of a rock freezes over a range of several degrees in temperature, so that the resistivity of water-bearing rock increases only moderately as the temperature is lowered through 0° C. Table 26-9 lists data on the amount by which resistivity of water-bearing rocks increases below 0° C.

At high temperatures (considerably above 100° C), rocks may be assumed to be water-free, and mineral conductivity is important. Figure 26-2 summarizes measurements of rock conductivity made at high temperatures, using direct current [10, 34]. Over limited ranges in temperature the conductivity of a rock varies according to the relationship:

$$\sigma_T = \sigma_0 e^{-A/T} \tag{3}$$

where σ_T is the conductivity, T is the absolute temperature, σ_0 and A are constants.

The constant, A, may be identified with the activation energy, E, of the charge carriers as follows [46]

$$\frac{E}{2k} = A \tag{4}$$

where k is Boltzmann's constant.

Table 26-8 lists values for the constants in equation 3 for measurements made over the temperature range 400° to 1300° Kelvin. Both the activation energy, E, and the constant, σ_0 are significantly larger at high temperatures than at low temperatures.

Conduction at high temperatures is frequency-dependent, as evidenced by data for several rock types shown in Figures 26-3, 26-4, and 26-5.

Hughes [25] has presented data on the effect of pressure on the conductivity of peridot (Table 26-10).

DIELECTRIC CONSTANT

Dielectric constant is frequency dependent, and data on values of dielectric constant for minerals and rocks may be specified for each of three frequency ranges: very high frequencies, in which polarization is due entirely to electron polarization; intermediate frequencies, in which ions and polar molecules also contribute to polarization; and low frequencies, where interfacial polarization may be important.

Table 26-11 lists values for the dielectric constant of minerals and rocks at intermediate and high frequencies. In most cases, the dielectric constant at optical frequencies was obtained by squaring the index of refraction. All measurements are made at temperatures near 20° C.

At low frequencies, variation in the mobility of charge carriers results in polarization which increases the dielectric constant. Dielectric constants measured at room temperature over a frequency range of 100 cps to 10 megacycles per second for various rocks and minerals are listed in Table 26-12. Dielectric constants measured at high temperatures are shown in Figures 26-6, 26-7, and 26-8.

At very low frequencies, large polarization may be induced in water-bearing rocks. Variations in ion mobility attributed to a number of mechanisms cause this polarization. At present, no standard way of describing low-frequency polarization has been adopted. Marshall and Madden [30] report low frequency polarization in terms of a "metal factor," defined as:

$$MF = 2\pi \frac{(\rho_{DC} - \rho_{AC}) \times 10^5}{\rho_{DC} \cdot \rho_{AC}}, \tag{5}$$

where ρ_{DC} is the resistivity of a rock measured with direct current, and ρ_{AC} is the magnitude of the specific impedance measured at a frequency of 10 cycles per second.

Table 26-14 lists values of "metal factor" reported by Marshall and Madden [30].

If polarization is measured by recording the transient voltage response of a rock to a step current, the ratio of the time integral of the transient voltage to the applied voltage equals the product of dielectric constant and resistivity (Table 26-15). Values for low-frequency dielectric constant and resistivity are listed separately in Table 26-16.

TABLE 26-1. ELECTRICAL RESISTIVITY OF MINERALS AND ELEMENTS

Mineral	Source	Reported resistivities			Number of samples	Ref.
		Low	High	Average		
	NATIVE ELEMENTS					
Antimony, Sb	Native metal	5.0×10^{-7}	1.0×10^{-6}		1	23
	Refined metal			4.17×10^{-7}		
Arsenic, As	Native metal	1.5×10^{-7}	3.0×10^{-7}		1	23
	Refined metal			3.33×10^{-7}		
Bismuth, Bi	Native metal	1.0×10^{-6}	1.3×10^{-6}		3	23
	Refined metal			1.20×10^{-6}		
Copper, Cu	Native metal	1.2×10^{-8}	3.0×10^{-7}		9	23
	Refined metal			1.72×10^{-8}		
Diamond, C	South Africa	2.7			1	3
		10^{16}				29
Gold, Au	Refined metal			2.44×10^{-8}		
Graphite, C	Refined			5.00×10^{-5}		
	Crystals from marble New York state					
	Parallel to basal plane	2.8×10^{-5}	6.4×10^{-5}	5.0×10^{-5}	9	38
	Across basal plane	3.6×10^{-7}	4.6×10^{-7}	3.8×10^{-7}	12	
	Ceylon					
	Parallel to basal plane	9.6×10^{-3}	9.9×10^{-3}	9.8×10^{-3}	25	18
	Across basal plane	9.8×10^{-7}	1.0×10^{-6}	1.0×10^{-6}	25	
Iron, Fe	Refined metal			1.0×10^{-8}		
Platinum, Pt	Refined metal			1.0×10^{-8}		
Silver, Ag	Native metal			2.0×10^{-8}	1	23
	Refined metal			1.59×10^{-8}		
Sulfur, S	Sublimed			1.6×10^{7}		
	Pure crystals			1.0×10^{16}		29
Tellurium, Te	Native metal	1.1×10^{-4}	2.5×10^{-3}			23
	SULFIDES					
Argentite, Ag$_2$S		8.0×10^{-1}	2.0		4	23
	USSR	1.5×10^{-3}	2.0×10^{-3}	1.7×10^{-3}	2	40

TABLE 26-1. *Continued*

Mineral	Source	Reported resistivities			Number of samples	Ref.
		Low	High	Average		
		SULFIDES (*continued*)				
Bismuthinite, Bi₂S₃	USSR	3.0	12	5.7 × 10²	2	23
	..	..	..	..	1	40
Bornite, Fe₂S₃(3–5)·Cu₂S	USSR	3.0 × 10⁻⁵	3.0 × 10⁻³	..	16	23
	USSR	1.6 × 10⁻⁶	6.0 × 10⁻³	9.3 × 10⁻⁵	36	40
Chalcocite, Cu₂S	USSR	8.0 × 10⁻⁵	1.0 × 10⁻⁴	..	2	23
	USSR	4.2 × 10⁻²		..	1	40
Chalcopyrite, Fe₂S₃·Cu₂S	USSR	3.0 × 10⁻⁵	2.0 × 10⁻¹	..	37	23
		1.5 × 10⁻⁴	8.3	1.4 × 10⁻³	13	40
	Smaland, Sweden	2.2 × 10⁻⁴	6.2 × 10⁻⁴	3.7 × 10⁻⁴	21	35
	Vasterbotten, Sweden	1 × 10⁻³	9 × 10⁻³		3	35
	Neudorf, Germany	3.5 × 10⁻⁴	4.7 × 10⁻⁴	4.1 × 10⁻⁴	60	35
Covellite, CuS		3.0 × 10⁻⁷	8.0 × 10⁻⁷		1	23
	USSR	1.0 × 10⁻⁶	8.3 × 10⁻⁵	1.32 × 10⁻⁵	..	40
Galena, PbS	USSR	1.8 × 10⁻⁵	9.0 × 10⁻²		17	23
	USSR	6.8 × 10⁻⁵	5.8 × 10⁻¹	1.87 × 10⁻²	25	40
	Sweden	3 × 10⁻⁵	3 × 10⁻⁴		9	35
Hauerite, MnS₂		10	20		1	23
Marcasite, FeS₂	USSR	1.0 × 10⁻³	1.5 × 10⁻¹		3	23
	USSR	2.8 × 10⁻²			1	40
Metacinnabarite, 4(HgS)	USSR	2.0 × 10⁻⁷	1.0 × 10⁻³		2	23
Millerite, NiS		2.0 × 10⁻⁷	4.0 × 10⁻⁷		1	23
Molybdenite, MoS₂		1.2 × 10⁻¹	1.5		3	23
	USSR	7.5	1.0 × 10⁶	1.15 × 10²	14	40
Pentlandite, (Fe,Ni)₉S₈		1.0 × 10⁻⁶	1.1 × 10⁻⁵		1	23
Pyrrhotite, Fe₇S₈	USSR	2.0 × 10⁻⁶	2.0 × 10⁻⁵		6	23
	USSR	6.5 × 10⁻⁶	1.6 × 10⁻⁴	1.23 × 10⁻⁴	5	40
	Vasterbotten, Sweden			2.0 × 10⁻⁵	8	35
	Ringerike, Norway			5.7 × 10⁻⁵	3	35
Pyrite, FeS₂	Norbotten, Sweden	1.4 × 10⁻⁵	2.6 × 10⁻⁵		21	23
		1.0 × 10⁻⁵	2.0 × 10⁻¹		29	35
	Jamtland, Sweden	6.0 × 10⁻⁵	2.6 × 10⁻¹	3.8 × 10⁻¹	10	35

Mineral and formula	Locality					
Sphalerite, ZnS	Gastrikland, Sweden			4.2×10^{-2}	8	35
	Gastrikland, Sweden			6.0×10^{-1}	6	35
	Vastmanland, Sweden			1.2×10^{-3}	5	35
	Vastmanland, Sweden			2.6×10^{-3}	5	35
	Vastmanland, Sweden	6.0×10^{-4}	7.0×10^{-2}		6	35
	Vastmanland, Sweden	3.0×10^{-4}	3.0×10^{-3}		5	35
	Vastmanland, Sweden	1.2×10^{-3}	1.0×10^{-1}		7	35
	Ostergotland, Sweden	7.2×10^{-4}	1.22	2.8×10^{-1}	32	35
	Smaland, Sweden	5.0×10^{-4}	5.0×10^{-2}		16	40
	USSR	1.8×10^{-2}	4.0×10^{-2}	2.7×10^{-2}	2	40
Stannite, Cu$_2$FeSnS$_5$	USSR	4.0×10^{3}	4.0×10^{4}	1.2×10^{4}	3	23
	USSR	3.0×10^{2}	6.0×10^{3}	35×10^{3}	2	40
Sulfo-Antimonides						
Berthierite, FeSb$_2$S$_4$	USSR	7.0×10^{-1}	2.0	1.44×10^{-2}	1	23
	USSR	8.3×10^{-3}	2.5×10^{-2}		2	40
Boulangerite, Pb$_5$Sb$_4$S$_{11}$	USSR	2.0×10^{3}	4.0×10^{5}	1.8×10^{4}	5	40
Cylindrite, Pb$_3$Sn$_4$Sb$_2$S$_{14}$(?)		2.5	60	13.5	3	40
Franckeite, Pb$_5$Sn$_3$Sb$_2$S$_{14}$		1.2	4.0		1	23
Hauchecornite, Ni$_9$(Bi,Sb)$_2$S$_8$	USSR	2.1×10^{-6}	8.3×10^{-5}	1.30×10^{-5}	2	40
	USSR	1.0×10^{-6}	1.2×10^{-6}		1	23
Jamesonite, Pb$_4$FeSb$_6$S$_{14}$	USSR	2.0×10^{-2}	1.5×10^{-1}		2	23
Tetrahedrite, Cu$_3$SbS$_3$	USSR	3.0×10^{-1}	3.0×10^{4}		5	23
Ullmannite, NiSbS	USSR	5.3×10^{-1}	1.0×10^{4}	1.1×10^{2}		40
	USSR	9.0×10^{-8}	1.2×10^{-6}		1	23
Sulfo-Arsenides						
Arsenopyrite, FeAsS	USSR	2.0×10^{-5}	1.5×10^{-4}	1.93×10^{-2}	3	23
	Sweden	3.0×10^{-4}	15	3.0×10^{-4}	18	40
Cobaltite, CoAsS		1.0×10^{-5}	1.2×10^{-2}		2	35
		6.5×10^{-3}	1.3×10^{-1}		7	23
Enargite, Cu$_3$AsS$_4$	Vastmanland, Sweden	1.0×10^{-3}	4.0×10^{-2}	2.66×10^{-2}	51	35
	Sodermanland, Sweden	2.0×10^{-4}	9.0×10^{-1}		19	35
Gersdorffite, NiAsS	USSR	5.5×10^{-3}	4.0×10^{-2}	2.0×10^{-2}	10	23
	USSR	1.0×10^{-6}	3.0×10^{-5}		3	40
	USSR	1.5×10^{-6}	1.6×10^{-4}	1.55×10^{-5}	2	23

TABLE 26-1. *Continued*

Mineral	Source	Reported resistivities Low	Reported resistivities High	Average	Number of samples	Ref.
SULFO-ARSENIDES (*continued*)						
Glaucodote, (Co.Fe)AsS	..	5.0×10^{-6}	1.0×10^{-4}	..	1	23
Tennantite, Cu₃AsS₃	..	7.0×10^{-4}	4.0×10^{-1}	..	4	23
	USSR	1.2×10^{-3}	6.0×10^{-3}	2.7×10^{-3}	2	40
ANTIMONIDES						
Breithauptite, NiSb	USSR	3.0×10^{-8}	5.0×10^{-7}	..	4	23
		..	..	1.6×10^{-4}	1	40
Dyscrasite, Ag₃Sb	USSR	1.2×10^{-7}	1.2×10^{-6}	..	2	23
ARSENIDES						
Allemonite, SbAs₃	USSR	70	6.0×10^{4}	2.0×10^{3}	2	40
Loellingite, FeAs₂	..	2.0×10^{-6}	1.5×10^{-5}	..	2	23
	USSR	8.3×10^{-5}	2.7×10^{-4}	1.5×10^{-4}	2	40
	Sweden	..	..	5.0×10^{-5}	9	35
Niccolite, NiAs	USSR	1.1×10^{-7}	5.0×10^{-7}	..	7	23
	..	2.0×10^{-6}	..	..	1	40
Skutterudite, CoAs₃	USSR	1.1×10^{-4}	4.0×10^{-6}	..	1	23
	..	1.6×10^{-4}	..	..	1	40
Smaltite, CoAs₂	USSR	1.1×10^{-6}	1.2×10^{-5}	..	2	23
TELLURIDES						
Altaite, PbTe	..	2.0×10^{-5}	2.0×10^{-4}	..	3	23
Calavarite, AuTe₂	..	6.0×10^{-6}	1.2×10^{-5}	..	5	23
Coloradoite, HgTe	..	4.0×10^{-6}	1.0×10^{-4}	..	2	23
Hessite, Ag₂Te	..	4.0×10^{-6}	1.0×10^{-4}	..	5	23
Nagyagite, Pb₆Au(S,Te)₁₄	..	2.0×10^{-5}	8.0×10^{-5}	..	2	23
Sylvanite, AgAuTe₄	..	4.0×10^{-6}	2.0×10^{-5}	..	1	23
OXIDES						
Barium priderite, BaTiO₃	Synthetic ceramic	1.6×10^{-1}	..	1.64×10^{7}	..	47
Braunite, Mn₂O₃	USSR	..	1.0	4.3×10^{-1}	6	40
Bromellite, BeO	Synthetic ceramic	..	..	2.29×10^{9}	..	47
Cassiterite, SnO₂	USSR	4.5×10^{-4}	1.0×10^{4}	1.73×10^{-1}	13	40

Mineral	Locality					
Cuprite, Cu_2O	..	10	50	..	1	23
Hollandite, $(Ba,Na,K)Mn_2^{\cdot\cdot}Mn_6^{\cdot\cdot\cdot}O_{16}\cdot H_2O$	Norbotten, Sweden	1.9×10^{-2}	1.0×10^{-1}	2.1×10^{-2}	24	35
Hematite, Fe_2O_3	Central India	2.0×10^{-3}	6.0×10^{-2}	1.7×10^{-2}	5	35
	USSR	2.1×10^{-3}	1.0×10^4	11.0	36	40
	Lango, Norway (along c axis)	..	..	6.0×10^{-3}	1	6
	(across c axis)	..	..	4.0×10^{-3}		
	Brazil (along c axis)	..	..	1.39×10^{-2}	1	28
	(across c axis)	..	..	$.54 \times 10^{-2}$		
	Norbotten, Sweden	4.0×10^{-3}	6.0×10^2	..	19	35
	Vastmanland, Sweden	8.2	120	..	7	35
Ice, H_2O	Temperature $-12°$ C	..	4.0	4.7×10^5	:	47
Ilmenite, $FeTiO_3$	USSR	1.0×10^{-3}	7.0×10^{-3}	7.1×10^2	5	23
Magnetite, Fe_3O_4	USSR	1.5×10^{-5}	1.0×10^4	1.70×10^{-3}	11	23
	USSR	38	7.2×10^{-1}	5.2×10^{-5}	31	40
		9.3×10^{-5}	..	1.0×10^{-4}	1	40
				1.08×10^{-4}		35
Manganite, $MnO\cdot OH$	USSR	1.8×10^{-2}	5.0×10^{-1}	7.1×10^{-2}	:	15
Melaconite, CuO	USSR	6.0×10^3	..	..	1	40
Periclase, MgO	Synthetic ceramic	..	..	6.2×10^{10}	8	40
Psilomelane	USSR	6.0×10^{-2}	6.0×10^3	2.4	1	46
$kMnO\cdot MnO_2,nH_2O$	Dalarna, Sweden	..	..	4.1×10^{-2}	6	40
	Orkney Islands	..	..	8.8×10^{-2}	4	35
	Elgersburg, Germany	.10	.90	1.27	8	35
	Morocco	..	3.0×10^{-1}	.40	4	35
	Brazil	5.0×10^{-2}	1.0×10^{-1}	.11	10	35
Pyrolusite, MnO_2	Vastergotland, Sweden	1.5×10^{-3}	5.4×10^{-2}	1.8×10^{-2}	3	23
	Donetz, USSR	7.2×10^{-3}	..	31.8 ± 5.3	28	35
Rutile, TiO_2	Synthetic blue crystals (across c axis)	3.8×10^2	9.1×10^2	5.0×10^2	5	35
	(along c axis)	29	120	59	8	13
Uraninite	..	1.5	200	..	1	23

TABLE 26-2. RESISTIVITY RANGES OF WATER-BEARING ROCKS

Geologic age	Rock type				
	Marine sand, shale, graywacke	Terrestrial sands, claystone, arkose	Volcanic rocks (Basalt, rhyolite, tuffs)	Granite gabbro, etc.	Limestone dolomite, anhydrite salt
Quaternary, Tertiary	1–10 ohm-m	15–50 ohm-m	10–200 ohm-m	500–2,000 ohm-m	50–5,000 ohm-m
Mesozoic	5–20	25–100	20–500	500–2,000	100–10,000
Carboniferous	10–40	50–300	50–1,000	1,000–5,000	200–100,000
Pre-Carboniferous Paleozoic	40–200	100–500	100–2,000	1,000–5,000	10,000–100,000
Precambrian	100–2,000	300–5,000	200–5,000	5,000–20,000	10,000–100,000

TABLE 26-3. COEFFICIENTS OF MACROANISOTROPY DERIVED FROM ELECTRIC LOG STUDIES

Rock type and area	Transverse resistivity	Longitudinal resistivity	Coefficient of anisotropy
Ordovician limestone in Jefferson County, Tennessee			
Lenoir Limestone	7,550 ohm-m	5,800 ohm-m	1.14
Mascot Dolomite	12,700	11,300	1.07
Kingsport Limestone	13,800	13,400	1.01
Rhyolitic tuffs in the Oak Spring Group (Tertiary), Nye County, Nevada			
Granular tuff	17.2 to 59.1 ohm-m	12.7–49.1	1.16–1.17
Welded tuff	217–1410	161–1160	1.10–1.21
Pierre Shale (Cretaceous), eastern Colorado	2.7–5.5	2.5–5.2	1.03–1.08
Paleozoic limestones, sandstone and shale, eastern Colorado	8–25	5–16	1.21–1.45
Helmet Fanglomerate (Tertiary), from southern Arizona	37–57	35–56	1.01–1.02

TABLE 26-4. COEFFICIENTS OF MACROANISOTROPY FOR LAYERED ROCK [14]

Rock type	Coefficient of anisotropy
Massive shale	1.02–1.05
Interbedded sandstone and shale	1.05–1.15
Bedded sandstone	1.10–1.59
Low-grade slate	1.10–1.59
Slate	1.41–2.25
Low-grade coal	1.73–2.55
Anthracite	2.00–2.55
Graphitic slate	2.00–2.75

TABLE 26-5. SUMMARY OF EQUATIONS RELATING RESISTIVITY AND POROSITY FOR FULLY WATER-SATURATED ROCKS [24, 53, 54]

Formations for which equations are valid	Porosity range	Number of measure- ments	Equation*
1. Bradford Sand (Devonian), Woodbine Sand (Cretaceous), Wilcox sand (Eocene)	.150–.367	30	$F = .62 \, \phi^{-2.15}$
2. Pennsylvanian sandstone, Oklahoma	.080–.200	97	$F = .65 \, \phi^{-1.91}$
3. Morrison sandstone (Jurassic), Montrose County, Colorado	.140–.230	243	$F = .62 \, \phi^{-2.10}$
4. Clean Miocene sandstone, Weeks Island, Louisiana	.11–.26	35	$F = .78 \, \phi^{-1.92}$
5. Clean Cretaceous sandstone, Paluxy Sand, Texas	.08–.25	50	$F = .47 \, \phi^{-2.23}$
6. Clean Ordovician sandstone, Simpson sand, Oklahoma	.07–.15	44	$F = 1.3 \, \phi^{-1.71}$
7. Shaly sandstone (Eocene), Wilcox Formation, Texas	.09–.22	72	$F = 1.8 \, \phi^{-1.64}$
8. Shaly sandstone (Oligocene), Frio sands, Texas	.07–.26	63	$F = 1.7 \, \phi^{-1.65}$
9. Shaly sandstone (Cretaceous), Taylor sand, Texas	.07–.31	36	$F = 1.7 \, \phi^{-1.80}$
10. Oölitic limestone (Cretaceous), Texas	.07–.19	13	$F = 2.3 \, \phi^{-1.64}$
11. Oölitic limestone (Jurassic), Smackover Limestone, Ark.	.09–.26	42	$F = .73 \, \phi^{-2.10}$
12. Siliceous limestone (Devonian), Texas	.07–.30	58	$F = 1.2 \, \phi^{-1.88}$
13. Limestone (Cretaceous)	.08–.30	37	$F = 2.2 \, \phi^{-1.65}$

* F is defined as the ratio of the resistivity of a rock to the resistivity of the water contained in it, when the pore space is filled with water.

TABLE 26-6. RESISTIVITIES OF NATURAL WATERS [4, 9, 12, 17, 32, 39, 43, 51]
Average values on a regional basis

Source of water samples	Number of samples	Resistivity at 20° C Median	Range
		(ohm-meters)	
Igneous rocks, Europe	314	7.6	3.0–40
Igneous rocks, South Africa	175	11.0	.50–80
Metamorphic rocks, South Africa	88	7.6	.86–80
Metamorphic rocks, Precambrian of Australia	31	3.6	1.5–8.6
Recent and Pleistocene continental sediments, Europe	610	3.9	1.0–27
Recent and Pleistocene sediments, Australia	323	3.2	.38–80
Tertiary sediments, Europe	993	1.40	.70–3.5
Tertiary (Miocene and Oligocene) sedimentary rocks, Australia	240	3.2	1.35–10
Mesozoic sedimentary rocks, Europe	105	2.5	.31–47
Paleozoic sedimentary rocks, Europe	161	.93	.29–7.1
Chloride waters from oil fields	967	.16	.049–.95
Sulfate waters from oil fields	256	1.20	.43–5.0
Bicarbonate waters from oil fields	630	.98	.24–10

TABLE 26-7. ELECTRICAL CONDUCTIVITY OF PURE ICE [42]
(Expressed as micromhos/meter)

Temperature °C	Frequency				
	60 KC/S	20 KC/S	5 KC/S	1 KC/S	.5 KC/S
−60	1.2	.24	.16	.11	.086
−40	2.58	.89	.69	.58	.55
−20	6.7	5.5	4.55	2.14	.86
−10	15.6	12.7	9.00	1.25	.40
−5	23.7	19.7	9.86	.81	.20
−3	27.5	23.3	9.62	.65	.17
−1	29.9	25.6	8.85	.57	.17

TABLE 26-8. PARAMETERS DESCRIBING THE BEHAVIOR
OF D.C. CONDUCTIVITY AT HIGH TEMPERATURES [10, 34, 46]

Rock	σ_0	E/K
	TEMPERATURE RANGE 300°–800° K	
Granite	4.5×10^{-6} mhos/m	.62 electron volt
Gabbro	7.0×10^{-5}	.70
Basalt	7.0×10^{-5} to 1.0×10^{-3}	.57 to .62
Gneiss	1.0×10^{-4}	.96
Peridotite	3.8×10^{-4}	.81
Eclogite	2.2×10^{-4}	.81
Andesite	6×10^{-5}	.7 to 1.4
	TEMPERATURE RANGE 900°–1400° K	
Granite	10^3	2.5
Gabbro	10^3	2.2
Basalt	10^3	2.0
Peridotite	10^3	2.3

TABLE 26-9. TEMPERATURE DEPENDENCE OF RESISTIVITY NEAR 0° C [1, 33]

Rock	Porosity	$\dfrac{\text{Resistivity at } -12° \text{ C}}{\text{Resistivity at } 20° \text{ C}}$
Sandstone	.119	184
Sandstone	.068	80
Conglomerate	.018	87
Conglomerate	.210	73
Orthoquartzite	.038	76
Orthoquartzite	.087	375
Orthoquartzite	.041	175
Shale	.101	255
Limestone, fine-grained	.022	17
Limestone	.011	4
Limestone	.073	178
Dolomite	.204	237
Granite	.034	430
Red porphyry	.122	343
Red porphyry	.100	100
Syenite	.049	27
Nepheline syenite	.008	62
Mariopolite	.008	47
Pyroxenite	0	32
Basalt	.064	21
Metaquartzite	.098	10
Metaquartzite	.071	40

TABLE 26-10. PRESSURE EFFECT ON THE CONDUCTIVITY OF PERIDOT [25]

Temperature	Pressure range	Percent change in conductivity per 1000 kg/cm² increase in pressure
1333° K	1000–8500 kg/cm²	−(2.9 ± .9) per cent
1429° K	1000–8500 kg/cm²	−(3.7 ± .3) per cent
1513° K	1000–8500 kg/cm²	−(2.3 ± .6) per cent

TABLE 26-11. DIELECTRIC CONSTANTS OF MINERALS, ROCKS, AND SOILS AT HIGH FREQUENCIES [16, 44, 45, 49]

Mineral or rock	Source and orientation of sample	Dielectric constant Radio frequencies	Optical frequencies
SULFIDE MINERALS			
Galena, PbS	..	17.9	
Sphalerite, ZnS	Titibu, Japan	7.90	5.61 to 6.10
	Nakatatu, Japan	12.1	
	Joplin, Missouri	69.9–7.90	
	Harz, Germany	69.7–7.88	
OXIDE MINERALS			
Corundum, Al₂O₃	..	11.0–13.2	
	along optic axis	..	3.10
	across optic axis	..	3.14
Cassiterite, SnO₂	..	23.4–24.0	
	along optic axis	..	3.98
	across optic axis	..	4.36
Diaspore, AlO(OH)	Mituisi, Japan		
	along a axis	7.70	2.90
	along b axis	8.38	2.96
	along c axis	7.27	3.05
Hematite, Fe₂O₃	..	25.0	
	along optic axis	..	8.65
	across optic axis	..	10.33
Rutile, TiO₂	..	31.0–170	
	along optic axis	..	6.82
	across optic axis	..	8.42
Anatase, TiO₂	..	425	
HALIDE MINERALS			
Halite, NaCl	..	5.70–6.20	2.39
Fluorite, CaF₂	..	6.79	2.06
	Akenobe, Japan	6.26	
	Saxony	6.61	
	Okuno, Japan	6.27	
	Switzerland	6.25	
	Durham, England	6.30	
	Freiburg, Saxony	6.60	
Sylvite, KCl	..	4.39–6.20	2.20
CARBONATE MINERALS			
Aragonite, CaCO₃	Bohemia		
	along a axis	6.46	2.34
	along b axis	9.72	2.82
	along c axis	7.55	2.84
Calcite, CaCO₃	..	7.80–8.50	
	across optic axis	..	2.21
	along optic axis	..	2.75
Dolomite, CaMg(CO₃)₂	..	6.80–8.00	
	across optic axis	7.53	2.28
	along optic axis	6.11	2.85

TABLE 26-11.　*Continued*

		Dielectric constant	
Mineral or rock	Source and orientation of sample	Radio frequencies	Optical frequencies
PHOSPHATE MINERALS			
Apatite, $Ca_5(F,Cl)(PO_4)_3$	..	7.40–10.47	
	Asio, Japan		
	across optic axis	7.60	2.69
	along optic axis	10.0	2.71
	Kamioka, Japan		
	across optic axis	7.43	
	along optic axis	6.07	
Vivianite, $Fe_3(PO_4)_2\cdot8H_2O$	..	6.07	2.49–2.67
SULFATE MINERALS			
Anglesite, $PbSO_4$	..	74.0–500	3.52–3.59
Anhydrite, $CaSO_4$	..	5.70–6.30	
	along a axis	..	2.48
	along b axis	..	2.49
	along c axis	..	2.61
Barite, $BaSO_4$	..	6.99–12.2	
	along a axis	7.10	2.68
	along b axis	8.85–10.0	2.38–2.69
	along c axis	6.72–7.60	2.40–2.71
	Trintington, England (nine samples)		
	along a axis	7.85 ± (0.09)	
	along b axis	12.31 ± (0.05)	
	along c axis	7.88 ± (0.05)	
Celestite, $SrSO_4$	Sicily		
	along a axis	7.60	2.62
	along b axis	..	2.64
	along c axis	8.26	2.66
Gypsum, $CaSO_412H_2O$	..	5.00 –11.5	
	along a axis	11.2	2.31
	along b axis	12.0	2.32
	along c axis	5.40	2.34
SILICATE MINERALS			
Analcime, $NaAlSi_2O_6\cdot H_2O$	Tyrol	5.88	2.21
Augite, $Ca(Mg,Fe,Al)(Al,Si)_2O_6$	..	6.90–10.27	
	along a axis	8.60	2.92
	along b axis	6.90	2.95
	along c axis	7.10	3.01
Beryl, $Be_3Al_2Si_6O_{18}$	..	5.48–7.80	
	across optic axis	6.59	2.53
	along optic axis	6.16	2.56
	Urals		
	along optic axis	6.18	
	across optic axis	5.67	
Biotite, $K(Mg,Fe)_3AlSi_3O_{10}(OH)_2$	..	6.19–9.30	
	along a axis	..	2.50
	along b axis	..	2.68
	along c axis	..	2.68
Epidote (average of 14 samples) $Ca_2(Al,Fe)_3(SiO_4)_3OH$	Tyrol		
	along a axis	7.60 ± .13	3.01
	along b axis	9.99 ± .14	3.11
	along c axis	15.36 ± .04	3.17
Leucite, $KAlSi_2O_6$	Italy	7.13	
	across optic axis	..	2.27
	along optic axis	..	2.27
Muscovite, $KAl_3Si_3O_{10}(OH)_2$	..	6.19–8.00	
	along a axis	..	2.46
	along b axis	..	2.55
	along c axis	..	2.60
Opal, $SiO_2\cdot nH_2O$	Bodai, Japan	7.15	2.10
	Takarasaka, Japan	7.43	

TABLE 26-11.   *Continued*

Mineral or rock	Source and orientation of sample	Dielectric constant Radio frequencies	Optical frequencies
SILICATE MINERALS *(continued)*			
Opal, var. Hyalite	Tateyama, Japan	4.21	
Orthoclase feldspar var. adularia, $KAlSi_3O_8$			
	along *a* axis	5.55	2.30
	along *b* axis	5.80	2.33
	along *c* axis	4.50	2.34
Phlogopite, $KMg_2Al_2Si_3O_{10}(OH)_2$	..	5.90–6.50	
	along *a* axis	..	2.44
	along *b* axis	..	2.58
	along *c* axis	..	2.58
Plagioclase feldspar			
var. albite $Ab_{97}An_3$	Basi-bergwerk, Japan	5.58	2.33
var. albite $Ab_{99}An_1$	Switzerland	5.45	2.34
var. albite $Ab_{95}An_5$	Tyrol	5.57	2.36
var. albite $Ab_{96}An_4$	Switzerland	5.52	2.36
var. albite $Ab_{98}An_2$	Italy	5.55	2.34
var. albite $Ab_{94}An_6$	Norway	5.63	2.36
var. albite $Ab_{99}An_1$	Urals	5.55	2.33
var. albite $Ab_{98}An_2$	Bavaria	5.39	2.34
var. oligoclase $Ab_{76}An_{24}$	North Carolina	6.03	2.39
var. oligoclase $Ab_{77}An_{23}$	Norway	6.06	2.39
var. andesine $Ab_{65}An_{35}$	Norway	6.20	2.41
var. andesine $Ab_{61}An_{39}$	Korea	6.47	2.41
var. andesine $Ab_{52}An_{48}$	Nakasiota, Japan	6.30	2.43
var. labradorite $Ab_{43}An_{57}$	Labradore, Italy	6.61	2.45
var. labradorite $Ab_{45}An_{55}$	North America	6.51	2.45
var. anorthite Ab_4An_{96}	Otaru, Japan	7.24	2.51
var. anorthite Ab_2An_{98}	Tsushima, Japan	7.14	2.51
var. anorthite Ab_7An_{93}	Hokkaido, Japan	7.05	2.49
var. anorthite Ab_4An_{96}	Miyakeshima, Japan	7.15	2.49
Quartz SiO_2	..	4.19–5.00	
	across optic axis	4.69	2.36
	along optic axis	5.05	2.41
	Naegi, Japan		
	normal to optic axis	4.11	
	parallel to optic axis	4.27	
	Kinbuzan, Japan		
	normal to optic axis	4.13	
	parallel to optic axis	4.27	
Quartz, bipyramidal	Cumberland, Maryland		
	normal to optic axis	4.09	
	parallel to optic axis	4.27	
Sericite	..	19.55–25.35	
Sillimanite	..	4.80	
Al_2SiO_5	along *a* axis	..	2.78
	along *b* axis	..	2.79
	along *c* axis	..	2.84
Topaz, $Al_2SiO_4(F,OH)_2$	..	6.30–7.60	
	along *a* axis	6.65	2.66
	along *b* axis	6.70	2.66
	along *c* axis	6.30	2.68
	Naegi, Japan		
	along *a* axis	6.31	
	along *b* axis	6.43	
	along *c* axis	6.27	
Tourmaline	..	5.60–7.10	
	Ceylon		
	normal to optic axis	6.75	2.76
	parallel to optic axis	5.52	2.89
	Cumberland, Maryland		
	normal to optic axis	6.76	
	parallel to optic axis	5.45	
Zircon, $ZrSiO_4$	..	8.59–12.0	~3.84

Table 26-11. *Continued*

Mineral or rock	Source and orientation of sample	Dielectric constant Radio frequencies	Optical frequencies
SEDIMENTARY ROCKS			
Anhydrite	..	6.19	
Limestone	..	15.1	
Sandstone, dry (4 samples)	..	4.69–4.99	
Sandstone, 1.5% water	..	7.40	
2.8% water	..	12.1	
4.2% water	..	10.9	
Packed sand, dry	..	2.93	
1.5% water	..	5.00	
3.0% water	..	11.0	
4.5% water	..	39.1	
6.0% water	..	105.	
Packed sand, 6% kerosene	..	2.89	
12% kerosene	..	3.01	
18% kerosene	..	3.20	
24% kerosene	..	3.30	
30% kerosene	..	3.59	
SOILS			
Soil, 7.78% water	Decca, India	3.95	
19.9% water	..	4.75	
26.8% water	..	5.23	
32.1% water	..	7.93	
36.8% water	..	21.9	
41.4% water	..	29.4	
IGNEOUS ROCKS			
Granite, dry (7 samples)	..	4.80–18.9	
Granite	..	14.9	
Granite porphyry, 2.16 per cent sulfides	..	27.1	
Nepheline syenite (6 samples)	..	6.93–12.7	
Gabbro containing 3.2–6.4 per cent sulfides (5 samples)	..	12.8–39.9	
Peridotite	..	8.59	
Fayalite (3 samples)	..	7.45–8.59	
Norite	..	61.3	
Quartz porphyry (4 samples)	..	14.1–49.3	
Diabase (2 samples)	..	18.1–34.5	
Trap (3 samples)	..	18.9–39.8	
Dacite (4 samples)	..	6.8–8.2	
Andesite basalt (6 samples)	..	6.54–11.9	
IGNEOUS GLASSES			
Obsidian (3 samples)	..	5.80–10.4	
Pitchstone	..	18.7	
Tuff (3 samples)	..	3.78–3.99	

TABLE 26-12. DIELECTRIC CONSTANTS OF ROCKS, MINERALS AND SOÏLS AS A
FUNCTION OF FREQUENCY [25]

Mineral	Source	100 cps	1 kcps	10 kcps	100 kcps	1 mcps	10 mcps
	MINERALS						
Apatite	Hull Township, Quebec, Canada	12.0	11.9	11.8	11.7	11.2	10.5
Biotite	Pontiac Township, Quebec, Canada	4.81	4.80	4.76	4.71	4.69	4.67
Calcite	..						
	Field parallel to cleavage	7.60	7.60	7.60	7.60	7.60	7.60
	Field across cleavage	7.31	7.31	7.31	7.31	7.31	7.31
Chalcedony	Trestia, Hungary	..	29.1	8.70	6.21	5.40	5.10
Chert	Joplin, Missouri	63.9	13.0	6.19	4.80	4.60	4.50
Halite	..	5.90	5.90	5.90	5.90	5.90	5.90
Lepidomelane	Faraday Township, Ontario, Canada	4.00	3.98	3.96	3.94	3.91	3.89
Microline	..	8.82	7.63	6.97	6.33	5.78	5.62
Muscovite	..	5.40	5.40	5.40	5.40	5.40	5.40
Novaculite	Hot Springs, Arkansas	5.93	5.34	5.00	4.94	4.89	4.86
Orthoclase	Twentynine Palms, California	3.27	3.03	2.98	2.97	2.93	2.89
Perthite	Keystone, South Dakota						
	Field across b axis	6.49	6.19	6.12	6.02	5.91	5.80
	Hybla Station, Ontario, Canada						
	Field across a axis	3.65	3.51	3.47	3.40	3.32	3.29
Phlogopite	Denholm Township, Quebec, Canada	6.20	6.16	6.15	6.13	6.10	6.10
Quartz	..						
	Field across c axis	4.60	4.60	4.60	4.60	4.60	4.60
	Field along c axis	4.60	4.60	4.60	4.60	4.60	4.60
Spodumene	Keystone, South Dakota	10.4	9.62	9.17	8.97	8.76	8.42
	SEDIMENTARY ROCKS						
Dolomite, dry, Warrior Limestone (Cambrian)	State College, Pennsylvania	11.9	9.67	8.70	8.11	7.90	7.72
Kaolinite, dry	Drybranch, Georgia	7.65	6.32	5.42	4.85	4.55	4.49
Limestone, dry, Lowville Limestone (Ordovician)	Bellefonte, Pennsylvania	10.4	9.35	9.01	8.86	8.69	8.56
Limestone, dry, Carlim Limestone (Ordovician)	Bellefonte, Pennsylvania	15.4	12.3	10.6	9.79	9.40	9.22
Arkose sandstone, dry	Edgewater, New Jersey	5.94	5.78	5.60	5.39	5.34	5.31
Graywacke sandstone, dry	McKean County, Pennsylvania	11.6	8.78	7.37	6.59	6.12	5.87
Quartzite sandstone	Millerstown, Pennsylvania	5.65	5.33	5.19	5.02	4.88	4.72
Sandstone, Morrison Formation (Jurassic) 6 samples, water content .7 per cent	Montrose County, Colorado	13.0	8.0	6.55	6.00	5.55	5.20
	SOILS						
Sandy soil, dry	..	3.41	2.90	2.75	2.65	2.59	2.56
Loamy soil, dry	..	3.06	2.83	2.69	2.60	2.53	2.43
Clayey soil, dry	..	4.72	3.93	3.26	2.79	2.56	2.44
	IGNEOUS ROCKS						
Anorthosite, dry	Crystal Bay, Minnesota	167	73	25.0	10.9	9.93	9.03
Diabase, dry	Rhenish, USSR	23.5	15.5	12.3	10.5	9.09	8.50
Diabase, dry	Princeton, New Jersey	13.4	11.2	9.95	9.10	8.31	7.76
Diorite, dry	Bavaria	17.0	13.4	10.8	9.45	8.78	8.57
Diorite, dry (average of 53 samples)	La Sal Mountains, Utah	7.21 +.67	6.61 .47	6.27 .40	6.05 .36	.. ..	.. ..

TABLE 26-12. *Continued*

Mineral	Source	100 cps	1 kcps	10 kcps	100 kcps	1 mcps	10 mcps
	IGNEOUS ROCKS *Continued*						
Dunite, dry (olivine rock)	Jackson County, North Carolina	10.0	8.47	7.83	7.60	7.37	7.18
Gabbro, dry	Bartons Peak, Minnesota	15.0	11.5	10.2	9.65	9.12	8.78
Gabbro, dry (fine-grained)	..	15.6	12.1	9.95	8.56	7.71	7.30
Granite, dry	Arknis, California	9.63	8.00	6.86	6.11	5.57	5.23
Granite, dry (fine-grained)	Braintree, Vermont	8.47	7.55	7.16	7.02	6.87	6.68
Hornblende granite, dry	Saxony	11.1	9.65	8.52	7.86	7.52	7.20
Obsidian (rhyolite glass)	Lake County, Oregon	7.31	7.09	6.90	6.80	6.69	6.59
Quartz pegmatite, dry	..	5.62	5.48	5.33	5.20	5.06	4.90
	METAMORPHIC ROCKS						
Argillite, dry	Princeton, New Jersey	11.9	10.4	9.22	8.65	8.30	7.97
Gneiss, dry (Sillimanite-garnet)	Warren County, New York	9.73	9.13	8.78	8.50	8.23	8.07
Hornblende schist, dry	Springfield, Vermont	10.3	9.91	9.52	9.23	9.10	8.88
Talc schist, dry	Perkinsville, Vermont	31.5	22.7	15.7	10.8	8.46	7.57
Serpentine (serpentine and chlorite)	Rochester, Vermont	10.1	7.79	6.91	6.60	6.40	6.24

TABLE 26-13.   DIELECTRIC CONSTANT OF ICE [42]

Temperature	500 cps	1 kcps	Frequency 5 kcps	20 kcps	60 kcps
−1° C	73.8	72.5	51.6	12.3	4.3
−3	73.8	72.5	46.3	10.4	4.2
−5	73.8	72.5	40.2	8.34	3.71
−10	73.6	69.4	24.4	5.46	3.33
−20	65.9	45.2	7.60	3.57	3.12
−40	8.78	5.37	3.32	3.06	3.03
−60	3.92	3.50	3.12	3.00	3.00

TABLE 26-14.   LOW-FREQUENCY POLARIZATIONS EXPRESSED AS METAL FACTORS [30]

Rock	Metal factor
Dirty sandstone and limestone	3–100
Granite	<2
Basalt	2–20
Tuff	3–300
Porphyry with 1–3 per cent sulfides	100–1000
Andesite (Arizona)	11–25
Trap rock (Michigan)	140–670

TABLE 26-15. LOW-FREQUENCY POLARIZATION [48]

Rock type	Number of measurements	Product of resistivity and specific capacity	
		Average	Range (in seconds)
Hematite ore (Precambrian Biwabik Formation, Minnesota)	14	10.8	1.5–35
Glacial till (Minnesota)	9	.80	.30–3.0
Rhyolite tuff, trap rock	19	.63	.25–2.6
Sandstone (Jurassic Morrison Formation)	306	.18	.015–4.0
Greenstone, granulite	10	.17	.022–.36
Granite, quartz porphyry	8	.16	.030–.57
Limestone, dolomite	18	.10	.030–.25
Diorite, monzonite	19	.085	.026–.23
Gabbro, chromite, troctolite	15	.0014	.00033–.033

TABLE 26-16. LOW-FREQUENCY DIELECTRIC CONSTANTS [48]

Rock	Number of measurements	Dielectric constant	Resistivity (Ohm-meters)
SEDIMENTARY ROCKS			
Graywacke sandstone	1	3.45×10^8	910
Sandstone with galena	2	$5.9–9.2 \times 10^7$	835–1290
Quartzitic sandstone	1	2.68×10^8	388
Shale	2	$5.4–15.2 \times 10^7$	163–192
Oil shale	3	$2.1–59 \times 10^6$	138–4250
Limestone	13	$4.9–620 \times 10^5$	292–29,000
Dolomite	5	$9.6–860 \times 10^5$	1435–9350
IGNEOUS PHANERITES AND MICROPHANERITES			
Granite	2	$1.34–1.68 \times 10^5$	19,800–23,400
Quartz porphyry	5	$9.9–67 \times 10^4$	48,000–143,000
Monzonite	2	$8.8–45 \times 10^6$	740–5500
Diorite	12	$10.8–940 \times 10^4$	2370–77,000
Feldspar porphyry	1	4.0×10^5	7400
Hornblendite	4	$6.5–25.4 \times 10^5$	2420–8500
IGNEOUS APHANITES			
Pyritic rhyolite	7	$1.66–12.7 \times 10^7$	14.1–830
Felsite	2	$2.52–3.96 \times 10^5$	7400–7900
Mineralized andesite	4	$1.22–10.0 \times 10^6$	10,000–32,000
Basalt	14	$7.5–213 \times 10^7$	81–1120
Mineralized tuff	2	$2.87–7.9 \times 10^8$	57–60
METAMORPHIC ROCKS			
Gneiss	8	$5.9–480 \times 10^5$	660–27,000
Granulite	8	$1.03–100 \times 10^5$	3600–195,000
Greenstone	2	$2.02–2.56 \times 10^5$	9900–11,800

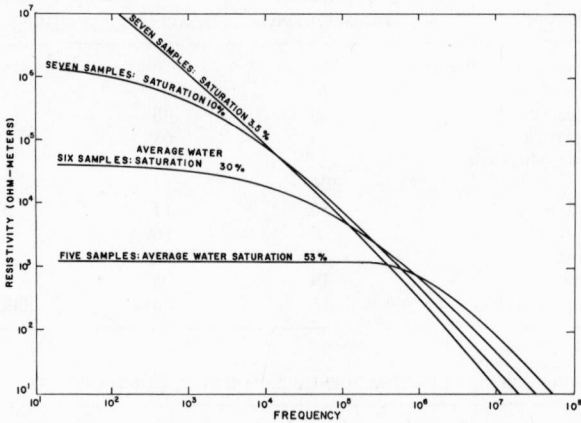

Figure 26-1. Resistivity of water-bearing sandstones as a function of frequency

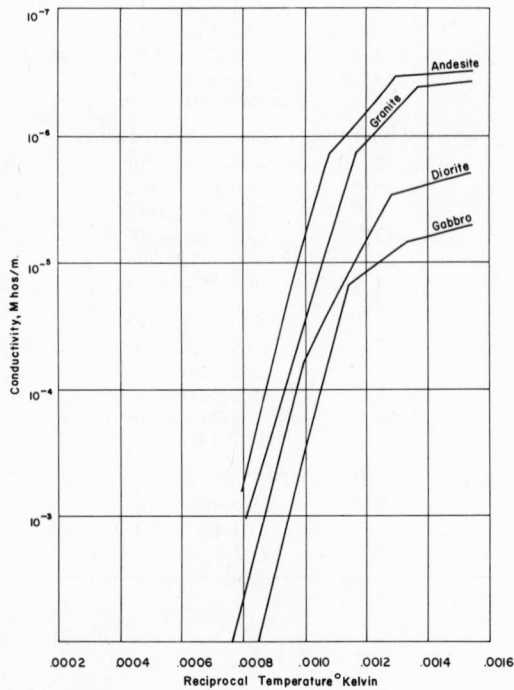

Figure 26-2. Conductivity of dry rocks as a function of temperature

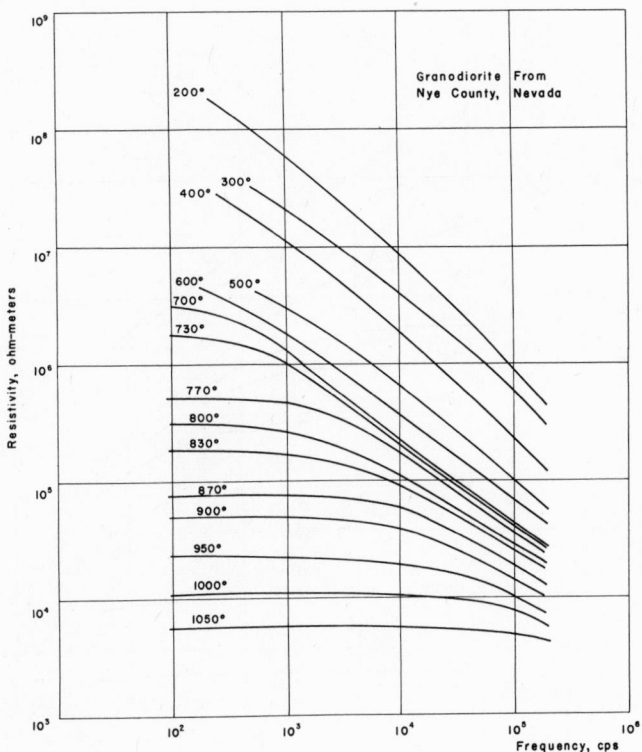

Figure 26-3. Resistivity of granodiorite as a function of temperature and frequency

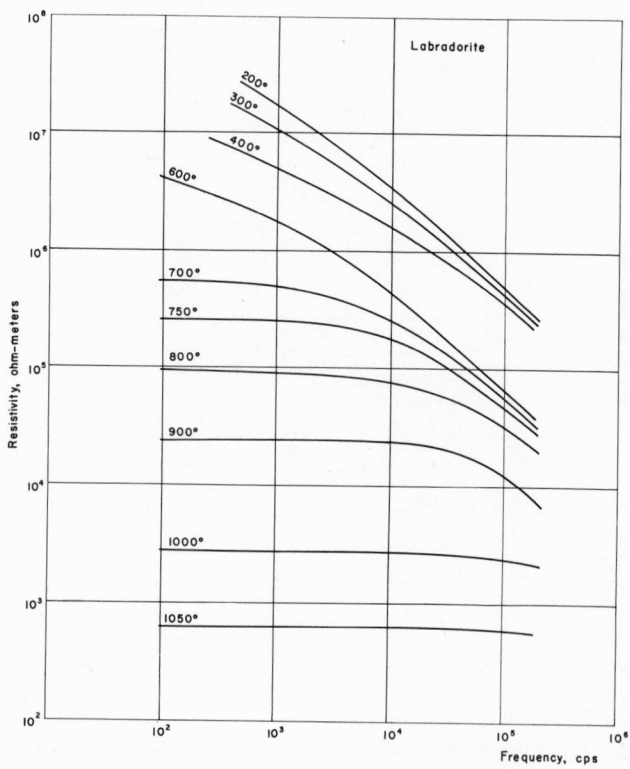

Figure 26-4. Resistivity of labradorite rock as a function of temperature and frequency

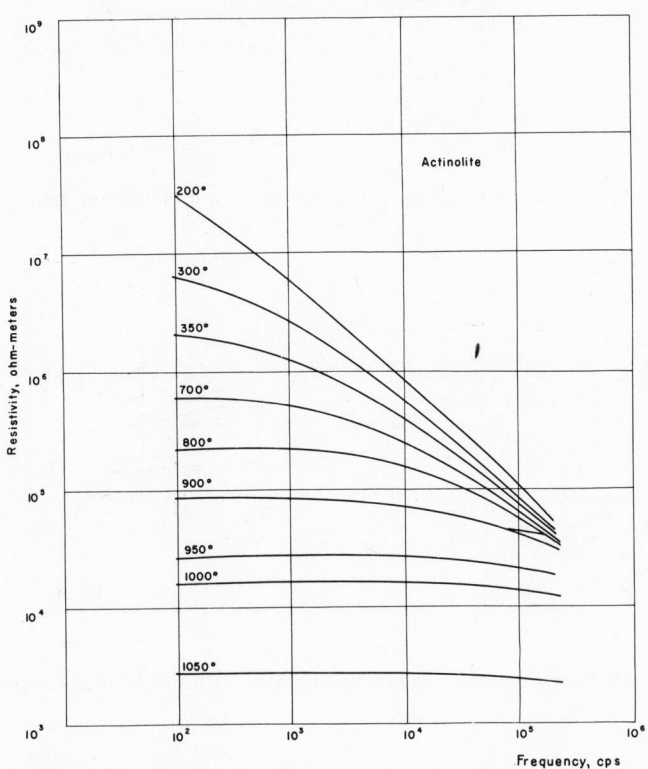

Figure 26-5. Resistivity of actinolite rock as a function of temperature and frequency

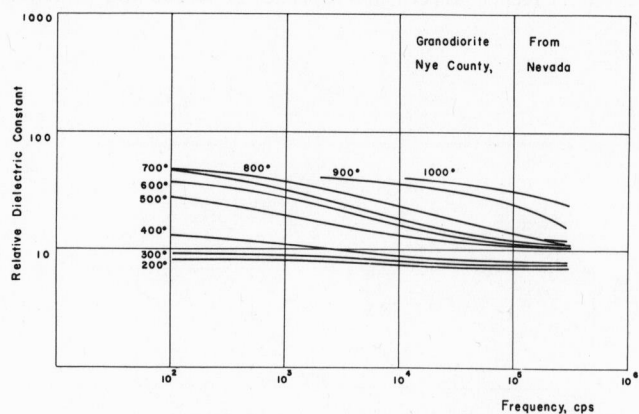

Figure 26-6. Dielectric constant of granodiorite as a function of temperature and frequency

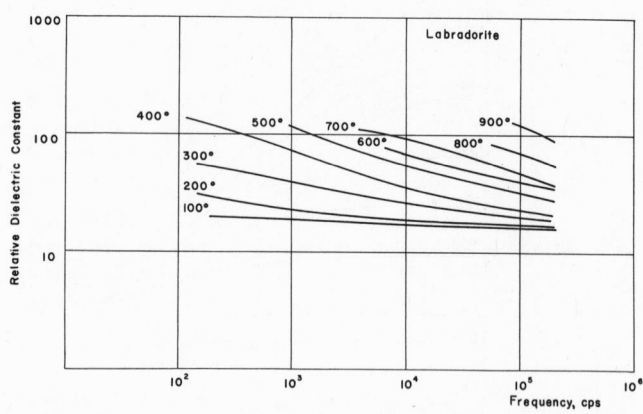

Figure 26-7. Dielectric constant of labradorite rock as a function of temperature and frequency

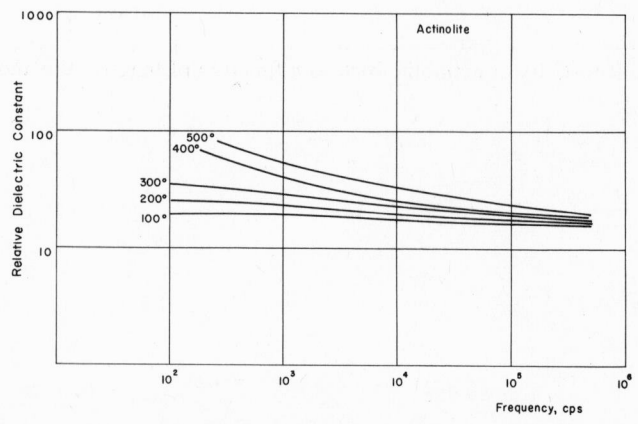

Figure 26-8. Dielectric constant of actinolite rock as a function of temperature and frequency

576

REFERENCES FOR SECTION 26

1. Ananyan, Izv. Akad. Nauk SSSR **12**, 1504, 1958
2. Archie, AIME Tech. Paper 1422, 1942
3. Austin and Wolfe, Proc. Phys. Soc., B. **69**, 329, 1956
4. Ayers, Dobyns, and Bussell, Pet. Eng. 24, B36, 1952
5. Birch, Schairer, and Spicer, Handbook of physical constants, Geol. Soc. America Special Paper 36, 1942
6. Backstrom, Ofv. of Kongl. Vet.-Akad. Fork 8, 533, 1888
7. Card, Trans. AIME **138**, 380, 1940
8. Chakravarty and Khastigir, Phil. Mag. **25**, 793, 1938
9. Chebotarev, Geochim. Cosmochim. Acta **8**, 53, 1955
10. Coster, M.N.R.A.S. Geophys. Supp. **5**, 193, 1948
11. Cownie and Palmer, Phys. Soc. London, B. **65**, 295, 1952
12. Crawford, Subsurface geologic methods, p. 272–296, Colorado School of Mines, 1951
13. Cronemeyer, Phys. Rev. **87**, 876, 1952
14. Dakhnov, Promyslovaya Geofizika, Gostoptekhizdat, Moscow, 1957
15. Domenicali, Phys. Rev. **78**, 458, 1950
16. Dostovalov, Trudy Petrograficheskoy Inst. Akad. Nauk SSSR **10**, 161, 1937
17. Dunlap and Hawthorne, Jour. Pet. Tech. **7**, 17, 1951
18. Dutta, Phys. Rev. **90**, 187, 1953
19. Finklea, Pet. Tech. **8**, 25, 1956
20. Fritsch, Grundzuge der angewandten Geoelektrik, Manzsche verlagsund Universitatsbuchhandlung, Vienna, 1949
21. Frueh, Am. Min. **44**, 1010, 1959
22. Fuoss and Kirkwood, Jour. Am. Chem. Soc. **63**, 385, 1941
23. Harvey, Econ. Geol. **23**, 778, 1928
24. Howell and Licastro, Am. Min. **46**, 269, 1961
25. Hughes, Jour. Geophys. Res. **60**, 187, 1955; AIME Trans., 207, 65, 1956
26. Keller, Oil and Gas Jour. **51**, 62, 1953
27. Kirby, Harman, Capps, and Jones, Nat. Bur. Standards Circ. 546, 1954
28. Konigsberger and Reichenheim, Neues Jahrb. f. Min: Geol. u. Pal. II, 20, 1906
29. Manning and Bell, Rev. Mod. Phys. **12**, 215, 1940
30. Marshall and Madden, Geophysics **24**, 790, 1959
31. McKelvey, Southwick, Spiegler and Wyllie, Geophysics **20**, 913, 1955
32. Miles, Econ. Geol. **46**, 193, 1951
33. Nesterova and Nesterov, Materialy Vses. Nauchno-Issled. Geol. Inst., Geofiz. **11**, 76, 1947
34. Noritomi, Sci. Repts. Tohoku Univ., 5th Ser. **6**, 119, 1955
35. Parasnis, Geophys. Prosp. **4**, 249, 1956
36. —— Jernkont. Ann. 140, 494, 1956
37. Parkhomenko and Bondarenko, Izv. Akad. Nauk SSSR **2**, 326, 1960
38. Primak and Fuchs, Phys. Rev. **95**, 22, 1954
39. Puzin, Pet. Eng. **24**, 9, B67, 1952
40. Semenov and Malchevskiy, Razvedka Nedr **9**, 35, 1939
41. Smith-Rose, Jour. Inst. Elec. Eng. **75**, 221, 1934
42. Smythe and Hitchcock, Jour. Am. Chem. Soc. **54**, 4631, 1932
43. Stringfield, Warren, and Cooper, Econ. Geol. **36**, 698, 1941
44. Takubo, Memoirs of the College of Science, Series B, Kyoto Imperial University **16**, 95, 1941
45. Tarkhov, Materialy Vses. Nauchno-Issled. Geol. Inst., Geofiz. **12**, 1, 1947
46. Tozer, The electrical properties of the earth's interior p. 414–436 *in* Physics and chemistry of the earth, vol. III, Pergamon Press, London, 1959
47. von Hippel, Dielectric materials and applications, The Technology Press of MIT, 1954
48. Wait, Overvoltage research and geophysical application, Pergamon Press, London, 1959
49. Weeks, Phys. Rev. **19**, 319, 1922
50. Wyllie, AIME Tech. Paper 2511, 1949
51. —— Am. Assoc. Petroleum Geologists Bull. **33**, 1192, 1949
52. Wyllie and Gregory, Jour. Pet. Tech. **198**, 103, 1953
53. Wyllie and Morgan, Producers Monthly **16**, 31, 1952
54. Winsauer, Perkins, and Brannon, Jour. Pet. Tech. **6**, 29, 1954

SECTION 27

CONVERSION FACTORS, NUMERICAL CONSTANTS, ATOMIC CONSTANTS

By SYDNEY P. CLARK, JR.

CONTENTS

Handbook of Physical Constants—*Revised Edition*
THE GEOLOGICAL SOCIETY OF AMERICA MEMOIR 97, 1966

Table 27-1. Conversion Factors

Length

1 m = 39.3700 in = 3.280833 ft
1 in = 2.540005 cm
1 ft = 30.48006 cm
1 mi = 1.60935 km
1 km = .62137 mi

Area

1 cm² = .15500 in² = .00107639 ft²
1 in² = 6.451626 cm²
1 mi² = 2.59001 km²
1 km² = .3861006 mi²
1 circular mil = .78540 × 10⁻⁶ in² = 5.0671 × 10⁻⁶ cm²

Volume

1 cm³ = .061023 in³
1 in³ = 16.387162 cm³
1 liter = .264178 gallon = .035316 ft³ = 1.05671 quarts
= 1000.027 cm³
1 gallon = .13368 ft³ = 231.00 in³ = 3785.4 cm³

Mass

1 kg = 2.2046223 lb
1 lb = .4535924 kg
1 oz (avoir.) = 28.3495 gm
1 oz (troy) = 31.10348 gm

Time

1 solar day = 24 hr = 1440 min = 86,400 sec
1 sidereal day = 86,164.09054 sec
1 sidereal year = 3.155815 × 10⁷ sec

Density

1 gm cm⁻³ = .036127 lb in⁻³ = 62.4298 lb ft⁻³
1 lb in⁻³ = 27,680 gm cm⁻³
1 lb ft⁻³ = .016018 gm cm⁻³

Thermal gradient

1 °C km⁻¹ = 5.48641 × 10⁻⁴ °F ft⁻¹
1 °F ft⁻¹ = 1822.68 °C km⁻¹
100 ft °F⁻¹ = 18.2268 °C km⁻¹
Thermal diffusivity (also kinematic viscosity)
1 cm² sec⁻¹ = 3.155815 km² 10⁻⁶ year

Thermal conductivity

	cal cm⁻¹ sec⁻¹ °C⁻¹	watt cm⁻¹ °C⁻¹	BTU ft⁻¹ hr⁻¹ °F⁻¹	BTU in ft⁻² hr⁻¹ °F⁻¹
1 cal cm⁻¹ sec⁻¹ °C⁻¹	1	4.1840	241.804	2901.65
1 watt cm⁻¹ °C⁻¹	.23901	1	57.7936	693.523
1 BTU ft⁻¹ hr⁻¹ °F⁻¹	.00413558	.0173033	1	12.0000
1 BTU in ft⁻² hr⁻¹ °F⁻¹	.000344632	.00144194	.0833333	1

Energy

	erg	joule	calorie	watt-hr	BTU	mev	AMU
1 erg	1	10⁻⁷	.23901 × 10⁻⁷	.2778 × 10⁻¹⁰	.94805 × 10⁻¹⁰	.624224 × 10⁶	.670142 × 10³
1 joule	10⁷	1	.23901	.2778 × 10⁻³	.94805 × 10⁻³	.624224 × 10¹³	.670142 × 10¹⁰
1 calorie	4.1840 × 10⁷	4.1840	1	1.1622 × 10⁻³	3.9666 × 10⁻³	2.61175 × 10¹³	2.80387 × 10¹⁰
1 watt-hr	3.60 × 10¹⁰	3600	860.42	1	3.4130	2.24721 × 10¹⁶	2.41251 × 10¹³
1 BTU	1.0548 × 10¹⁰	1054.8	252.10	.29300	1	.658432 × 10¹⁶	.706866 × 10¹³
1 mev	1.60199 × 10⁻⁶	1.60199 × 10⁻¹³	3.82885 × 10⁻¹⁴	.44500 × 10⁻¹⁶	1.51876 × 10⁻¹⁶	1	1.07356 × 10⁻³
1 AMU	1.49222 × 10⁻³	1.49222 × 10⁻¹⁰	.356650 × 10⁻¹⁰	.414506 × 10⁻¹³	1.41470 × 10⁻¹³	9.31476 × 10²	1

Pressure

	bar	normal atmosphere	kg cm⁻²	lb in⁻²
1 bar (10⁶ dynes cm⁻²)	1	.986924	1.01972	14.5038
1 Normal atm.	1.01325	1	1.03323	14.6960
1 kg cm⁻²	.980665	.967842	1	14.2234
1 lb in⁻²	.0689474	.0680458	.0703070	1

1 Torr = 1 mm Hg = 1.33322×10^{-3} bars

Electromagnetic quantities

(Dimensions of the various quantities are given in square brackets. $c = 2.997930 \times 10^{10}$ cm sec⁻¹)

	mks	cgs esu	cgs emu
Electric charge	1 coulomb $[Q]$	$.1c$ statcoulombs $[M^{1/2}L^{3/2}T^{-1}]$	$.1$ abcoulombs $[M^{1/2}L^{1/2}]$
Electromotive force	1 volt $[Q^{-1}ML^2T^{-2}]$	10^8c^{-1} statvolts $[M^{1/2}L^{1/2}T^{-1}]$	10^8 abvolts $[M^{1/2}L^{3/2}T^{-2}]$
Capacitance	1 farad $[Q^2M^{-1}L^{-2}T^2]$	$10^{-9}c^2$ statfarads $[L]$	10^{-9} abfarads $[L^{-1}T^2]$
Current	1 ampere $[QT^{-1}]$	$.1c$ statamperes $[M^{1/2}L^{3/2}T^{-2}]$	$.1$ abamperes $[M^{1/2}L^{1/2}T^{-1}]$
Resistance	1 ohm $[Q^{-2}ML^2T^{-1}]$	10^9c^{-2} statohms $[L^{-1}T]$	10^9 abohms $[LT^{-1}]$
Inductance	1 henry $[Q^{-2}ML^2]$	10^9c^{-2} stathenries $[L^{-1}T^2]$	10^9 abhenries $[L]$
Magnetic flux	1 weber $[Q^{-1}ML^2T^{-1}]$	10^8c^{-1}	10^8 maxwells $[M^{1/2}L^{3/2}T^{-1}]$
	Magnetic induction = B	Magnetic field = H	Magnetization = M

Magnetic induction, **B**, is related to magnetic field, **H**, by $\mathbf{B} = \mu\mathbf{H} = \mathbf{H} + 4\pi\mathbf{M}$. In cgs emu, μ is dimensionless and all three vectors have dimensions $[M^{1/2}L^{1/2}T^{-1}]$.
In mks units **B** has dimensions $[Q^{-1}MT^{-1}]$ and **H** and **M** have dimensions $[QL^{-1}T^{-1}]$.
In mks units the magnetic permeability of free space, $\mu_0 = 10^{-7}$ kg m coulomb⁻² and the dielectric constant of free space $\varepsilon_0 = 10^{11}\ c^{-2}$ coulombs² sec² kg⁻¹ m⁻³.

TABLE 27-2. NUMERICAL CONSTANTS

$\pi = 3.14159265$	$2\pi = 6.28318531$
$4\pi = 12.56637061$	$4\pi/3 = 4.18879020$
$\pi/2 = 1.57079633$	$\pi^2 = 9.86960438$
$\pi^{-1} = .31830989$	$\pi^{1/2} = 1.77245385$
$\pi^{-1/2} = .56418958$	$2\pi^{-1/2} = 1.12837917$
$180\pi^{-1} = 57.295780$	

$e = 2.71828183$ $\log_e 10 = 2.3025851$ $\log_{10} e = .43429448$

$\gamma =$ Euler's constant $= .57721566$

TABLE 27-3. ATOMIC CONSTANTS BASED ON THE 1961 ADJUSTMENT
by J. W. M. DuMond, E. R. Cohen, and A. G. McNish

N	Avogadro's number	$(6.02257 \pm .00009) \times 10^{23}$ (g mole)$^{-1}$
c	Speed of light	$(2.997925 \pm .000002) \times 10^{10}$ cm sec^{-1}
e	Electronic charge	$(4.80296 \pm .00006) \times 10^{-10}$ esu
		$(1.602095 \pm .000022) \times 10^{-20}$ emu
m	Electron rest mass	$(9.10904 \pm .00013) \times 10^{-28}$ g
h	Planck's constant	$(6.62554 \pm .00015) \times 10^{-27}$ erg sec
$F = Ne$	Faraday	$(2.892616 \pm .000012) \times 10^{14}$ esu (g mole)$^{-1}$
		$(9.64873 \pm .00004) \times 10^3$ emu (g mole)$^{-1}$
$\alpha = 2\pi e^2/hc$	Fine structure constant	$(7.29720 \pm .00003) \times 10^{-3}$
α^{-1}		$(1.370389 \pm .000006) \times 10^2$
e/m		$(5.272741 \pm .000015) \times 10^{17}$ esu g^{-1}
		$(1.758797 \pm .000005) \times 10^7$ emu g^{-1}
h/e		$(1.379469 \pm .000013) \times 10^{-17}$ erg sec esu^{-1}
$\lambda_{ce} = h/mc$	Compton wavelength of electron	$(2.426206 \pm .000022) \times 10^{-10}$ cm
$\lambda_{cp} = (Nm/H^+)\lambda_{ce}$	Compton wavelength of proton	$(1.321397 \pm .000013) \times 10^{-13}$ cm
$a_0 = h^2/4\pi^2me^2$	First Bohr radius	$(5.291659 \pm .000026) \times 10^{-9}$ cm
$r_0 = e^2/mc^2$	Classical radius of electron	$(2.81776 \pm .00004) \times 10^{-13}$ cm
Nm	Atomic mass of electron	$(5.485981 \pm .000019) \times 10^{-4}$ amu
Nm_p	Atomic mass of proton	$(1.00727663 \pm .00000008)$ amu
H	Atomic mass of hydrogen	$(1.00782522 \pm .00000008)$ amu
$\sigma = 2\pi^5 R_0^4 / 15_c^2 h^3 N^4$	Stefan-Boltzmann constant	$(5.6697 \pm .0009) \times 10^{-5}$ erg cm^{-2} deg^{-4} sec^{-1}
$k = R_0/N$	Boltzmann constant	$(1.38053 \pm .00006) \times 10^{-16}$ erg deg^{-1}
$c_1 = 8\pi hc$	First radiation constant	$(4.99208 \pm .00011) \times 10^{-15}$ erg cm
$c_2 = hcN/R_0$	Second radiation constant	$1.43879 \pm .00006$ cm deg
h/k	Atomic specific heat constant	$(4.79928 \pm .00020) \times 10^{-11}$ sec deg
$\lambda_{max}T$	Wien displacement constant	$.289779 \pm .000012$ cm deg
$(3k/N)^{1/2}$	Multiplier of (Curie constant)	$(2.62235 \pm .00007) \times 10^{-21}$ (erg g mole deg^{-1})$^{1/2}$
$\Lambda = \lambda_g/\lambda_p$	Conversion factor from Siegbahn X—units to milliangstroms	$1.002063 \pm .000006$
$R\infty$	Rydberg constant for infinite mass	$(1.09737309 \pm .00000012) \times 10^5$ cm^{-1}
R_H	Rydberg constant for hydrogen	$(1.09677576 \pm .00000012) \times 10^5$ cm^{-1}
$n_0 = N/V_0$	Loschmidt's number	$(2.68702 \pm .00008) \times 10^{19}$ cm^{-3}
ν_0	Frequency associated with 1 ev	$(2.418061 \pm .000022) \times 10^{14}$ sec^{-1} (ev)$^{-1}$
λ_0	Wavelength associated with 1 ev	$(1.239805 \pm .000012) \times 10^{-4}$ cm ev
$1/\lambda_0$	Wave number associated with 1 ev	$(8.06579 \pm .00008) \times 10^3$ cm^{-1} (ev)$^{-1}$
$e \times 10^8$	Energy associated with 1 ev	$(1.602095 \pm .000022) \times 10^{-12}$ ergs (ev)$^{-1}$
$e/k \times 10^{-8}$	Temperature associated with 1 ev	$(1.16049 \pm .00005) \times 10^4$ deg (ev)$^{-1}$
E_0	Conversion, atomic mass unit to ev	$(9.31476 \pm .00004) \times 10^8$ (ev) amu^{-1}
E_g	Conversion, grams to ev	$(5.60988 \pm .00008) \times 10^{32}$ (ev) g^{-1}
mE_g	Energy equivalent of electronic mass	$(5.110058 \pm .000014) \times 10^5$ ev m^{-1}
m_pE_g	Energy equivalent of proton mass	$(9.38254 \pm .00004) \times 10^8$ ev m$_p^{-1}$

TABLE 27-3. *Continued*

$\mu_1 = eh/4\pi mc$	Bohr magneton	$(9.27314 \pm .00021) \times 10^{-21}$ erg gauss^{-1}
μ_1/hc	Zeeman displacement	$(4.668583 \pm .000013) \times 10^{-5}$ cm^{-1} gauss^{-1}
μ_e	Magnetic moment of the electron	$(9.28389 \pm .00021) \times 10^{-21}$ erg gauss^{-1}
$(\mu_e/\mu_0) - 1$	Correction for anomalous moment of the electron	$(1.159615 \pm .000005) \times 10^{-3}$
μ_n	Nuclear magneton	$(5.05048 \pm .00011) \times 10^{-24}$ erg gauss^{-1}
γ'	Gyromagnetic ratio of proton in spherical H$_2$O sample	$(2.675118 \times .000007) \times 10^4$ rad sec^{-1} gauss^{-1}
γ	Gyromagnetic ratio of proton corrected for diamagnetism	$(2.675192 \pm .000007) \times 10^4$ rad sec^{-1} gauss^{-1}
R_0	Gas constant	$(8.31432 \pm .00034) \times 10^7$ erg (g mole)$^{-1}$ deg^{-1}

INDEX

Individual substances are not listed below. Look instead for the desired property.